2nd Edition

Sport & Exercise Sciences

Adam Gledhill
Chris Mulligan
Graham Saffrey
Louise Sutton
Richard Taylor

www.harcourt.co.uk

✓ Free online support
✓ Useful weblinks
✓ 24 hour online ordering

01865 888118

Heinemann is an imprint of Harcourt Education Limited, a company incorporated in England and Wales, having its registered office: Halley Court, Jordan Hill, Oxford OX2 8EJ. Registered company number: 3099304

www.harcourt.co.uk

Heinemann is the registered trademark of Harcourt Education Ltd

First published 2007

12 11 10 09 08 07[1]
10 9 8 7 6 5 4 3 2 1

British Library Cataloguing in Publication Data is available from the British Library on request.

ISBN 9780435465162

Edited by Melanie Gray and Felicity Kendal
Typeset by Techtype, Oxfordshire, UK
Illustrated by Tek-art, Surrey, UK
Cover design by Pentacor Ltd
Picture research by Kath Kollberg
Cover photo/illustration © Science Photo Library / Gustoimages
Printed at Scotprint Ltd

Websites
The websites used in this book were correct and up-to-date at the time of publication. It is essential for tutors to preview each website before using it in class so as to ensure that the URL is still accurate, relevant and appropriate. We suggest that tutors bookmark useful websites and consider enabling students to access them through the school/college intranet.

Contents

Acknowledgements

The authors and publisher would like to thank the following individuals and organisations fro permission to reproduce photographs:

Front cover: © Science Photo Library / Gustoimages
Feature icons: Getty Images / PhotoDisc, Photos.com, Corbis

Getty Images / Ross Kinnaird – page 2
Action Plus / Neil Tingle – page 22
Getty Images / PhotoDisc – page 23
PA Photos / Panoramic – page 23
Getty Images – page 44
Action Plus / Glyn Kirk – page 46
Getty Images / AFP / Pascal Guyot – page 60
Getty Images / Adam Pretty – page 65
PA Photos / John Giles – page 69
Getty Images / Jonathan Ferrey – page 76
Action Plus / Neil Tingle – page 79
Action Plus / Robert Beck – page 87
Getty Images – page 91
Action Plus / Grabowski – page 104
Action Plus / Glyn Kirk – page 124
Getty Images – page 137
PA Photos / AP / Efrem Lukatsky – page 150
Getty Images – page 168
PA Photos / Owen Humphreys – page 172
Getty Images / Eliot J Schechter – page 174
Getty Images / PhotoDisc – page 175
Author supplied – page 180
Author supplied – page 182
Getty Images – page 183
Getty Images / Daniel Berehulak – page 202
Alamy / George S de Blonsky – page 208
Getty Images / Tom Shaw – page 224
Getty Images – page 228
PA Photos / AP / Martin Meissner – page 239
Getty Images – page 258
PA Photos / Anthony Devlin – page 261
Corbis / Tim McGuire – page 262
Alamy / John Powell Photographer – page 274
Getty Images / PhotoDisc – page 276
Action Plus / Glyn Kirk – page 290
PA Photos / Kirsty Wigglesworth – page 292
Action Plus / Neil Tingle – page 296
Action Plus / Neil Tingle – page 299
Getty Images / Ezra Shaw – page 307
PA Photos / EMPICS / Barry Coombs – page 321
PA Photos / AP / Jasper Juinen – page 334
Getty Images – page 340
Getty Images – page 340
Action Plus / Steve Bardens – page 345
Action Plus / Neil Tingle – page 352
PA Photos / EMPICS / Adam Davy – page 353
Getty Images / AFP / Romeo Gacad – page 360
Getty Images / Bongearts / Friedemann Vogel – page 362
Action Plus / Mike King – page 368
Getty Images / PhotoDisc – page 378
Getty Images – page 388
Getty Images – page 401

The authors and publisher would like to thank the following individuals and organisations fro permission to reproduce copyright material:

1. Unit 3 pg 83-85. Questionnaires adapted from Myers Briggs (MBTI) Type Indicator, Isabel Briggs Myers
2. Unit 22 pg 380, World Health Organisation: Caring for the elderly: a report on the status of care for the elderly in the Eastern Mediterranean Region *G. Hafez,* K. Bagchi and R. Mahaini
3. Unit 22 pg 385, http://www.abc.net.au/health: Quote from an article on stroke risk to the elderly by Angela Williams Published 25/08/2005

Every effort has been made by the publisher to contact copyright holders of material reproduced in this book. Any omissions will be rectified in subsequent printings if notice is given to the publishers

Introduction

Welcome to this BTEC National Sport and Exercise Sciences course book, specifically designed to support students on the following programmes:

- BTEC National Award in Sport and Exercise Sciences
- BTEC National Certificate in Sport and Exercise Sciences
- BTEC National Diploma in Sport and Exercise Sciences.

For the BTEC National Award the book covers all four core units, that is:

- Anatomy for Sport and Exercise
- Sport and Exercise Physiology
- Sport and Exercise Psychology
- Research Methods for Sport and Exercise Sciences

It also provides three specialist units from which you can choose two to complete the qualification. These are:

- Research Project in Sport and Exercise Sciences
- Sports Biomechanics in Action
- Exercise, Health and Lifestyle

For the BTEC National Certificate/Diploma programmes, the book covers the five/six core units, that is:

- Anatomy for Sport and Exercise
- Sport and Exercise Physiology
- Sport and Exercise Psychology
- Research Methods for Sport and Exercise Sciences
- Research Project in Sport and Exercise Sciences
- Sports Biomechanics in Action (Diploma)

It also provides four of the specialist units required for this qualifications. These are:

- Exercise, Health and Lifestyle (Certificate and Diploma)
- Applied Sport and Exercise Psychology (Diploma)
- Applied Exercise Physiology (Diploma)
- Exercise for Specific Groups (Diploma)

The aim of this book is to provide a comprehensive source of information for your course. It follows the BTEC specification closely, so that you can easily see what you have covered and quickly find the information you need.

Due to the scientific nature of the units, especially the core units a great deal of attention has been paid to breaking down the scientific terminology to make the information accessible to all students.

Examples and case studies from Sport and Exercise Science are used to bring your course to life and make it enjoyable to study. We hope you will be encouraged to find your own examples of current practice too.

You will often be asked to carry out research for activities in the text, and this will develop your research skills and enable you to find many sources of interesting Sport and Exercise Sciences information, particularly on the Internet.

The book is also a suitable core text for students on HND, foundation degree and first-year degree programmes. To help you plan your study, an overview of each unit and its outcomes is given at the beginning of each unit.

Features of the book

This book has number of features to help you relate theory to practice and reinforce your learning. It also aims to help you gather evidence for assessment. You will find the following features in each unit.

Case studies

Interesting examples of real situations, for example laboratory data are described in case studies that link theory to practice. They will show you how the topics you are studying affect real people and businesses.

Theory into practice

These features allow you to consider theoretical knowledge and relate this to Sport and Exercise Science tasks or research.

Taking it further

Facilitating the knowledge from each unit and extending your thinking is what Taking it further is all about. Questions will be posed that will stretch the learning and build on what has already been explained.

Knowledge checks

At the end of each unit is a set of quick questions to test your knowledge of the information you have been studying. Use these to check your progress, and also as a revision tool.

Case study

Title

A basketball coach wants to measure the overall flexibility of the team's players and has decided to use the sit-and-reach test to measure this. However, although this test is a measure of flexibility, it would not be valid.

1. **Explain to the coach why the sit-and-reach test is not a valid measure of overall flexibility.**
2. **The coach needs some advice about fitness testing with his players. He has come to you for some advice. Your job is to suggest a more appropriate method of testing the players' overall flexibility. Make sure you can explain why your suggestions will increase the validity of testing.**

Reliability

Reliability relates to whether, if you carried out the research again, you would get the same results. However, reliability can be claimed without the results being correct. For example, if you always ask the wrong questions in research, you would always get the same wrong answers. This would mean the test would be reliable because you have received the *same* wrong answers, even though they are not the ones you have been wanting.

In quantitative research, reliability can be one researcher conducting the same test on the same individual on a number of occasions, and getting the same (or similar) results. Alternatively, it can be different researchers conducting the same test on the same individual and getting the same (or similar) results.

In qualitative research, reliability relates to the same researcher placing results into the same categories on a number of different occasions, or different researchers placing results into the same or similar categories.

Remember!

You need to be careful, as reliability can be claimed without the results being correct!

There are certain factors you need to take into account that can affect reliability. For example:

- errors can happen when researchers don't know how to use the equipment correctly
- the equipment is poorly maintained
- the wrong type of equipment is selected.

There are two main types of reliability.

- Inter-researcher reliability: This looks at whether different researchers in the same situation would get the same (or similar) results. An example of when inter-researcher reliability is a problem comes through body composition assessment. When people are learning to use the skinfold calliper technique (see page 129) of assessing body composition, it is sometimes difficult to take accurate measurements from the correct sites. Researchers often come up with different values. When this happens, you cannot claim to have achieved inter-researcher reliability.
- Test-retest reliability: This relates to doing the same test on a number of different occasions and getting the same (or similar) results. An example of a test-retest reliability issue in sport or exercise research is the measurement of heart rate. Heart rate can be affected by a number of factors, such as temperature, time of day, diet, sleep patterns, physical activity levels and alcohol. Therefore, if you were to measure heart rate on the same person at the same time of day, but on different days, it is likely you would get different measurements.

[128] BTEC National | Sport & Exercise Science | Book 1

Your tutor should check that you have completed enough activities to meet all the assessment criteria for the unit.

Tutors and students should refer to the BTEC standards for the qualification for the full BTEC grading criteria for each unit (www.edexcel.org.uk).

I do hope that you enjoy your course and find this book an excellent support for your studies. Good luck!

Graham Saffery

Assesment practice/Activities

Activities are also provided throughout each unit. These are linked to real situations and case studies and they can be used for practice before tackling the preparation for assessment or completing your own actual assessment.

4.1

Assessment practice

A newly-qualified fitness instructor has been asked to measure the body fat percentage of a client. They are a little unsure of how to use the skinfold callipers, but take the measurements anyway. However, they take the measurements in the wrong places and record the results. The results of the tests are shown below.

Site	Measurement 1 (mm)	Measurement 2 (mm)	Measurement 3 (mm)	Mean (mm)
Biceps	7	7	7	7.0
Triceps	7	6	7	6.6
Subscapular	8	11	6	8.3
Suprailiac	13	6	7	8.6
				30.5

1 What validity issues can you identify? P2
2 What reliability issues can you identify? P2
3 Which results in the table do you think are unreliable? Explain your answer. M2

grading tips

Grading Tip P2

Say how you know when something is not valid or reliable.

Grading Tip M2

Give examples from the case study and data that you have been provided with, to show where the validity and reliability issues are.

Think it over

Can something be valid without being reliable? Can something be reliable without being valid?

Accuracy

Accuracy relates to how close your measurement is to the 'gold standard', or what you are actually intending to measure. Imagine you are looking at the weight of a boxer before a fight. If the boxer had an actual weight of 100 kg and your weighing device showed him to weigh 100.1 kg, you could say this is accurate. However, if the measuring device showed him to weigh 103 kg, you would say this is not accurate as it is not close to their actual body weight.

Key Term

Gold standard The norm value closest to what you are actually intending to measure. For example, in darts if you wanted to hit the bulls eye, the gold standard would be hitting the bulls eye.

Precision

When working in a research setting, any measurement you take will have some unpredictability about it. This degree of unpredictability relates to the amount of precision the tool selected for measurement has. Precision is related to the refinement of the measuring process. It is mainly concerned with how fine or small a difference the measuring device can detect. Precision is closely related to repeatability/reliability (see page 128).

An example involves measuring the bowling speed of Steve Harmison in the Ashes series using a speed gun and light gates. The speed gun gives you three speeds, all to the nearest mile per hour (e.g. 80mph, 81mph,

4: Research methods for sport and exercise sciences [129]

Think it over

These are points for individual reflection or group discussion. They will widen your knowledge and help you reflect on issues that impact on Sport and Exercise Science.

Key terms

Issues and terms that you need to be aware of are summarised under these headings. They will help you check your knowledge as you learn, and will prove to be a useful quick-reference tool.

Preparation for assessment

Each unit concludes with a suggested full unit assessment which, taken as a whole, fulfils all the unit requirements from Pass to Distinction.

Each task is matched to the relevant criteria in the specification.

If you are aiming for a Merit, make sure you complete all the Pass (P) tasks

If you are aiming for a Merit, make sure you complete all the Pass (P) and Merit (M) tasks.

If you are aiming for a Distinction, you will also need to complete all the Distinction (D) tasks. P1 means the first of the Pass criteria listed in the specification, M1 the first of the Merit criteria, D1 the first of the Distinction criteria, and so on.

Anatomy for sport and exercise

Introduction

Have you ever wondered how our body is able to undertake a variety of sport or exercise activities? This unit investigates just that: how the many parts of the human body are pieced together, what they are made from and how these various parts work, regardless of whether you are a footballer, sprinter, table tennis player, cyclist or marathon runner, etc.

As a sport and exercise scientist, your understanding of an athlete's anatomy is important. In this unit you will learn the structure and function of the skeletal system, how muscles are constructed and their various roles in exercise, why the heart works the way it does and how it works with the lungs to allow athletes to take part in sport- and exercise-related activities.

After completing this unit you should be able to achieve the following outcomes:

- understand the structure and function of the skeletal system
- understand the structure and function of the muscular system
- understand the structure and function of the cardiovascular system
- understand the structure and function of the respiratory system.

Think it over

A runner completes a marathon in 2 hours and 10 minutes. At the end of the race he is tired, sweaty and his muscles ache. During the past 2 hours or so, he has covered just over 26 miles, taking on small amounts of fluid through the race.

How many times do you think the marathon runner's heart has beaten during the race and how many litres of air have passed in and out of his lungs?

Would it surprise you to learn that the athlete's heart has beaten somewhere between 15,000 and 20,000 times during the course of the race? The lungs have breathed in somewhere between 5,000 and 10,000 litres of air – enough to fill a room as big as your classroom.

How do these anatomical processes happen? What can they tell us about athletes?

1.1 Understand the structure and function of the skeletal system

The skeletal system is made up of bones and joints. Without bones we would be shapeless heaps of muscles and organ tissue. Our joints allow movement. You need to know how the structure and the function of the skeletal system contribute to the range of motion required in sport and exercise.

Structure of skeletal system

The human skeleton is made up of 206 bones in total held together by connective tissue known as ligaments, whilst joints at the junction between two or more bones provide the mobility. Your skeleton forms a frame under which your internal organs sit and over which your muscles and skin are carefully situated.

Axial and appendicular skeleton

The bones of the human skeleton are divided into two groups: axial and appendicular. This distinction enables you to understand the functions of the skeleton more clearly.

The axial and appendicular skeleton ▶

Key

Axial skeleton

Appendicular skeleton

▼ **Bones of the human skeleton**

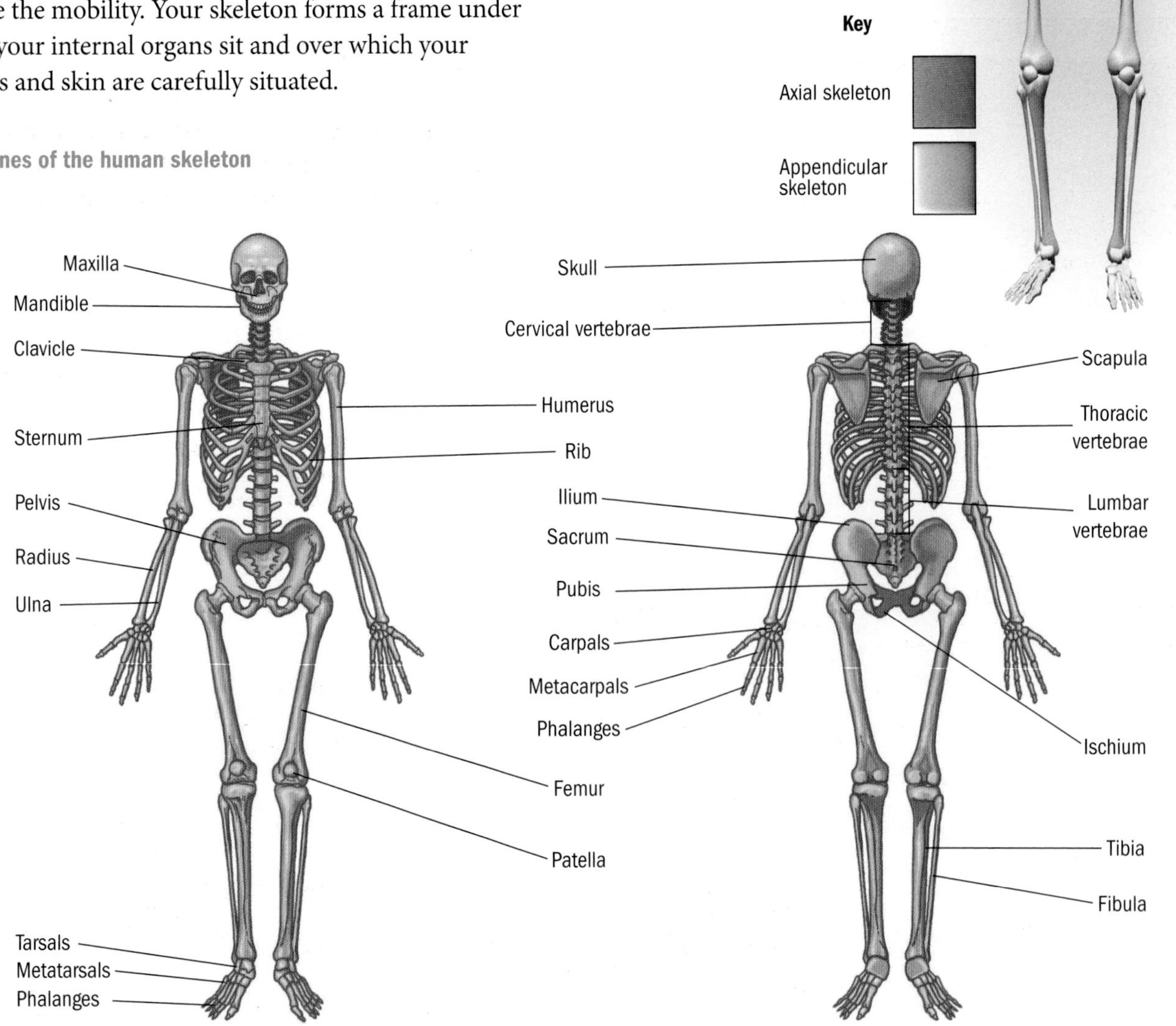

The axial skeleton: (a) the skull, (b) the rib cage and (c) the spine

- The axial skeleton forms the long axis of the body and includes the bones of the skull, rib cage and spine. These bones are most involved in protecting, supporting or carrying other body parts. For example, the skull is part of the axial skeleton and its purpose is to protect the brain.
- The appendicular skeleton consists of the bones of the upper and lower limbs, shoulders and pelvis. These bones help you get from place to place by directing and affecting your movement.

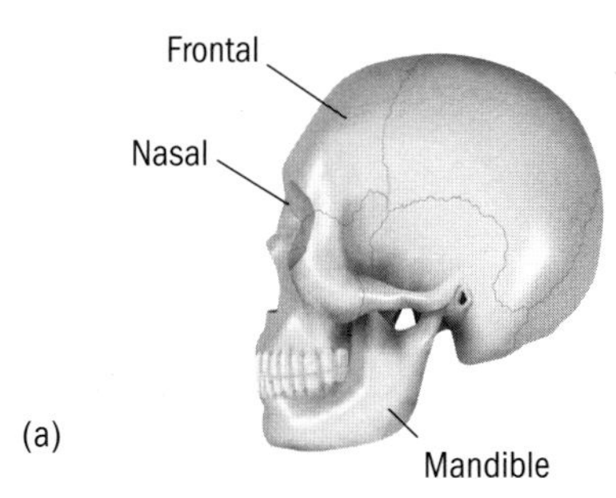

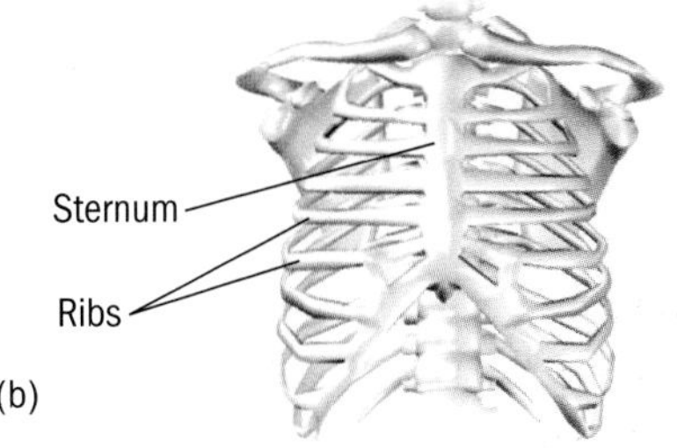

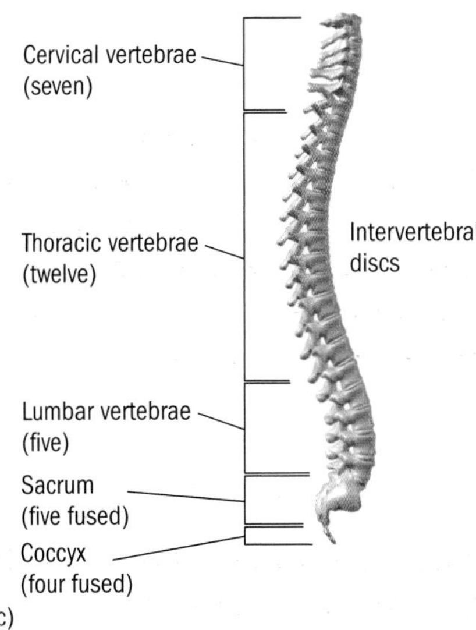

Activity

Using the diagram of the human skeleton opposite, make a list of the major bones in the axial and appendicular skeletons that play an important role in sport.

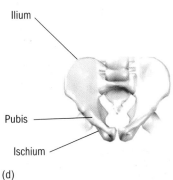

The appendicular skeleton: (a) the upper limbs, (b) the lower limbs, (c) the shoulder girdle and (d) the pelvis

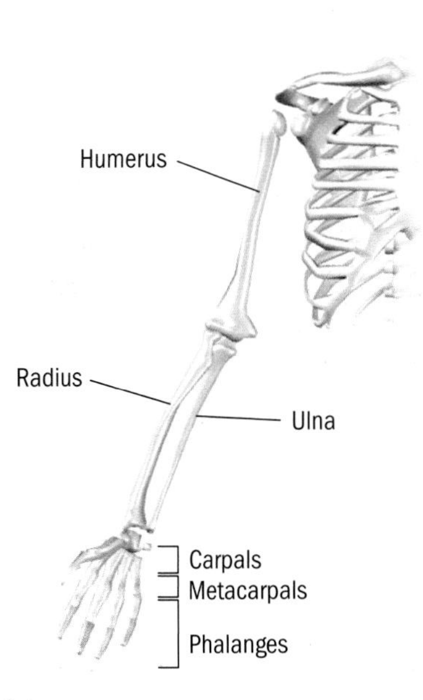

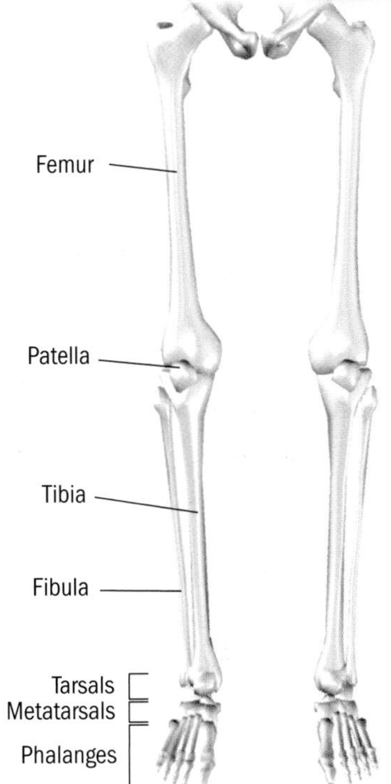

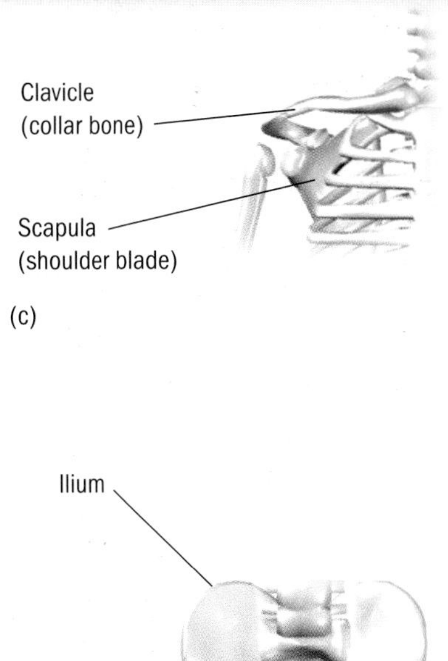

Key Terms

Axial skeleton Provides the main area of support and protection for the body. It includes the cranium (skull), the thorax (rib cage) and the vertebral column (spine).

Appendicular skeleton Consists of the bones of the limbs. It includes the femur, fibula and tibia in the legs, and the humerus, radius and ulna in the arms, together with the girdles that join on to the axial skeleton.

Types of bone

Bones come in a variety of shapes and sizes according to their specific functions. They are generally classified by their shape as long, short, flat, irregular or sesamoid.

Long bones

Long bones are longer than they are wide. A long bone has a shaft and two ends. All limb bones – with the exception of the patella (kneecap), wrist and ankle bones – are long bones. Examples are the fibula and tibia (bones in the lower leg).

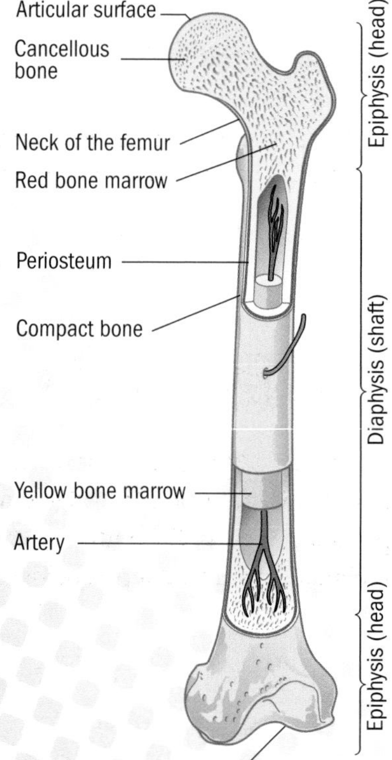

Long bones include the bones of the lower limbs, such as the femur, tibia and fibula

Short bones

Short bones are small, cube-shaped bones consisting of cancellous bone surrounded by a thin layer of compact bone. Short bones are like a sweet with a hard shell and a soft centre. Examples are the metacarpals, which are small bones in the hand.

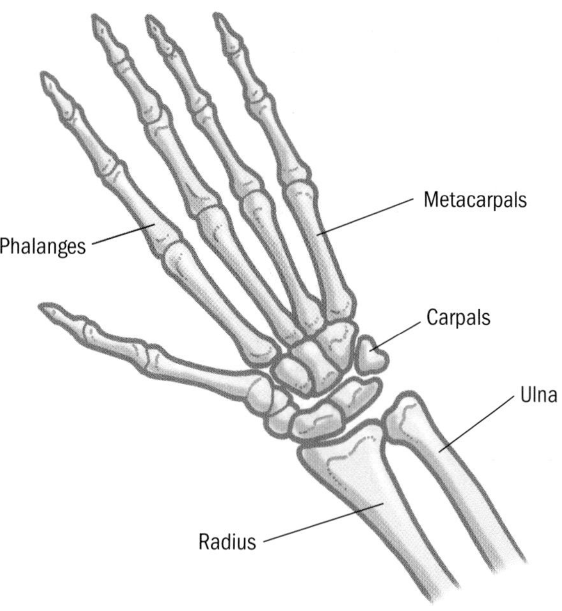

The metacarpals of the hand are examples of short bones

Key Terms

Cancellous bone Lightweight, honeycomb bone with a spongy appearance. It is found at the ends of long bones and in the centre of other bones.

Compact bone Forms the dense outer shell of bones. It has a smooth appearance.

Flat bones

Flat bones are thin, flattened and slightly curved. They have two outer layers of compact bone with cancellous tissue between them. The sternum (breast bone) and scapula are flat bones.

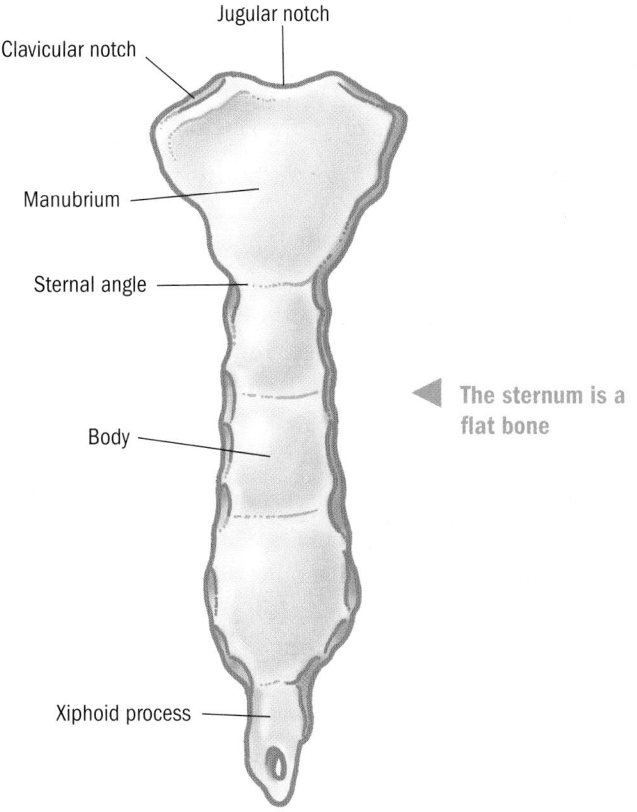

The sternum is a flat bone

Irregular bones

Irregular bones have complex shapes that fit none of the other categories of bone. The facial bone and vertebrae are good examples.

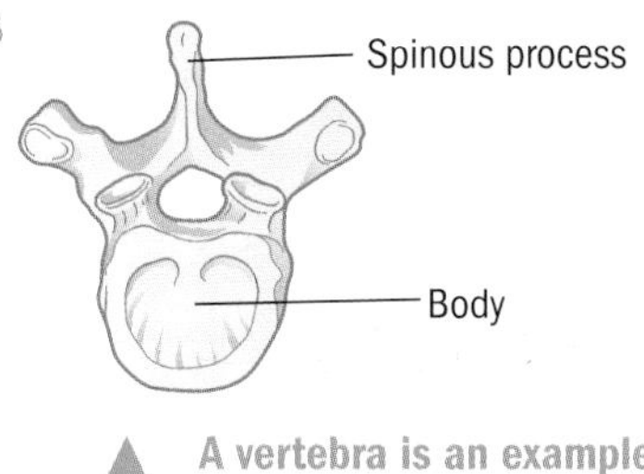

A vertebra is an example of an irregular bone

Sesamoid bones

Sesamoid bones have a specialised function: they ease joint movement and resist friction. They are usually found within tendons. They are covered with a layer of cartilage as they are found where bones articulate. Although usually small in appearance, sesamoid bones vary in size. The largest is the patella (kneecap), which is situated in the quadriceps femoris tendon.

The patella is a sesamoid bone

Activity

1. Look at the diagram of the skeleton on page 4. Identify at least two examples each of long, short, flat, irregular and sesamoid bones.
2. Explain the function of each type of bone in relation to physical activity.

Key Terms

Periosteum Connective tissue surrounding the bone. It has a supporting function, and when strong tendons, ligaments or muscle are attached to a bone, the periosteum is incorporated with them.

Bone marrow Fat- or blood-forming tissue found within bone cavities.

Remember!

Bones are made up of periosteum, compact bone, cancellous bone and bone marrow (see page 6).

Location of major bones

When considering the location and orientation of bones, it is important to understand how they relate to a particular view of the body. The table on page 8 explains the main anatomical terms below it.

Term	What it means
Anterior	To the front or in front
Posterior	To the rear or behind
Medial	Towards the mid-line
Lateral	Away from the mid-line
Proximal	Near to the root or origin
Distal	Away from the root or origin
Superior	Above
Inferior	Below

Main anatomical terms

Anatomical positions

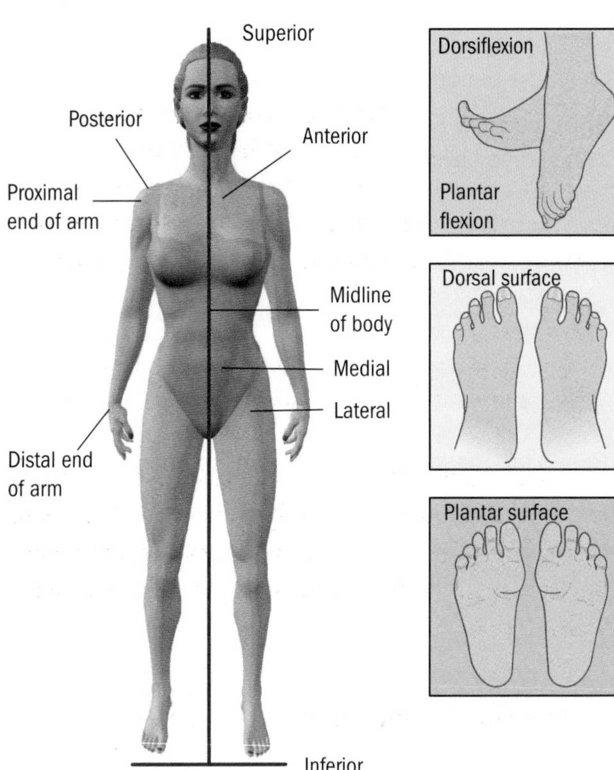

From top to bottom, the human skeleton is made up of the following groups.

- Skull: the bony framework of the head made up of facial and cranial bones, which form the cranium.
- Shoulder girdle: composed of four bones, two clavicles and two scapulae. The clavicle (collar bone) connects the humerus to the torso. One end of the clavicle is connected to the sternum and the other end to the scapula (shoulder blade). The scapula is a large, triangular, flat bone located on the back of the rib cage.
- Chest (thorax): made up of the ribs and sternum (breast bone) and exists to protect the heart and lungs. The sternum is a flat bone situated in the middle of the chest. Ribs are thin and flat, and number 24 in total (in 12 pairs). The first seven pairs from the top (superior) are connected to the spine and the sternum by cartilage. The next three pairs are attached to the spine at the rear and the rib above at the front. The last two pairs are known as floating ribs.
- Arm: made up of the humerus, radius and ulna. The humerus is the upper arm bone and fits into the scapula of the shoulder. The radius is located on the side away from the body (on same side as the thumb), while the ulna is located on the side towards the body.

Key Term

Innominate bone The hip bone, consisting of the ilium, ischium and pubis.

- Pelvic girdle: this is made of three bones: the ilium, ischium and pubis. These three bones fuse together with age and are collectively known as the innominate bone. The pelvic girdle supports the weight of the body from the vertebral column and offers protection for the digestive and reproductive organs.
- Hand: made up 27 bones located in three separate parts: the wrist, the palm and the fingers. The wrist contains eight small bones known as carpals. The palm consists of five metacarpals, one aligned with each of the fingers which, themselves, are made up of 14 bones called phalanges.
- Leg: the thigh is composed of a single bone called the femur, which is the longest, largest and strongest bone in the body. The lower leg contains the fibula and tibia (shin bone). The fibula is located on the lateral side of the body and the tibia on the medial side. The tibia is larger than the fibula because it bears most of the weight. The patella (kneecap) is

a large, triangular bone located within a tendon between the femur and tibia. It protects the knee joint and strengthens the tendon that forms the knee.

- Foot: made up of 26 bones located in three separate parts: the ankle, the instep and toes. The ankle contains seven tarsals. The metatarsals and phalanges of the foot are similar in number and position to the metacarpal and phalanges of the hand.
- Vertebral column (see page 5): also known as the spine, backbone or spinal column, this supports body parts, allows you to bend and twist, and protects the spinal cord. It is made up of 33 vertebrae that are divided into five categories: cervical, thoracic, lumbar, sacrum and coccyx.
- Cervical: the seven cervical vertebrae support the neck and head and let you bend, tilt and turn your head.
- Thoracic: the twelve thoracic vertebrae are connected to the ribs. They do not move much so that the heart and lungs do not get squashed.
- Lumbar: the five lumbar vertebrae allow twisting and turning. Powerful back muscles are attached to these vertebrae.
- Sacrum: the sacrum (five fused vertebrae) is fused to the pelvic girdle, making a solid base for the trunk and legs.
- Coccyx: the coccyx (four fused vertebrae) is the evolutionary remains of a tail.

Theory into practice

Using your knowledge of joints and anatomical movements, give examples of sporting activities you might witness an athlete performing and their associated movements. You may wish to use the table to help you.

Function of skeletal system

Bones give the body shape, protect and support the organs, provide levers for muscles to pull on, store calcium and other minerals, and are the site of blood cell production.

Support

Bones provide a framework that supports the body and gives it shape. For example, the lower limbs act as a support to the torso. The 206 bones of the skeleton provide a framework and points of attachment for many of the soft tissues of the body.

Protection

Bones protect the internal organs such as the brain, heart and lungs from damage. Our internal organs are particularly delicate compared with our muscles and bones. Therefore, the bones of the skull protect the brain, whereas the vertebrae surround and protect the spinal cord.

Attachment for skeletal muscle and leverage

Skeletal muscles, which are attached to bones by tendons, use bones as levers to initiate body movement. As a result we can walk, run, jump, etc., but remember that the type of joint (see page 10) determines the types of movement possible.

Sporting action	Major bone(s) involved	Joints involved
Javelin throw (upper body)	Humerus, radius and ulna	Shoulder and elbow

Source of blood cell production

Bones make blood. Some bones such as the femur and ribs contain red bone marrow, which produces red blood cells, some white blood cells and platelets. The main bones that are responsible for red blood cell production are the sternum, the vertebrae and the pelvis.

Store of minerals

Bone is a reservoir for minerals such as calcium and phosphate. The stored minerals are released into the bloodstream as required for distribution throughout the body when needed.

Deposits and withdrawals of minerals from bones are an ongoing process. These mineral bone stores have other additional uses, for example, the most important for adolescents is the storage of important growth factors that allow bones to grow and your body to take on an increased proportional appearance.

Remember!

The functions of the skeleton are shape, protection, movement, blood production and mineral storage.

Assessment practice

Create a large poster of the human skeleton to describe its structure and function, and illustrating the major bones. Your poster should describe the axial and appendicular skeleton, the different types of bone in the skeleton and visibly locate all major bones mentioned on pages 4 to 9. You also need to list the five functions of the skeleton. **P1**

Joints

Key Terms

Articulating surface The part of a bone which acts as a cushion between joints.

Articular (or hyaline) cartilage A smooth, slippery covering over bones that reduces friction.

Fibrocartilage A tough cartilage capable of absorbing heavy loads.

A joint is a site in the body where two or more bones meet. Joints are classified according to the amount of movement there is between the articulating surface of a bone. There are three types of joint in the human body: fixed, slightly movable and synovial.

Fixed

Fixed joints do not move. They interlock or overlap and are held together by bands of tough, fibrous tissue. An example of this type of joint is between plates in the cranium.

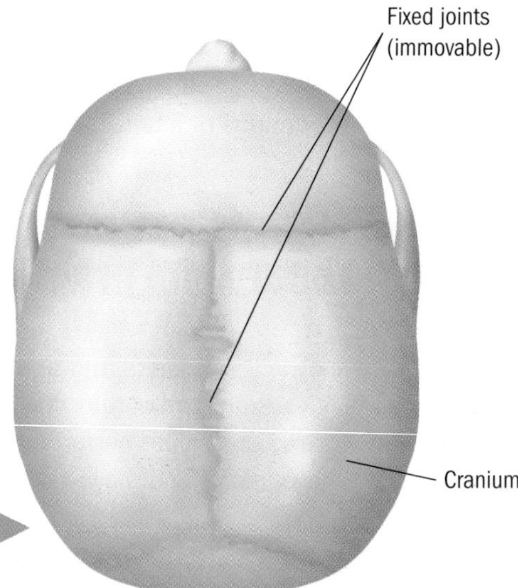

Fixed joints in the cranium

Slightly movable

Slightly movable (or cartilaginous) joints allow some slight movement. The ends of the bone are covered in articular cartilage which is separated by pads of white fibrocartilage. Slight movement at these articulating surfaces is made possible because the pads of cartilage compress. An example of this type of joint is between most vertebrae.

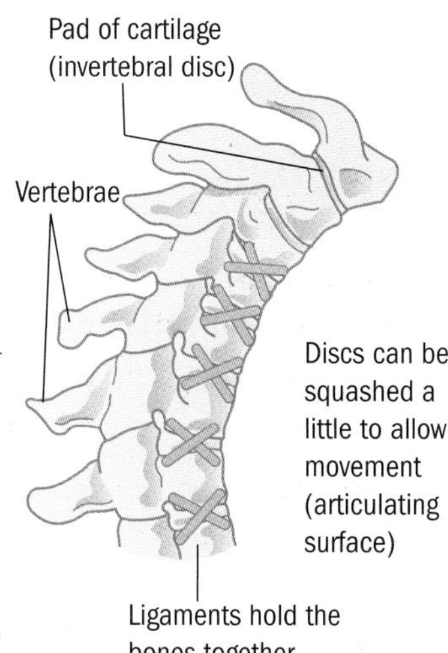

A slightly movable joint in the vertebral column

Synovial/freely moveable

A synovial joint is a freely moving joint in which the bones are separated by a joint cavity containing fluid. The bones are connected by ligaments while the ends of the bones are covered with articular cartilage.

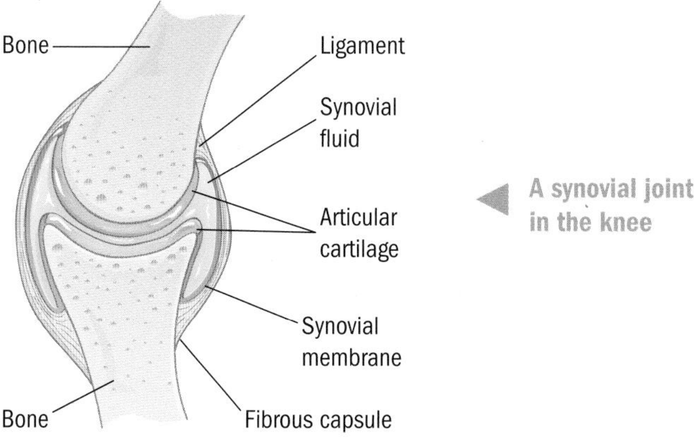

A synovial joint in the knee

All synovial joints contain the following parts.

- An outer sleeve or joint capsule: to help to hold the bones in place and protect the joint.
- A synovial membrane: the capsule lining that oozes a slippery, viscous liquid called synovial fluid. This acts as a lubricant to the knee joint.
- A joint cavity: the gap between the articulating bones. This is where the synovial fluid pools to lubricate the joint so that the bones can move more easily.
- Articular cartilage on the end of the bones: to provide a smooth and slippery covering to stop the bones knocking or grinding together.
- Ligaments: to hold the bones together and keep them in place.

Remember!

Here are the main differences between cartilage and ligaments.

Cartilage:

- protects bones and stops them knocking together
- forms a gristly cushion between bones in cartilaginous or slightly moveable joints
- forms a smooth, slippery coating on the end of bones in synovial joints.

Ligaments:

- are a strong binding material that fasten bones together
- hold a joint in place
- are slightly elastic to allow bones to move the way they should.

Movement at each joint

- Fixed joints: these are also known as fibrous joints and, as the name implies, allow no movement across the joint. Examples include the joints found in the skull.
- Slightly moveable joints: these are also known as cartilaginous joints. They allow a small amount of movement and are linked by cartilage. These types of joints can be found between the ribs and sternum, and the vertebrae in the spine.
- Synovial joints: there are 70 synovial joints in the skeletal system and they account for much of our wide range of movement. There are several types of synovial joint, each of which has a different structure and function.

- Gliding: flat surfaces can glide over each other providing a little movement in all directions. Examples include the joints between carpals in the hand.
- Hinge: the joint can swing open until it is straight, rather like a car door. Examples include the elbow and knee joints.
- Pivot: a ring on one bone fits over the peg of another, allowing controlled rotational movement. Examples include the head of the radius rotating within a ring-like ligament secured to the ulna.
- Condyloid: a bump on one bone sits in the hollow formed by another. Movement is backwards and forwards and from side to side. Ligaments often prevent rotation. An example is the wrist joint.
- Saddle: the ends are shaped like saddles and fit neatly together. Movement is backwards and forwards and from side to side. An example is the joint at the base of the thumb.
- Ball and socket: the round end of one bone fits into a hollow in the other bone and can move in numerous directions. Examples include the hip and shoulder joints.

Types of movement at a synovial joint

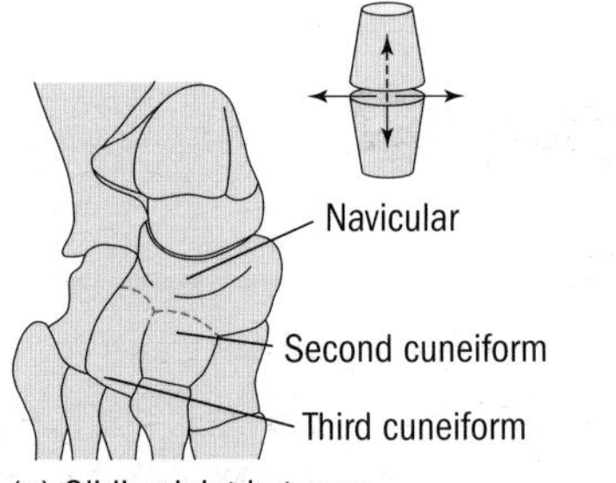

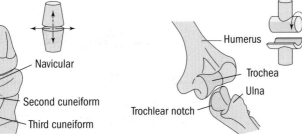

(a) Gliding joint between the navicular and second and third cuneiforms of the tarsus in the foot

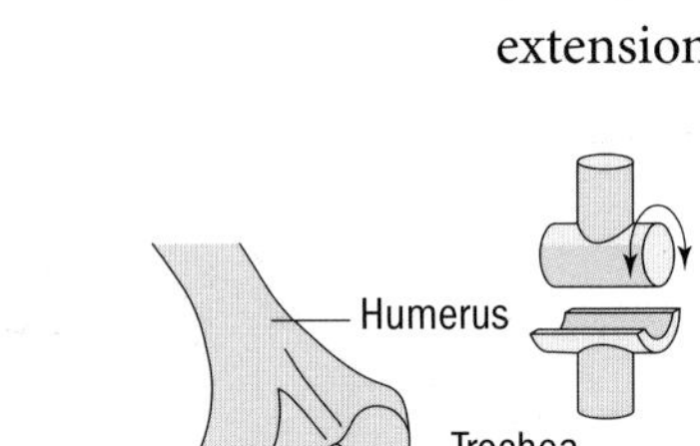

(b) Hinge joint between trochlea of humerus and trochlear notch of ulna at the elbow

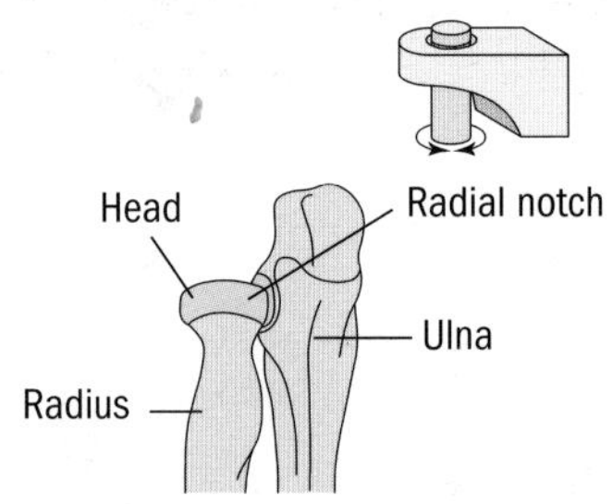

(c) Pivot joint between head of radius and radial notch of ulna

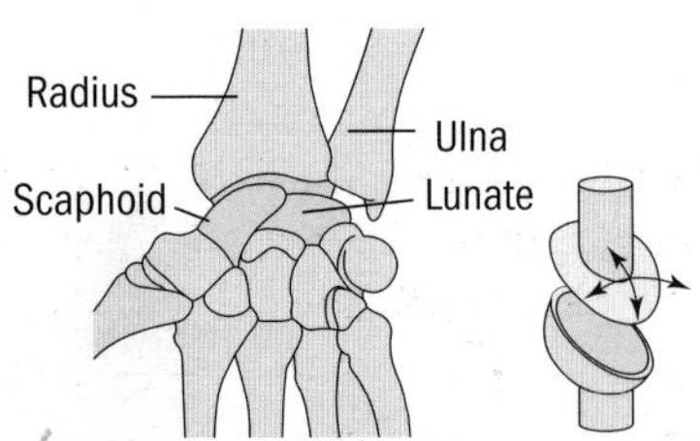

(d) Condyloid joint between radius and scaphoid and lunate bones of the carpus (wrist)

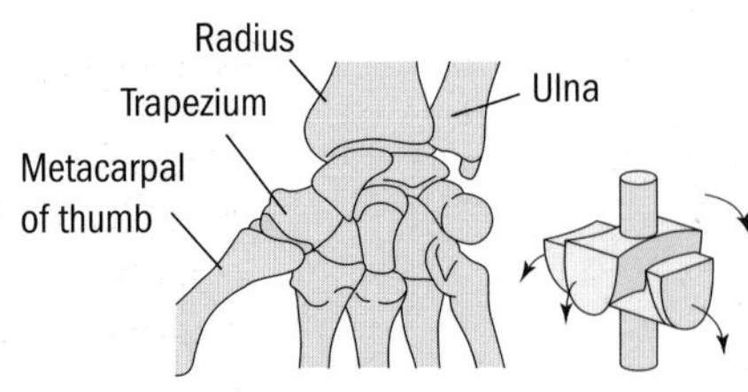

(e) Saddle joint between trapezium of carpus (wrist) and metacarpal of thumb

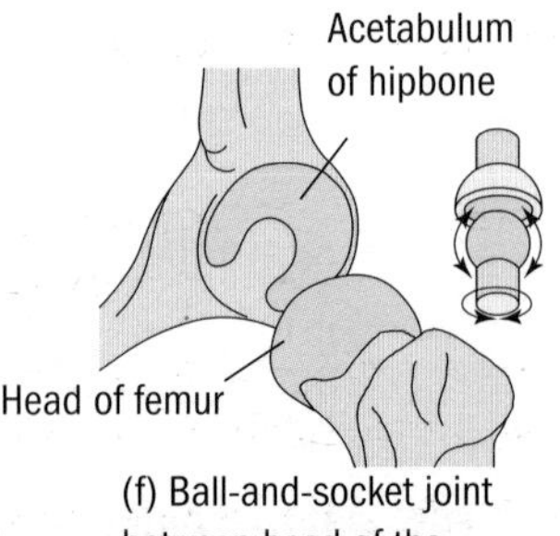

(f) Ball-and-socket joint between head of the femur and acetabulum of the hipbone

Movement available

Flexion

This means to bend the limb, reducing the angle at the joint. This occurs at the knee when you prepare to kick a football or rugby ball.

Extension

This means to straighten a limb, increasing the angle at the joint. This occurs at the elbow when you shoot in netball.

Adduction

This means movement towards the body. This occurs at the shoulder when you pull on an oar while rowing.

Abduction

This means movement away from the body. This occurs at the hip during a side step in gymnastics.

Rotation

This means that the limb moves in a circle. Rotation or circumduction is simply a combination of flexion, extension, adduction and abduction. True circumduction

– which means moving a limb through a full 360° circle – can only occur at ball and socket joints such as the shoulder and hip. Rotation occurs at the shoulder joint during a tennis serve.

Pronation

Pronation is an inward rotation of the forearm so that the palm of the hand is facing backwards and downwards. This occurs at the wrist joint during a table tennis forehand topspin shot.

Supination

Supination is an outward rotation of the forearm so that the palm of the hand is facing forwards and upwards. This occurs at the wrist joint during a table tennis backhand topspin shot.

Plantar flexion

This is a movement that points the toes downwards by straightening the ankle. This occurs at the ankle when jumping to shoot in basketball.

Hyper-extension

This involves movement beyond the normal anatomical position in a direction opposite to flexion. This occurs at the spine when a cricketer arches his or her back when approaching the crease to bowl.

Case study

Wayne Rooney

Before the 2006 FIFA World Cup in Germany, Wayne Rooney suffered a fractured metatarsal in his right foot during a premiership match while playing for Manchester United. His place in the England football squad was in serious doubt given the nature of his injury.

1 **Draw and label a diagram to identify exactly which bone Wayne Rooney fractured.**
2 **Give details of the bone's type, function and location, and type of the nearest joint.**
3 **Explain why such an injury might cause problems for a footballer.**

Assessment practice

1 Draw a table that describes the different types of joints and the range of movement available to them. Your table should describe all three classifications of joint and be able to describe the amount of movement allowed at each. **P2**

2 Within your table, compare and contrast joints, highlighting the differences in their construction and their range of movement. Provide examples from different sports that illustrate your comparisons. Your table should examine each of the classification of joints, including all six synovial joints, and their relevance to sporting activities. Explain how and why the range of movement differs. **M1**

Taking it further

Carry out some research to find out how many weeks a broken metatarsal would usually take to heal.

grading tips

Grading Tip M1

You must be able to describe the different classifications of joints and the range of movement available at each. If you can provide real working examples, these will help to show this. Ensure you choose different sports (as that will determine your grade as well).

Grading Tip M1

The merit criteria demands a bit more from you, in terms of the quality of what you produce as evidence and in terms of complexity, so pay attention to detail in your responses. 'Explaining' means showing that you know how to compare and contrast the different classifications of joints and the range of movement available at each.

1.2 Understand the structure and function of the muscular system

Muscular system

The muscles that move your bones when you exercise are skeletal muscles. There are over 640 named muscles in the human body.

Major muscles

Trying to remember all the names, locations and actions of the major muscles is a huge task. Therefore, from a sports perspective, the main ones you should remember are outlined in the table opposite.

Key Terms

Origin A muscle's origin is attached to the immovable (or less moveable) bone.

Insertion A muscle's insertion is attached to the movable bone.

Olecranon process Forms part of the elbow; located at the proximal end of the ulna.

Acromion Roughened triangular projection atop of the scapula.

Xiphoid process Forms the inferior (or sword-like) end of the sternum.

Pubic crest An inferior and anterior portion of the pelvis located next to the pubic arc.

Striations Skeletal muscle is striated. This means that the fibres contain alternating light and dark bands (striations) that are perpendicular to the long axes of the fibres.

▼ (a) Posterior muscular system and (b) anterior muscular system

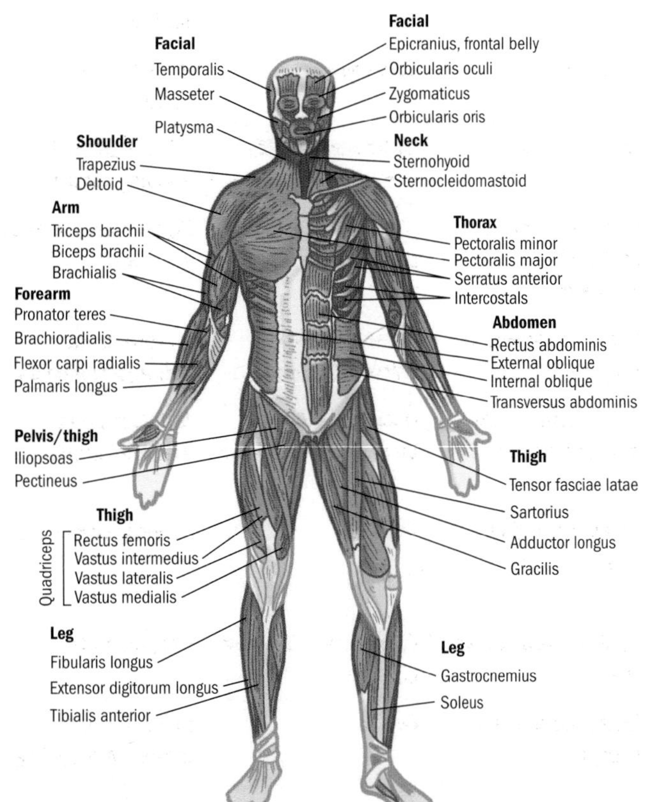

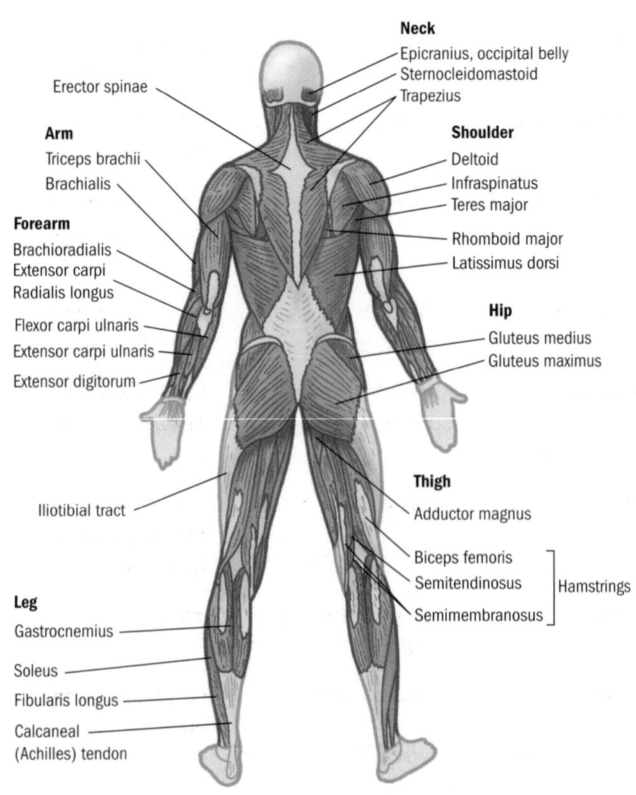

Muscle	Function	Location	Origin	Insertion	Exercise
Biceps	Flexes lower arm	Inside upper arm	Scapula	Radius	Arm curls, chin-ups
Triceps	Extends lower arm	Outside upper arm	Humerus and scapula	Olecranon process	Press-ups, dips, overhead pressing
Deltoids	Abducts, flexes and extends upper arm	Forms cap of shoulder	Clavicle, scapula and acromion	Humerus	Forward, later and back-arm raises, overhead lifting
Pectoralis major	Flexes and adducts upper arm	Large chest muscle	Sternum, clavicle and rib cartilage	Humerus	All pressing movements
Rectus abdominis	Flexion and rotation of lumbar region of vertebral column	'Six-pack' muscle running down abdomen	Pubic crest and symphysis	Xiphoid process	Sit-ups
Quadriceps -- rectus femoris -- vastus lateralis -- vastus medialis -- vastus intermedius	Extends lower leg and flexes thigh	Front of thigh	Illium and femur	Tibia and fibula	Knee bends, squats
Hamstrings -- semimembranosus -- semitendinosus -- biceps femoris	Flexes lower leg and extends thigh	Back of thigh	Ischium and femur	Tibia and fibula	Extending leg and flexing knee (running)
Gastrocnemius	Plantar flexion flexes knee	Large calf muscle	Femur	Calcaneius	Running, jumping and standing on tip-toe
Soleus	Plantar flexion	Deep to gastrocnemius	Fibula and tibia	Calcaneius	Running and jumping
Tibialis anterior	Dorsiflexion of foot	Front of tibia on lower leg	Lateral condyle	By tendon to surface of medial cuneiform	All running and jumping exercises
Erector spinae	Extension of spine	Long muscle running either side of spine	Cervical, thoracic and lumbar vertebrae	Cervical, thoracic and lumbar vertebrae	Prime mover of back extension
Teres major	Rotates and abducts humerus	Between scapula and humerus	Posterior surface of scapula	Intertubercular sulcus of humerus	All rowing and pulling movements
Trapezius	Elevates and depresses scapula	Large triangular muscle at top of back	Continuous insertion along acromion	Occipital bone and all thoracic vertebrae	Shrugging and overhead lifting
Latissimus dorsi	Extends and adducts lower arm	Large muscle covering back of lower ribs	Vertebrae and iliac crest	Humerus	Rowing movements
Obliques	Lateral flexion of trunk	Waist	Pubic crest and iliac crest	Fleshy strips to lower eight ribs	Oblique curls
Gluteus maximus	Extends thigh	Large muscle on buttocks	Ilium, sacrum and coccyx	Femur	Knee-bending movements, cycling

Major muscles and their functions

Key Terms

Calcaneius Major portion of the heel bone.

Occipital bone Forms most of the skull's posterior wall and base.

Iliac crest When you rest your hands on your hips, you are resting them on the iliac crests.

Theory into practice

Find an anatomical model of a skeleton (preferably half size), and a large piece of modelling clay.

Use the clay to construct the following muscles and fix them over the skeleton in their correct positions:

- deltoids
- biceps
- trapezius
- pectoralis major
- hamstrings.

Once completed, ask your tutor to verify you have completed the task successfully.

Assessment practice

Find a poster-sized piece of paper and draw the outline of a human on it (use page 14 to help). Identify the location, function, origin and insertion of the major muscles and draw them on the poster (see page 15).

Your poster should identify the location of all the major muscles and indicate the origin and insertion of each of these muscles. You should also include a clear description of the function of the muscular system. **P3**

Types of muscle

All movement that takes place in the body depends on the actions of muscles. They work by shortening, lengthening and, in some cases, remaining static or still. There are three main types of muscle tissue: cardiac, skeletal and smooth.

Key Terms

Cardiac muscle Specialised muscle of the heart.

Skeletal muscle Voluntary muscle with obvious striations that attaches to the body's skeleton.

Smooth muscle Muscle with no visible striations found mainly in the walls of hollow organs.

Cardiac

Cardiac muscle is found only in the wall of the heart. Its contractions help force blood through the blood vessels to all parts of the body.

Remember!

Cardiac muscle:

- forms the walls of the heart
- works non-stop throughout life
- is involuntary (meaning not under conscious control)
- has its own blood supply.

Skeletal

Skeletal or voluntary muscle accounts for much of the muscle tissue in the body. This type of muscle is voluntary, which means it is under conscious control and you control the contraction. It is attached to bones or occasionally skin. When stimulated, skeletal muscle moves a part of the skeleton such as the arm or leg.

Remember!

Skeletal muscle:

- is attached to bones
- works when you want it to (for example, when you take part in sport)
- is also known as voluntary muscle
- is also called striped or striated muscle, which means the muscle fibres are marled with striations.

Smooth

Smooth muscle is an involuntary muscle that lines the walls of organs. It is well adapted to producing long and slow contractions that are not under voluntary control. Smooth muscle is found in the body where movement occurs without conscious thought, such as with the passage of food or blood in the system. These long, slow contractions would be of little use to skeletal muscles, as they require fast or deliberate movement.

Except for the heart, which is made of cardiac muscle, the muscle in the walls of all the body's hollow organs – such as the stomach, intestines and blood vessels – are almost entirely smooth muscle.

Remember!

Smooth muscle:

- works without you knowing, as its contractions are involuntary
- is found in the walls of internal organs such as arteries, stomach and intestines, (for example, when the smooth muscle in the intestines contracts, it forces food through the digestive system)
- is also known as involuntary muscle.

Key Terms

Aerobic Requires oxygen.

Anaerobic Does not require oxygen.

This table summarises the different characteristics of each muscle type.

Muscle	Location	Speed of contractions	Respiration
Cardiac	Heart	Slow	Aerobic
Skeletal	Attached to bones	Slow to fast	Aerobic and anaerobic
Smooth	Hollow organs and arteries	Slow	Mainly aerobic

Characteristics of each muscle type

Fibre types

Key Terms

Sarcomeres The smallest unit of a contractile muscle.

Myofilaments Filaments that make up myofibrils and constitute either actin or myosin.

Smooth muscle fibres contain no striations and sarcomeres. However, the fibres do contain filaments, but they are much longer than those in skeletal muscle and the type of myosin contained differs in smooth muscle. The proportion and organisation of myofilaments are also different.

Two main types of striated skeletal muscle can be distinguished on the basis of their speed of contraction: type 1 (slow twitch) and type 2 (fast twitch). The human body consists of both types of fibre.

Key Terms

Adenosine triphosphate (ATP) Stores and releases chemical energy for use in body cells.

Myoglobin Oxygen-binding pigment in muscle.

Haemoglobin Oxygen-transporting protein found in red blood cells.

Oxyhaemoblogin Oxygen-bound form of haemoglobin.

Mitochondria Organelles responsible for ATP production for energy use.

Type 1

Type 1 fibres are also called slow-twitch muscle fibres. They have a slower contraction time, and consequently are better suited to low intensity, long-duration endurance work (see table, page 19).

Type 1 fibres have a high capacity for aerobic respiration, a process that uses oxygen to produce energy in the form of adenosine triphosphate (ATP), because of their blood supply. Type 1 fibres have a greater number of capillaries per fibre than Type 2 fibres. Type 1 fibres also have greater levels of myoglobin, an iron-containing pigment present in muscle tissue that acts as a store for oxygen and can be used during strenuous exercise. Myoglobin has a greater attraction for oxygen than haemoglobin, the oxygen-transporting component of red blood cells. As a result, myoglobin takes oxygen from the oxyhaemoglobin in the blood, and in turn acts as a store of oxygen within the muscle, releasing it to the mitochondria for production of energy in the form of ATP.

Remember!

Type 1 fibres:

- contract slowly and with minimal power
- do not tire easily
- suit activities that need endurance, such as long-distance running and swimming.

Type 2a

Type 2a fibres (also called fast-twitch or fast-oxidative fibres) contain large amounts of myoglobin, many mitochondria and blood capillaries.

Type 2a fibres are red, have a high capacity for generating ATP by oxidative metabolic processes and split ATP at a rapid rate. They also have a fast contraction velocity and are resistant to fatigue (see table, page 19).

Key Terms

Lactic acid Product of anaerobic metabolism, especially in muscle tissue.

Anaerobic glycolycis Conversion of glucose to lactic acid in muscle tissue when sufficient oxygen is not available.

Type 2b

Type 2b fibres (also called fast-twitch or fast-glycolytic fibres) contain a low content of myoglobin, relatively few mitochondria, blood capillaries and large amounts glycogen.

Type 2b fibres are white, generate ATP by anaerobic metabolic processes and are not able to supply skeletal muscle fibres continuously with sufficient ATP.

Type 2b fibres also fatigue easily, split ATP at a rapid rate and have a very fast contraction velocity (see table, page 19).

Remember!

Type 2 fibres:

- contract quickly with fast, powerful contractions
- tire easily
- suit activities that require sudden bursts of power, such as weightlifting or sprinting.

Characteristics

Type 1	Type 2a	Type 2b
Red	Red	White
Contract slowly	Contract rapidly (but not as fast as type 2b)	Contract rapidly
Aerobic	Aerobic	Anaerobic
Endurance-based such as cycling and long-distance running	Middle-distance such as ice skating	Speed- and strength-based such as sprinting and rugby
Can contract repeatedly	Fairly resistant to fatigue	Easily exhausted
Exert minimal force	Exert medium	Exert great force

Characteristics of each fibre type

Types of sport each are associated with

All types of muscle fibre are used in all types of exercise. Although Type 1 fibres are particularly adapted to low-intensity aerobic endurance work, they are generally employed at the beginning of exercise (regardless of the intensity of exercise). Type 2 fibres adapt to high-intensity anaerobic exercise involving explosive or powerful movements, but they are also increasingly employed during low intensity endurance-workouts as performer fatigue increases.

Think it over

Long-distance runners, especially those racing on the track, are generally able to finish their race with a sprint if needed. If they have a dominant number of Type 1 fibres, how is this possible?

Force production

The forces involved in muscular contractions in Type 2 (fast twitch) fibres are far greater than in Type 1 (slow twitch) fibres. The greater force is related to the size of the individual fibres and the number of fibres making up the muscle unit. Both the size and number of fibres are greater in Type 2 muscles.

Think it over

Every athlete in the 100-metre final at the Athens Olympics in 2004 was of African-Caribbean descent. Is this coincidence or do African-Caribbean sprint athletes possess an advantage in terms of their concentration of Type 2 muscle fibres that are so vital for sprinting?

Muscle movement

In order to understand the different types of muscle movement, it is necessary to know about the structure of muscle tissue.

Skeletal muscle contains bundles of cells called muscle fibres, together with nerves that carry messages to and from the brain. A muscle contracts when messages from the brain race along the nerves to the fibres, telling them to shorten, lengthen or tense.

Each fibre is made up of many contractile protein myofibrils. A myofibril is a rod-like bundle of myofilaments running the length of a muscle fibre. Each myofibril is in turn composed of many overlapping protein threads or filaments known as myofilaments. Each myofibril is divided along its length into a repeating series of units or sarcomeres, which are the fundamental functional units of muscle.

Each skeletal muscle fibre is a long cylindrical cell surrounded by a sarcolemma, the cell membrane surrounding a muscle fibre. It consists of a multinucleate fibre and is designed specifically for contraction. The sarcolemma is very thin to enable efficient diffusion of oxygen and glucose into the cell, and carbon dioxide out of the cell.

Muscles work across joints. One end is usually attached to a fixed bone and the other end to a movable bone. When the muscle contracts, it pulls on the movable bone.

Remember!

- The origin is where the muscle joins the fixed bone.
- The insertion is where it joins the moving bone.
- On contraction, the insertion moves towards the origin.

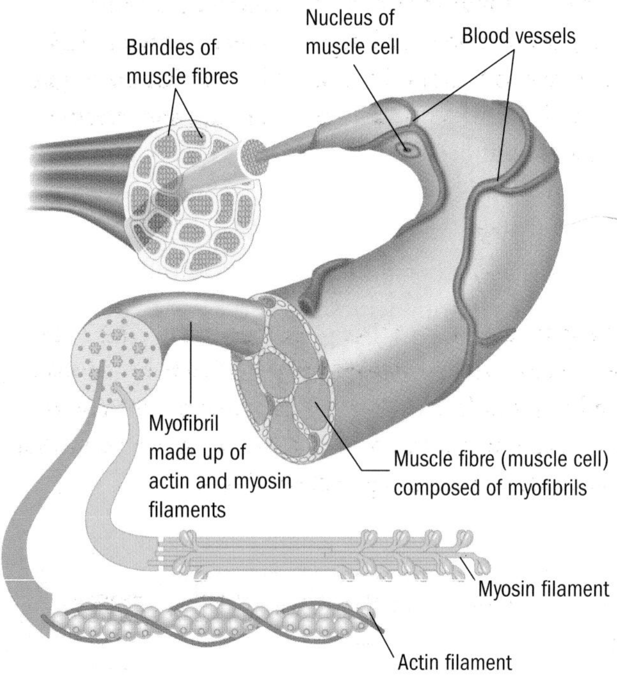

▲ Cross-section of skeletal muscle

Key Term

Contractile protein myofibrils Rod-like bundle of contractile filaments found in muscle fibres.

Key Terms

Sarcolemma Plasma membrane surface of a muscle fibre.

Multinucleate fibre Fibre made up of cells consisting of more than one nucleus.

Isometric contractions Muscle contracts but does not shorten, giving no movement.

Sliding filament theory

The sliding filament theory explains how muscles contract. During contraction, myosin (green filaments in diagram) attach on to actin (blue filaments) by forming chemical bonds called crossbridges.

Muscle cells are composed of actin and myosin molecules in series. This basic unit of a muscle cell is known as a sarcomere. It is sarcomeres that give skeletal muscle tissue its striated appearance.

The mechanisms involved for muscular contraction are simple. The myosin molecules act like a ratchet, whilst the actin molecules form passive filaments that transmit the force generated by the myosin to the ends of the muscle tissue.

In short, the mechanism of the sliding filament theory involves the myosin progressing along an actin filament, constantly binding, ratcheting, and then letting go. This process of binding and ratcheting is what allows muscles to contract (i.e. shorten).

When the muscle does not need to contract, thin strands of a further protein (called tropomyosin) are wrapped around the actin filaments to stop the myosin from bonding.

As a muscle undergoes contraction:

- molecules called troponin attach to the tropomyosin
- calcium ions are introduced into the muscle cell and these bind with the troponin
- calcium binding changes the shape of the troponin, causing the tropomyosin to move and exposing the actin
- myosin is now free to bind with the actin and the muscle contracts (according to the sliding filament theory).

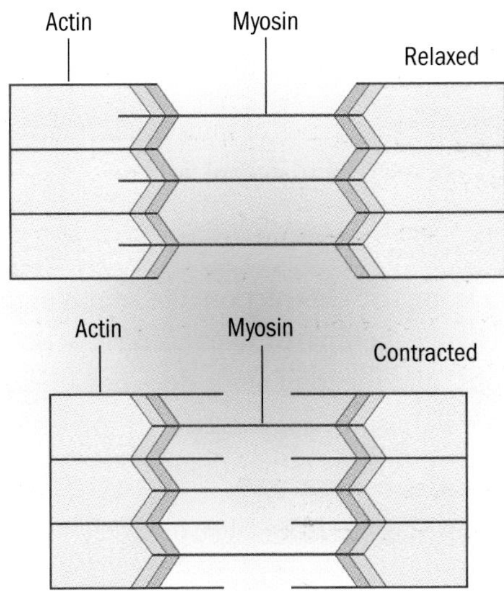

Sliding filament theory 

Troponin and tropomyosin

Troponin and tropomyosin are proteins that form part of the thin or actin filament. Tropomyosin is a rod-shaped protein that spirals about the actin core to stiffen it. Troponin, on the other hand, binds to the tropomyosin and helps it bind to the actin.

Calcium ions

Calcium plays a vital role in the anatomy and physiology of the cell. The skeleton acts as a major mineral storage site for the element and releases calcium ions into the bloodstream under controlled conditions. Circulating calcium is either in ionised form or bound to blood proteins such as troponin. The ions are stored in the sarcoplasmic reticulum of muscle cells.

Antagonistic pairs

Skeletal muscles are normally arranged in pairs, so that one muscle is contracting while the opposing muscle is relaxing. The muscle that shortens to move a joint is called the agonist (or prime mover). The muscle that relaxes in opposition is called the antagonist.

A muscle that acts as an agonist for one movement can act as an antagonist for the opposite movement. For example, the bicep contracts (agonist) while the tricep (antagonist) relaxes during the up-phase of an arm-curl. However, during the down-phase of an arm curl, the reverse occurs. The tricep contracts (agonist) while the bicep (antagonist) relaxes. This action of the muscles working in pairs is known as antagonistic muscle action.

Fixator

Fixators stabilise the origin, so that the agonist can achieve maximum and effective contraction. When synergists immobilise a bone or a muscle's origin, they are known as fixators. These muscles stabilise the origin so that the agonist can achieve maximum and effective contraction.

Synergist

Synergists are muscles that work together to enable the agonists to operate more effectively. They help agonists by adding a little extra force to the same movement, or by reducing unnecessary or undesirable movements that might occur when the agonist contracts.

Activity

Copy and complete this table by filling in details about the agonist, antagonist, fixators and synergists involved in each type of exercise. Use the major muscle table on page 15 to help you.

Exercise	Agonist	Antagonist	Fixator	Synergist
Squat				
Upright row (standing)				
Sit-up				
Barbell curl (standing)				

Remember!

The agonist is the prime mover, the antagonist is the muscle that works opposite the agonist, synergists assist the agonist, and fixators immobilise the bone (or agonist muscle's origin).

Assessment practice

Produce a guide or leaflet for professional athletes to aid their understanding of muscle types. Include the following information in your guide.

1 a Details to explain each of the three classifications of muscle types.

b Details about the different muscle fibre types. **P4**

2 a An explanation for why the three classifications of muscle have different properties related to their functions.

b Details about why and how the various fibre types differ. **M2**

grading tips

Grading Tip **P4**

You must be able to describe the different types of muscle and the different muscle fibre types. If you can provide real working examples, these will help to show this. Ensure you choose different sports (as that will determine your grade as well).

Grading Tip **M2**

The merit criteria demands a bit more from you, in terms of the quality of what you produce as evidence and in terms of complexity, so pay attention to detail in your responses. 'Explaining' means showing how to compare and contrast the properties of the different types of muscle and the different muscle fibre types.

Types of contraction

There are three main types of muscle contraction: isometric, concentric and eccentric.

Isometric

During an isometric contraction, the length of the muscle does not change (compared to concentric or eccentric contractions) and the joint angle does not alter. As there is no movement, isometric exercises or movements are done in static positions rather than being dynamic.

During an isometric contraction, the gymnast's muscles do not shorten but they work hard nonetheless

Concentric

Concentric contraction is the main type of muscle contraction. In this type of contraction, the muscle gets shorter and the two ends of the muscle move closer together. This type of contraction is seen in the biceps muscle of the arm when performing a bicep curl.

In a concentric contraction, the muscle shortens

Eccentric

In eccentric muscle contraction, the muscle increases in length while still producing tension. The two ends of the muscle move further apart. For example, in the lowering phase of a bicep curl, the biceps are working eccentrically to control the lowering of the weight.

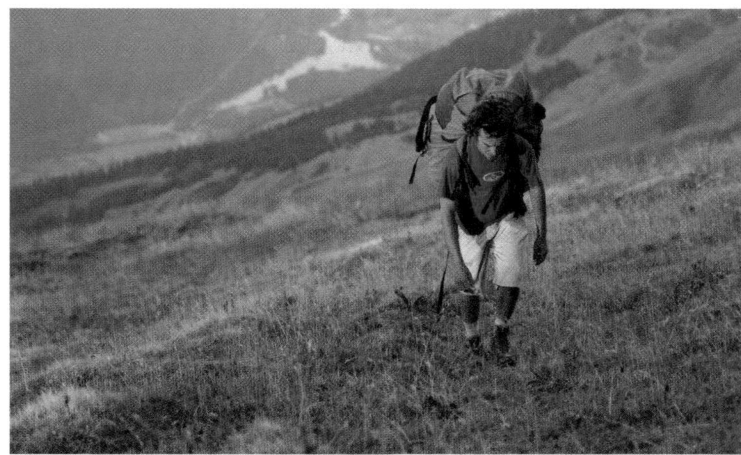

Eccentric contractions, in which the muscle generates force as it lengthens, occurs in the calf muscle when walking uphill

Assessment practice

1 Using the example of the press-up (on the upwards phase), describe how the muscles produce movement (agonist, antagonist, fixator and synergist) and the different types of contraction that occur during the movement. **P2**

2 Using the aid of a flow diagram, explain how the muscles of the body produce movement during the press-up and the different types of contraction that occur, further explaining the sliding filament theory. **M3**

grading tips

Grading Tip  **P5**

You must be able to describe how muscles produce movement and the different types of contraction. If you can provide real working examples, these will help to show this. Ensure you choose different sports as that will determine your grade as well.

Grading Tip **M3**

The merit criteria demands a bit more from you, in terms of the quality of what you produce as evidence and in terms of complexity, so pay attention to detail in your responses. 'Explaining' means showing how to explain how muscles produce movement and the different types of contraction.

1.3 Understand the structure and function of the cardiovascular system

Structure

Heart

The heart is a muscular organ in the circulatory system that constantly pumps blood throughout the body. Approximately the size of a clenched fist, the heart is composed of cardiac muscle tissue that is very strong, and able to contract and relax rhythmically throughout life.

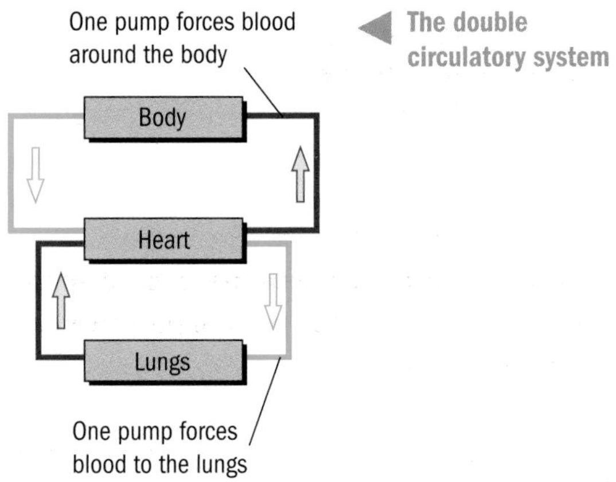
One pump forces blood around the body
Body
Heart
Lungs
One pump forces blood to the lungs

The double circulatory system

The heart is in effect two pumps in one. The right side receives oxygen-poor blood from the body and delivers it to the lungs. In the lungs, oxygen is taken in by the blood. The left side of the heart receives the oxygen-rich blood from the lungs and delivers it to the rest of the body.

Heart wall

The heart wall is made up of three layers.

- Endocardium lines the inner heart chambers and allows the blood to flow freely.
- Myocardium is the middle layer. It is composed mainly of cardiac muscle and forms the bulk of the heart. The myocardium is the layer that contracts.

> **Key Term**
>
> **Serous pericardium** A thin, slippery, two-layer serous membrane that, on the one hand lines part of the internal surface of the heart and, on the other, lines a cavity that lubricates the heart and allows it to work in a relatively friction-free environment.

- Epicardium is a superficial layer of the serous pericardium, a double-layered envelope surrounding the heart that prevents overextension during heart beats.

Atria and ventricles

The heart has four separate chambers: two atria and two ventricles. The upper chambers on each side are called the left atrium and the right atrium. The lower chambers are called the left and right ventricles.

The atria receive and collect the blood coming to the heart. They then deliver blood to the lower left and right ventricles, which pump blood away from the heart through powerful, rhythmic contractions.

The atria are the receiving chambers for blood returning to the heart from the body. They need to contract only minimally to push blood into the ventricles, so the atria are relatively small, thin-walled chambers.

The left and right ventricles make up most of the volume of the heart. They are the discharging chambers of the heart. When ventricles contract, blood is pumped out of the heart into the circulation and around the body.

- The right ventricle pumps blood into the pulmonary artery, which routes the blood to the lungs where gas exchange occurs.
- The left ventricle pumps blood into the aorta, the largest artery, which takes the oxygenated blood away from the heart and around the body. This ventricle has a thick wall because it has to pump blood around the body.

The heart ▶

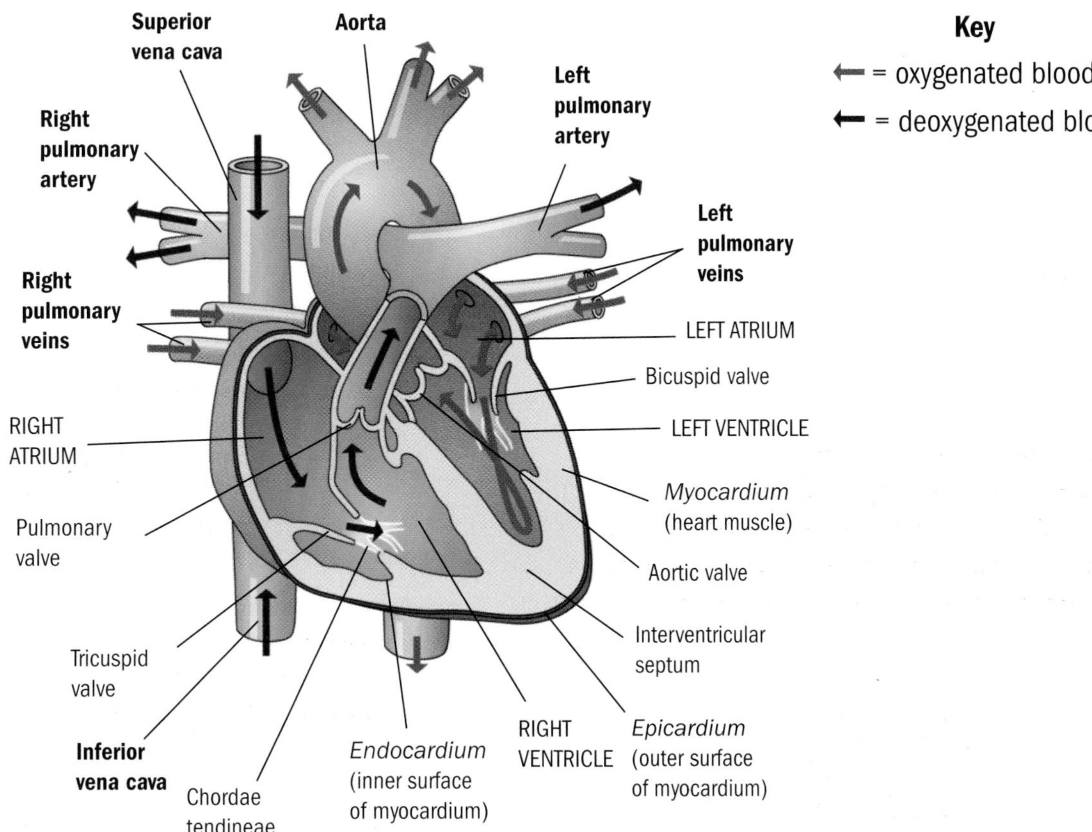

■ Bicuspid valve and tricuspid valve

The bicuspid valve is situated between the left atrium and the left ventricle. It permits blood to flow one way only, from the left atrium into the left ventricle.

The tricuspid valve is situated between the right atrium and the right ventricle. It allows blood to flow from the right atrium into the right ventricle.

The job of the bicuspid and tricuspid valves is to prevent backflow into the atria when the ventricles are contracting and forcing blood into the circulatory system.

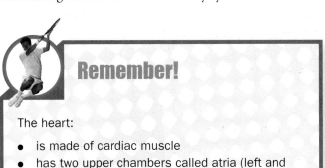

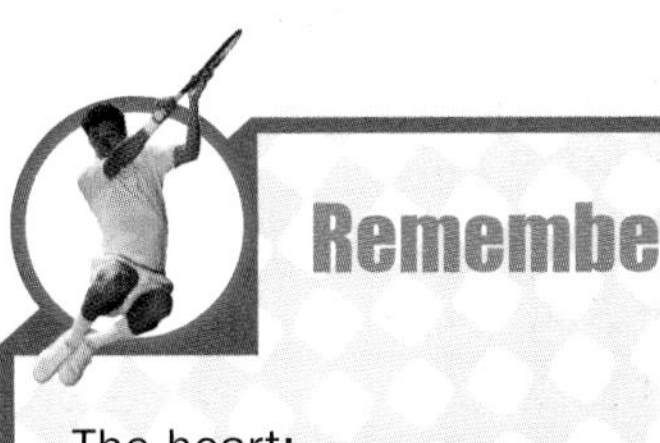

Remember!

The heart:

- is made of cardiac muscle
- has two upper chambers called atria (left and right atrium)
- has two lower chambers called ventricles.

■ Chordae tendineae

These are chord-like tendons that connect to the bicuspid and tricuspid valves. They prevent the valves from turning inside out.

■ Aortic valve and pulmonary valve

The aortic and pulmonary valves guard the bases of the larger arteries attached to the ventricles and prevent backflow into the ventricles. The aortic and pulmonary valves are known as semilunar valves. These valves open and close in response to differences in pressure. When the ventricles are contracting, the valves are forced open as the blood rushes past them. When the ventricles relax, and the blood (no longer propelled forward by the pressure of ventricular contraction) flows backwards toward the heart, the valves close.

Key Term

Semilunar valves Valves that prevent blood from returning to the ventricles after contraction.

Aorta

The aorta is the largest artery in the human body, originating from the left ventricle of the heart and transporting oxygenated blood to all parts of the body.

Vena cava

Superior

The superior vena cava is a large but short vein that carries deoxygenated blood from the upper half of the body to the right atrium.

Inferior

The inferior vena cava is the large vein that carries deoxygenated blood from the lower half of the body into the heart. It enters the right atrium at the lower right, posterior side of the heart.

Pulmonary vein

The pulmonary vein carries oxygen-rich blood from the lungs to the left atrium of the heart.

Pulmonary artery

The pulmonary artery carries deoxygenated blood from the heart to the lungs. It is the only artery in the body that carries deoxygenated blood.

Remember!

- The heart acts as a double pump.
- The right side pumps blood to the lungs to collect oxygen.
- The left side pumps oxygenated blood to the rest of the body.
- Arteries carry blood away from the heart.
- The aorta is the largest artery.
- Veins carry blood back to the heart.
- The vena cava is the largest vein.
- The pulmonary artery is the only artery that carries deoxygenated blood.

Activity

1 Draw an outline diagram of the heart using page 25.

2 Label the valves located between the top and bottom chambers on both sides of the heart.

3 Label the valves that prevent backflow into the ventricles.

4 Write notes to explain the function of the heart valves.

Blood vessels

Blood vessels are often compared to a system of plumbing for the body. They are vibrant structures that constrict and relax. These blood vessels form a closed delivery system that starts and finishes with the heart.

The walls of all blood vessels have three layers. These layers surround the lumen, which is the blood-containing vessel.

- The inner tunica initima lines the lumen and creates a slick surface that minimises friction as the blood passes through.
- The middle layer, known as the tunica media, is composed of smooth muscle cells and elastic tissue. Depending on the body's needs at any given moment, either vasodilatation (increase in lumen diameter as the smooth muscle relaxes, see page 28) or vasoconstriction (reduction in lumen diameter as smooth muscle contracts, see page 28) can be the result.
- The outer layer is known as the tunica externa. It is composed of collagen fibres that protect and reinforce the vessel, and keep it in place within the body's structure.

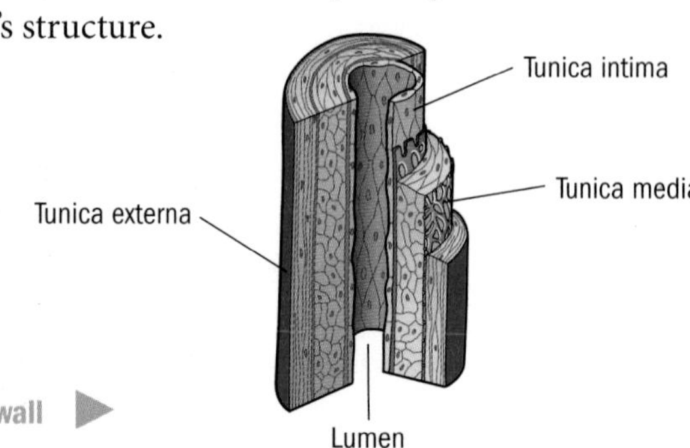

An artery wall

Key Terms

Lumen The cavity inside a blood vessel.

Tunica initima The innermost layer of a blood vessel wall.

Tunica media The middle layer of a blood vessel wall.

Tunica externa The outermost layer of a blood vessel wall.

There are three major types of blood vessels: arteries, capillaries and veins.

Arteries

Arteries take oxygenated blood away from the heart to be delivered around the body. The large artery that leaves the right ventricle is called the pulmonary artery and the artery that leaves the left ventricle is the aorta (see page 25). The blood moves under pressure into smaller arteries, finally reaching the smallest branches known as arterioles, which feed into the capillary beds of body organs, skeletal muscles and other tissues.

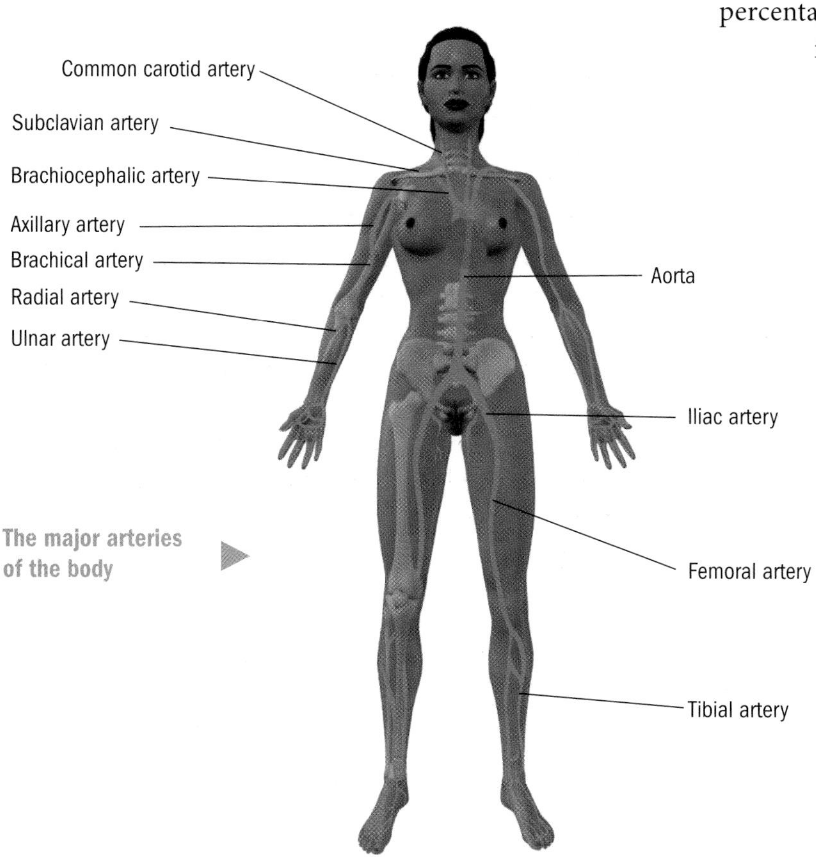

The major arteries of the body

Deoxygenated blood drains from the capillaries into venules, the smallest veins, and then on into larger and larger veins. These veins eventually merge to form the superior and inferior vena cava (see page 25), which ultimately takes the deoxygenated blood back to the heart.

Key Terms

Capillary bed An interwoven network of capillaries.

Capillary exchange Where oxygen, carbon dioxide, nutrients and metabolic waste pass between blood and interstitial fluid by diffusion.

Elastic arteries are thick-walled arteries near the heart, such as the aorta. These arteries are the largest in diameter and the most elastic. Elastic arteries contain more elastin in their tunica than any other vessel. Although elastic arteries also contain a large percentage of smooth muscle, they are relatively inactive during vasoconstriction and, consequently, operate more as simple elastic tubes. These elastic arteries transport blood under high pressure to the muscular arteries and larger arterioles.

Arterioles

These are smaller versions of arteries and they connect arteries to capillaries. Major arterioles are thick-walled with small diameters. The tunica media consists of some elastic tissue but a large amount of smooth muscle. This combination controls the blood flow into the capillary bed.

The smooth muscle controls the shape of the lumen by contracting and reducing the width of the vessel (vasoconstriction) and relaxing to allow the expansion of the vessel (vasodilatation).

Arterioles are responsible for the redistribution of blood flow and blood pressure. They contain muscles that allow the vessel to constrict and stop blood flow to certain areas if it is not required.

Capillaries

Arterioles subdivide into capillaries, which are the smallest blood vessels in the body. They are microscopic – just one cell thick – to allow for capillary exchange.

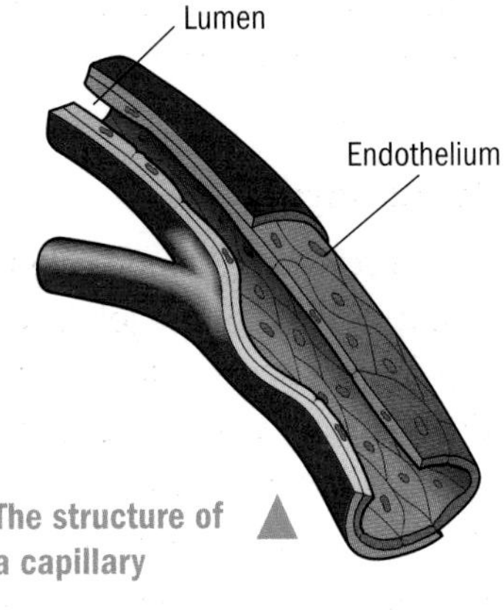

The structure of a capillary

A capillary bed is the capillary structure found in a body organ or skeletal muscle. Capillary beds contain thousands or millions of capillaries for each muscle structure or body organ. As blood passes through the muscle or organ capillary system, it gives up oxygen and nutrients and takes in carbon dioxide and other waste products.

Each capillary has a venous end, which connects to a vein, and an arterial end, which connects to an artery. On leaving the venous end of the capillary bed with waste products, the blood then enters the venules, which transport the blood to the larger veins.

Key Terms

Endothelium The thin layer of cells that lines the interior surface of blood vessels, forming an interface between circulating blood in the lumen and the rest of the vessel wall. Endothelial cells line the entire circulatory system, from the heart to the smallest capillary.

Vasodilation This is the increase in the lumen of blood vessels in the body following the relaxation of the smooth muscle in the vessel wall. Vasodilation results in an increase in blood flow to the area supplied by the vessels.

Vasoconstriction This is the decrease in the lumen of blood vessels in the body following the contraction of the smooth muscle in the vessel wall. Vasoconstriction results in a decrease in blood flow to the area supplied by the vessels.

Veins

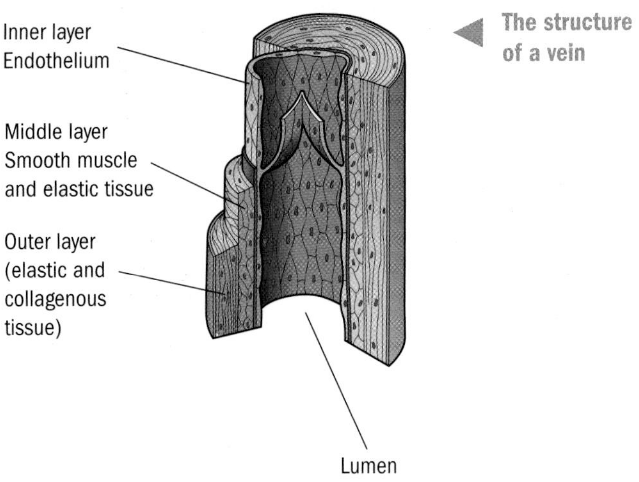

The structure of a vein

Veins are supported by a thick tunica externa and contain less smooth muscle and elastic tissue than arteries. Veins also differ in that they are supported by valves. Valves prevent a backflow of blood and ensure that the blood in veins is not under pressure. Veins act as low pressure reservoirs, and move stored blood into general circulation during exercise (in order to transport blood towards the vena cava).

Venules

Venules are small veins which, unlike capillaries, have some connective tissue in their walls. Venules collect the outflow of blood from the capillary bed at low pressure.

Remember!

- Arteries carry blood away from the heart.
- Arteries are said to diverge (or fork) as they form smaller and smaller elements.
- Veins carry blood toward the heart.
- Veins are said to join (or merge) into larger vessels as they near the heart.
- Blood pressure decreases and blood travels slower as it flows from arteries to veins.
- Veins are wider than arteries.

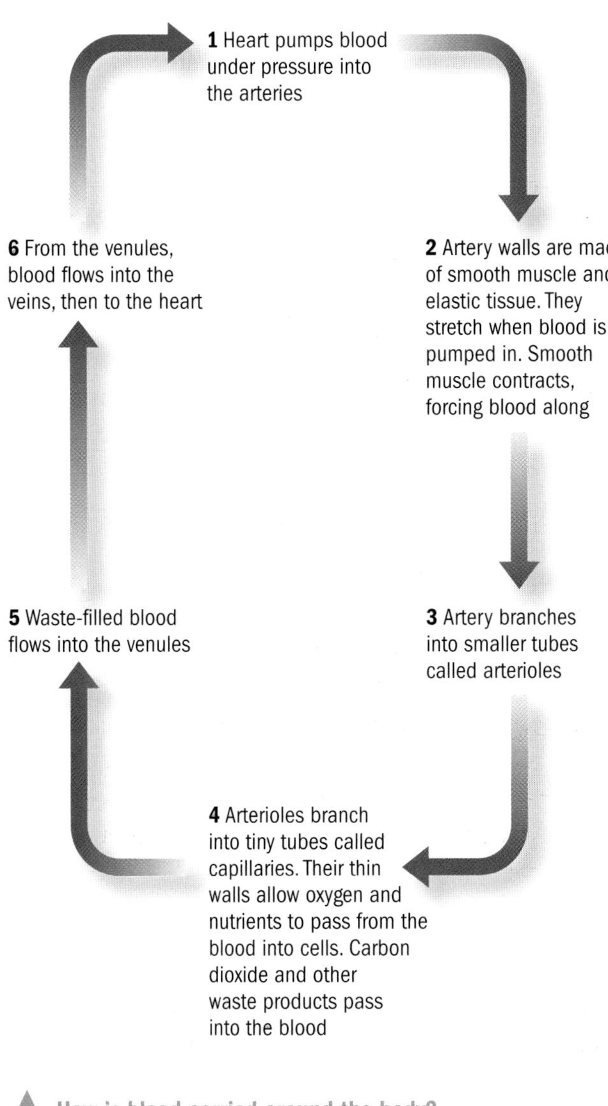
1 Heart pumps blood under pressure into the arteries
2 Artery walls are made of smooth muscle and elastic tissue. They stretch when blood is pumped in. Smooth muscle contracts, forcing blood along
3 Artery branches into smaller tubes called arterioles
4 Arterioles branch into tiny tubes called capillaries. Their thin walls allow oxygen and nutrients to pass from the blood into cells. Carbon dioxide and other waste products pass into the blood
5 Waste-filled blood flows into the venules
6 From the venules, blood flows into the veins, then to the heart

▲ How is blood carried around the body?

Blood

Composition

Blood is a thick, tacky fluid that accounts for approximately 8 per cent of body weight. Its average volume in a healthy adult male is 5 to 6 litres and 4 to 5 litres for a healthy female. Blood is the only fluid tissue in the human body. It has both cellular and liquid components that are visible under a microscope. In other words, blood is very complex!

Blood contains plasma, erythrocytes, leucocytes and thrombocytes.

Plasma

This is a sticky, straw-coloured fluid composed mostly of water. Plasma also contains glucose and other nutrients for cells, hormones, gases, enzymes, antibodies and waste products.

Erythrocytes

Erythrocytes (red blood cells) are a major factor of blood viscosity. Their job is to take on oxygen in the capillary beds of the lungs, and release this oxygen to tissue cells across capillaries throughout the body (via the circulatory system). They also remove carbon dioxide from the tissues, to be excreted by the lungs.

Haemoglobin, the protein that gives red blood cells their colour, binds easily with oxygen. A single red blood cell contains about 250 million haemoglobin molecules, so each red blood cell can transport a relatively high level of oxygen.

Leucocytes

Leucocytes (white blood cells) account for less than 1 per cent of blood volume, so there are fewer of them in the body than red blood cells. They are crucial to our defence against disease. They form a 'mobile army' that helps to protect the body from damage by bacteria, viruses and parasites. When white blood cells are mobilised for action, the body starts to speed up their production, and twice the number may appear in the blood within hours to fight infection.

The approximate composition of blood ▶

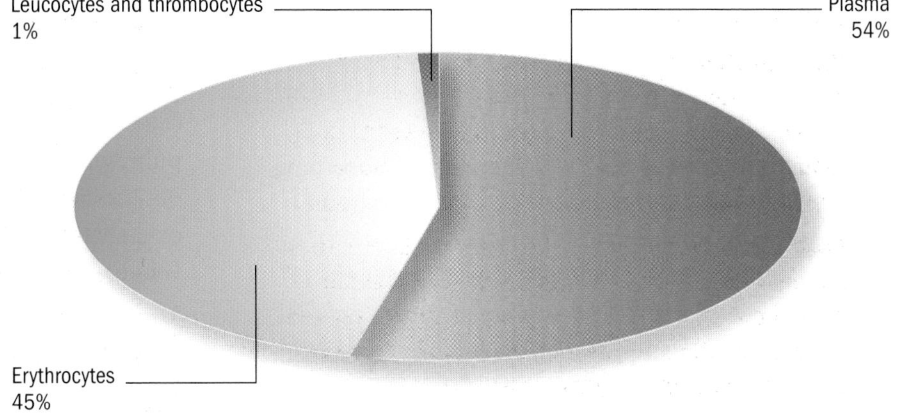
Leucocytes and thrombocytes
1%
Plasma
54%
Erythrocytes
45%

Thrombocytes

Thrombocytes (platelets) are essential for the clotting process. This is a complex process that starts when a blood vessel is ruptured or the lining damaged. As the blood escapes, thrombocytes stick to the damaged area and to each other, to form a temporary plug that helps to seal the break. Red blood cells get trapped within the seal and form a blood clot. This turns into a scab.

Function

Delivery of oxygen and nutrients

The main role of the cardiovascular system is transportation. Exercise increases the demand from the cells in the body for nutrients from the digestive system and oxygen from the lungs. Blood is the specialised tissue that carries out these functions and the cardiovascular system is the method of delivery.

The cardiovascular system also acts as a distribution network for hormones and heat around the body.

Removal of waste products

The cardiovascular system's role is to transport nutrients and oxygen to where they are required in the body, and to remove the waste products from the organs and tissues to the lungs and kidneys, where they are excreted.

Blood

Function

Blood has a number of functions, including distribution, regulation and protection.

Blood helps to maintain body temperature by absorbing and distributing heat throughout the body, and to the skin, to encourage heat loss.

■ Oxygen transport

Thanks to the circulatory system, blood delivers oxygen, nutrients and hormones to the parts of the body that require them. It also transports metabolic waste from cells to areas of disposal. For example, carbon dioxide is extracted from cells and transported to the lungs, where it is expelled into the air.

■ Clotting

Clotting is a complex process during which blood forms solid clots. A damaged blood vessel wall is covered by a fibrin clot to assist repair of the damaged vessel. If an injury occurs, platelets form a plug at the site of the damage. Plasma components known as coagulation factors respond to form fibrin strands, which strengthen the platelet plug. This is all possible due to the constant supply of blood to the damaged site via the cardiovascular system.

■ Fighting infection

Blood helps prevent infection. It contains antibodies and white blood cells, which help to defend against viruses and bacteria. They do this by attacking and, hopefully, destroying them once they enter the body or blood stream.

Cardiac cycle

The vessels that carry the blood supply to and from the lungs form the pulmonary circuit, which takes deoxygenated blood to the lungs and returns oxygenated blood to the heart (see page 25). The vessels that carry the blood supply to and from all other body tissues is known as the systemic circuit.

The heart is divided into two halves, with each providing a pump consisting of two chambers. The right side of the heart is the pulmonary circuit pump. Blood returning from the body is oxygen-deficient and carbon dioxide-rich. The blood enters the right atrium and passes into the right ventricle, which pumps it to the lungs via the pulmonary artery. While in the lungs, the blood gives out the carbon dioxide and takes in oxygen. The freshly oxygenated blood is then carried along the pulmonary vein back to the left side of the heart.

The left side of the heart is the systemic circuit pump. Freshly-oxygenated blood enters the left atrium and passes into the left ventricle (the strongest part of the heart), which pumps it around the body via the aorta. While it passes around the body, the blood gives out the oxygen and nutrients via a system of arteries and smaller capillaries to the organs and tissues. The blood is then oxygen-deficient and carbon dioxide-rich. It returns to the right side of the heart via the superior and inferior vena cava. This cycle repeats itself continuously.

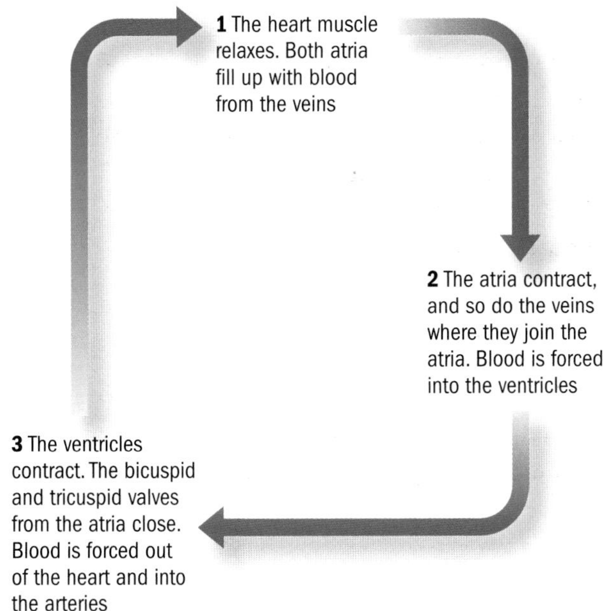
1 The heart muscle relaxes. Both atria fill up with blood from the veins
2 The atria contract, and so do the veins where they join the atria. Blood is forced into the ventricles
3 The ventricles contract. The bicuspid and tricuspid valves from the atria close. Blood is forced out of the heart and into the arteries

Steps 1–3 repeat as a cycle known as the cardiac cycle. A heart beat is one complete cardiac cycle and the heart rate is the number of beats (or cardiac cycles) per minute

The heart undergoes some dramatic movements as it contracts – forcing blood out of its chambers – it then relaxes, allowing the chambers to refill with blood.

Taking it further

In small groups, gather in a sports hall. On the floor (using chalk, tape or ready-made cut-outs), mark the various chambers of the heart and the main veins and arteries that make up the cardiovascular system.

Take on the role of blood. Slowly walk around the marked-out areas of the cardiovascular system so that everyone understands blood flow within the human body.

The contraction of the cardiac muscle tissue in the ventricles is called systole. When the ventricles contract, they force the blood into the arteries leaving the heart. The left ventricle empties into the aorta and the right ventricle into the pulmonary artery. The increased pressure due to the contraction of the ventricles is called systolic pressure.

The relaxation of the cardiac muscle tissue in the ventricles is called diastole. When the ventricles relax, they allow the heart to accept the blood from the atria. The decreased pressure due to the relaxation of the ventricles is called diastolic pressure.

The heart is composed mainly of muscle tissue. A network of nerve fibres coordinates the contraction and relaxation of the cardiac muscle tissue to obtain an efficient, wave-like pumping action of the heart.

Key Terms

Systole Cardiac-cycle period when either the ventricles or the atria are contracting.

Diastole Cardiac-cycle period when either the ventricles or the atria are relaxing.

Sino atrial node (SAN) and atrio ventricular node (AVN)

The sino atrial node (SAN) is the natural pacemaker for the heart. Nestled in the upper area of the right atrium, it sends the electrical impulse that triggers each heartbeat. The impulse spreads through the atria, prompting the cardiac muscle tissue to contract in a coordinated, wave-like manner.

The impulse that originates from the sino atrial node strikes the atrio ventricular node (AVN), which is situated in the lower section of the right atrium. The atrio ventricular node in turn sends an impulse through the nerve network to the ventricles, initiating the same wave-like contraction of the ventricles.

The electrical network serving the ventricles leaves the atrio ventricular node through the right and left bundle branches. These nerve fibres send impulses that cause the cardiac muscle tissue to contract.

Atrio ventricular bundle

The atrio ventricular bundle is a bundle of specialised fibres in the heart that transmit the cardiac impulses from the atria to the ventricles.

Purkinje fibres

These are found in the inner ventricular walls of the heart, beneath the endocardium (see page 25). These fibres are specialised myocardial fibres that conduct an electrical stimulus, enabling the heart to contract in a rhythmical routine.

Nervous system

Sympathetic and parasympathetic

The continual regulation of the heart rate is controlled by the sympathetic and parasympathetic nervous systems.

When the sympathetic nervous system is activated by emotional or physical stressors (such as anxiety or exercise), sympathetic fibres release a chemical called norepinephrine. This makes the heart beat faster.

Key Terms

Norepinephrine Chemical transmitter substance released at nerve endings to increase the heart rate.

Acetylcholine Chemical transmitter substance released at nerve endings to relax the heart rate.

The parasympathetic system opposes sympathetic effects and effectively reduces heart rate when a stressful situation has passed. Parasympathetic responses are managed by a chemical called acetylcholine.

Activity

This activity requires a fresh animal heart (sheep or pig) for dissection under appropriate supervision (suitable safety clothing, dissection equipment and an appropriate working environment). Care must be taken when using dissection blades. If no heart is available, appropriate models or charts can be used.

1. Identify the external features of the heart.
2. Identify the vessels branching over the surface of the ventricles. These blood vessels supply the heart with oxygen and transport carbon dioxide away from it.
3. Cut the heart along its front plane – each half should show all four chambers. Identify each chamber and the various heart valves. If possible, record your dissection either on camcorder or photographs for future reference and analysis.

Assessment practice

1. Give an oral presentation that describes the structure and function of the cardiovascular system. You should complement your presentation by drawing the structure of the heart and blood vessels on a whiteboard and relating its function to exercise where appropriate. **P6**
2. During your presentation, explain the function of the cardiovascular system – what it does and how each part of the system is designed to meet its function. To meet the D1 criteria, you need to analyse the cardiovascular system. **M4** **D1**

grading tips

Grading Tip P6

You must be able to describe the structure and function of the cardiovascular system. If you can provide real working examples, that will help to show this. Ensure you choose different sports as that will determine your grade as well.

Grading Tip M4

The merit criteria demands a bit more from you, in terms of the quality of what you produce as evidence and in terms of complexity, so pay attention to detail in your responses. 'Explaining' means showing the function of the cardiovascular system.

Grading Tip D1

Analyse is more difficult than explaining. During your presentation, think about the factors that influence the cardiovascular system and, in particular, what might happen if one of those factors suddenly failed or went wrong.

1.4 Understand the structure and function of the respiratory system

Structure

The respiratory system includes the nasal cavity, pharynx, larynx, trachea, bronchi and the lungs. Its job is to take in oxygen for the body cells and get rid of carbon dioxide.

With each inhalation, air is pulled through the windpipe (trachea) and the branching passageways of the lungs (bronchi), filling thousands of tiny air sacs (alveoli) at the ends of the bronchi. These sacs (which resemble bunches of grapes), are surrounded by small blood vessels (capillaries). Oxygen passes through the thin membranes of the alveoli and into the bloodstream. The red blood cells pick up the oxygen and carry it to the body's organs and tissues. As the blood cells release the oxygen, they take in carbon dioxide, a waste product of metabolism. The carbon dioxide is then carried back to the lungs and released into the alveoli. With each exhalation, carbon dioxide is expelled from the bronchi and out through the trachea.

The respiratory tract is divided into two main parts: the upper respiratory tract, consisting of the nose, nasal cavity, pharynx and larynx; and the lower respiratory tract, consisting of the trachea, bronchi and lungs.

Key Term

Alveoli They are found at the end of bronchioles and are the site for gaseous exchange. Alveoli are microscopic air sacs that have thin walls and are surrounded by capillaries.

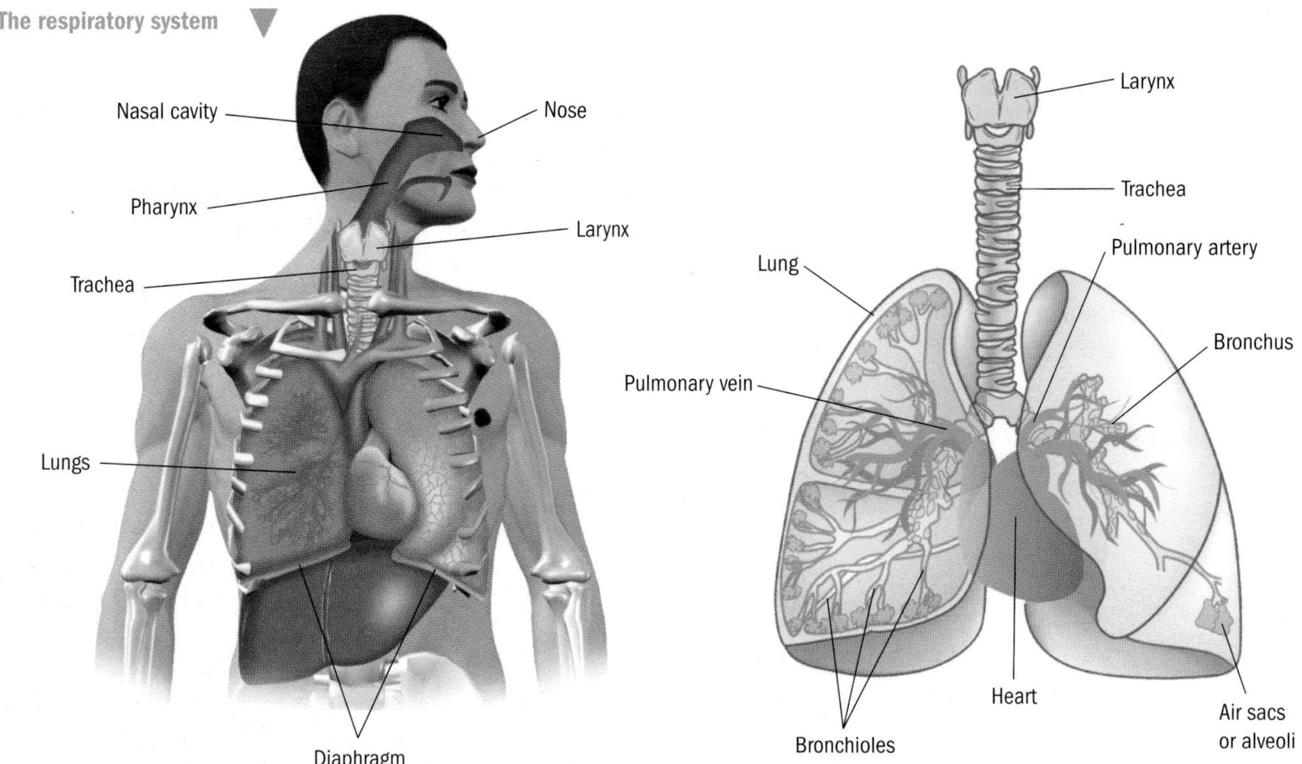

Nasal cavity

The nose is the only external part of the respiratory system. The structure of the nose is divided into the external nose and the internal nasal cavity. When you breathe, air enters the cavity by passing through the nostrils. The roof of the nasal cavity is formed by the ethmoid and sephenoid bones of the skull. The hairs of the nasal cavity filter particles of dust or pollen from inspired air. The rest of the nasal cavity is lined with two types of mucous membrane. These secrete a watery fluid containing antibacterial enzymes. The sticky mucous also traps inspired dust, bacteria and other debris, while the antibacterial enzymes attack and destroy bacteria chemically.

Pharynx

The funnel-shaped pharynx connects the nasal cavity and mouth to the larynx (air) and oesophagus (food). Commonly called the throat, the pharynx is a small length of tubing that measures approximately 10 to 13cm from the base of the skull to the level of the sixth cervical vertebra. The muscular pharynx wall is composed of skeletal muscle throughout its length. It is a passageway for food as well as air.

Larynx

The larynx or voice box extends for about 5cm from the level of the third to the sixth vertebra. It is made of cartilage and has a protruding section known as the Adam's apple.

The larynx is located between the pharynx and the trachea and has three functions: Its two main tasks are to provide an open airway and to act as a switching mechanism to guide air and food into the correct channels. It also houses the vocal cords, so its third function is voice production.

Trachea

The trachea, or windpipe, descends from the larynx through the neck and ends by splitting into two main bronchi prior to entering the lungs. The trachea is about 12cm long and 2cm in diameter, and it is very flexible and mobile.

Bronchus and bronchioles

Key Terms

Lobar bronchi Thin-walled air sacs within the lung where gaseous exchange takes place.

Segmental bronchi (third-order bronchus). A sub-division of the lobar bronchi that further divides into small bronchioles.

Gaseous exchange Loading oxygen and unloading carbon dioxide at the lungs.

The right and left bronchi are formed by the division of the trachea. The bronchi carry air into the lungs. The right bronchus is wider, shorter and more vertical than the left and is a more common site for foreign objects to become lodged. By the time inhaled air reaches the bronchi, it is warm, clear of most impurities and saturated with water vapour.

Once inside the lungs, each bronchus subdivides into lobar bronchi: three on the right and two on the left. The lobar bronchi branch into segmental bronchi, which divide again into smaller and smaller bronchi. Overall, there are approximately 23 orders of branching bronchial airways in the lungs. Passages smaller than 1mm in diameter are called bronchioles. Because of this branching pattern, the bronchial network within the lungs is often known as the bronchial tree.

Remember!

- The alveoli are where gaseous exchange takes place.
- The alveoli walls are thin and moist, which helps oxygen and carbon dioxide pass through.
- The bunches of alveoli are surrounded by capillaries.
- The capillaries also have thin walls to let the gases through.
- Each alveolus is smaller than a grain of sand.

Lungs

The paired lungs occupy most of the thoracic cavity and extend down to the diaphragm. The heart is situated slightly to the left, so the lungs differ slightly in shape and size. The left lung is smaller than the right.

The lungs

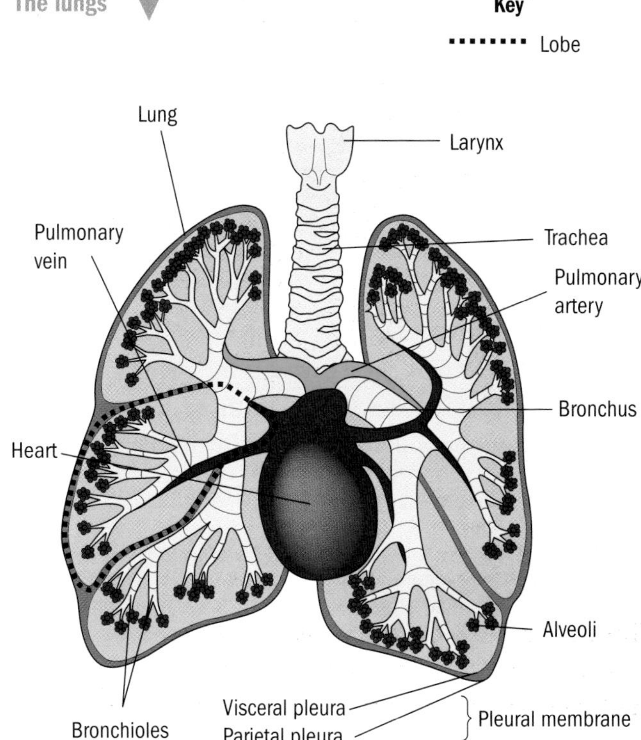

Lobes

The lungs are divided into lobes. The left lung contains two lobes, whereas the right lung has three. Each lobe is served by its own artery and vein, and receives air from an individual bronchus.

Pleural membrane

Each lung is enclosed in a pleural membrane that helps to keep the two lungs away from each other and air tight. Therefore, if one lung is punctured and collapses due to an accident, the other pleural cavity will still be air tight and the other lung will work normally.

Pleural cavity

In between the parietal pleura and the visceral pleura is a thin space known as the pleural cavity or pleural space. It is filled with pleural fluid.

Parietal pleura

The parietal pleura is the outermost of the two pleural membranes (see page 35). It covers the thoracic wall and the top of the diaphragm. It continues around the heart and between the lungs, forming the lateral walls of the mediastinal enclosure.

Key Term

Mediastinal enclosure Lies between the right and left pleura in and near the median sagittal plane of the chest. It extends from the sternum in front to the vertebral column behind, and contains all the thoracic viscera except the lungs.

Thoracic cavity

The thoracic cavity, or chest cavity, is the chamber of the human body that is protected by the thoracic wall. It is separated from the abdominal cavity by the diaphragm.

Visceral pleura

The visceral pleura is the innermost of the two pleural membranes (see page 35). It covers the surface of the lung and dips into the spaces between its lobes.

Pleural fluid

The pleural membranes produce pleural fluid, which fills the pleural cavity between them. This lubricating secretion allows the lungs to glide easily over the thorax wall during respiration. Although the membranes slide easily across each other, their separation is resisted by the surface tension of the pleural fluid. The pleural fluid provides the surface tension that keeps the lung surface in contact with the chest wall.

During breathing, the pleural cavity experiences a negative pressure (compared to the atmosphere) which helps adhere the lungs to the chest wall. This means that movements of the chest wall during breathing are coupled closely to movements of the lungs.

Alveoli

The bronchioles end in air sacs called alveoli. The 300 million gas-filled alveoli in each lung account for most of the lung volume and provide an enormous area for gaseous exchange. The external surfaces of the alveoli are densely covered with a host of pulmonary capillaries. Together, the alveolar and capillary walls form the respiratory membrane that has gas on one side and blood flowing past on the other side. Gas exchanges occur readily by simple diffusion across the respiratory membrane. Oxygen passes from each alveolus into the blood and carbon dioxide leaves the blood to enter the gas-filled alveolus.

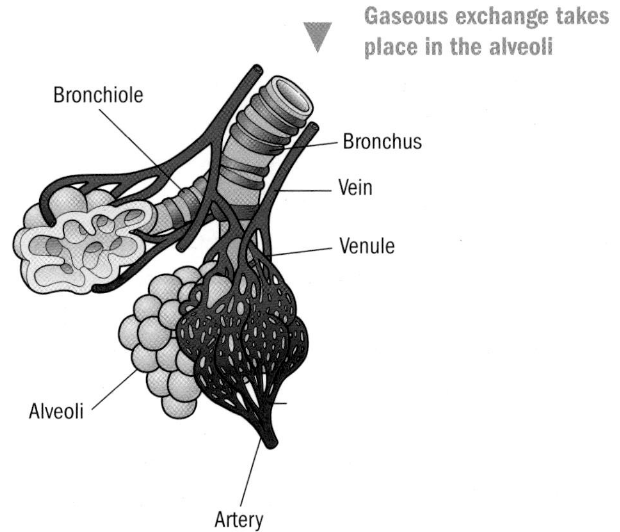

Gaseous exchange takes place in the alveoli

Diaphragm

The diaphragm plays an important role in the mechanics of breathing. Contraction of the diaphragm increases the volume of the chest cavity, drawing air into the lungs during inspiration, while relaxation involves recoil of the diaphragm and decreases the volume of the chest cavity, pumping out air.

Intercostal muscles

The intercostal muscles lie between the ribs. To help with inhalation and exhalation, the muscles extend and contract.

External

The external intercostals pull the ribs upwards and outwards, increasing the volume of the chest cavity and drawing air into the lungs during inspiration.

■ Internal

The internal intercostals draw the ribs downward and inwards, decreasing the volume of the chest cavity and forcing air out of the lungs during expiration.

Function

Transport

Gaseous exchange occurs by diffusion between air in the alveoli and blood in the capillaries in the walls of the alveoli.

The concept of partial pressure applies to the diffusion of gases from a gas mixture to a gas in solution, and vice versa. Gases in contact with a liquid dissolve into solution by diffusion until equilibrium is achieved. At equilibrium, the partial pressure of the gases is the same in both gaseous and liquid states, and the gases are diffusing in and out of each state at the same rate. This same principle applies to the exchange of gases in the lungs: between the alveolar air (gaseous) and the blood circulating (liquid) in the capillaries of the alveoli walls.

Blood entering the capillaries from the pulmonary arteries has a lower oxygen content and higher carbon dioxide content than the air in the alveoli. Oxygen diffuses into the blood via the surface of the alveoli, through the thin walls of the capillaries, through the red blood cell membrane and finally latches on to the haemoglobin. Carbon dioxide diffuses in the opposite direction to the oxygen: from blood into the alveoli.

Key Terms

Diffusion A substance moves by diffusion from a region of higher concentration to a region of lower concentration until equilibrium is reached.

Partial pressure Pressure exerted by a single gas in a mixture of gases.

■ Oxygen

The oxygen absorbed into the blood in the capillaries combines with haemoglobin in the red blood cells to form oxyhaemoglobin. The concentration of red blood cells and their haemoglobin affects the amount of oxygen taken up by the blood. The red blood cells typically make up roughly 45 per cent of blood volume. These concentrations increase during exercise, as more fluid moves from the plasma to the tissues, and more water is lost from the plasma as sweat. Long-term endurance training can result in an increase in red blood cells and, therefore, haemoglobin.

■ Carbon dioxide

This is excreted as a waste product of aerobic metabolism. It is carried to the veins via the cardiovascular system and diffused into the lungs, where it is expired.

■ Haemoglobin

This is a large protein that can combine reversibly with oxygen. Haemoglobin is the oxygen-transporting component of red blood cells.

■ Oxyhaemoglobin

Oxygen attaches to haemoglobin to form oxyhaemoglobin. Blood carries oxyhaemoglobin to tissue sites, where the oxygen is released during a process known as tissue respiration.

Mechanisms of breathing

Breathing in is referred to as inspiration and breathing out as expiration.

■ Inspiration

When the air pressure inside the lungs decreases, more air flows in. Air pressure inside the lungs is decreased by increasing the size of the thoracic cavity. Due to surface tension between the two pleural membranes, the lungs follow the chest wall and expand.

The muscles involved in expanding the thoracic cavity include the diaphragm and the external intercostal muscles. As the diaphragm contracts, it flattens out. As a result, the superior-inferior dimension of the thoracic cavity increases. Contraction of the intercostal muscles lifts the rib cage and pulls the sternum upwards.

Although these actions expand the thoracic cavity by only a few millimetres, this is enough to increase the thoracic volume by almost 500ml – the usual volume of air that enters the lungs during normal inspiration.

At rest and during exercise

When at rest, the external intercostal muscles contract and the internal intercostal muscles relax. This action causes the ribs and sternum to move upwards and outwards, increasing the chest volume.

During forced inspirations that occur when exercising, the thoracic volume increases further. Assistance from muscles such as the pectorals help to raise the rib cage even more, extending the thoracic volume beyond the normal 500ml. The trapezius and back muscle also contract to increase the size of the thorax, which allows a greater volume of air into the lungs.

■ Expiration

Expiration is a passive process that depends more on lung elasticity than on muscle contraction. As the inspiration muscles relax, the rib cage descends and the lungs recoil. Thus, the thoracic volume decreases.

Remember!

When you breathe in:

- the intercostal muscles contract: this pulls the rib cage upwards, so the chest expands
- the diaphragm contracts: this pulls it down and flattens it, making the chest cavity larger
- the lungs expand because their moist surface clings to the chest lining
- air is sucked down the trachea and into the lungs.

When you breathe out:

- the intercostal muscles relax: this lowers the rib cage and makes the chest cavity smaller
- the diaphragm relaxes so it bulges upwards again, making the chest cavity even smaller
- the lungs get compressed, forcing air out and up the trachea.

At rest and during exercise

During expiration at rest, the diaphragm and external intercostal muscles relax and return to their original positions. The ribs and diaphragm exert pressure on the pleural fluid. This reduces the lung volume and increases air pressure inside, so air is forced out via the respiratory passage.

When exercising, the combined contraction of the internal intercostal and abdominal muscles, mainly the oblique and transverse muscles, forces air out of the lungs.

Taking it further

Explain why your breathing rate changes during exercise compared to when you are at rest.

Respiratory volumes

Key Terms

Tidal volume Volume of air inhaled and exhaled in one breath.

Inspiratory reserve volume Air that can be forcibly inspired during normal breath.

Expiratory reserve volume Air that can be forcibly expired over and above tidal volume.

Vital capacity Maximum volume of air forcibly expired after maximal respiration.

Residual volume Air remaining in the lungs after maximal respiration.

Total lung capacity Volume of air following maximal inspiration.

Maximal inspiration Inhale fully, exhale completely, and then take another full inhalation and hold the breath for as long as possible.

The average pair of human lungs can hold about 6 litres of air, but only a small amount of this capacity is used during normal breathing. Lung volumes refer to physical differences in volume, while lung capacities represent different combinations of lung volumes, usually in relation to respiration and exhalation. These values vary depending on the age and height of the person.

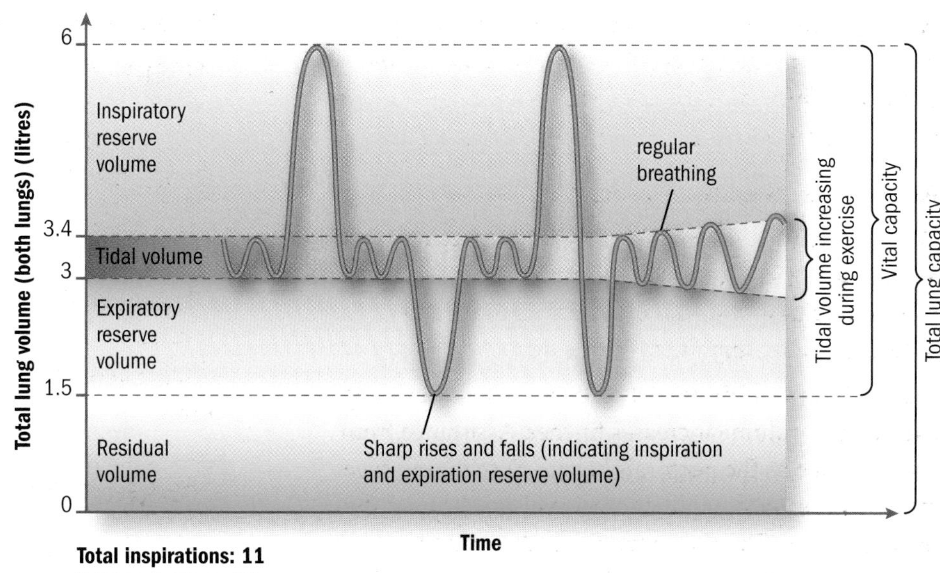

Lung volume and capacities of a healthy adult

Tidal volume

Tidal breathing means that air goes into the lungs in the same way that it comes out and, under normal conditions, this equates to approximately 500cm^3 of air breathed (both inhaled or exhaled). Of this inhalation, approximately 350cm^3 reaches the alveoli in the lungs (the site of gaseous exchange). The remainder fills the pharynx, larynx, trachea, brochi and bronchioles. This 150cm^3 is known as dead or stationary air.

The 350cm^3 of air from the inhalation that makes it to the alveoli mixes with 150cm^3 of dead air in the pharynx, larynx, trachea, bronchi and bronchioles (which was left from the previous exhalation), so that 500cm^3 does in fact reach the alveoli in a single breath.

The diagram illustrates the breathing rate of a healthy adult. The continuous oscillating line is an indication of a breathing pattern; where the line dips denotes an exhalation, and where the line rises denotes an inhalation.

Much of the breathing is located within the tidal volume band. This indicates regular steady breathing. The exceptions on the diagram are as follows:

- two sharp rises – forced deep inspirations (which are the inspiration reserve volume)
- two sharp falls – forced deep exhalations (which are the expiratory reserve volume).

Inspiratory reserve volume

By breathing in deeply, it is possible to take in more than the usual 350cm^3 of fresh air that reaches the alveoli. This is especially important during exercise. In addition to the tidal volume, you can also breathe in up to an additional 3,000cm^3 of fresh air. This is known as the inspirational reserve volume.

Expiratory reserve volume

The expiratory reserve volume can be up to 1,500cm^3 and is the amount of additional air that can be breathed out after normal expiration. At the end of a normal breath, the lungs contain the residual volume plus the expiratory reserve volume. If you then exhale as much as possible, only the residual volume remains.

Vital capacity

Vital capacity is the amount of air that can be forced out of the lungs after maximal respiration. The volume is around 4,800cm^3.

Residual volume

Residual volume is the amount of air left in the lungs after maximal respiration (when you breath out as hard as you can). The volume is around 1,200cm^3 for an average male.

Total lung capacity

Total lung capacity is the volume of air contained in the lungs after maximal inspiration. The volume is usually between 4,000cm^3 and 8,000cm^3, with 6,000cm^3 for an average-sized male.

Control of breathing

Neural control

Although breathing seems simple, its control is complex, It involves neurones (cells that conduct nerve impulses) in the reticular formation of the medulla and pons (both parts of the brain stem).

Neurones in two areas of the medulla are critical in respiration. These are the dorsal respiratory group (DRG) and the ventral respiratory group (VRG). The VRG is thought to be responsible for rhythm generation.

Key Terms

Neurones Cells of the nervous system that conduct nerve impulses to generate and transmit electrical signals.

Reticular formulation Part of the brain essential for the basic functions of life such as breathing, sleep and walking.

Medulla Lower portion of the brain stem responsible for controlling several major autonomic functions of the body including respiration, blood pressure, heart rate and reflex arcs.

Pons Located on the brain stem and responsible for providing linkage between the upper and lower levels of the central nervous system.

Chemoreceptors Receptors sensitive to various chemicals in solution.

Aortic arch The major artery that has three branches to deliver oxygenated blood throughout the body.

Carotid arteries These feed the head and brain with oxygenated blood.

Chemical control

Others factors that control breathing are the continually changing levels of oxygen and carbon dioxide. Sensors responding to such chemical fluctuations are called chemoreceptors. These are found in the medulla and in the aortic arch and carotid arteries.

Assessment practice

1. Describe the structure and function of the respiratory system. **P7**
2. Explain the function of the respiratory system, detailing why humans require such a system and how it works. **M5**
3. To analyse the function of the respiratory system, examine the many different factors involved and the effect each of these has on the respiratory system. **D2**

grading tips

Grading Tip 

You must be able to describe the structure and function of the respiratory system. If you can provide real working examples, these will help to show this. Ensure you choose different sports as that will determine your grade as well.

Grading Tip M5

The merit criteria demands a bit more from you, in terms of the quality of what you produce as evidence and in terms of complexity, so pay attention to detail in your responses. 'Explaining' means demonstrating the function of the respiratory system.

Grading Tip D2

To be graded at distinction level means you can show an in-depth understanding, use appropriate terminology well and have a really thorough approach. Above all, you must analyse the function of the respiratory system, which means showing you can break up the components of the question and respond to them with critical insight. In other words, you have the ability to see important points that others miss, as well as identifying faults and making realistic suggestions as to how something could have been done better.

Knowledge check

1 What is the purpose of the skeleton?

2 Why do we have joints?

3 Examine the skeletal and muscular systems and describe how the human body is able to move.

4 Explain what is meant by the terms 'isometric' and 'isotonic'.

5 Explain how the heart and lungs work together to supply muscles with oxygen.

6 Draw a diagram to show how blood travels around the body and to the lungs. Include the blood vessels and a labelled heart.

7 Explain why taking part in exercise is good for the skeletal, muscular, respiratory and circulatory systems.

8 Describe how the skeletal, muscular, cardiovascular and respiratory systems work together to allow someone to take part in any given sport.

9 Explain what is meant by the term 'tidal volume'.

10 Draw a flow diagram to show the various stages involved, from nasal cavity to alveoli, in air inhalation.

End of Unit assessment

Preparation for assessment

Imagine yourself in ten years' time and you are now a full-time lecturer. You are teaching a class of 20 sport and exercise students who are keen to learn about human anatomy. Your job is to provide a one-hour lecture on this topic. Imagine you have a detailed anatomical model that incorporates all the anatomical parts you must consider.

You need to prepare a lecture plan to help you through the various explanations and interpretations that will take place. Bear in mind that this plan will form part of the student handout material. Therefore, your lecture plan should make detailed reference to the:

- structure and function of the skeletal system **P1**
- anatomical joints **P2 M1**
- location and function of major muscles **P3**
- types of muscle and muscle fibre types **P4 M2**
- muscle movement and contraction **P5 M3**
- cardiovascular system **P6 M4 D1**
- respiratory system. **P7 M5 D2**

grading tips

Grading Tip 

You must describe the axial and appendicular skeleton, the different types of bone in the skeleton and be able to locate all of the bones named in the content. You must also be able to describe all five functions of the skeleton.

Grading Tip 

You must be able to describe the different classifications of joints and the range of movement available at each.

Grading Tip 

You must be able to identify the location, function, origin and insertion of the major muscles.

Grading Tip P5

You must be able to describe how muscles produce movement and the different types of contraction.

Grading Tip P6

You must be able to describe the structure and function of the cardiovascular system.

Grading Tip P7

You must be able to describe the structure and function of the respiratory system.

Grading Tip M1

You must be able to compare and contrast the different classifications of joints and the range of movement available at each.

Grading Tip M2

You must be able to compare and contrast the properties of the different types of muscle and the different muscle fibre types.

Grading Tip M3

You must be able to explain how muscles produce movement and the different types of contraction.

Grading Tip M4

You must be able to explain the function of the cardiovascular system.

Grading Tip M5

You must be able to explain the function of the respiratory system.

Grading Tip D1

You must be able to analyse the function of the cardiovascular system.

Grading Tip D2

You must be able to analyse the function of the respiratory system.

Grading criteria

To achieve a pass grade the evidence must show that the learner is able to:	To achieve a merit grade the evidence must show that, in addition to the pass criteria, the learner is able to:	To achieve a distinction grade the evidence must show that, in addition to the pass and merit criteria, the learner is able to:
P1 describe the structure and function of the skeletal system **Assessment practice pages 10, 42**		
P2 describe the different classifications of joints and the range of movement available at each **Assessment practice pages 13, 42**	**M1** compare and contrast the different classifications of joints and the range of movement available at each **Assessment practice pages 13, 42**	
P3 identify the location, function, origin and insertion of the major muscles **Assessment practice pages 16, 42**		
P4 describe the different types of muscle and the different muscle fibre types **Assessment practice pages 22, 42**	**M2** compare and contrast the properties of the different types of muscle and the different muscle fibre types **Assessment practice pages 22, 42**	
P5 describe how muscles produce movement and the different types of contraction **Assessment practice pages 23, 42**	**M3** explain how muscles produce movement and the different types of contraction **Assessment practice pages 23, 42**	
P6 describe the structure and function of the cardiovascular system **Assessment practice pages 32, 42**	**M4** explain the function of the cardiovascular system **Assessment practice pages 32, 42**	**D1** analyse the function of the cardiovascular system **Assessment practice pages 32, 42**
P7 describe the structure and function of the respiratory system **Assessment practice pages 40, 42**	**M5** explain the function of the respiratory system **Assessment practice pages 40, 42**	**D2** analyse the function of the respiratory system **Assessment practice pages 40, 42**

Sport and exercise physiology

Introduction

As you sit reading this book, your body is coping well as it is doing little in the way of physical exercise. Your oxygen and energy demands are low and are easily met by your shallow breathing and relatively low pulse rate. The blood circulating around your system delivers glucose and oxygen to your cells and takes waste products, such as carbon dioxide, away.

However, were you to get up and run around a sports field, significant changes would take place. To fuel this activity and maintain its equilibrium, your body must adapt quickly and it does so in a variety of ways involving many complex processes. This unit is designed to examine these processes and the implications on sports performance.

After completing this unit you should be able to achieve the following outcomes:

- understand the initial responses of the body to exercise
- understand how the body responds to steady-state exercise
- understand fatigue and how the body recovers from exercise
- understand how the body adapts to long-term exercise.

Think it over

Paula Radcliffe is the current world record holder for the women's marathon, which she set in the 2003 London marathon with a time of 2 hours, 15 minutes and 25 seconds. During the 26 miles, her body kept her skeletal muscles supplied with fuel and oxygen while it eliminated waste products such as carbon dioxide.

A number of physiological processes occur when Paula is competing in this gruelling event. You might be surprised to learn that these same processes occur in your body when you exercise. The only difference is that Paula is a highly trained athlete who can push these physiological processes further than you. What exactly is going on under Paula's grimace? What is her body doing? How much blood do you think her heart is pumping around her body in a minute? How many litres of air are her lungs breathing in and out in the same minute? What energy systems are at work and how do they fuel her muscles? Without these processes working effectively and efficiently, Paula would simply grind to a halt. Why do you think you cannot run a marathon in the same time as Paula?

2.1 Understand the initial responses of the body to exercise

For the past five years, Paula Radcliffe has been considered to be among the world's elite female aerobic athletes due mainly to her success in the marathon event. How does her body respond to the demands of such a gruelling event?

As Paula runs a marathon significant changes take place thoughout her body. To fuel this activity and maintain its equilibrium, Paula's body must adapt quickly and it does so in a variety of ways, involving many complex physiological processes. This unit examines these processes and the implications on sport and exercise performance.

Exercise

Aerobic

Aerobic literally means 'with oxygen' and refers to the use of oxygen in energy production.

During aerobic exercise, oxygen is used to burn fats and glucose in order to produce adenosine triphosphate (ATP), the basic energy carrier for all cells in the human body. Initially during aerobic exercise, glycogen is broken down to produce glucose, but in its absence fat metabolism is used instead. This is a slow process that is accompanied by a decline in performance levels. The switch to fat as a fuel is a major cause of what marathon runners call 'hitting the wall'.

There are various types of aerobic exercise. In general, aerobic exercise is one performed at a moderate level of intensity over a long period of time. For example, running a long-distance at a moderate pace is an aerobic exercise, but sprinting is not. Playing badminton, with near-continuous motion, is generally considered aerobic activity, while rugby union or cricket bowling, with their more frequent breaks, may not be.

Anaerobic

Anaerobic exercise means 'without oxygen'. It is a short-lasting, high-intensity activity, where the demand for oxygen from the exercise exceeds the oxygen supply.

Anaerobic exercise relies on energy sources that are stored in the muscles and, unlike aerobic exercise, is not dependent on oxygen from breathing the air.

Anaerobic exercise includes heavy weightlifting, sprints (running, cycling), jumping rope, hill climbing, intervals, isometrics (in which one part of the body is used to resist the movement of another part) or any rapid burst of hard exercise.

▲ At a sprint finish with 100 metres to go, many cyclists are travelling at speeds approaching 40mph. These sprints entail short bursts of intense anaerobic exercise. How do you think their bodies feel once they cross the finish line?

Key Terms

Aerobic exercise An activity that uses oxygen as part of the energy production process.

Adenosine triphosphate (ATP) Stores and releases chemical energy for use in body cells.

Anaerobic exercise Activity that does not use oxygen as part of the energy production process.

Cardiovascular responses

When exercising, a number of changes occur within the cardiovascular system (see page 24). It is important that a sports scientist understands these changes as they will have a significant impact on an athlete's training and performance.

Heart rate

The heart rate changes according to the needs of the body. It increases during exercise to deliver extra oxygen to tissues and remove excess carbon dioxide (see page 24). At rest, a normal adult heart beats approximately 75 beats per minute, peaking at around 200 beats per minute for strenuous activity, but this figure depends on the person's age.

Heart rate is controlled by the sino atrial node (SAN) (see page 31). The rate goes up or down when the SAN receives information via nerves that link the SAN with the cardiovascular centre in the brain (see page 31). Consequently, when you begin to exercise, information is sent and the heart adapts accordingly. It does so by the following methods:

- the sympathetic nerve speeds up the heart: the synapses at the end of this nerve secrete a hormone called noradrenalin
- the vagus nerve (parasympathetic nerve) slows down the heart: the synapses at the end of the nerve secrete a hormone called acetylcholine.

Key Terms

Sympathetic nerve Speeds up heart rate through release of noradrenalin.

Parasympathetic nerve Slows heart rate through release of acetylcholine.

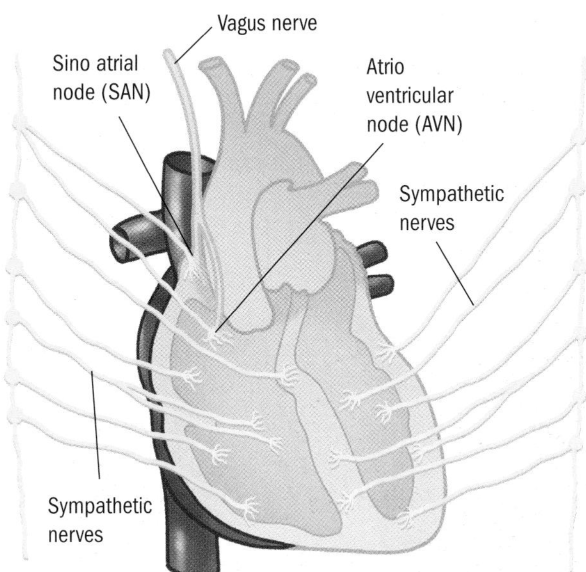

▲ **The heart is connected via the vagus and sympathetic nerves to the brain. How does this work to make the heart beat continually?**

■ Anticipatory increase and activity response

An anticipatory increase in heart rate occurs following impulses originating in the brain's central command system. This occurs not only during exercise but also during the period when athletes are about to exercise. Therefore, the anticipatory increase can depend on an athlete's emotional state, often belying his or her true resting state. This causes heart rate to rise rapidly in anticipation of exercise.

For example, just before the start of a running race the athlete's heart rate is likely to increase in anticipation of the event about to be undertaken. The highest level of anticipatory rise in heart rate is known to be that of 100m sprinters.

Stroke volume

Stroke volume is the amount of blood pumped by one of the ventricles of the heart in one contraction. The stroke volume is not all of the blood contained in the left ventricle because the heart does not pump all the blood out. About two-thirds of the blood in the ventricle is normally put out with each beat. Stroke volume and heart rate together determine the cardiac output.

With the onset of exercise, stroke volume increases progressively and then gradually levels off at a relatively high level until the exercise has ended. Assuming normal stroke volume ranges between 70 and 80ml per beat, a trained athlete's stroke volume can be as much as 110ml. With the onset of exercise, the blood flow of a trained athlete increases sharply, levelling out at between 180 and 200ml^3. This increase in blood flow via an increase in stroke volume allows for a greater oxygen supply to the skeletal muscles.

Cardiac output

Cardiac output is the volume of blood being pumped out of the heart in one minute (see page 30). It is equal to the heart rate multiplied by the stroke volume.

If the heart beats 70 times a minute, and 70ml of blood is pumped each time, the cardiac output is 4,900ml per minute, or about 5 litres. This value is typical for an average adult at rest, although cardiac output may reach up to 30 litres per minute during extreme exercise.

When cardiac output increases in a healthy but untrained individual, most of the increase can be attributed to an increase in heart rate. A change of posture, increased sympathetic nervous system activity and decreased parasympathetic nervous system activity can also increase cardiac output.

Key Terms

Stroke volume The volume of blood pumped by the heart per beat.

Cardiac output The volume of blood pumped being pumped out of the heart in one minute.

Blood pressure

Blood pressure is the pressure of the blood against the walls of the arteries (see page 27) and results from two forces. One is created by the heart as it pumps blood into the arteries and through the circulatory system. The other is the force of the arteries as they resist the blood flow.

During exercise, although both cardiac output and blood pressure increase, these mechanism act to restrict the blood pressure rise and eventually bring it down to more efficient levels.

Calculating – resistance to flow multiplied by cardiac output

Blood pressure is the force exerted by the flow of blood against the walls of blood vessels. It is determined by two factors:

- The resistance offered by the vessel walls to the flow of blood. This can be dependent on several factors including blood vessel length and radius.
- Cardiac output or the volume of blood pumped out of the left ventricle in one minute.

Therefore, blood pressure is defined as:

cardiac output × resistance

Blood pressure increases when either cardiac output or resistance increases.

Readings

Medical staff such as doctors or nurses sometimes measure blood pressure manually in the brachial artery of a patients arm. A blood pressure cuff is wrapped around the arm from above the elbow and inflated until a brachial pulse cannot be felt or heard. The doctor or nurse will then gradually release the pressure on the arm and listen (with a stethoscope) for the first sounds of blood being forced through to the brachial artery. This will give the systolic pressure. As the cuff pressure reduces further, and the sounds of the blood being forced disappear, this reading will give the diastolic pressure. Nowadays, blood pressure is easily measured at the touch of a button using digital instruments. However, these instruments, whilst easy to use, still operate using the same principles as the manual method outlined above.

At rest, normal adult systolic pressure varies between 110 and 140mm Hg, and distolic pressure between

70 and 80mm Hg. Blood pressure varies with age, sex, race and physical activity levels (see Unit 21). Remember, what is normal for one person may not be normal for another.

Blood pressure below 120/80mm Hg is considered optimal for adults. Someone with a systolic pressure of 120 to 139mm Hg or a distolic pressure of 80 to 89mm Hg is considered to have prehypertension and needs to be watched carefully. A blood pressure reading of 140/90mm Hg or higher is considered high and the individual concerned will be considered to be hypertensive. Hypertension is high blood pressure and it can increase the risk of cardiovascular diseases or kidney failure because it adds to the workload of the heart.

Aerobic exercises depend mainly on energy derived from consuming oxygen (aerobic). Thus they increase the body's need for oxygen. Because blood delivers oxygen to the body, aerobic activity challenges the heart and circulatory system to meet this increased need. During aerobic exercise, oxygen consumption and heart rate increase in relation to the intensity of the activity. Systolic blood pressure rises progressively, while diastolic blood pressure stays the same or decreases slightly. Pulse rate rises and blood flow to the muscles increases.

To detect changes in cardiovascular activity and oxygen consumption, measure your pulse rate before, during and after exercise or sports activity. Aerobic exercise increases the heart rate, and the more intense the activity (that is, the more energy demanding), the more the heart rate will increase. When exercising ceases, the heart rate does not return to normal immediately. Instead it gradually returns to its resting level. The greater your fitness level, the sooner your pulse rate will fall.

Key Terms

Systolic pressure The pressure when the heart contracts.

Diastolic pressure The pressure when the heart relaxes between beats.

Prehypertension This means you don't have high blood pressure now but you are likely to develop it in the future.

Hypertension High blood pressure, which is when systolic blood pressure is above 140mm Hg and diastolic pressure is above 90mm Hg.

Theory into practice

Under guidance from your tutor, use a digital blood pressure monitor to determine your own blood pressure.

Respiratory responses

Your body is surprisingly insensitive to falling levels of oxygen required for exercise. However, it is much more sensitive to an increase in levels of carbon dioxide. This is, therefore, a much more reliable indicator of the need for oxygen.

The levels of oxygen in arterial blood vary little, even during exercise, but carbon dioxide levels vary in direct proportion to the level of physical activity. The more intense the exercise, the greater the carbon dioxide concentration in the blood. To combat this, your body adapts by increasing its breathing rate (see page 33) to ensure the carbon dioxide is expelled.

Think it over

Although blood pressure goes up during any kind of exercise, the changes brought on vary according to whether the exercise is aerobic or anaerobic.

Aerobic exercise involves large muscle groups engaged in rhythmic, repeated movements. Examples of aerobic activities include jogging, brisk walking, swimming, bicycling and jumping rope.

Anaerobic exercise is defined as a sustained contraction of a muscle group and is typified by weightlifting.

Increase in breathing rate

Moderate to heavy physical exercise greatly increases the amount of oxygen skeletal muscles use.

For example, a trained athlete at rest might use about 250ml of oxygen per minute, but he may require 3,600ml per minute during maximal exercise. While oxygen utilisation is increasing, the volume of carbon dioxide produced increases also. A decreased blood oxygen and increased blood carbon dioxide concentration stimulate the respiratory centre, which, in turn, is accompanied by an increased breathing rate.

Key Term

Maximal exercise The level of training intensity when an athlete approaches their maximal heart rate and performs the exercise increasingly anaerobically rather than aerobically.

A minor increase in breathing rate prior to exercise is known as an anticipatory rise because it is a result of anticipating the exercise about to be undertaken.

When exercise begins, there is an immediate and much greater increase in breathing rate. This rise is believed to be as a result of the receptors working in both the muscles and joints.

After several minutes of aerobic exercise, breathing continues to rise but at a much slower rate, levelling off (so long as the exercise intensity remains constant) until the end of the exercise. If, however, the exercise is maximal, then the breathing rate continues to rise until exhaustion. In both cases, after exercise is finished, breathing returns towards normal – rapidly to begin with and then more slowly.

The increase in breathing rate during any exercise demands an increase in blood flow to the skeletal muscles. Exercise therefore increases demands on the respiratory and circulatory systems. Should either of these systems fail to keep up with demands, the athlete will feel out of breath. This is generally due to the inability of the heart and circulatory system to move enough blood between the lungs and the skeletal muscles, and not necessarily an inability of the respiratory system to provide sufficient oxygen.

Activity

List the following activities in order of their likely effects on the respiratory system, with '1' having the most effects and '6' the fewest:

- chess
- squash
- football (90 minutes)
- running a marathon
- archery
- rowing (2,000 metres).

Intercostal muscles

During the breathing process (see pages 33 to 40), the external intercostal muscles contract, causing the ribs and the sternum to move upwards and outwards. While this process takes place, the diaphragm muscles contract, causing the central part of the diaphragm to move down so that the diaphragm effectively flattens. The combined movements of the ribs, sternum and diaphragm cause the thorax and lungs to increase in volume, while the air pressure within the lungs decreases below the external air pressure. The result is that the external air pressure forces air from the external environment into the lungs.

During relaxed breathing, expiration is passive. The external intercostal muscles relax so that the ribs and the sternum move downwards and inwards. While this process takes place, both ribs and sternum regain their original positions. At the same time, the diaphragm muscles relax and the central part of the diaphragm rises, regaining its dome shape. The combined movements of the ribs, sternum and diaphragm, aided by the recoil of the abdominal muscles, cause the thorax and the lungs to decrease in volume. The air pressure within the lungs increases above the external air pressure. The result is that the internal air pressure forces air from the lungs into the external environment.

During exercise, forced breathing is used. This differs from normal breathing because, in the case of expiration, the internal intercostal muscles contract, moving the ribs and sternum upwards and outwards more forcibly. The abdominal muscles also contract, increasing the pressure of the abdominal cavity, which helps the central part of the diaphragm rise more forcibly. In terms of exercise and performance, the strength and efficiency of the intercostal muscles are increased as a consequence of the work they perform. During strenuous exercise the muscles involved in the breathing process can themselves utilise up to 10 per cent of the total oxygen uptake. Cramp in these muscles is thought to be one possible explanation of the 'stitch'.

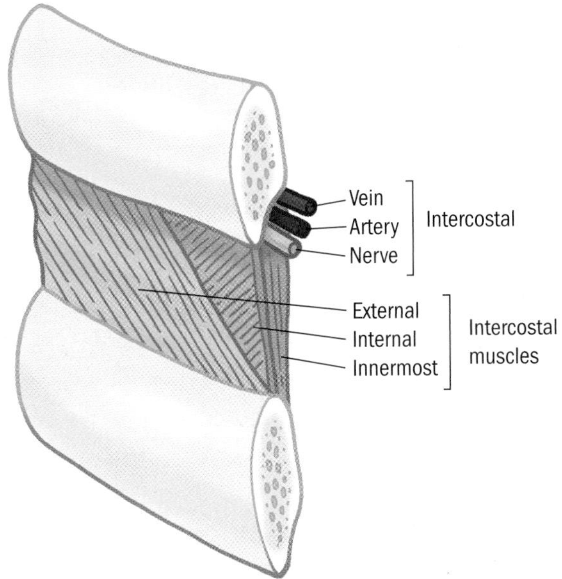

Eleven pairs of intercostal muscles occupy the spaces between 12 pairs of ribs. Their contraction and relaxation change the intrapulmonary pressure and constitute the mechanics of breathing

Increase in tidal volume

Tidal volume is the air ventilated per breath (see page 39). Exercise results in an increase in minute ventilation (the volume of gas ventilated in one minute). This rapid rise is due to nervous influences generated from receptors located in the working muscles and joints. Consequently, both tidal volume and frequency of breath increase. After exercise ends, minute ventilation returns to resting values.

Key Term

Minute ventilation Tidal volume × frequency of breaths per minute.

Valsalva manoeuvre

The Valsalva manoeuvre is performed by forcibly exhaling with the mouth closed and the nose pinched, forcing air into the middle ear. This manoeuvre can be used as a test of cardiac function and autonomic nervous control of the heart or to 'clear' the ears (equalise pressure) when external pressure increases, as in diving or aviation.

The normal physiological response consists of four phases:

- Initial pressure rise: on application of expiratory force, pressure rises inside the chest and forces blood out. This causes a transient rise in blood pressure.
- Reduced venous return and compensation: return of blood to the heart is impeded by the pressure inside the chest. The output of the heart is reduced and blood pressure falls. The fall in blood pressure causes blood vessels to constrict with some rise in pressure. This compensation can be quite marked with pressure returning to near or even above normal, but the cardiac output and blood flow to the body remains low. During this time the pulse rate increases.
- Pressure release: the pressure on the chest is released, allowing the aorta to expand again, causing a further initial slight fall in pressure. Venous blood can once more enter the chest and the heart. Cardiac output begins to increase.
- Return of cardiac output: blood returning to the heart is enhanced by the effect of entry of blood which had been dammed back, causing a rapid increase in cardiac output and blood pressure. The pressure usually rises above normal before returning to a normal level. With return of blood pressure, the pulse rate returns to normal.

Pulmonary ventilation

Pulmonary ventilation is commonly referred to as breathing. It is the process of air flowing into the lungs during inspiration (inhalation) and out of the lungs during expiration (exhalation). Air flows because of pressure differences between the atmosphere and the gases inside the lungs.

Air, like other gases, flows from a region with higher pressure to a region with lower pressure. Muscular breathing movements and recoil of elastic tissues create the changes in pressure that result in ventilation. Pulmonary ventilation involves three pressures:

- atmospheric pressure – the pressure of the air outside the body
- intra-alveolar (intrapulmonary) pressure – the pressure inside the alveoli of the lungs
- intrapleural pressure – the pressure within the pleural cavity.

These three pressures are responsible for pulmonary ventilation.

During exercise, the breathing rate of an athlete increases. The respiratory centre sends impulses to the internal intercostal muscles to speed up the expiratory process. This is a response to the chemical composition of the blood. The response of the body to exercise often results in an increased concentration of carbon dioxide in the blood following an increased utilisation of oxygen. It is this level of carbon dioxide that speeds up the expiratory process.

Think it over

Paula Radcliffe completed the London Marathon in 2 hours 17 mins and 42 seconds. When Paula crossed the finish line, she was clearly tired, but did you notice her breathing? She took several rapid and deep breaths in and out once she had stopped. Within a few minutes, her breathing rate had slowed enough for her to hold a brief television interview comfortably. Explain why you think it would be virtually impossible for Paula to give a televison interview immediately after she had crossed the finish line. Concentrate on the physiology of the pulmonary ventilation and why Paula needed these extra few minutes.

Assessment practice

Draw a table to illustrate the initial responses of the cardiovascular and the respiratory systems to exercise. Using the example of a middle-distance runner, use the following factors in your table and describe what happens to them: heart rate, stroke volume, cardiac output, blood pressure, breathing rate, intercostal muscles, tidal volume and pulmonary ventilation. **P1**

grading tips

Grading Tip 

You must be able to show a basic understanding in describing the initial responses of the cardiovascular and respiratory systems to exercise. Try to mention different sports as that will determine your grade as well.

Neuromuscular responses

The term 'neuromuscular' refers to both the nervous system and the muscular system (see page 14). There are two kinds of nerves:

- sensory neurons (or nerves) carry information from our extremities (the skin) to the central nervous system (the brain and spinal cord)
- motor neurones (or nerves) carry information from our central nervous system to our muscles.

Nervous control of muscular contraction

Muscles contract when they are stimulated by nerves. There are three basic types of contraction each with a variation of contraction pattern. All these types of contraction occur to some extent during exercise.

- Isotonic contraction: the muscle shortens as it develops tension. It is the most familiar type of contraction, the kind used in lifting or curling exercises.
- Isometric contraction: the muscle develops tension but does not change length. Holding a weight at arm's length is a good example. Isometric contractions occur regularly in sports such as wrestling.
- Isokinetic contraction: the muscle contracts to its maximum at a constant speed over the full range of movement. Isokinetic contractions occur within the arm stroke of a front crawl swimmer.

Neuromuscular junction

Neuromuscular junctions connect the end of a myelinated motor neurone to a muscle fibre. Generally, one neuromuscular junction is attached to one muscle fibre, to which it transmits nerve impulses.

Motor unit

A motor unit is made up of a motor neurone and all the associated muscle fibres it affects. Motor units generally work together to coordinate the contractions of a single skeletal muscle, although the number of fibres in each unit varies on the muscle size and role.

Muscle spindles

Muscle spindles are found in skeletal muscles. They are proprioceptors that contain small muscle fibres and sensory receptors. They detect muscle stretch and initiate a reflex that resists the stretch.

When a muscle is stretched, primary sensory sensors in the muscle spindle respond to both the velocity and the degree of stretch, and send this information to the spinal cord. Secondary sensory sensors detect and send information about the degree of stretch (but not the velocity) to the central nervous system. This information is transmitted to a motor neurone, which activates the muscle to contract, thus reducing stretch.

Key Term

Proprioceptor A sense organ found in muscle joints and tendons that give information concerning movement.

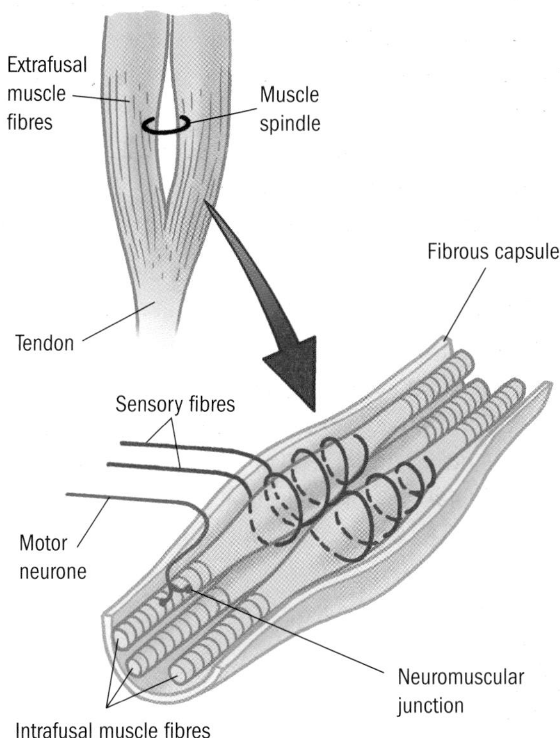

▲ **Muscle spindles provide information about any changes in length and tension of muscle fibres**

Energy system responses

The body takes in chemical energy in the form of food. This is stored in the body in the form of adenosine triphosphate (ATP), a high-energy compound that is converted into kinetic energy and used to create movement. The movement of muscles requires ATP, so it follows that the ability of an athlete to move his or her muscles requires a continued supply of ATP.

Remember!

The energy systems do not operate in isolation; they interact to supply the energy required for muscular movement. Energy systems are like 'taps' that are never fully turned off – the energy flows continually (like water at differing pressures) according to the exercise being undertaken.

Adenosine triphosphate production

Energy is required for all kinds of bodily processes including growth and development, repair, the transport of various substances between cells and, of course, muscle contraction.

Whether it's during a 26-mile marathon run or one explosive movement like a tennis serve, skeletal muscle is powered by one compound: ATP. However, the body stores only a small quantity of this 'energy currency' in the cells – enough to power only a few seconds of all-out exercise. Therefore, the body must replace or resynthesise ATP on a continual basis. Understanding how it does this is the key to understanding energy systems.

ATP consists of a base (adenine) and three phosphate groups. It is formed by a reaction between an adenosine diphosphate (ADP) molecule and a phosphate. When a molecule of ATP is combined with water, the last phosphate group splits off and energy is released.

(a) ATP is formed when adenosine diphosphate (ADP) binds with a phosphate

(b) A lot of energy is stored in the bond between the second and third phosphate groups, which can be used to fuel chemical reactions

(c) When a cell needs energy, it breaks the bond between the phosphate groups to form ADP and a free phosphate molecule

ATP and energy released from the breakdown of ATP

Creatine phosphate system

ATP and creatine phosphate (phosphocreatine or PCr) make up the ATP-PCr system. PCr is broken down, releasing a phosphate and energy, which is then used to rebuild ATP. The enzyme that controls the breakdown of PCr is called creatine kinase.

The ATP-PCr energy system can operate with or without oxygen, but because it does not rely on the presence of oxygen it said to be anaerobic. During the first five seconds of exercise, regardless of intensity, the ATP-PCr system is relied on almost exclusively. ATP concentrations last only a few seconds, with PCr buffering the drop in ATP for another five to eight seconds or so. The ATP-PCr system can sustain all-out exercise for three to 15 seconds and it is during this time that the potential rate for power output is at its greatest.

If activity continues beyond this immediate period, the body must rely on another energy system to produce ATP.

Remember!

ATP is a relatively small molecule that is generated inside the mitochondria of cells. ATP delivers instant energy in small but usable amounts.

Think it over

Think about the various movements of a footballer during a match (e.g. heading, shooting, tackling, jogging, standing, etc). Which of them are primarily aerobic metabolism, and which are primarily anaerobic metabolism?

Lactic acid system

Glycolysis is the breakdown of glucose and consists of a series of enzymatic reactions. The carbohydrates we eat supply the body with glucose, which can be stored as glycogen in the muscles or liver for later use.

The end product of glycolysis is pyruvic acid. This can then be either used in a process called the Krebs cycle (see page 61) or converted into lactic acid. Traditionally, if the final product was lactic acid, the process was called anaerobic glycolysis; and if the final product was pyruvic acid, the process was called aerobic glycolysis. However, oxygen availability only determines the fate of the end product and is not required for the actual process of glycolysis itself. In fact, oxygen availability has been shown to have little to do with which of the two end products – lactic acid or pyruvic acid – is produced. Therefore, the terms 'aerobic' meaning 'with oxygen' and 'anaerobic' meaning 'without oxygen' can be misleading.

Alternative terms that are often used are fast glycolysis if the final product is lactic acid, and slow glycolysis for the process that leads to pyruvic acid being funnelled through the Krebs cycle. As its name would suggest, the fast glycolitic system can produce energy at a greater rate than slow glycolysis. However, because the end product of fast glycolysis is lactic acid, it can quickly accumulate and is thought to lead to muscular fatigue.

Remember!

Glycolysis is the breakdown of glucose or glycogen to produce ATP.

Key Terms

Pyruvic acid A chemical precursor to lactic acid.

Lactic acid system An anaerobic energy system in which ATP is made when carbohydrate is broken down into lactic acid.

Anaerobic glycolysis

Anaerobic glycolysis is the process by which the normal pathway of glycolysis is routed to produce lactic acid. It occurs at times when energy is required in the absence of oxygen. It is vital for tissues with high energy requirements, insufficient oxygen supply or in the absence of oxidative enzymes.

Glycolysis results in the formation of pyruvic acid and hydrogen ions (H+). A build up of H+ makes the muscle cells acidic and interferes with their operation, so carrier molecules called nicotinamide adenine dinucleotide (NAD+) remove the H+. The NAD+ is reduced to NADH, which deposit the H+ during the electron transport chain (see page 62) to be combined with oxygen to form water.

If there is insufficient oxygen, NADH cannot release the H+ and they build up in the cell. To prevent the rise in acidity, pyruvic acid accepts H+ forming lactic acid that then dissociates into lactate and H+. Some of the lactate diffuses into the blood stream and takes some H+ with it as a way of reducing the H+ concentration in the muscle cell. The normal pH of the muscle cell is 7.1, but if the build up of H+ continues and pH is reduced to around 6.5, then muscle contraction may be impaired.

This table gives some examples of the three energy systems, their duration and their uses.

Energy system	Time	Use	Example
Creatine phosphate	10–15 seconds	Explosive activity	Weightlifting
Lactic acid	Post creatine phosphate; 60–90 seconds	High-intensity, submaximal activity	400m run
Aerobic*	90+ seconds to exhaustion	Continuous submaximal activity	1500m swim

Energy systems and their uses

* The aerobic energy system (see page 46) is a long-term energy system that is used in steady-state exercise.

Activity

What sports activities depend on aerobic metabolism for their source of ATP?

Key Term

Submaximal exercise Exercise conducted, generally at a steady state, below the anaerobic threshold.

Assessment practice

You've recently been employed as a fitness instructor at a large health club. The senior Personal Trainer is particularly busy at the moment and has asked you to assist him with three important clients. These are a weightlifter, a 400m runner and a 1500m swimmer, all of whom compete at a high level. The Personal Trainer is stepping up their preparation for an important competition and has asked you to help them by preparing a handy A2-poster that illustrates to each athlete the likely efffects of their individual training programmes.

1 Using specific examples, describe the initial responses of the neuromuscular and energy systems to the athletes' events. In other words, what are the likely neuromuscular responses and energy system responses to the individual events? Illustrate your findings on a poster with three columns for each athlete and their event. **P2**

2 Further explain on your poster the initial response of the cardiovascular, respiratory, neuromuscular and energy systems to the individual events and their participants. **M1** **D1**

grading tips

Grading Tip 

You must be able to show a basic understanding in describing the initial responses of the neuromuscular and energy systems to exercise.

Grading Tip 

The merit criteria demands a bit more from you in terms of the quality of what you produce as evidence and in terms of complexity, so pay attention to detail in your responses. 'Explaining' means showing that you know why something happens and can give that explanation clearly.

Grading Tip D1

To be graded at distinction level you need to show an in-depth understanding, use appropriate terminology well and have a really thorough approach. Above all, you must analyse, which means showing you can break up the components of the question and respond to them with critical insight. In other words, you have the ability to see important points to do with the response of the cardiovascular, respiratory, neuromuscular and energy systems that others might overlook.

2.2 Understand how the body responds to steady-state exercise

Regular aerobic training results in a type of cardiac hypertrophy. (In this case the heart increases in efficiency, size and blood volume.) The wall of the left ventricle thickens, increasing the strength potential of its contractions (see page 25). This has an important effect on heart rate, stroke volume and cardiac output.

Steady-state exercise

Once you undertake exercise, there is an elevated energy usage. This is reflected in the increased oxygen consumption.

Under certain conditions where the work rate is constant, the pattern of this increased oxygen consumption shows an initial rise for a few minutes and then it levels off. Once this plateau has been reached, oxygen consumption remains relatively steady over the course of the exercise. This is known as steady-state exercise.

For example, if you undertake 20 minutes of continuous same-speed jogging, 20 minutes of an aerobics class or 20 minutes of continuous same-speed swimming, a number of responses occur. Your heart and respiratory states increase to accommodate the demands placed on the body. A greater amount of ATP is synthesised and a number of neuromuscular changes occur. After three or four minutes your body has adapted to the increase in exercise intensity, so your increase in physiological demands levels out. For the remaining 15 minutes or so, you will undergo what is known as steady-state exercise, and what this involves is discussed below.

Cardiovascular responses

Heart rate

Prior to exercise, the heart usually beats between 60 and 80 beats per minute in untrained men and women, but this rate is generally much lower (40 to 60 beats per minute) in trained athletes. The heart rate increases during exercise and it does so in relation to the intensity of the exercise performed, as shown in the graph below.

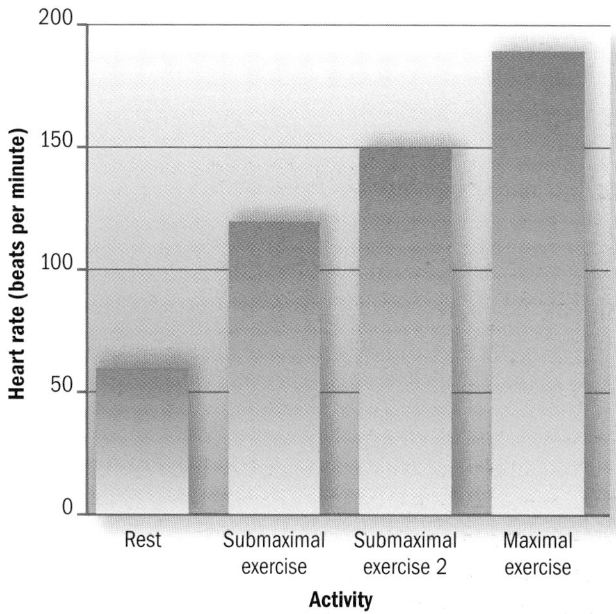

Heart rate during exercise. 'Submaximal exercise 2' is aerobic exercise of a greater intensity than 'Submaximal exercise' given the increased heart rate, although it is still below the anaerobic threshold

Stroke volume

Stroke volume increases to its highest levels during submaximal exercise and does not increase further during maximal exercise.

Stroke volume actually achieves its maximum amounts at between 40 and 50 per cent of VO_2 maximum (see page 345). In trained athletes, this generally means 120–140 beats per minute. The greatest increase in stroke volume occurs in the transition from rest to moderate exercise. During maximal exercise, stroke volume does not increase from its peak at 120–140 beats per minute as the left ventricle is, at this point, already full to capacity. The body tolerates maximal activity for as long as it can by simply increasing heart rate and maintaining stroke volume, although eventually the body will fatigue if the demands of the maximal exercise are too great.

Cardiac output

Each litre of arterial blood carries about 200ml of oxygen. The oxygen-carrying capacity of blood normally varies only slightly because haemoglobin content fluctuates little regardless of the exercise intensity. Approximately five litres of blood are circulated each minute at rest for trained or untrained athletes, so approximately one litre of oxygen is available to the body.

An increase in cardiac output has huge benefits for trained athletes as they can transport more blood to the working muscles and, therefore, more oxygen (page 289).

Given the formula for cardiac output is stroke volume × heart rate, and say the average stroke volume is 70ml and the average resting heart rate is 70 beats per minute, the average cardiac output of a healthy adult is:

70 × 70 = 4,900ml of blood per minute

However, a key adaptation of steady-state exercise is that the resting heart rate decreases while the stroke volume increases. A trained athlete can have a stroke volume of 110ml and a resting heart rate of 50 beats per minute. Therefore, the average cardiac output of a trained athlete is:

110 × 50 = 5,500ml of blood per minute

Therefore, a greater cardiac output (oxygen to working muscles) maintained with fewer beats is an indication of how steady-state exercise can increase the fitness levels.

Blood flow

Increased energy expenditure due to exercise requires adjustment in blood flow that affects the entire cardiovascular system (see page 29).

Vasodilation

During exercise, the vascular portion of active muscles increases through dilation of arterioles. This process is known as vasodilation and involves an increase in the diameter of the blood vessels resulting in an increased blood flow to the muscle area supplied by the vessel (or arteriole).

Vasoconstriction

Vessels can also shut down blood flow to tissues, which can temporarily lessen their blood supply. This process is known as vasoconstriction and involves a decrease in the diameter of a blood vessel by contraction of involuntary muscle fibres in the vessel walls, resulting in the reduction of blood flow.

For example, kidney function illustrates regulatory capacity for adjusting renal blood flow. At rest, renal blood flow comprises about 20 per cent of cardiac output. During maximal exercise, renal blood flow decreases to approximately 1 per cent of cardiac output.

Blood pressure

During steady-state exercise, dilation of the blood vessels in the active muscles increases the vascular area for blood flow. The alternate rhythmical contraction and relaxation of the skeletal muscles forces blood through the vessels and returns it to the heart.

Thermoregulation

Steady-state exercise increases sweating. This beneficial response is because of the significant increase in plasma volume that occurs during steady-state exercise. Increased plasma volume supports sweat gland function during heat stress, and maintains the correct plasma volume for the cardiovascular demands of the exercise. Therefore, a trained person will store less heat early during steady-state exercise, reaching a thermal steady-state sooner and at a lower core temperature than an untrained person. The training advantage for thermoregulation occurs only if the individual fully hydrates during exercise.

Increased venous return

Veins (see page 28) solve the potential problem related to the low blood pressure of venous blood. Valves spaced at short intervals within the vein permit one-way blood flow back to the heart. Veins compress because of low venous blood pressure or, in the case of steady-state exercise, muscular contractions.

Alternate venous compression and relaxation, combined with the one-way action of valves, provides a 'milking' effect similar to the action of the heart. Venous compression imparts considerable energy for blood flow, whereas a relaxation of the vessels allows blood to move towards the heart.

Without valves, blood would stagnate or pool in the veins and athletes would faint or pass out every time they undertook exercise.

Starling's law

Starling's law states that the stroke volume of the heart increases in response to an increase in the volume of blood filling the heart. The increased volume of blood stretches the ventricular wall, causing cardiac muscle to contract more forcefully. The stroke volume may also increase as a result of greater contractions in the cardiac muscles during exercise. Therefore, the reduced heart rate of a trained athlete allows a greater filling during the longer diastole, so the amount of stretch of the cardiac muscle is greater. This in turn increases the stroke volume.

Respiratory responses

Tidal volume and breathing rate

Increases in breathing rate maintain alveolar ventilation during steady-state exercise. During steady-state exercise, trained athletes achieve the required alveolar ventilation by increasing tidal volume and only minimally increasing breathing rate. With deeper breathing, alveolar ventilation usually increases from 70 per cent of minute ventilation (see page 35) at rest to over 85 per cent of total ventilation in exercise. This increase occurs because deeper breathing causes a greater percentage of the incoming tidal volume to enter the alveoli.

Effects of pH and temperature on the oxygen dissociation curve

The oxygen dissociation curve is a graph that shows the relationship between the percentage of oxygen saturation of blood and the partial pressure of oxygen. During steady-state exercise, increased temperature and lower blood pH concentration affect the oxygen–haemoglobin dissociation curve in such a way that more oxygen can be unloaded to supply the active muscle. In prolonged high-intensity exercise, large amounts of lactate enter the blood from active muscle. At exhaustion, blood pH can approach 6.8. Only after exercise ceases does blood pH stabilise and return to 7.4.

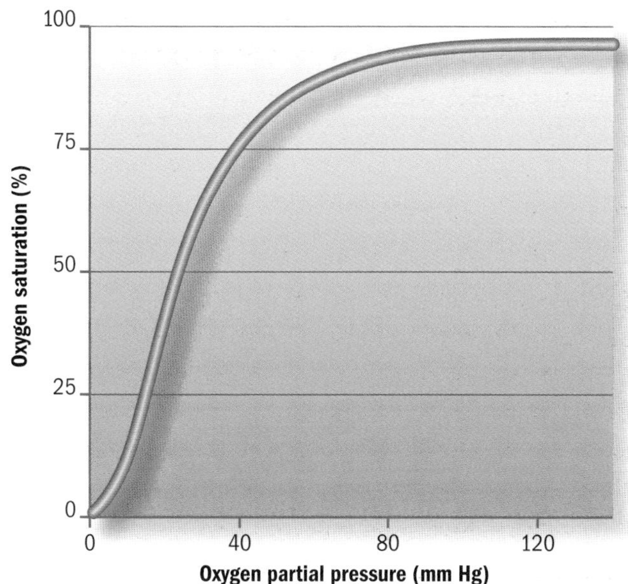

▲ The oxygen dissociation curve

Neuromuscular responses

Muscle spindles and Golgi tendon organs provide sensory information in relation to the intensity of exercise, providing smooth, coordinated movement patterns.

Increased pliability of muscles

Muscle spindles are located within muscle fibres known as intrafusal fibres (see page 53). When the spindle is stretched, nerve impulses are generated and information relative to the degree of stretch is sent to the central nervous system. The central nervous system sends back information concerning how many motor units should be contracted in order to implement a smooth movement. The more your body is used to a particular steady-state exercise, the more efficient the muscle spindles become at transmitting the same information, and the more pliable the muscles become.

Increased transmission rate of nerve impulses

Golgi tendon organs are located within the tendons and are also sensitive to stretch. The information that the Golgi tendon organs send to the central nervous system is concerned with the strength of the muscle contraction. The Golgi tendon organs complement the muscle spindles and together they facilitate efficient and movement patterns.

Key Term

Golgi tendon organ A proprioceptor located within the muscle tendon.

Energy system responses

On arrival at the skeletal muscle, fuel is consumed with or without oxygen as the muscles convert chemical energy to mechanical energy. Before examining how the muscles respond to this process, the various energy systems should be explained. However, at any period in time, one of the three energy systems is dominant in contributing the energy required for the resynthesis of adenosine triphosphate (ATP). The contribution of each energy system is dependent on the intensity and duration of the exercise. The continual interaction of the three systems is known as the energy continuum.

Remember!

During exercise, the body does not switch from one energy system to the other – energy at any time is derived from all three systems. However, the emphasis changes depending on the intensity of the activity relative to the efficiency of your aerobic fitness, i.e. your ability to deliver and utilise oxygen.

Adenosine triphosphate (ATP) production

As a general rule, training to enhance intramuscular ATP energy transfer capacity requires repetitive, intense, short-duration exercise.

The training activities selected should engage the muscles in the movement for which the athlete desires improved anaerobic power. This achieves two goals:

- it enhances the metabolic capacity of engaged muscle tissue or fibres
- it improves the neuromuscular adaptations to the sport-specific pattern of movement.

When ATP is split, some of the energy is used to power muscle contractions but, as no energy is 100 per cent efficient, some is always lost as heat. This is why vigorous exercise produces large amounts of heat that must escape from the body.

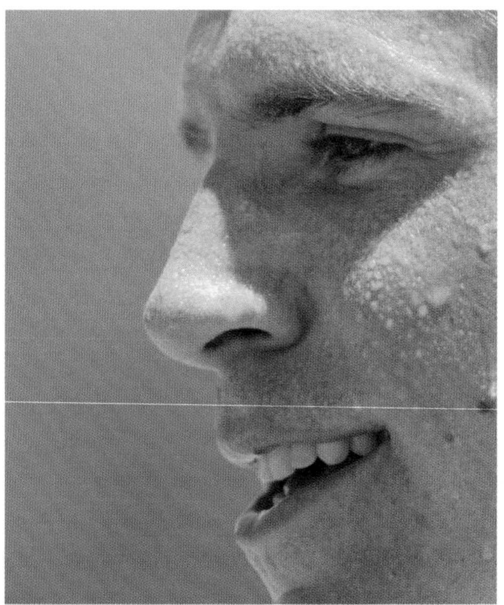

▲ Our bodies are able to exercise due to the supply of energy from ATP. This process not only produces energy but also large amounts of heat. Is it possible to tell when an athlete is consuming much energy?

Aerobic energy system

This aerobic energy system involves the oxygen transporting system and the use of mitochondria in the working muscle for oxidation of glycogen and fatty acids. Due to this system's reliance on oxygen, it is referred to as the aerobic energy system.

This system is involved in prolonged work at low intensity and is of increasing importance the longer the sport goes on. Only lack of fuel, overheating or dehydration will end exercise using this system.

It seems that the fuelling system for combustion in aerobic exercise varies according to its duration and intensity. In prolonged aerobic exercise, the preferred fuel is free fatty acids because glycogen stores are limited compared to our large fat stores.

Unlike glycogen, fatty acids can only be used in the aerobic energy system, whereas higher-intensity exercise involving aerobic and anaerobic energy systems prefer glycogen as fuel.

Anaerobic glycolysis

Anaerobic glycolysis involves the breakdown of glycogen (glycolysis) in the absence of oxygen, with the formation of ATP plus lactate (lactic acid and associated by-products).

The accumulation of lactate terminates the use of this energy system after 40 to 60 seconds of maximum effort. Consequently, it is the system called upon by athletes whose sports demand high-energy expenditure for up to 60 seconds, such as 400m runners and those in compound sprint sports such as squash, football or rugby.

Mitochondria

Mitochondria are the site of aerobic respiration. Pyruvate oxidation and the Krebs cycle take place in the matrix (fluid) of the mitochondria, while the electron transport chain takes place in the inner membrane itself.

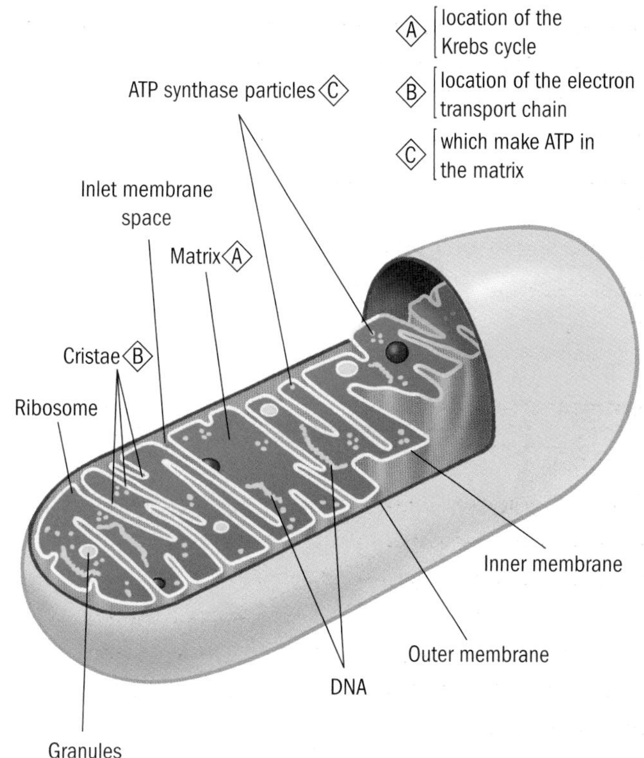

▲ A typical mitochondrion

Krebs cycle

The Krebs cycle is a series of aerobic chemical reactions occurring in the matrix in mitochondria. The main purpose of the Krebs cycle is to provide a continuous supply of electrons to feed the electron transport chain.

Key Term

Krebs cycle A series of chemical reactions occurring in mitochondria in which carbon dioxide is produced and carbon atoms are oxidised.

This cycle begins when the 2-carbon acetyl CoA joins with a 4-carbon compound to form a 6-carbon compound called citric acid. Citric acid (6C) is gradually converted back to the 4-carbon compound ready to start the cycle once more. The carbons removed are released as CO_2. The hydrogens, which are removed, join with NAD to form $NADH_2$.

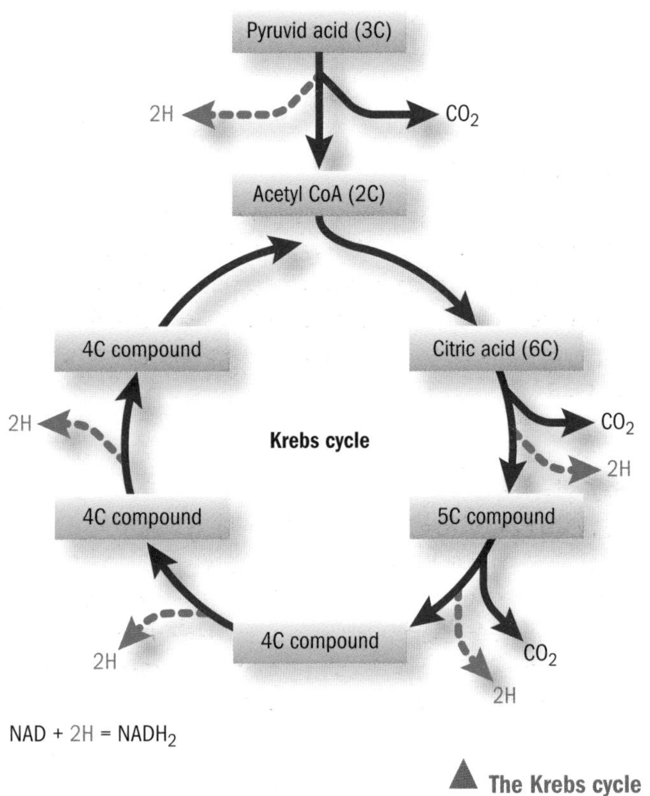

▲ **The Krebs cycle**

Electron transport chain

The electron transport chain is also known as the cytochrome system. It is a series of biomechanical reactions during which free energy contained within hydrogen (derived from the Krebs cycle) is released, so that it can be used to synthesise ATP during aerobic metabolism. The electron transport chain occurs in the many cristae in mitochondria. Each reaction involves a specific electron-carrier molecule which has a particular attraction for hydrogen. The final link in the electron transport chain is oxygen, which combines with the hydrogen and electrons to form water.

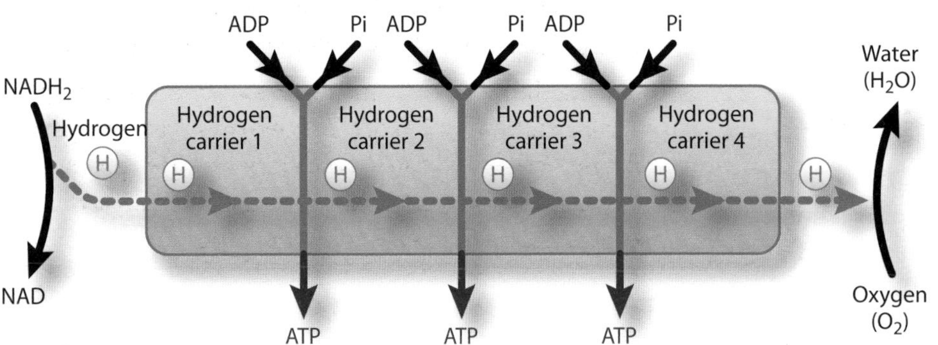

◀ **The electron transfer chain**

Assessment practice

Following the success of your last training poster, the 1500m swimmer has asked if you could assist his fitness and training programme. He is keen to learn more about sport and exercise physiology and has asked you to explain his training regimes, so that he understands in more detail the effects of his training.

1 Describe how the cardiovascular, respiratory, neuromuscular and energy systems respond to the swimmer's steady-state exercise training (i.e. swimming at a constant rate for 20–30 minutes). **P3 P4**

2 You decide to produce four flash cards, one for each topic area. These flash cards are designed for your swimmer to keep in his kit bag and will describe the responses in bullet-point format for future reference. Further explain on your flash cards how the cardiovascular, respiratory, neuromuscular and energy systems respond to steady-state exercise. **M2**

3 Analyse the cardiovascular, respiratory, neuromuscular and energy systems' responses to steady-state exercise. Your flash cards should refer to fitness testing results taken from the swimmer during training to illustrate your findings. **D2**

grading tips

Grading Tip  P3

You must be able to show a basic understanding in describing how the cardiovascular and respiratory systems respond to steady-state exercise. If you can provide real working examples, these will help to show this. Ensure you choose different sports as that will determine your grade as well.

Grading Tip  M2

The merit criteria demands a bit more from you in terms of the quality of what you produce as evidence and in terms of complexity, so pay attention to detail in your responses. 'Explaining' means showing that you know why something happens and can give that explanation clearly.

Grading Tip P4

You must be able to show a basic understanding in describing how the neuromuscular and energy systems respond to steady-state exercise. If you can provide real working examples, these will help to show this. Ensure you choose different sports as that will determine your grade as well.

Grading Tip D2

To be graded at distinction level means you can show an in-depth understanding, use appropriate terminology well and have a really thorough approach. Above all, you must analyse, which means showing you can break up the components of the question and respond to them with critical insight.

2.3 Understand fatigue and how the body recovers from exercise

Fatigue

Fatigue involves the exhaustion of muscle resulting from prolonged exertion or over-stimulation. We cannot exercise indefinitely because of neuromuscular fatigue, which occurs as a result of different methods and systems.

The symptoms of fatigue include:

- depletion of energy sources, primarily creatine phosphate and glycogen
- increase in lactic acid
- dehydration
- electrolyte loss.

Exercise places demands on the body. Think about the changes that occur when you exercise:

- oxygen levels fall
- carbon dioxide and lactate levels increase
- body temperature increases
- blood glucose and glycogen levels fall
- fluid and electrolytes (salts) are lost as you sweat.

During short-term maximal exercise, insufficient oxygen and/or an increased lactate accumulation can bring about fatigue. Reliance on anaerobic metabolism ultimately impairs energy transfer via glycolysis and inhibits the contractile mechanisms of muscle fibres.

Depletion of energy sources

The body needs energy in order to function effectively. As an athlete begins to exercise, the body has to ensure a supply of energy so that the heart rate increases, forcing more blood to the skeletal muscles so they can contract more frequently in response to the activity undertaken.

The energy required comes from the food you eat.

- Carbohydrate (e.g. pasta, bread, rice and potatoes) is broken down into glucose in the body to provide energy.
- Fats (e.g. cheese, butter, oils) are broken down into fatty acids in the body to provide energy.
- Proteins (e.g. fish, meat, eggs) are broken down into amino acids that provide energy in extreme circumstances.

The breakdown of all three fuels in the body produces adenosine triphosphate (ATP), the only substance the body is able to utilise to provide energy. All forms of anatomy and physiology – be it digestion, transmission of nerve impulses or muscular contractions – require energy in the form of ATP. Therefore, if an athlete fails to take in enough carbohydrate, fat or protein, it is likely they will deplete their energy sources quickly when exercise is undertaken.

Creatine phosphate

Creatine phosphate is synthesised in the liver and transported to skeletal muscles for storage. It is used to form ATP from ADP (see page 54) and is particularly important for intense efforts of physical exercise with a time limit of approximately ten seconds.

Muscle and liver glycogen

A reduction in muscle and liver glycogen and blood glucose during submaximal exercise can occur despite the availability of sufficient oxygen and ATP through metabolic pathways.

Once glycogen stores are depleted, muscles cease contracting – even during steady-state exercise – as the body is unable to use fat as a sole source of fuel. Marathon runners in particular must be careful not to deplete their glycogen stores early in a race by running too fast. The premature depletion of these stores brings the athlete to the point of exhaustion. To combat this, marathon runners run at a pace that metabolises fats so that the rate at which glycogen depletes is lessened.

Effects of waste products

The principle waste products of exercise are urea, carbon dioxide, water, lactic acid and other metabolites. Urea and water are filtered through the kidneys and expelled from the body. Carbon dioxide is carried in the blood to the lungs, where it passes into the alveoli and is then expelled from the body.

Blood lactate accumulation, carbon dioxide and increased acidity

During exercise, however, raised levels of carbon dioxide increase the level of blood acidity. Carbon dioxide is carried in chemical combinations in the blood. In red blood cells, enzymes speed up the reaction of carbon dioxide and water to form carbonic acid.

$$H_2O + CO_2 \rightarrow H_2CO_3$$

Carbonic acid breaks down into hydrogen ions (H+) and bicarbonate ions (HCO_{3-}).

$$H_2CO_3 \rightarrow H+ + HCO_{3-}$$

The increase in hydrogen ions is responsible for the increase in blood acidity. Metabolites other than lactate are disposed of by oxidation. Lactic acid is disposed of as follows:

- Muscle lactate is disposed of first by oxidation to pyruvate and then by dissimilation to carbon dioxide and water.
- Some blood lactate is taken in by the liver, which reconstructs it to glycogen.
- The remaining blood lactate diffuses back into the muscle or other organs, to be oxidised then dismantled. This oxidation forms carbon dioxide, which is later excreted by the lungs.

Neuromuscular fatigue

Depletion of acetylcholine

Acetylcholine is a neurotransmitter that is released to stimulate skeletal muscles and the parasympathetic nervous system. Its effect is short-lived because it is destroyed by acetylcholinesterase – an enzyme released into the sarcolemma of muscle fibres, thus preventing continued muscle contraction in the absence of additional nervous stimulation.

Reduced calcium-ion release

As part of the sliding filament theory (see page 20), calcium ions are known to be released allowing actin and myosin to couple and form actomyosin. During relaxation (once stimulation has ceased), the calcium ions are removed and the muscle returns to its resting state. If the store of calcium ions is reduced, the ability of the actin and myosin to couple is compromised, thus preventing continued muscle contraction.

▲ **Fatigue is an unpleasant but often inevitable result of elite competition. It is vital that sport scientists understand the impact and consequences of fatigue and recovery**

Recovery

Four processes have to be satisfied before the exhausted muscle can perform to its optimum level again. These are:

- restoration of muscle phosphogen stores
- removal of lactic acid
- replenishment of myoglobin stores with oxygen
- replacement of glycogen.

Activity

What causes muscle fatigue?

Excess post-exercise oxygen consumption (EPOC)

The need for additional oxygen to replace ATP and remove lactic acid is known as oxygen debt or excess post-exercise oxygen consumption (EPOC). The two major components of EPOC are:

- fast components (alactacid oxygen debt) – this is the amount of oxygen required to synthesise and restore muscle phosphagen stores (ATP and creatine phosphate)
- slow components (lactacid oxygen debt) – this is the amount of oxygen required to remove lactic acid from the muscle cells and blood.

Bodily processes do not immediately return to normal or resting levels after exercise. After light exercise such as golf or walking, recovery to a resting state takes place quickly and generally without realising it. With steady-state exercise, however, it takes time for the body to return to normal.

EPOC defines the excess oxygen uptake above the resting level in recovery. It means the total oxygen consumed after exercise is in excess of a pre-exercise baseline level. Oxygen consumption after exercise restores the energy demands used during exercise.

Fast components

Restoration of muscle phosphogen stores

Alactacid oxygen debt (without lactic acid) represents that portion of oxygen used to synthesise and restore muscle phosphogen stores (ATP and creatine phosphate) which have been almost completely exhausted during high-intensity exercise. During the first three minutes of recovery, EPOC restores almost 99 per cent of the ATP and creatine phosphate used during exercise (see the table on page 66).

Recovery time (seconds)	Muscle phosphogen restored (%)
10	10
30	50
60	75
90	87
120	93
150	97
180	99
210	101
240	102

Restoration of muscle phosphogen

Slow components

Removal of lactic acid

The slow component of EPOC is concerned with the removal of lactic acid from the muscles and the blood. This can take several hours, depending on the intensity of the activity and whether the athlete was active or passive during the recovery phase (continuous activity can significantly speed up recovery). Around half of lactic acid is removed after 15 minutes, and most is removed after an hour.

Lactacid recovery converts most of the lactic acid to pyruvic acid, which is oxidised via the Krebs cycle to create ATP. Once exercise is over, the liver synthesises lactic acid into glycogen while the remainder of the body can remove small amounts of lactic acid through respiration, perspiration and excretion.

Replenishment of myoglobin stores

Myoglobin is an oxygen-storage protein found in muscle. Like haemoglobin, it forms a loose combination with oxygen while the oxygen supply is plentiful, and stores it until the demand for oxygen increases. Consequently, muscle has its own built-in oxygen supply. However, during exercise, the oxygen from myoglobin is quickly used up. After exercise, additional oxygen is required to pay back any oxygen that has been borrowed from myoglobin stores.

Replacement of glycogen

The replenishment of muscle and liver glycogen stores depends on the type of exercise. Short-distance, high-intensity exercise may take two or three hours, whereas long endurance activities such as a marathon may take several days. Replenishment of glycogen stores is most rapid during the first few hours after training. Complete restoration of glycogen stores is accelerated with a high carbohydrate diet.

Activity

How long does it take to replenish the stores of muscle glycogen?

Assessment practice

1 Your swimmer has successfully completed his six-month training programme and is now much more knowledgeable about the physiological responses to steady-state exercise. He is due to start an important competition in one month and has enquired about how his body recovers from exercise. Describe the mechanisms of fatigue, including the waste products, neuromuscular fatigue and depletion of energy sources. **P5**

2 Your swimmer is away training elsewhere for the next month, but he has asked you to record a CD or MP3 which he can take with him to listen to while travelling. The audio file should describe fatigue and how the body recovers from exercise. Naturally, you agreed and set to work immediately. You decide on a simple format describing how fatigue and recovery apply to swimming training. Your CD or MP3 should explain fatigue, and how the body recovers from exercise. **M3**

grading tips

Grading Tip 

You must be able to show a basic understanding in describing fatigue, and how the body recovers from exercise. If you can provide real working examples, these will help to show this. Ensure you choose different sports as that will determine your grade as well.

Grading Tip 

The merit criteria demands a bit more from you in terms of the quality of what you produce as evidence and in terms of complexity, so pay attention to detail in your responses. 'Explaining' means showing that you know why something happens and can give that explanation clearly.

2.4 Understand how the body adapts to long-term exercise

There are differences between responses to exercise and how the body adapts to exercise. The immediate changes that occur to the energy and neuromuscular systems during exercise are called responses. How the body adapts are more permanent changes, that take place as a result of long-term exercise.

If you exercise regularly your body adapts and you get fit. This means you are able to cope more easily with exercise that previously you might have found difficult. Consequently, the human body is able to adapt and respond to exercise, allowing you to cope with your chosen sport.

Chronic exercise

A chronic (long-term) exercise programme is one in which the exercise period is not less than eight weeks. Responses to long-term exercise include changes to the heart, lungs and muscles, although the extent of the changes depends on the type and intensity of exercise undertaken.

Cardiovascular adaptations

Cardiac hypertrophy

An increase in heart size indicates the adjustment of a healthy heart to exercise training. Regular aerobic exercise (e.g. four 30-minute jogging sessions per week for eight weeks) stimulates the increase in both the thickness of the muscle fibres and the number of contractile elements contained in the fibres (see page 25).

Increase in stroke volume and cardiac output, and decrease in resting heart rate

Over time, aerobic training increases the size of the heart. This is due to an increase in the muscle mass of the four heart chambers. This increase in size increases the athlete's stroke volume (see page 48). As a result of increased stroke volume and cardiac hypertrophy, the athlete's resting heart rate decreases. When the heart can pump more blood per beat, it does not have to beat as often when the body is a rest. This is why getting fitter causes a decrease in resting pulse rate. Some of the world's top athletes have a resting pulse rate between 30 and 40 beats per minute.

Blood volume

Blood volume is the amount of blood circulating in the body. It varies from athlete to athlete and will increase with training. In trained males, blood volume equates to approximately to 75ml per kilogram of bodyweight, and in trained females it equates to approximately 60ml per kilogram of bodyweight.

Blood volume increases because of capillarisation during long-term exercise. Consequently, there is more space for blood to circulate which, in turn, allows for a greater supply of oxygen to skeletal muscles.

Capillarisation

Long-term exercise can lead to the development of a capillary network to a part of the body. Aerobic training improves the capillarisation of cardiac and skeletal muscle by increasing the number of capillaries and the capillary density (the number of capillaries in a given area of muscle tissue).

Respiratory adaptations

Increase in minute ventilation

Minute ventilation depends on breathing rate and tidal volume. During exercise, adults can generally achieve 100 litres per minute or approximately 15 times the resting value. In trained athletes, however, minute ventilation can increase by 50 per cent to 150 litres per minute.

Respiratory muscles

An increase in strength allows the external intercostal muscles a greater degree of contraction, while the internal intercostal muscles relax during inspiration, thus forcing more air into the lungs. Likewise, during expiration the greater degree of contraction of the internal intercostals and the relaxation of the external intercostals allows the athlete to breath out a greater volume of air.

Increase in resting lung volumes

An increased surface area allows a greater volume of deoxygenated blood access to the sites of gaseous exchange (see page 36) within the lungs. The carbon dioxide is offloaded and a greater amount of oxygen is diffused into the blood for its journey back to the heart, followed by circulation to the skeletal muscles. The increased ability of the blood to take on more oxygen due to the increased surface area of alveoli, aids trained athletes tremendously.

Increase in oxygen diffusion rate

An increase in diffusion rates in tissues favours oxygen movement from the capillaries to the tissues, and carbon dioxide from the cells to the blood. Long-term exercise causes these rates to increase, allowing both oxygen and carbon dioxide to diffuse more rapidly.

Neuromuscular adaptations

Hypertrophy

As a general rule, long-term exercise improves muscle tone and stamina. Training with a greater resistance brings about an increase in muscle size, a process known as hypertrophy. Muscular hypertrophy involves an increase in the cross-sectional size of existing muscle tissue. This is because of the increase in the number of myofibrils and connective tissue (tendons and ligaments), which then become more pliable.

Increase in tendon strength

As the skeletal muscles of a trained athlete become larger, stronger or more efficient, the connective tendons have to adapt to meet these increased demands of the muscle. Without such adaptations, serious injury may follow if the increased forces of contraction developed by the muscle cannot cause the lever or bone to move properly.

Increased myoglobin stores, increased numbers of mitochondria, and increased storage of glycogen and triglycerides

With training, muscles tend to increase their oxidative capacity. This is achieved by an increase in the number of mitochondria in the muscle cells, an increased supply of ATP and an increase in the quantity of the enzymes involved in respiration. The ability of the muscles to store glycogen and myoglobin, and the ability to use triglycerides as an energy store, can also be increased.

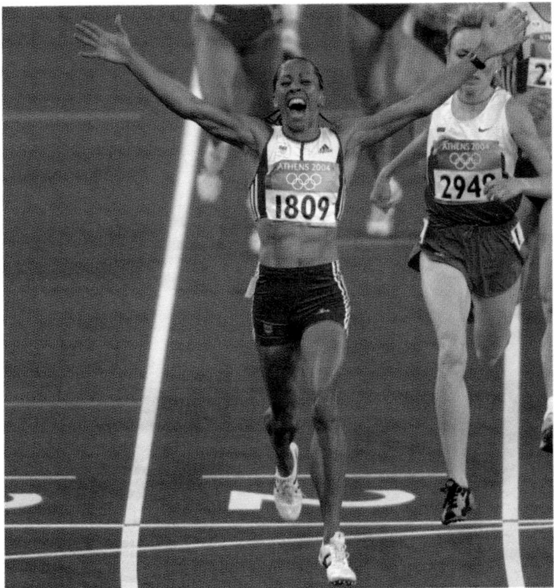

▲ Persistence with training and an understanding of the responses and adaptations to training and competition can be a winning combination

Key Terms

Cellular adaptations Changes within the cell structure (e.g. increase in mitochondrial size).

Neurotransmitters Chemicals used to carry signals or information between neurons and cells.

Neural pathways

Neural structures and pathways show changes as a result of long-term exercise training. These changes include cellular adaptations, modifications of neurotransmitters, alterations in reflex, and chemical and biochemical responses.

For example, sprint training actually produces relatively small metabolic changes but has substantial effects on performance. Therefore, neuromuscular adaptations brought about by sprint training are important given those changes in performance.

Energy system adaptations

Increased anaerobic and aerobic enzymes

Long-term exercise brings about a number of cellular changes that enhance the ability of muscle tissue to generate ATP. Cellular adaptation such as the increase in size of mitochondria is usually accompanied by an increase in the level of aerobic system enzymes. A combination of these changes probably accounts for why an athlete can sustain prolonged periods of aerobic exercise as a result of longer-term training. The anaerobic system also undergoes a number of changes, including the increase in enzymes (especially in fast-twitch muscles) that control the anaerobic phase of glucose breakdown.

Increased use of fats as an energy source

The use of fats as an energy source occurs during low-intensity exercise. During exercise, fat combustion powers almost all exercise at approximately 25 per cent of aerobic power. Carbohydrate and fat contribute in equal measures during moderate exercise. Fat oxidation increases if exercise extends to over an hour as glycogen levels deplete. In fact, towards the end of an exercise session beyond an hour, fats account for approximately 75 per cent of the total energy required.

Therefore, when considering the effects of long-term exercise, it is clear that trained athletes have far greater opportunity to burn fat as fuel than non-trained adults.

Higher tolerance to lactic acid

If your lactate threshold is reached at low-exercise intensity, it means that the aerobic energy system in your muscles is not working very well. If you are performing at a high level, you would use oxygen to break down lactate to carbon dioxide and water, preventing lactate from pouring into the blood.

If your lactate threshold is low, it is because of one of the following factors:

- you are not getting enough oxygen inside your muscle cells
- you do not have enough mitochondria in your muscle cells
- your muscles, heart and other tissues are not good at extracting lactate from the blood.

One of the longer-term adaptations to exercise is to saturate the muscles in lactic acid, which educates your body in dealing with it more effectively. The accumulation of lactate in working skeletal muscles is associated with fatigue after 50 to 60 seconds of maximal effort. Therefore, training continuously at about 85 per cent to 90 per cent of your maximum heart rate for 20 to 25 minutes improves the body's tolerance to lactic acid.

Skeletal adaptations

Increased calcium stores

Long-term exercise slows the rate of skeletal aging. Regardless of age, athletes who maintain physically active lifestyles have significantly greater bone mass compared with those who participate in less exercise.

Exercise of moderate intensity provides a safe and potent stimulus to maintain and even increase bone mass. Weight-bearing exercises such as running or walking are particularly beneficial, but this is dependent on adequate calcium availability for the bone-forming process.

Increased tendon strength

Tendons attach muscles to bones or to muscles, whereas ligaments attach bone to bone and are usually found at joints. Both are able to withstand great tensile stress when forces are applied. However, both types of tissue are poorly supplied with blood (vascularised). In terms of construction, both types of tissues are constructed of closely-packed bundles of collagen fibres. Crowded among the collagen fibres are rows of fibroblasts. The main function of the fibroblasts is to maintain the structural integrity by secreting compounds to help manufacture replacement fibres.

Key Term

Fibroblast A connective tissue cell that makes and secretes collagen proteins.

Increased stretch of ligaments

When considering the effects of long-term exercise, it is important to remember that the human body responds to stimulus. An athlete requires stronger tendons and more pliable ligaments to handle heavy weights or an increase running distance. If an athlete lifts progressively heavier weights as part of a strength-training exercise programme, the athlete's muscles will gain strength. Therefore, to accommodate this increase, the athlete's tendons have to increase their load-bearing capacity relative to the increased strength of the muscle, while the ligaments need to adapt their pliability accordingly. This adaptation occurs when fibroblast secretions increase the production of collagen fibres relative to the training undertaken. Without this relationship, injury is likely to occur.

Assessment practice

On return from his competition, your swimmer was successful and finished second in his event. He commented that he owes much of his success to your training and advice. To remember exactly what he has achieved so far and how, he has asked for a series of reminders that he can take away with him.

1 First, he would like a printed T-shirt that lists, on both sides, in short, concise sentences (a maximum of ten words per sentence) how the cardiovascular and respiratory systems adapt to long-term exercise. He maintains this will serve as a timely reminder every time he wears it to go training. **P6**

2 Second, he would like a flipcard book that summarises how the neuromuscular, energy and skeletal systems adapt to long-term exercise. He can keep this in his pocket and flick through it wherever he is. **P7**

3 Third, and in more detail, he would like a laminated A4 sheet of paper (which he can take on poolside) that explains how the cardiovascular, respiratory, neuromuscular, energy and skeletal systems adapt to long-term exercise. He says this would remind him why he should train so hard. **M4**

4 Finally, your swimmer has asked for a simplified log of his training with you over a six month period. This log should highlight times and instances that analyse how the cardiovascular, respiratory, neuromuscular, energy and skeletal systems adapt to chronic exercise. The log should provide evidence as to how these adaptations materialised. **D3**

grading tips

Grading Tip 

You must be able to show a basic understanding in describing how the cardiovascular and respiratory systems adapt to long-term exercise. If you can provide real working examples, these will help to show this. Ensure you choose different sports as that will determine your grade as well.

Grading Tip 

You must be able to show a basic understanding in describing how the neuromuscular, energy and skeletal systems adapt to long-term exercise. If you can provide real working examples, these will help to show this. Ensure you choose different sports as that will determine your grade as well.

Grading Tip 

The merit criteria demands a bit more from you in terms of the quality of what you produce as evidence and in terms of complexity, so pay attention to detail in your responses. 'Explaining' how the cardiovascular, respiratory, neuromuscular, energy and skeletal systems adapt to long-term exercise means showing that you know why something happens and can give that explanation clearly.

Grading Tip 

To be graded at distinction level means you can show an in-depth understanding, use appropriate terminology well and have a really thorough approach. Above all, you must analyse, which means showing you can break up the components of the question and respond to them with critical insight. In other words, you have the ability to see important points that others miss, as well as identifying faults and making realistic suggestions as to how something could have been done better.

Knowledge check

1 What is aerobic exercise?
2 What does 'systolic' refer to?
3 Examine the nervous control of muscular contraction and then describe how this enables the body to move.
4 Explain what is meant by the term 'steady-state exercise'.
5 Explain how your heart and lungs work together to respond to a form of steady-state exercise such as 20 minutes on a running machine.
6 Draw a diagram to describe the Krebs cycle.
7 Why does taking part in exercise deplete energy sources and what waste products are produced?
8 Explain the process of excess post-exercise oxygen consumption (EPOC).
9 Explain the difference between responses and adaptations to exercise.
10 Think of a sport and then describe how the cardiovascular, respiratory, neuromuscular, energy and skeletal systems adapt to long-term changes as a result of taking part in this sport.

Preparation for assessment

Following on from the success of your training relationship with the 1500m swimmer, you have come to the attention of the local swimming club. They are impressed with your ability to pass on complex physiological knowledge and have asked you to produce a CD-ROM for all their competetive swimmers, to aid with their training.

This CD-ROM is designed to educate athletes on the basic principles of sport and exercise physiology. It should, therefore, contain four sections:

1 Initial responses of the body to exercise.

2 How the body responds to steady-state exercise.

3 Fatigue and how the body recovers from exercise.

4 How the body adapts to long-term exercise.
P6 P7 M4 D3

Your CD-ROM should take the form of a PowerPoint® presentation rather than a written report. It is designed as an educational tool to complement an elite athlete's training programme, regardless of the sport they specialise in. The presentation should be brief and to the point and consist of no more than 20 slides (a maximum of five slides per section).

If possible, your slides should make use of pictures to further illustrate the points being made. The actual reading time of the CD-ROM presentation should be no more than 30 minutes.

grading tips

Grading Tip 

Ensure your presentation describes, explains and analyses the initial responses of the cardiovascular, respiratory, neuromuscular and energy systems to exercise. It is a good idea to devote one slide to each category, using sport-specific examples to illustrate and analyse your findings. Keep your analysis brief and in the form of bullet points.

Grading Tip P3 P4 M2 D2

Your presentation should describe, explain and analyse how the cardiovascular, respiratory, neuromuscular and energy systems respond to steady-state exercise. Use the same steady-state form of exercise for the analysis of your findings for the sake of continuity. Keep your analysis brief and in the form of bullet points.

Grading Tip P5 M3

Describe and explain the process of fatigue and how the body recovers from exercise. Concentrate on what happens to the body when it approaches fatigue or exhaustion; what particular factors occur and how they affect an athlete's physiology. Explain the various methods by which an athlete recovers from a period of exercise.

Grading Tip P6 M4 D3

Describe, explain and analyse how the cardiovascular, respiratory, neuromuscular and energy systems adapt to long-term exercise. To achieve this, it is perhaps best to construct a case history for an athlete, analysing how their training schedule progresses over time and outlining the evidence that emerges to show how the athlete has adapted to long-term exercise.

Grading criteria

To achieve a pass grade the evidence must show that the learner is able to:	To achieve a merit grade the evidence must show that, in addition to the pass criteria, the learner is able to:	To achieve a distinction grade the evidence must show that, in addition to the pass and merit criteria, the learner is able to:
P1 describe the initial responses of the cardiovascular and respiratory systems to exercise **Assessment practice pages** 52, 73	**M1** express the initial responses of the cardiovascular, respiratory, neuromuscular andd energy systems to exercise **Assessment practice pages** 56, 73	**D1** analyse the initial responses of the cardiovascular, respiratory, neuromuscular and energy systems to exercise **Assessment practice pages** 56, 73
P2 describe the initial responses of the neuromuscular and energy systems to exercise **Assessment practice pages** 56, 73		
P3 describe how the cardiovascular and respiratory systems respond to steady-state exercise **Assessment practice pages 62, 73**	**M2** explain how the cardiovascular, respiratory, neuromuscular and energy systems respond to steady-state exercise **Assessment practice pages 62, 73**	**D2** analyse how the cardiovascular, respiratory, neuromuscular and energy systems respond to steady-state exercise **Assessment practice pages 62, 73**
P4 describe how the neuromuscular and energy systems respond to steady-state exercise **Assessment practice pages 62, 73**		
P5 describe fatigue, and how the body recovers from exercise **Assessment practice pages 66, 73**	**M3** explain fatigue, and how the body recovers from exercise **Assessment practice pages 66, 73**	

Grading criteria		
P6 describe how the cardiovascular and respiratory systems adapt to long-term exercise **Assessment practice pages 71, 73**	**M4** explain how the cardiovascular, respiratory, neuromuscular and energy systems respond to long-term exercise **Assessment practice pages 71, 73**	**D3** analyse how the cardiovascular, respiratory, neuromuscular and energy systems respond to long-term exercise **Assessment practice pages 71, 73**
P7 describe how the neuromuscular, energy and skeletal systems adapt to long-term exercise **Assessment practice pages 71, 73**		

Sport and exercise psychology

Introduction

Sport and exercise psychology is a relatively new field. It involves the scientific study of people and how they act in sport and exercise environments.

The first stage of developing and using sport and exercise psychology techniques with clients is what works and how it works. After we know this, we can begin to identify the practical applications of this knowledge to sport and exercise.

Athletes are continually seeking to increase their levels of performance, and sport psychology has a really important role within this as it can help athletes to have an advantage over their opponents. In exercise and health settings, exercise psychology also has an important role to play in helping the government to reduce levels of obesity and improve mental health through regular exercise.

After completing this unit you should be able to achieve the following outcomes:

- understand the effect of personality in sports situations
- understand the impact of stress, arousal and anxiety on performance
- understand the psychology of group dynamics in sports environments
- understand psychological factors that affect people in exercise environments.

Think it over

How do the symptoms of stress affect a person's concentration? Will a football player have a different personality type to a sprinter? Is aggression necessarily a bad thing? Can exercising benefit your mental health and self-esteem? These are some of the questions that this unit will help you to answer.

Now think about the World Cup final. It's a penalty shoot-out and the player taking the last penalty has taken many penalties before and scored most of them. The player blazes the ball way over the bar. Why has someone who can take penalties up to an elite level missed so badly?

Personality

Definitions

Personality is one of the hardest terms to define in sport and exercise psychology, as has been shown through the range of definitions offered from previous research. As a result, it is difficult to understand what personality actually is and how it can affect sporting performance. However, a widely-accepted definition of personality is that it is the sum of those characteristics that make a person unique.

Some theorists believe that personality affects sports participation and performance, whereas others argue that there is not a strong relationship between the two. A number of theories and arguments have been put forward to argue and counter-argue these statements.

Theories

Sport psychologists have looked at personality and how it affects sports performance from a number of different perspectives. Some of the most frequently-used theories that have attempted to explain how personality can affect sport behaviour are outlined below.

■ Trait theory

Trait theory suggests that individuals have certain characteristics that will partly determine how they behave.

Traits are relatively stable aspects of personality and early trait theorists such as Eysenck and Cattell argued that traits were mainly inherited. According to Eysenck, there are two main dimensions to personality:

- an introversion-extroversion dimension
- a stable-neurotic dimension.

Introverts are individuals who do not actively seek excitement and would rather be in calm or quieter environments. They tend to prefer tasks that require a great deal of concentration and dislike the unexpected. Extroverts tend to become bored quickly, are poor at tasks that require a great deal of concentration, and constantly seek change and excitement. Extroverts are less responsive to pain than introverts. It has also been argued that extroverts are more successful in sporting situations because they can cope with competitive situations better than introverts, and because they can cope better with the distraction from external stimuli such as audiences.

Stable individuals are people who tend to be more easy-going and even tempered. Neurotic (unstable) people tend to be more restless and excitable than their stable counterparts, they have a tendency to become anxious and they are more highly aroused.

The trait approach has been applied to sport by several researchers. Personality traits are enduring characteristics across a variety of situations, and the trait approach suggests that the cause of behaviour lies within a person. Therefore, trait theorists say that the reasons someone takes part in sport come from within them and are determined by their personality traits. This approach argues that the environment or situation play a minimal role.

Theory into practice

Introverts tend to be drawn to more individual sports such as long-distance running, whereas extroverts prefer team- and action-orientated sports, such as football. Why do you think introverts or extroverts could be drawn to different sports?

Trait theories have been seen as too simplistic in their views and claims. For example, trait theorists have argued that personality traits are more stable and enduring than they actually are, and the theories fail to take into account the significance of the situation the individual may find themselves in. Another limitation of trait theories is that they do not take into account the fact that individuals can be actively involved in shaping their own personalities.

The conclusion is that personality alone cannot predict athletic success, but it can be used to help to explain some of the reasons why people choose some of the sports they do. At best, personality traits can predict a limited amount of behaviour, but traits alone cannot successfully predict behaviour in a particular situation. Personality can be used with physiological and situational factors in order to suggest whether an athlete will be more or less successful in a sporting situation.

Think it over

Based on the trait theory of personality, do you think you are suited to your particular sport?

Remember!

Although personality traits can be used with physiological and situational factors to try to predict success, there is no single athletic personality that will guarantee sporting success.

Social learning theory

Social learning theory suggests that personality is not a relatively stable or enduring characteristic. It is constantly changing and is created as a result of our experiences of different social situations. It is highly unlikely that an individual will behave in the same way in a variety of different situations.

This theory suggests that individuals learn in sporting situations through two distinct processes: modelling and reinforcement. Modelling suggests that individuals are more likely to model themselves on people they feel they can relate to, such as individuals in the same sport or of the same gender, and that as they observe their behaviour, they attempt to copy it. Reinforcement is important because if an individual's behaviour is reinforced or rewarded in some way, it is likely that the behaviour will be repeated.

Bandura, a leading psychologist, identified four main stages of observational learning that demonstrate how modelling can influence personality and behaviour.

1 Attention: to learn through observation, the athlete must have a certain level of respect and admiration for the model they are observing. The amount of respect the athlete has will depend on the status of the model. If the model is successful, attractive, powerful and of a high status, and if their behaviour can be seen to have a function or purpose, they will gain more attention.
2 Retention: for modelling to be effective, the athlete must be able to retain the observed skill or behaviour to memory and be able to recall it when needed.
3 Motor reproduction: the athlete must be able to physically perform the task he or she is observing. The athlete needs time to practise the skill in order to learn how it should be performed.
4 Motivational response: unless the athlete is motivated, he or she will not go through the first

High-profile athletes such as Wayne Rooney are able to keep the attention of others and make people want to act like them in a sporting environment because of the level of skill they display and the level of success they experience

three stages of modelling. Motivation is dependent on the amount of reinforcement (e.g. praise, feedback, sense of pride or achievement), the perceived status of the model and the perceived importance of the task.

Interactional approach

To more accurately predict behaviour in a sporting situation, you need to consider the interaction of both the situation and the individual's personality traits. This is known as the interactional approach to personality and sport behaviour.

The interactional approach is widely accepted by most sports psychologists when considering behaviour. This theory suggests that when situational factors are particularly strong, (for example, during competitive sporting situations such as penalty shoot-outs in football), they are more likely than personality traits to predict behaviour. The athlete who tends to be quiet and shy in an everyday situation, is likely to run towards an ecstatic crowd screaming if he scored the winning penalty.

Theory into practice

An eight-year-old aspiring footballer is watching Ronaldinho play for Barcelona in the European Champions League. Ronaldinho becomes a model for the young footballer as he is a powerful model and is similar to the aspiring footballer (same sport and same gender). Ronaldinho is stepping up to take a free kick and the young footballer pays particular attention to this as he is the free-kick taker for his local football team. The four stages of observational learning are as follows.

1. Attention: the young footballer pays attention to Ronaldinho's approach to the free kick; his confident posture when he picks up the ball and then places it down for the free kick; the confident strike of the ball; the ball going into the back of the net.
2. Retention: the young footballer remembers Ronaldinho's confident approach to taking the free kick; his run-up and body shape as he steps up to take the kick; the strike of the ball; the ball going into the back of the net.
3. Motor reproduction: the next time the young footballer is in the position of taking a free kick for his team, he tries to imitate the actions of the player he has modelled himself on. He attempts to copy the confident approach and displays this by confidently placing the ball down in the spot he is comfortable taking the kick from before striking the ball.
4. Motivational response: the young player feels more confident and as a result becomes more comfortable with his performance. As a result of this change in his behaviour, his performance is reinforced due to his higher levels of self-confidence, which further motivates him to behave in the same way in future situations like this (e.g. free kicks within shooting distance).

This example demonstrates that the aspiring player's personality and behaviour have been shaped by observing the behaviour of people they model themselves on and by reinforcement experienced. However, it cannot be argued that his increased confidence would be apparent in any other situation, which suggests that it is the situation change, rather than changes in his personality traits, that have shaped his behaviour.

Who has influenced you in your chosen sport? How?

Think about a situation where you have applied all of these stages of observational learning into practice. You may find that you don't consciously think about it.

Case study

Interactional approach

Basketball training sessions at a development club have been set up so that players can get the opportunity to coach sessions, to help with their coach education portfolios. Two players at the club, Jack and Tyreese, have been selected to lead and be assessed in their sessions today.

Jack has a great deal of self-confidence because he knows he is a good coach and has a high level of skill in his particular sport. He looks forward to leading his session because he is aware of his levels of ability and has practised the session a number of times. He is now thinking about a career as a basketball coach. He completes a good session and achieves a good grade for his assessment.

Tyreese, on the other hand, doesn't have a great deal of self-confidence as he is not as experienced or as skilled as Jack when it comes to playing or coaching basketball, yet he is placed in the same evaluative social situation as Jack. As a result, Tyreese becomes nervous and anxious during his coaching session and is concerned that the assessor and the players are making negative comments about his session. Although Tyreese really likes playing basketball, he finds the situation too stressful and doesn't want to be put in the same situation again.

1 **Do Jack and Tyreese behave differently in the same situations?**

2 **How does the interactional approach explain the way Jack and Tyreese behave?**

Marten's schematic view of personality

Marten developed anxiety traits questionnaires that were tailored specially to sport known as the Sport Competition Anxiety Test (SCAT). He recognised that any measure of sport anxiety must take into consideration cognitive anxiety and somatic anxiety.

Key Terms

Cognitive anxiety The thought component of anxiety that most people refer to as worrying about something.

Somatic anxiety The physiological response to anxiety.

Sheldon's constitutional theory

In 1942, an American psychologist called Sheldon proposed the constitutional theory, which suggests that an athlete's constitution or somatotype will affect their personality type and traits. Sheldon studied images of approximately 4,000 male participants from anterior, posterior and lateral viewpoints, and produced the notion of somatotypes and their accompanying traits. This has raised questions over whether the theory can be applied to females as well.

Key Term

Somatotype One of the three body shapes.

There are three somatotypes: ectomorph, endomorph and mesomorph, as shown in the table on page 82.

Somatotype	Predominant physical characteristics	Personality type
Ectomorph	Lean or skinny	Normally shy and introverted; displays personality traits such as sensitivity and apprehension; fairly self-aware; generally found in sports such as marathon running
Endomorph	Fat or pear-shaped	Normally happy, sociable, friendly and outgoing; considered to be more extroverted; tend to be fairly tolerant
Mesomorph	Muscular	Normally quite assertive, competitive and aggressive; often risk takers; like excitement and are attracted to team sports that have a high level of interaction, such as football or rugby.

The three types of body frame

There are some problems with constitutional theory. For example, people that are clinically obese would fall under the endomorph somatotype, so according to constitutional theory should be happy, lively and outgoing. However, people who suffer from obesity can often suffer from depression, and be shy and introverted. The opposite of this are stereotypical supermodels. They are often under the ectomorph bracket, which according to constitutional theory means they are introverted, shy and apprehensive.

Think it over

Do you think the somatotype of a typical supermodel describes someone who is happy to be photographed and on show to thousands of people? Look back at some of the images of athletes in this book. Do you think their somatotype reflects the personality they display?

Can you think of any other sports people that have certain physical characteristics, yet exhibit different personality traits?

Theory into practice

Rugby players such as Leslie Vainakolo tend to fall under the mesomorph category and to show more extroverted traits such as confidence and risk taking, whereas a marathon runner such as Haile Gebrselassie would be an ectomorph body type and is generally more introverted.

There has been some support for Sheldon's constitutional theory. However, we can conclude that although your somatotype can influence how you act in different situations, we should not take for granted that people will act (or play a sport) in a certain way because of the way they look. If you think about Justin Gatlin, Lebron James, Jonny Wilkinson and Joe Calzaghe for example, they would all fall under the mesomorph somatotype, but publicly display different personality characteristics.

Activity

Make a note of your answers to the following questions with a tick (yes) or a cross (no). You should answer them quickly, based on how you usually behave, feel or act. You need to answer all of the questions.

1. Do you seek excitement regularly?
2. Do you need people around you to cheer you up?
3. Do you find that you just go ahead and do things rather than thinking them over before you do them?
4. If you say you will do something, do you always do it?
5. Do you find your moods swing?
6. Are you willing to do almost anything for a dare?
7. Do you get shy when you want to talk to an attractive stranger?
8. Do you occasionally lose your temper?
9. Would you rather read something instead of meeting somebody new?
10. Can your feelings be easily hurt?
11. Do you sometimes think things you don't want anybody to know about?
12. Do you prefer to have a few close friends instead of many distant friends?
13. Do you find yourself daydreaming a lot?
14. Do you have only good habits?
15. Can you enjoy yourself at a lively party?
16. Are you tense?
17. Are you mainly quiet around other people?
18. Do you gossip?
19. Do thoughts and ideas running through your head keep you awake at night?
20. Do you like having to pay close attention to work or tasks?
21. Do you shake a lot?
22. Would you always declare everything at customs and excise on your way back from holiday, even if you knew you wouldn't get caught?
23. Do you like doing things where you have to act quickly?
24. Do you find yourself worrying about bad things that could happen to you?
25. Have you ever turned up late for an appointment?
26. Would you talk to a stranger because you like talking to people so much?
27. Do you have aches and pains that bother you?
28. Are there some people you are acquainted with whom you don't like?
29. Are you self-confident?
30. When people are inspecting work you have done, does it hurt when they find things wrong with it?
31. Can you be the 'life and soul' of a party?
32. Do you sometimes talk about things you know nothing about?
33. Do you find yourself worrying about your health?

Scoring

Copy the two tables on page 84. For each answer you gave that corresponds to the ones in the tables, give yourself one mark.

Give yourself two separate scores out of 12 for your E score and your N score.

Your E score describes to what extent you are introverted or extroverted, with a score closer to 1 meaning you are more introverted, and a score of 12 meaning you are more extroverted.

Your N score describes how stable or unstable (neurotic) you are. This relates to your thoughts and emotions, with a score closer to 1 meaning you are more stable and a score closer to 12 meaning you are more unstable.

Question number	Answer	Marks
1	Yes	
3	No	
6	Yes	
9	No	
12	No	
15	Yes	
17	No	
20	No	
23	Yes	
26	Yes	
29	Yes	
31	Yes	
		E score =

Question number	Answer	Marks
2	Yes	
5	Yes	
7	Yes	
10	Yes	
13	Yes	
16	Yes	
19	Yes	
21	Yes	
24	Yes	
27	Yes	
30	Yes	
33	Yes	
		N score =

You now need to chart your score to get an indication of your personality type and your characteristics. To do this, you will need graph paper, a ruler and a pencil. This is a fun activity to quickly test your personality type, don't worry if the results aren't what you expect.

Your N score:

Look at the example below. The student's E score was 9 and N score 3. This has been plotted on the graph. The location of the plot indicates the quarter that corresponds to the student's personality characteristics (e.g. passive, calm, etc).

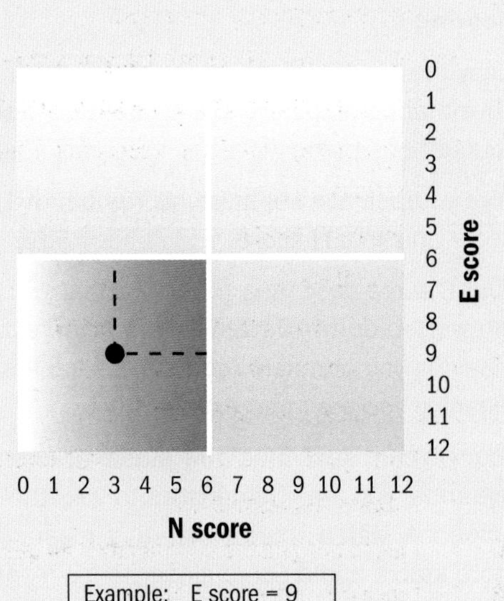

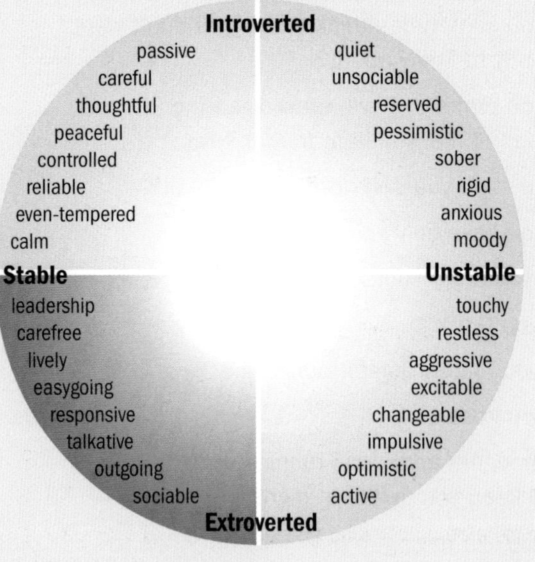

Type A and type B

Another approach common in sport psychology is the one that suggests that personality traits can be grouped under two headings: type A and type B.

People who fall under the type A personality bracket are those who tend to lack patience, have a strong urge for competition, have a high desire to achieve goals, always rush to complete activities, will happily multi-task when placed under heavy time constraints, lack tolerance towards others and tend to experience higher levels of anxiety.

People in the type B category are those who tend to be more tolerant towards others, are more relaxed than their type A counterparts, are more reflective, experience lower levels of anxiety and display higher levels of imagination and creativity.

Activity

Try this activity to work out your personality type.

Use tracing paper to complete this questionnaire by circling the score that most closely represents your feelings. For example, if you answered 1 to the first statement, this means you feel very strongly that you don't mind leaving things uncompleted temporarily.

If you answered 7, this means you feel very strongly that you must get things completed as soon as you have started on them.

When you have completed all the questions, add up your total score.

Statement	Score							Statement
I don't mind leaving things uncompleted temporarily	1	2	3	4	5	6	7	I must get things completed as soon as I have started them
I don't hurry to get to appointments	1	2	3	4	5	6	7	I'm never late for appointments
I'm not competitive	1	2	3	4	5	6	7	I'm very competitive
I let others finish speaking before I start to speak	1	2	3	4	5	6	7	I interrupt others in conversation
I don't hurry, not even when I'm under pressure	1	2	3	4	5	6	7	I'm always in a hurry
I can wait calmly for things	1	2	3	4	5	6	7	I don't like waiting because I get uneasy
I'm laid back and easy going	1	2	3	4	5	6	7	I'm always going at full speed
I do one thing at a time	1	2	3	4	5	6	7	I try to do more than one thing at a time
I'm very deliberate in my speech	1	2	3	4	5	6	7	I'm speak quickly and use a lot of hand gestures
I want to be satisfied with myself: I don't need recognition from others	1	2	3	4	5	6	7	I want recognition from others when I have done a good job
I do things slowly	1	2	3	4	5	6	7	I do things quickly
I'm relaxed	1	2	3	4	5	6	7	I'm restless
I can talk openly about my feelings	1	2	3	4	5	6	7	I tend to keep my feelings to myself
I'm interested in a lot of things	1	2	3	4	5	6	7	I only have a few interests
I'm content and happy in life	1	2	3	4	5	6	7	I'm always pushing myself further
I never set myself targets and deadlines	1	2	3	4	5	6	7	I set myself lots of targets and deadlines
I feel little responsibility	1	2	3	4	5	6	7	I always feel responsible
I judge things more on quality than quantity	1	2	3	4	5	6	7	I judge things more on quantity than quality
I'm very casual about my work	1	2	3	4	5	6	7	I take my work very seriously
I'm not very precise	1	2	3	4	5	6	7	I'm very precise and pay attention to detail.
My total score is:								

Scoring

- 0–29: you are a type B personality who is normally relaxed and copes well with stressful situations.
- 30–59: you are a type B personality who is generally relaxed and copes adequately with stress.
- 60–79: you are a mixed personality who needs to be careful when displaying type A traits.
- 80–109: you are a type A personality who is generally less relaxed and are more prone to stress-related issues and illnesses.
- 110–140: you are a type A personality who is very restless. You are in a high-risk group for stress-related illnesses and could be more prone to stress-related problems.

Effects on sports performance

There is no direct link between personality type and successful sporting performance. Some research has suggested that some personality types may be more attracted to certain sports, but little says that your personality will make you a better athlete.

In 1980, Morgan devised the credulous-sceptical argument relating to the ability of traits to predict sport behaviour. Those who support the credulous argument say that personality traits can be used to predict sporting behaviour, whereas those who support the sceptical argument say that personality traits cannot be used.

All human beings are different, and we constantly change over time and in different situations or environments. Therefore, you should appreciate that you will never find two people whose personalities are exactly identical.

Athletes versus non-athletes

Previous research suggests that there is no such thing as an athletic personality. This means that when you look at athletes versus non-athletes, there is little difference between personality types. However, if you look further, some differences start to appear. For example, compared with non-athletes, athletes who take part in team sports tend to be more extroverted. On the other hand, when compared to non-athletes, athletes in individual sports tend to be more introverted. This suggests that in order to study the differences between athletes and non-athletes, we need to consider the sports the athletes play before we can reach any meaningful conclusions.

Elite versus non-elite

In the past, it was thought that successful athletes had more positive mental health than athletes who were not as successful, or who were unsuccessful. It was also suggested that more successful athletes display lower levels of neuroticism, depression, fatigue, confusion and anger, but higher levels of vigour. However, it has more recently been suggested that evidence which was originally used to draw these conclusions was insufficient, partly because the original work was based on only 16 athletes from one sport, and partly because more recent research has shown that personality accounts for less than 1 per cent of the performance variation.

Team versus individual

Some studies have reported that individual sports participants show greater state anxiety than team sports participants, while other researchers have reported no significant differences in state anxiety between team and individual sport athletes.

Type A versus type B

Although the type A/type B approach to personality does have some application to sports settings, its greater use has come in exercise and health psychology related to predicting coronary heart disease. It has been widely suggested that people of a type A personality are more prone to heart disease because of the amount of stress they put themselves under. In sport, type A individuals are more likely than type B people to continue participating in a sporting setting when the situation becomes unfavourable, or when they are not particularly motivated to take part.

Think it over

Can personality traits alone be used to predict both sport participation and performance success?

Assessment practice

1. Describe the effects of personality on behaviour in a sporting environment. 
2. Explain how it has been suggested that personality affects behaviour in sports environments. M1
3. Use a range of theories to analyse how personality can affect behaviour in sports environments. D1 

grading tips

Grading Tip 

Give a brief summary to say whether personality alone affects sporting behaviour.

Grading Tip 

You need to make it clear how personality affects behaviour in a sports setting, if at all.

Grading Tip 

Use a range of theories to support all of the arguments you make about whether personality affects behaviour in a sports environment.

Motivation

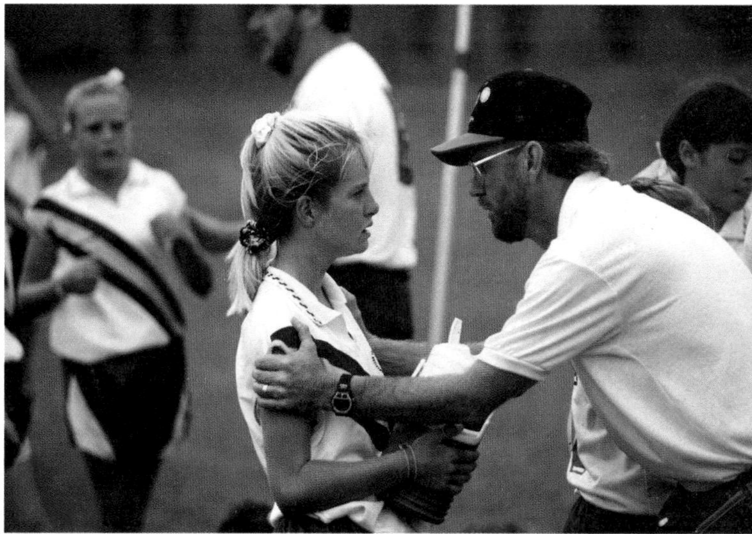

▲ Motivating athletes can range from a hand on the shoulder to rousing speeches resulting in team cheers – the key to being a good motivator is knowing which method to use and when

Definition

Motivation has been defined as the direction and intensity of your efforts. Most definitions of motivation refer to having a drive to take part in some form of activity and to persisting in that activity. However, these are general definitions that do not apply specifically to sport. A sport-specific definition is the tendency of an individual or team to begin and then to carry on with the activities relating to their sport.

Motivation is an interesting factor in sports psychology because it is one of the most controllable aspects. There are many examples of when athletes have appeared to be in control of their motivation, often demonstrated when the athletes or teams show an apparent ability to simply change motivation.

For example, in the 2005 European Champions League final: Liverpool went in at half-time 3-0 down, seemingly having already lost the final. However, the team came out in the second half with a significantly different performance that showed a great deal more motivation and confidence, and ended up winning the match.

Factors

Individual personality

The trait-centred view of motivation suggests that someone is motivated simply because they have personality traits that make them a motivated person. Some highly motivated people do appear to have attributes that make them more likely to be successful in a sporting situation. However, personality factors alone cannot account for what motivates someone. An example of this can be seen when a particular person acts differently when the same coaching session is taken by two different coaches. Therefore, most psychologists argue that viewing personality traits as the primary cause of motivation is too simplistic. The effects of the situation need to be considered when considering athlete motivation.

Situational

The opposite argument to the trait-centred view of motivation is known as the situation-centred view of motivation. People who support the situational view claim that the situation in which the athlete finds themselves is the primary reason behind motivation levels. However, if this were the case, how can an athlete's motivation to continue participating be explained when the situation is unfavourable?

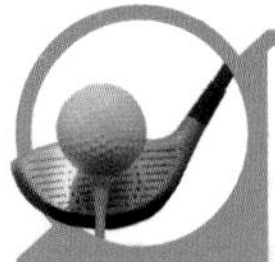

Think it over

Think about when you play your sport. It is cold and rainy, and your coach is screaming at you from the sidelines, constantly criticising your performance when you think you are playing well. This is not a situation that you like to be in, yet you carry on playing because you don't want to let down your team mates and want to finish the game. Is the situation your main reason behind carrying on? Can the situation alone account for motivation levels?

Interaction of personality and situation

The interactional view of motivation suggests that neither personality factors nor situational factors alone can accurately predict the motivation of an individual. You need to consider how personality traits and the situational factors interact.

The interactional approach is the view most widely accepted by most sports psychologists when considering motivation.

Remember!

When trying to understand how people are motivated in a sport or exercise setting, consider the interaction of personality traits and the situation.

Assessment practice

Describe how an individual's personality and different situational factors can influence motivation levels in the athlete. 

Intrinsic and extrinsic rewards

Intrinsic motivation is when someone is taking part in an activity without the presence of some form of external reward and/or without the primary motivation being the achievement of some form of external reward. Intrinsic motivation in its purest form is when the athlete participates in his or her sport primarily for enjoyment. When people are asked why they play sport, if they reply with 'for fun', 'because I enjoy it' or 'because it makes me feel good' (or similar responses), they can be said to be intrinsically motivated.

However, be careful when assessing motivation. An athlete may say to you that they play sport because it makes them feel good which, on the face of it, is intrinsic motivation. If you were to probe a little further and ask them why playing their sport makes them feel good, and they gave reasons such as 'because I like winning medals', this would actually be a form of extrinsic motivation as it is the external reward, not the feeling good, that is the primary motivator.

There are three parts of intrinsic motivation:

- being motivated by accomplishments – this occurs when athletes wish to increase their level of skill in order to get a sense of accomplishment
- being motivated by stimulation – this refers to seeking an 'adrenaline rush' or extreme excitement
- being motivated by knowledge – this means being curious about your own performance, wanting to know more about it and having a desire to develop new techniques or skills that can benefit performance.

Taking it further

Which factors that affect motivation do you think are the most important?

Extrinsic motivation is when someone behaves the way they do mainly because of some form of external mechanism.

The most common forms of extrinsic motivation come through the use of tangible and intangible rewards.

Tangible rewards are things that can physically be given to you, such as money, medals and trophies, whereas intangible rewards are non-physical things such as praise or encouragement.

For extrinsic motivation to be effective, the coach needs to make sure that he or she uses them effectively. The coach needs to consider how often the reward is used and the size of the reward offered. If the reward is given too frequently, it will be of little value to the athlete after a period of time, invalidating its potential impact on performance. The coach needs to have an in-depth knowledge of the athletes he or she is working with, to maximise the effect of extrinsic rewards.

Extrinsic motivation can potentially decrease intrinsic motivation. If the extrinsic motivator is used as a method of controlling the athlete, generally intrinsic motivation will decrease. On the other hand, if the extrinsic motivator is used to provide information or feedback to the athlete, this can benefit intrinsic motivation. The way in which the athlete perceives and understands the original extrinsic motivator, determines whether it will benefit or hinder intrinsic motivation.

Case study

Extrinsic and intrinsic motivation

A group of young children are playing basketball one day, much to the annoyance of an old man whose house they are playing outside. The old man asks the children to stop playing, but they carry on because they enjoy it so much. After a while, the old man comes out and offers them £5 each to play for him. As the children enjoy playing so much anyway, they gladly accept the offer. The next day, the children come back and play outside the old man's house again. Sure enough, the old man comes out and offers them money to play again, but this time he offers them only £4 each. As the children enjoy playing basketball, they agree to carry on even though the amount is less than the day before. This pattern continues for the next few days until the old man comes out and tells the children that if they want to carry on playing, they will have to do it free of charge as he has no more money to give them. The children, rather disgruntled, tell the old man that they refuse to play for him again if he doesn't pay them.

1. **What motivates the children to play basketball at the start of the story? Is this intrinsic or extrinsic motivation?**
2. **At the end of the case study, what has been the motivating factor for the children? Is this intrinsic or extrinsic motivation?**
3. **What effect has extrinsic motivation had on intrinsic motivation?**

Activity

1 In pairs, discuss all the reasons why each person in your group takes part in their chosen sports.

2 Produce a mind map (or spider diagram) of all of the reasons why the people in your group all take part in your chosen sports. Under each reason, classify what type of motivation is involved.

Aggression

Definition

The most widely-accepted definition was offered by Barron and Richardson in 1994, who stated that aggression is any form of behaviour directed towards the goal of harming or injuring another living being who is motivated to avoid such treatment.

Gill's criteria for aggression behaviour

Aggression is often confused with assertion or anger, so it is important to understand exactly what aggression is. Aggression has four main criteria, which were identified by Gill in the 1980s.

1 It is a form of behaviour: aggression can be either physical or verbal behaviour.
2 It involves causing harm or injury: aggression is designed to cause either physical or psychological harm.
3 The injury or harm is directed towards another living being: it does not have to be towards humans to be aggressive, it can be towards other living creatures such as animals.
4 The aggression must be done on purpose: if it is done genuinely by accident, it cannot be classed as aggression.

Assessment practice

Using Gill's criteria and Baron and Richardson's definition, decide whether the following are aggressive or non-aggressive behaviour. Justify your answers.

1 A football player throws his shirt at the ground when he is substituted in the World Cup final.

2 A basketball coach calls time-out when a player is standing on the free-throw line waiting to take a free throw.

3 In rugby, a scrum-half tackles his opponent very hard – but legally – with a view to stopping him attempting to run with the ball in future.

4 A boxer punches his opponent square in the face during a bout, with a view to gaining points to win the fight.

5 A netball player throws her water bottle at the wall during half-time.

6 A Formula One driver collides with a fellow driver and kills them during a race.

7 An ice hockey player is concerned about her performance during previous penalty shoot-outs. Fans behind the goal attempt to make her worry about taking a penalty during a match by distracting her with banners, booing and jeering. **P3 M2**

grading tips

Grading Tip 

Make sure you relate your answers to the different theories of aggression.

Grading Tip M2

Make sure that you relate your answer to the intended outcome of the performer.

Types of aggressive behaviour

There are two main types of aggression: hostile and instrumental. These categories were first proposed by Husman and Silva in 1984. They should not be confused with assertive behaviour, which is another key aspect of sport.

Hostile aggression

Hostile aggression means inflicting some form of harm (either physical or psychological) on someone else (e.g. an opponent). It is sometimes referred to as reactive aggression and is often accompanied by anger. A high-profile example of hostile aggression in sport came in the 2006 World Cup final when Zinedine Zidane headbutted Marco Materazzi in the chest. This is hostile aggression as the sole intention was to harm, and the headbutt was in reaction to an earlier incident.

◀ Aggression has a variety of causes and can be displayed in a number of ways

Instrumental aggression

Instrumental aggression means displaying aggressive behaviour in the pursuit of a non-aggressive goal. It is sometimes referred to as channelled aggression and most aggression in sport falls into this category. Instrumental aggression often occurs in contact sports. For example, in karate you may attempt to hit a round kick on your opponent, but this is because you would like to win the bout rather than hurt your opponent. This is instrumental aggression because you would have to harm your opponent in some way in order to execute the skill, but you are doing this with a view to winning rather than because you want to harm your opponent.

Assertion

Assertive behaviour (see Think it over, page 92) differs from aggressive behaviour because the individual is playing with emotion and within the rules of the game.

Assertive behaviour demonstrates four main criteria:

- it is goal-directed
- it is not intended to harm or injure
- it uses only legitimate force, even if this amount of force could be classed as aggression in a non-sporting or non-game setting
- it does not break any of the rules of the game.

Key Terms

Hostile aggression The main aim is to cause injury or harm (either physiological or psychological).

Instrumental aggression The main aim is to achieve some form of non-aggressive goal.

Assertion Playing with emotion and within the rules of the game.

For example, in a game of rugby, a player may tackle an opponent hard around the waist in order to stop that player progressing. In a non-sporting setting, running up and jumping into someone could be classed as aggressive (and illegal) behaviour. In this setting it is classed as assertion because it is goal-directed (the player wants to stop his opponent from winning the game), the player has no intention of harming or injuring (the intention is to stop the opponent from progressing), the tackle is performed with legitimate force and it does not break any rules of the game.

Assessment practice

Decide which type of behaviour the following scenarios fall under. Choose from hostile aggression, instrumental aggression and assertion. Justify your answers.

1. A boxer delivering a body blow during a boxing match.
2. A boxer pinning an opponent against the ropes and repeatedly delivering blows to the head without trying to end the bout.
3. A footballer tackling an opponent hard during a game of American football to gain possession of the ball.
4. A defender in football, shoulder-barging a player when challenging for the ball.
5. A basketball player blocking off the boards.

grading tips

Grading Tip 

Use your background knowledge on the different types of aggression and assertion to support your answers.

Grading Tip 

Relate your answers to the intended outcome of the individual to explain the type of aggression or assertion you have suggested.

Causes of aggression

Think about the different situations where you have become aggressive. What made you aggressive? This is a question that many researchers have tried to answer. They have devised a number of theories to try to explain the various causes of aggression.

■ Instinct theory

Instinct theory suggests that all actions, thoughts, emotions and intentions can be traced back to our instincts as human beings.

Freud suggested that as human beings we have two distinct needs: one is to have sex and the other is to be aggressive. Therefore, instinct theory suggests that we display aggression because it is innate.

Think it over

Think again about the incident regarding Zinedine Zidane and Marco Materazzi in the 2006 World Cup final. Zidane's reaction to his provocation was to headbutt his tormentor. Although this was the most recent, and the last, red card of Zidane's career, it came after these similar incidents that involved a violent reaction after some form of provocation (e.g. a bad challenge): stamping (World Cup, 1998), headbutting (Champions League, 2000/01), slapping (Copa Del Rey, 2003/04), kicking (Primera Liga, 2003/04). As similar incidents have happened on a number of occasions, you could argue that Zidane reacted in the way he did because it was in his nature to do so. Do you agree?

■ Frustration-aggression theory

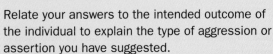

The frustration-aggression hypothesis was originally devised by Dollard, Doob, Miller, Mowrer and Sears in 1939. The hypothesis stated that aggression only occurs in frustrating situations, that it is caused only by frustration, and that frustration will always result in aggression. The hypothesis further stated that the frustration that causes the aggression will normally be brought about by some form of goal blockage or goal failure. Examples of cues that can initiate agressive acts are some playing equipment such as bats or sticks, and significant others reinforcing aggressive acts.

This theory has received little support and is generally dismissed. The main argument against it disagrees with its premise that frustration always leads to aggression and that aggression is always caused by frustration. Empirical and anecdotal evidence have shown that athletes are able to cope with their frustration, or are able to express their frustration through non-aggressive channels.

Key Terms

Empirical evidence Evidence that is based on scientific research.

Anecdotal evidence Evidence that is based on people's experiences and is often provided through short stories with no research-based support.

Think it over

A right back in hockey is beaten by the left winger who goes on to assist a goal. The left winger has beaten the full back on numerous occasions, which has frustrated the full back. When the winger is running back to the halfway line, the full back hits out at, and injures, the winger without the referee seeing. This is accepted by the full back's manager. Why would this scenario be more likey to occur in the future after this event? What are other possible consequences?

In 1941, Miller developed a revised frustration-aggression hypothesis. He claimed that frustration is more likely to lead to aggressive behaviour, but at times aggressive behaviour may not be demonstrated. Therefore, the frustration response is dependent on the individual's personality and the situation they are in.

Activity

1 In small groups, discuss the following scenarios:
   - someone purposefully frustrating you
   - someone being close to achieving a goal but not managing it
   - goal blockage being unfair, illogical or down to chance or luck.

2 As a group, produce a list of sporting examples for each of the above situations.

3 For one of each of the scenarios you have listed, discuss how you would feel if it happened during your sporting event.

In 1941, Berkowitz revised Miller's hypothesis and introduced arousal into the equation. His theory agrees that frustration will not always cause aggression, but he claimed that it does make aggressive behaviour more likely, because of increased levels of arousal and anger. However, this theory also proposes that the mere presence of increased arousal and anger alone will not cause increased levels of aggression. For this to happen, there must be environmental cues, and it is these that draw aggressive behaviour out of an individual.

The environmental cues must show that aggressive behaviour is appropriate in that particular situation, and only in their presence will aggressive behaviour result. If the cues in the situation indicate that aggressive behaviour is inappropriate, then aggressive behaviour will not result.

This version of the hypothesis is one of the more popular and widely-supported theories of aggression. One of the reasons for this is that the theory says we have a pre-disposition to become more aggressive in certain situations that frustrate us, but we are also likely to become angry and it is possible that we can control that anger.

■ Social learning theory

As discussed on pages 79–80, social learning theory claims that behaviour is learned by observing the behaviour of significant others that you can model yourself on, and then being rewarded (or having your behaviour reinforced in some way) for exhibiting similar behaviours.

In 1973, Bandura found that children who observed violent behaviours by significant adults were more likely to copy those acts than children who had not observed such behaviour. He also found that children were more likely to repeat these behaviours if they had their actions reinforced.

In modern society, the media has played a significant role in its portrayal of high-level sports stars and social learning. If a young child sees an elite sports star behave in an aggressive manner on the sports field, they are more likely to attempt to copy such behaviour.

Assessment practice

Research three sporting scenarios where an aggressive act has been observed. (For example, Zidane headbutting Materazzi, and Shane Warne throwing the cricket ball at Kevin Pieterson during the 2006 Ashes series). For each situation, answer the following questions.

1 What has caused the aggression?

2 What type of aggression have you observed?

3 What theories can you use to explain the aggression you have observed? **P3 M2**

grading tips

Grading Tip 

You need to describe both the type of aggression and the factors that have caused the aggression in that particular situation.

Grading Tip 

You need to use the different theories to explain why aggression has occurred in that situation.

Case study

Social learning theory

An 8-year-old boy is watching a tennis match with his father on television. A player that the boy and his father both support scores a clear point, but the umpire thinks the ball crossed the line and disallows the point. The player who scores the point turns to the umpire. He delivers a barrage of foul and abusive language and hand gestures to them, which is clearly displayed on the television. The boy's father cheers at the player doing this as he feels that the referee has made a serious mistake.

1 **When the boy is playing in his next match, he has a point disallowed unfairly. What is the boy's response likely to be in this situation?**

2 **What factors do you think will have influenced the boy to act in this way? Use appropriate theories to justify your answer.**

3.2 Understand the impact of stress, arousal and anxiety on performance

Stress, arousal and anxiety all have key functions when analysing sporting performance, because they can affect it either positively or negatively. An understanding of stress arousal and anxiety is central to most of the work you will do within sport and exercise psychology.

Arousal

Definition

Arousal is referred to as a physiological state of alertness and anticipation that prepares the body for action. It is generally considered to be neutral, because in itself it is neither positive nor negative. It involves both physiological activation (for example, increased heart rate, sweating rate or respiratory rate) and psychological activity (for example, increased attention). Arousal is typically viewed along a continuum, with one extreme of deep sleep to the other extreme of excitement. Individuals who are optimally aroused are those who are mentally and physically activated to perform.

Relationship between arousal level and performance

The relationship between arousal level and performance is demonstrated through a series of theories including drive theory, the inverted U hypothesis and the catastrophe theory.

Theories

Drive theory

This view of the relationship (Hull, 1943) between arousal and performance is a linear one. This means that as arousal increases, so does performance. It suggests that the more 'learned' a skill is, the more likely it is that a high level of arousal will result in a better performance. Therefore, drive theory is often summarised through the following equation:

$$\text{performance} = \text{arousal} \times \text{skill}$$

However, there is a lot of evidence to suggest that athletic performance is benefited by arousal only up to a certain point, and when you become too aroused your performance decreases.

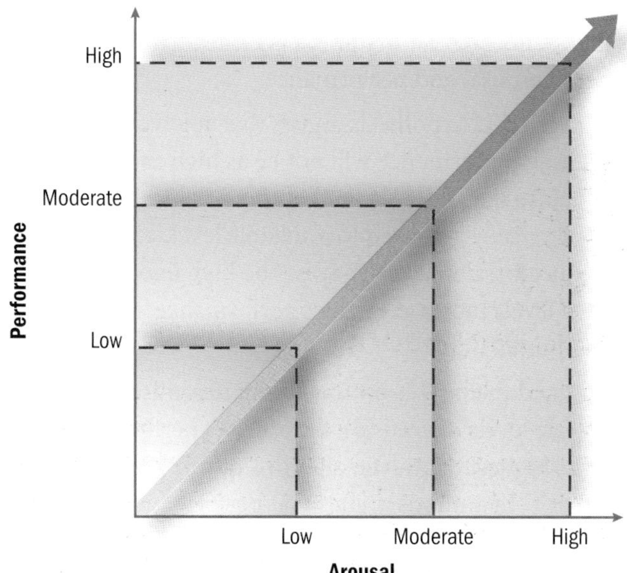

▲ Drive theory

Case study

What is drive theory?

A NBA basketball player is at the free-throw line, shooting his second of two free throws needed to tie the game. There are 30 seconds to play in the fourth quarter. He has a good record of free-throw shooting, having hit 87 per cent of free throws through the season, so his team mates are confident of his ability to hit the shot. The player is sweating heavily, his heart rate is very high and his hands are shaking. The player hits the ring and the board with his shot, his opponents win the rebound and score a 3 pointer, giving them a 4 point lead with 10 seconds left to play.

1. **What effect has arousal had on performance in this case?**
2. **Does this case study support or reject claims made by drive theory? Explain your answer.**

Inverted U hypothesis

The inverted U hypothesis is different from drive theory, as it does not suggest that there is a linear relationship between arousal and performance.

The inverted U hypothesis argues that at lower levels of arousal, performance will not be as high as it should be, because the athlete is neither physiologically nor psychologically activated to a suitable level (e.g. heart rate and concentration levels may not be high enough). As arousal levels increase, so does performance, but only up to an optimal point.

It is argued that at this optimal point of arousal (normally moderate levels of arousal), the athlete's performance will be at its highest. However, after this optimal point, the inverted U hypothesis argues that performance levels will start to decrease gradually.

In summary, the inverted U hypothesis suggests that at optimal arousal levels, performance levels will be at their highest, but when arousal is either too low or too high, performance levels will be lower.

Remember!

The inverted U hypothesis states that arousal will only affect performance positively up to an optimal point, but after this you will get a steady decrease in performance.

The inverted U hypothesis is more widely-accepted than drive theory because most athletes and coaches can report personal experience of under-arousal (boredom), over-arousal (excitement to the point of lack of concentration) and optimum arousal (focus on nothing but sport performance).

However, there has been some question over the type of curve demonstrated through this hypothesis: does it give an optimal point, or do some athletes experience optimal arousal for a longer period of time?

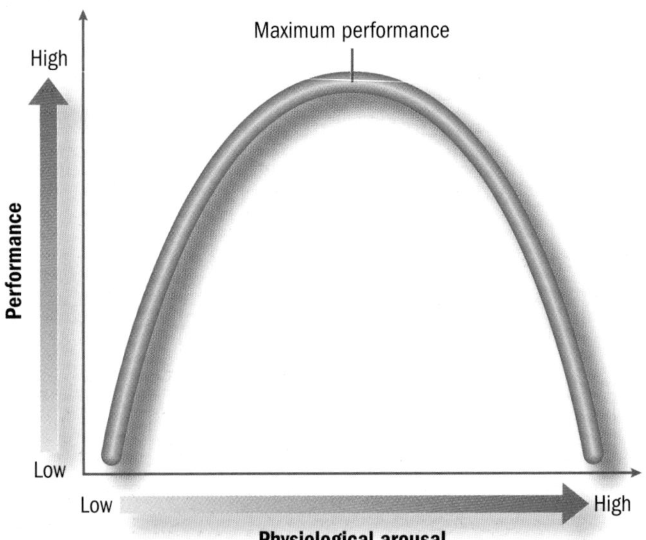

▲ The inverted U theory

Case study

What is the inverted U theory?

In the Rugby Union World Cup final, a player is getting ready to take a penalty kick that will certainly win his country the tournament. The player is motivated by his coach and other team mates, his heart rate starts to rise, as does his body temperature; but he is able to maintain his levels of concentration and focuses on the aspects of the techniques he needs to concentrate on in order to complete a successful kick. He scores the penalty and his country wins the World Cup.

Does this case study support or reject the inverted U hypothesis? Justify your answer.

■ Catastrophe theory

Catastrophe theory is based on a similar theory to the inverted U hypothesis, but it introduces an important concept called cognitive anxiety.

Catastrophe theory suggests that performance is affected by arousal in an inverted U fashion only when the individual has low levels of cognitive anxiety. If the athlete is experiencing higher levels of cognitive anxiety (see page 102), and arousal levels increase up to the athlete's threshold, the player experiences a dramatic (or catastrophic) drop in performance levels. The key difference between catastrophe theory and the inverted U hypothesis is that the reported drop in performance does not have to be a steady decline when arousal levels become too high.

However, catastrophe theory does not argue that cognitive anxiety is completely negative. The theory actually suggests you will perform at a higher level if you have a certain degree of cognitive anxiety because your attention and concentration levels increase; it is only when levels of cognitive anxiety are combined with hyper-elevated levels of arousal that performance levels decrease dramatically.

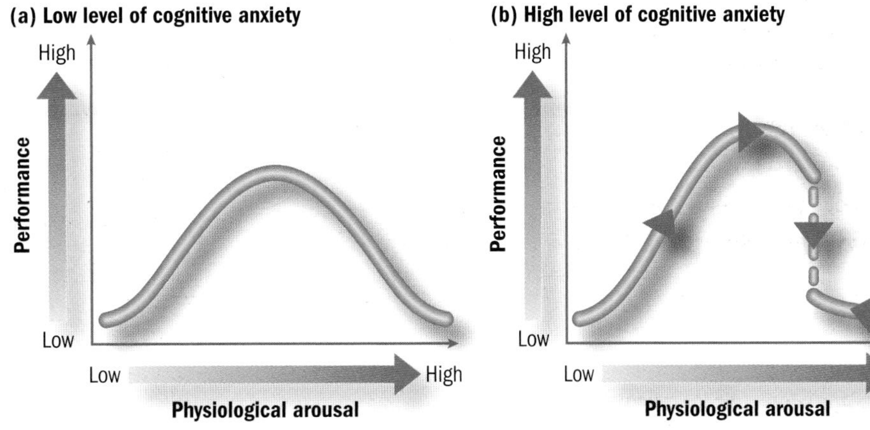

▲ Catastrophe theory

Activity

Discuss with a group of classmates the different theories of arousal. Which do you think is most likely to explain the effects of arousal on performance? Can you think of any occasions when you have been playing your sport that would provide examples of each of the theories?

Think it over

What are the key differences between the inverted U hypothesis, and the catastrophe theory?

Assessment practice

In pairs, produce a poster presentation for each of the theories of arousal. Make sure you include the following information.

- A diagram and an explanation of each theory.
- Details about which theory of arousal you think is most likely to explain the relationship between arousal and performance.
- Practical, sport-based examples of each of theory to develop your points. P4 M3 D2

grading tips

Grading Tip P4

Make sure you discuss how arousal can be caused, as well as the effects of arousal.

Grading Tip M3

Make sure you use the different theories of arousal to explain how arousal affects performance.

Grading Tip D2

Make sure that you discuss which theory is the most likely to explain the arousal–performance relationship and the effects of arousal on performance.

Effects

Attention

Arousal influences attention and concentration by narrowing your field during heightened states of arousal. This means that the more aroused you become, the lower the number of relevant cues you can concentrate on.

Concentration

During a game of netball, when at optimal states of arousal, the centre will be able to focus on the opposing player in possession of the ball as well as her position on the court, and the position of other players around her.

During heightened states of arousal, the centre may only be able to focus on the opposition player who has the ball, and may simply disregard other important cues.

Just as a heightened a state of arousal can narrow the player's attention, it can also broaden it to the point where performance is decreased. In this scenario, the netball player would not be concentrating only on all the relevant game cues; she would also concentrate on a lot of irrelevant information such as crowd noise.

Assessment practice

These questions will help you to provide evidence for criteria P4, M3 and D2.

Imagine you are working with an international sprinter, whose coach has contacted you because the sprinter is becoming aroused on a regular basis. The coach thinks this may be affecting performance in different events. The coach has asked you to give some feedback after your initial meeting. You have spoken to the sprinter, who has given permission for you to give feedback to the coach.

Write a letter to the coach, in which you answer the following questions.

1 What are the causes of arousal in a sports setting? P4

2 What are the effects of arousal on sports performance? M3

3 Using the different theories of arousal, analyse how arousal can affect sport performance. D2

grading tips

Grading Tip 

Define arousal and include a range of causes of arousal. Name and describe the theories that try to explain how arousal affects performance.

Grading Tip 

Use all of the different theories to explain how arousal affects performance. Then tell the coach which is most likely to explain the relationship between arousal and performance. Make sure you discuss how arousal can be both positive and negative.

Grading Tip 

Make sure you analyse how changes in arousal levels can influence changes in performance.

Key Terms

Eustress Known as 'good' stress and is a form of stress that some individuals (mainly in extreme sports) seek out. They feel it benefits their performance, either by helping them to focus or by enhancing intrinsic motivation because they know they have coped with a stressful situation.

Distress 'Bad' stress and is what you will more commonly know as stress. It is negative, normally viewed as threatening by the individual and is detrimental to performance.

Stress

Lazarus and Folkman (1984) provide us with a widely accepted definition of stress: 'a pattern of negative physiological states and psychological responses occurring in situations where people perceive threats to their well-being, which they may be unable to meet.'

Eustress and distress

The influences of stress on performance are shown in the diagram. Two terms have been introduced in sports psychology that contribute to this explanation: eustress and distress.

Eustress is a good form of stress that can give you a feeling of fulfilment. Some athletes actually actively seek out stressful situations as they like the challenge of pushing themselves to the limit. This can help them increase their skill levels and enables them to focus their attention on specific aspects of their chosen sport. The benefit of this is that increases in intrinsic motivation generally follow.

Distress is the bad form of stress. It is normally what we are talking about when we discuss the notion of stress. It is an extreme form of anxiety, nervousness, apprehension or worry as a result of a perceived inability to meet demands placed upon ourselves.

At stage 1 of the stress process, some form of demand is placed on the athlete in a particular situation. At stage 2,

STAGE 1	STAGE 2	STAGE 3	STAGE 4
Demand (e.g. last penalty in shoot-out)	**Perception of demand by athlete**	**Increased arousal levels**	**Outcome**
	Positive perception (challenge)	Eustress (increased energy and motivation)	Increased performance
	or		
	Negative perception (threat)	Distress (increased worry)	Reduced performance

Stress process flow diagram

the athlete perceives that demand either positively or negatively. It is this perception that increases the arousal levels of the performer (stage 3) and ultimately determines the outcome of performance (stage 4).

Theory into practice

A key aspect of stress process diagram is the perception of demand.

If we use the example of a penalty shoot-out in Ice hockey in an important event such as the Stanley Cup Final, the players have a demand placed upon them which they can perceive as either positive or negative. If a player views the demand as positive, he will see this as a challenge which will then motivate him to succeed (known as eustress). This generally results in an increased performance (increasing the player's chance of scoring the penalty).

However, if he perceives the demand as negative or too great, he sees this as a threat, which increases his levels of nervousness, apprehension and worry. When levels of distress become too high, they can reduce the performance (reducing the chance that the penalty will be scored).

Think of an example where this theory is relevant in other sports situations with which you are familiar.

Effects of stress on the body

When you find yourself in a situation you find threatening, your stress response is activated. The way you respond depends on how serious you view the threat, and the response is controlled by two parts of your nervous system: the sympathetic nervous system and the parasympathetic nervous system.

■ Sympathetic and parasympathetic nervous systems

The sympathetic nervous system is responsible for the 'fight or flight' response in your body (Cannon, 1932). It provides you with the energy you need to either confront the threat or run away from it. In order to do this, the sympathetic nervous system produces the following physiological responses:

- diverts blood to working muscles to provide more oxygen
- increases heart rate, breathing rate, heat production, adrenaline production, muscle tension, metabolism
- makes the hairs stand on end
- dilates the pupils
- slows digestion
- brings about a dry mouth.

Once the stress has passed, the parasympathetic nervous system begins to work. The parasympathetic system helps you to relax. It achieves this by producing the following responses:

- makes the muscles relax
- slows metabolism
- increases digestion rate, saliva production
- decreases body temperature, heart rate, breathing rate
- constricts the pupils.

Causes

There are a number of causes of stress, but the key aspect to understanding them is knowing that they are specific to the individual athlete. It is common to have a number of athletes in similar situations, yet each have an entirely different stress response.

Assessment practice

What sorts of things cause you to become stressed? Think about things in your everyday life and in a sporting situation. **P5**

grading tips

Grading Tip 

Describe factors that can cause stress in sporting environments.

Internal

Internal causes of stress include illnesses such as infections, psychological factors such as cognitive anxiety (worrying about something), not having enough sleep, being overly self-critical or being a perfectionist (e.g. type A personality).

External

External causes of stress include the environment in which you find yourself (e.g. too noisy, too quiet), negative social interactions with other people (e.g. somebody being rude to you), major life events (e.g. a death in the family) and day-to-day hassles (e.g. travel to and from games, training schedules).

Remember!

The key difference between internal and external sources of stress is that internal causes of stress are things that we think about (cognitive) whereas external sources come from the environment.

Personal

People who are significant in our lives – such as friends, family and partners – can also be a source of stress. Other lifestyle factors can also be personal sources of stress, such as health and financial circumstances.

Occupational

This relates to your job as a source of stress. It may be that you are unemployed and because of this you suffer from stress. Your boss could be getting at you constantly, which can cause stress. In a sporting situation, it may be that you have had a disagreement with a coach or a manager and you have been dropped as a result of this, causing you to suffer from stress.

Sport as a source of stress

There are two key aspects of sport performance that can cause stress: the importance of the event you are taking part in, and the amount of uncertainty that surrounds it.

The more important the event, the more stressful we find it. This doesn't mean that you have to be playing in a World Cup Final or sprinting in the 100m final in the Olympics; the importance of the event can be specific to the individual.

For example, someone who is playing their first mid-season game after a serious injury, could show the same symptoms of stress as someone who is about to go in to bat in the last innings of a baseball game when the scores are tied and their team already have two outs.

On the face of it, the mid-season game against a team you should beat would not be as important as the game-saving situation the baseball player finds himself in, but it is the importance that the individual attaches to the event that is key.

Anxiety

Definition

Anxiety is frequently referred to as a negative emotional state that is either characterised by, or associated with, feelings of nervousness, apprehension or worry.

Types

There are two main types of anxiety: state anxiety and trait anxiety.

Key Terms

State anxiety A temporary, ever-changing mood state that is an emotional response to any situation considered to be threatening.

Trait anxiety A behavioural tendency to feel threatened even in situations that are not really threatening, and then to respond to this with high levels of state anxiety.

State

State anxiety is a temporary, ever-changing mood state that is an emotional response to any situation considered to be threatening. For example, at the start of a show jumping event, the rider may have higher levels of state anxiety and then settle down once the event has started. State anxiety levels may increase when coming up to particularly high jumps, and then be at their highest level when coming towards the final jump which, if they were to clear quickly and cleanly, would result in a win. There are two types of state anxiety: cognitive state anxiety and somatic state anxiety (see below).

Key Terms

Cognitive state anxiety The amount you worry.

Somatic state anxiety Your perception of the physiological changes that happen in a particular situation.

Trait

Someone who has a high level of trait anxiety is predisposed to become worried in a variety of situations, whether they are in a situation they should find worrying or not. As the name suggests, trait anxiety is an aspect of personality and is part of an individual's pattern of behaviour. It is argued that somebody who has high levels of trait anxiety will respond to situations they find themselves in with higher levels of state anxiety because of their tendency to worry.

Symptoms

Cognitive

Cognitive state anxiety refers to the negative thoughts, nervousness and worry experienced in certain situations. The symptoms of cognitive state anxiety include concentration problems, fear and bad decision-making.

When a performer's concentration levels drop, their performance decreases generally because of the number of mistakes they have made. As the performance levels decrease, the levels of anxiety increase further, as do arousal levels. These increased levels of arousal can further lead to increased levels of cognitive state anxiety, which can further increase the number of mistakes made in performance. The performer is now caught in a negative cycle that can seriously harm performance.

Somatic

Somatic state anxiety relates to the perception of changes in physiological activation, such as increases in heart rate, sweating and increased body heat when you start to play sport. Somatic state anxiety doesn't necessarily mean the actual physiological changes are greater than those you would normally expect; it is more concerned with how the athlete interprets these changes. For example, an athlete could be concerned because they sense an increase in heart rate if they have gone into a game slightly less prepared than normal. This increase in heart rate is nothing different, and is actually beneficial to performance, but the athlete can perceive it as something negative. The symptoms of increased somatic state anxiety include: increases in heart rate, respiratory rate and sweating rate and even complete muscle tension which prevents the athlete from moving (known as 'freezing').

Case study

What is anxiety?

A sprinter is standing at the start line of the 100m final in the Olympic Games. She starts to think 'What happens if I don't get the right start? What happens if I false start? Why did I have to have her in the lane next to me?' As she is thinking all of these things, she starts to sweat, senses her heart rate starting to rise, and starts to feel tense. As this happens, she thinks 'Oh no! I'm tense, I'm not going to be able to start as quickly,' which makes her more tense.

1. **What are the symptoms of cognitive anxiety in the sprinter?**
2. **What are the symptoms of somatic anxiety in the sprinter?**
3. **How have the two types of anxiety affected each other?**

Causes

Athletes experience all of the day-to-day causes of anxiety that everyone else does. Major life events and the hassles of daily routines can be sources of anxiety, but athletes also have other factors that are anxiety-provoking such as injuries, training schedules, contractual issues and concerns about levels of performance.

Theory into practice

There are three main causes of anxiety: the importance of the event, uncertainty about the opposition and the competition itself.

1 Importance of the event: the more important the event, the greater the levels of stress and anxiety. Do you agree?

2 Uncertainty: think back to when you have played against an opponent who was equally matched to you in terms of skill and ability levels. Now think about when you played against someone who was far less skilled than you and also against someone who you knew you had no chance of beating. Who did you experience the greater levels of anxiety against? As a rule, greater levels of uncertainty lead to greater levels of anxiety.

3 Competition: when a player is constantly anxious about competing, they are said to have high levels of competitive trait anxiety. Think back to when you have been in a competitive situation. How did you feel when you knew that people were watching you and your performance? In athletes, this evaluative situation creates a threatening situation for the athlete, and as the athlete has high levels of competitive trait anxiety this can lead to higher levels of competitive state anxiety.

Effects

Anxiety can adversely affect sport performance in a number of ways. In skills that require a great deal of concentration (such as darts, golf putting and potting a ball in snooker or billiards), anxiety can lead to lower performance levels due to reduced concentration and attention levels. In more gross motor skills, anxiety can have a negative effect on performance, due to factors such as hyper-elevated muscle tension (freezing) and coordination faults.

However, some of the symptoms of anxiety can be beneficial for sporting performance. Think about some of the needs of the body to be active. You need to have an increased blood flow and an increased breathing and respiratory rate to aid oxygen transport, and increased sweating rates to keep the body cool. These symptoms of anxiety are physiologically beneficial for performance, but if the athlete thinks they are happening because of their inability to meet some form of demand, it is the perception of the athlete that will make these symptoms negative.

Assessment practice

For a sport of your choice, produce a coach information booklet that explains the following information:

- the symptoms of anxiety
- the causes of anxiety
- the effects of anxiety.

grading tip

Grading Tip 

Using practical, sport-based examples will help you to provide good descriptions.

3.3 Understand the psychology of group dynamics in sports environments

In this section we will look at how group dynamics affect team performance in a range of sports. How groups function is a constantly changing process rather than a static event, and is affected by a number of factors.

'Talent wins games, teamwork and intelligence wins championships' (Michael Jordan)

Group dynamics

Group processes

Throughout your sporting life, you will work with a number of people who together will make sure that your sporting performance is as good as it can be. Teams with the greatest array of talent don't necessarily win every game, so what is it that prevents the best collections of players from winning? What is it that allows less talented teams to win? To answer these questions, we need to consider teamwork.

Group or team

For a collection of individuals to be classed as a group, there must be interaction between the group members. This is normally characterised by communication over an extended period of time. The individuals need to get on with each other (interpersonal attraction) and there needs to be some form of collective identity – the members of the group must perceive themselves to be a distinct unit that is different to other groups. The group must also have shared goals and targets, norms and values, and be prepared to achieve these goals collectively.

All of these characteristics are common in teams, but for the group to become a team there are some key differences. The main difference relates to the pursuit of shared goals and objectives, both team and individual. For a group to be classed as a team, the members can depend on each other and offer support to each other in order to try to achieve the team goals, and the members interact with each other to accomplish these goals and objectives.

Stages of group development

A collection of people in the same place does not necessarily make a team. In order for a group of people to become a team, they must go through four developmental stages (Tuckman, 1965): forming, storming, norming and performing. All groups go through all stages, but the time they spend at each stage and the order in which they go through the stages may vary.

Once a team has progressed through the four stages, it does not mean that they will not revert back to an earlier stage. Teams often go through each stage on a number of different occasions. For example, if key members of the team leave, it is common for the team to revert back to the storming stage as the members of the team begin to vie for position within the team.

Forming

During the forming stage, group members familiarise themselves with other group members, get to know each other and try to decide whether they feel they belong in that group. During this stage, group members will start to assess the strengths and weaknesses of the group members, as well as starting to test their relationships with others in the group. Individuals within the group will try to get to know their roles within the group, and will start to make decisions about whether or not they feel they can fulfil (or want to fulfil) their role within the group. Formal leaders in the group tend to be directive during the forming stage.

Storming

During this stage, conflict begins to develop between individuals in the group. It is common for individuals or cliques within the group to start to question the position and authority of the leader, and they will start to resist the control of the group. Often, conflicts develop because demands start to be placed on the group members, and because some individuals start to try to acquire more important roles within the group. During the storming stage, the formal leader in the group tends to take on more of a guidance role when it comes to decision-making, and helps the team to move towards what is expected in terms of professional behaviour.

Norming

During the norming stage, the instability, hostility and conflict that occurred in the storming stage is replaced by cooperation and solidarity. The members of the group start to work towards common goals rather than focusing on individual agendas, and group cohesion begins to be developed at this stage. As group cohesion develops, group satisfaction increases (mainly due to satisfaction from achieving tasks) and levels of respect for others in the group start to increase. In the norming stage, the formal leader will expect the group members to become more involved in the decision-making process, and will expect the players to take more responsibility for their own professional behaviour.

Performing

The performing stage involves the team progressing and functioning effectively as a unit. The group works without conflict towards the achievement of shared goals and objectives, and there is little need for external supervision as the group is more motivated. The group is now more knowledgeable, and is able to make its own decisions and is responsible for those decisions.

Steiner's model of group effectiveness

Steiner's model was put forward to explain group effectiveness. It is described as:

actual productivity = potential productivity – losses due to faulty group processes

Actual productivity refers to how the team performs (the results they get and the level of performance they put in). Potential productivity refers to the perfect performance the team could produce, based on the individual skill and ability of each athlete in the team and the resources available. According to Steiner's model, if a basketball team contained the best five players in the world, the team would be the best team in the world. This is because each player's skills and ability are the most important resource for the team. Losses due to faulty group processes relate to the issues that can get in the way of team performance, preventing the team from reaching its potential performance. Losses are normally due to two main areas: motivational faults/losses and coordination faults/losses.

Key Terms

Motivational faults/losses These occur when some members of the team do not give 100 per cent effort.

Coordination faults/losses These occur when players do not connect with their play, the team interacts poorly or ineffective strategies are used. Generally, sports that require more interaction or cooperation between players are more susceptible to coordination faults or losses.

Case study

Motivational and coordination losses

In a volleyball team, two players seem to be putting in little effort. When they are setting, they don't appear to be on the same wavelength as the other players on the team, and when they are blocking they don't seem to be putting a great deal of effort into their jumps. The other players on the team appear to be working harder to try to make up for this. However, despite their efforts, there is little interaction between spikers and setters.

1 **Where are the coordination losses in this scenario?**
2 **Where are the motivational losses in this scenario?**
3 **What do you think would be your role as the coach to improve these faults?**

Ringlemann effect

The Ringlemann effect is a phenomenon whereby as the group size increases, the individual productivity of the people in the group decreases, by as much as 50 per cent in some cases. It has been widely assumed that the Ringlemann effect is caused not by coordination losses but by motivation faults or losses. This means that the Ringlemann effect can occur when people are not as accountable for their own performance – as the group gets larger, athletes can 'hide' behind other athletes and it not get noticed.

Social loafing

Social loafing refers to when group members do not put in 100 per cent effort when they are in a group- or team-based situations. This is generally due to losses in motivation. Losses in motivation that cause social loafing are most evident when the individual contributions of group members are not identified or are dispensable. It can also occur when some players seem to be working harder than other players.

Theory into practice

A rowing team was being assessed on its rowing performance by researchers looking at its effects on rowing performance. They found the following information.

One rower gave 100 per cent effort, but when two rowers performed together they put in only 90 per cent effort each. When this was doubled again to four people, each person's individual effort reduced to just 80 per cent. When this was doubled again to eight people in the rowing team, each person's effort reduced to 65 per cent.

Can you think of when this has occured in your chosen sport?

Individuals who display social loafing often lack confidence, are afraid of failure and tend to be highly anxious. It is often also the case that players who display social loafing do not feel they can make any form of useful contribution to overall team performance, which can be the reason why they don't want to participate.

Theory into practice

When the ball is with the right winger in an attacking play during a football match, the winger's team mate, who plays at left wing, may not work too hard to get in position because he knows that most of the attention will be focused on the winger. However, if the left wing knew that his performance would be noticed (for example, if the national team manager had come to watch them play a club game), he would work harder to make sure he was contributing to the game more fully.

Can you think of any examples when you have experienced this?

Interactive and coactive groups

The amount of team cohesion required for successful sports performance varies between different types of team.

- Interactive teams: these are teams that require the team members to work directly with each other in order to achieve a successful performance. Their performance is dependent on a great deal of interaction and coordination between members for performance to be successful. Interactive teams include volleyball and hockey teams.
- Mixed teams: mixed teams are teams that at times require players to interact directly with each other to achieve a successful performance, while at other times require players to focus solely on individual performance in order to achieve overall team success. Mixed teams include rowing and swimming relay teams.
- Co-active teams: co-active teams require individuals to achieve success in their individual games, events or performances in order to achieve overall team success. There is no direct interaction between team members during the performance. Co-active teams include archery and skiing teams.

Think it over

Think about the different teams you have played in or been involved with outside sport. Were they interactive, mixed or co-active teams?

Activity

For the following sports, say which type of team they are and justify your answer.

- 100m relay
- cricket
- basketball
- baseball.
- football
- ten-pin bowling
- golf.

Cohesion

Cohesion is defined as a dynamic process, that is reflected in the tendency for a group to stick together and remain united in the pursuit of its goals and objectives. There are two main types of cohesions: task and social.

Task cohesion

Task cohesion is how much group or team members work together to achieve the group's common goals and objectives. Although both types of cohesion influence performance to a certain degree, task cohesion is more closely related to successful sporting performance.

Theory into practice

A team may have the goal of winning a championship and even though the players don't get on really well outside the game, they all work together to achieve the goal.

How can this happen?

Social cohesion

Social cohesion is how well the team members get on with and enjoy each other's company. For example, in recreational sport all of the players may get on well with one another and enjoy playing the game, regardless of whether they win or lose.

Task and social cohesion are independent of each other. It is possible that team members may not get on particularly well with one another, but they are successful because they are focused on achieving the task. The team could be said to have a high degree of task cohesion, but a small degree of social cohesion. A team that gets on really well while not being very successful, can be said to have a high level of social cohesion.

Case study

Cohesion

An example of the importance of task cohesion comes through the Chicago Bulls teams of the 1990s. The Chicago Bulls won six championships between 1991 and 1998, yet it is widely reported that some players did not get on with each other away from the court and very rarely spoke to each other outside a game situation. However, as the players were focused on achieving the team goals and objectives (i.e. winning championships), the team was dominant at this time.

1 **Which type of cohesion does this team display?**

2 **Based on this case study, which type of cohesion do you think more closely affects sports performance?**

Remember!

When you are thinking about the importance of cohesion on performance, you need to think about the type of sport you are talking about.

■ Factors affecting cohesion

Carron's conceptual model of cohesion was put forward to explain the factors effecting cohesion. It suggests that four main factors can affect team cohesion:

- environmental
- personal
- leadership
- team.

Environmental

Groups that are closer to each other (in terms of location) tend to be more cohesive, as this gives members greater opportunities to communicate with each other and to develop the group as a whole. The size of the group is also important. Think about when you are in a big group and when you are in a small group. In smaller groups, you will have the opportunity to speak to other people more. The same applies to sports teams: the smaller the team, the greater the opportunity to interact with others and to form relationships.

Personal

The individual characteristics of the group members are an important factor in group cohesion. If players are motivated to achieve the group's aims and objectives, and are from similar social backgrounds, and have similar attitudes and opinions and similar levels of commitment, you are more likely to be satisfied with the group members and the group is more likely to be cohesive.

Leadership

The main leadership factor that affects group cohesion is the style that the leader adopts. Three main leadership styles are commonly used: autocratic, democratic and consultative (see pages 109–110). Another key leadership factor that affects cohesion is how the leader communicates with the team about different aspects of performance, such as goals, player roles and tasks that need to be completed.

Team

Stability is key to cohesion developing within the group. If the team can stay together for a long period of time, this allows relationships to develop between the group members. A more productive group is also likely to be more cohesive, especially if the members have been involved in the decision-making process regarding what is considered as productivity for the group. Another important consideration is what the group has been through together. Group cohesion is larger (and is maintained for longer) in groups who have experienced a range of successes and failures together over a period of time. This is known as shared experiences.

Relationship between cohesion and performance

It is easy to say that the greater the level of cohesion, the higher level of performance. However, some research has shown that cohesion has little or no effect on performance. Interactive sports (such as football, basketball and volleyball) require a greater deal of direct interaction and coordination between players. Co-active sports, (such as bowling, archery or golf), on the other hand, require little, if any, direct interaction or coordination. Therefore, cohesion has a greater influence on performance in interactive sports than it does on co-active sports.

Leadership

There are a variety of leadership styles and leadership roles that can influence how a team performs, but the best leaders are the ones that can attempt to make sure that the team is successful by helping everyone.

Activity

In small groups, brainstorm all the different types of leader that you have been involved with, for example a coach.

Qualities

The best leaders can match their styles, behaviours and qualities to the different situations in which they find themselves. The following qualities will contribute to making a good leader.

- Patience: not everything will work the first time you try it. A good leader is able to give athletes the necessary time to be able to develop their skills.
- Self-discipline: if the leader expects players to display professional standards at all times, the players expect the same of the leader. The athletes will expect the leader to lead by example.
- Intelligence: a good leader is expected to be able to come up with ideas and formulate plans to improve team performance. This could include the ability to introduce new tactics and discuss ideas with the team.
- Optimism: the leader needs to remain positive and enthusiastic at all times, even when everything else is negative. This is one of the essential aspects of a good leader, as it helps to motivate team members. It can be very demoralising to see a down-beat and pessimistic leader.
- Confidence: if you want to build confidence in your players and others who work with you, you must first display confidence in yourself. A good leader needs to give the people they work with the responsibility and the capabilities to make decisions, and to support them in these decisions.

Styles

Autocratic

Think about when you have been working with a coach, tutor or manager who is says things like 'do this', 'do it like this' or 'do it how I said'. These are all examples of how autocratic leaders approach the people they work with.

Autocratic leaders have very firm views about how and when things should be done. They tend to be inflexible with their approach to the group. This type of leader dictates to the group who does what tasks and when to do them, and they often dictate how the task should be done. The views and comments of the people within the group are not sought and it is rare that the leader gets involved on a personal level with the members of the group. This means group members tend to be passive. When working with this type of leader, group members can stop working or work more slowly when the leader is not there, and they have a tendency to become aggressive towards each other.

Democratic (consultative)

Think about when you have been working with a leader who has used questions such as 'How do you think we can do this?', 'Do you think this could work?' or 'How do you feel about doing it this way?' These questions are commonly used by democratic (consultative) leaders. This type of leader makes decisions only after they have been through a process of consultation with the group members. They actively encourage the involvement of the group, tend to adopt a more informal and relaxed approach to leadership, and listen to ideas relating to the prioritisation and completion of goals and objectives.

Democratic leaders maintain their status as the leader by making the final decision, based on all the information collected from the group members and their own thoughts and ideas. Generally, when the leader is not present, group members tend to continue working towards agreed goals and do not become aggressive towards each other when things start to go wrong.

Activity

In small groups, produce a list of all of the qualities that you think make a good leader.

Prescribed leaders

Prescribed leaders are those who are appointed by some form of higher authority. For example, Brian Noble was appointed Wigan Warriors' coach.

Emergent leaders

Emergent leaders are those who achieve their leadership status by gaining the respect and support of the group. These leaders generally achieve their status through showing specific leadership skills or being particularly skilful at their sport. For example, Andrew Flintoff emerged within the team and became the leader of the England national team before he was appointed to captain. He emerged because of his impressive performances, gaining the respect of other players.

Theories

The three main theories of leadership are trait, behavioural and interactional.

Trait

Trait approach (often referred to as the 'great man' theory) suggests that there are certain personality characteristics that predispose an individual to being a good leader. It suggests that leaders are born, not made. This theory says that leadership is innate and that a good leader would be a good leader in any situation, not necessarily just the domain he or she is currently working in.

This approach has not had a great deal of support since the late 1940s, and it is generally accepted now that there is no definitive set of traits that characterise a good leader.

Behavioural

Behavioural theories of leadership argue that a good leader is made, not born, and suggests that anyone can be taught to be a good leader. The behavioural approach has its roots in social learning theory (see page 79), so it suggests that people will learn to be good leaders by observing the behaviours of other good leaders in a variety of situations, reproducing those behaviours in similar situations and then continuing them should they be reinforced.

Theory into practice

An assistant coach of a rugby union team is watching the head coach deal with a disagreement between two players in training. The head coach deals with the situation well and the conflict is resolved. Imagine you are the assistant in this situation and have witnessed how the coach dealt with the situation. How do you think you would handle a similar situation? Why would you act in this way?

Interactional

Trait and behavioural approaches to leadership place a lot of emphasis on the personal qualities of a coach. The interactional approach considers other factors that could affect leadership, mainly the interaction between the individual and the situation in which they find themselves. Two main types of leader are identified through the interactional approach: relationship-orientated leaders and task-orientated leaders.

- Relationship-orientated leaders: these leaders are focused on developing relationships with the people in the group. They work hard to maintain communication with members; always help to maintain levels of social interaction between members and themselves; and develop respect and trust with others. Relationship-orientated leaders are generally more effective with experienced, highly skilled athletes.

- Task-orientated leaders: these leaders are more concerned with meeting goals and objectives. They tend to create plans; decide on priorities; assign members to task; and ensure members stay on task, all with the overall focus of increasing overall group productivity. Task-orientated leaders tend to be more effective with less experienced, less skilled performers who need constant instruction and feedback.

Different athletes will have a preference for task-orientated or relationship-orientated leaders. In principle, it is getting the right balance between providing a supportive environment and focusing on getting the job done that makes the most effective leader. It is a leader's role to get to know their performers so they know on which area to concentrate.

Social facilitation

Have you ever been in a sporting situation when you have played better when you have had an audience? If so, you have experienced social facilitation. How about playing worse when you have been playing in front of people watching you? If so, you have experienced impairment of performance, which is another aspect of the theory of social facilitation.

Audience effect

Social facilitation suggests that the effect of the audience is to increase arousal levels in athletes. In skills that are well learned or relatively simple, the increased arousal levels will improve performance levels. However, in skills that are not well learned, or in tasks that are relatively complex, performance levels can be reduced or impaired.

Co-action effect

Social facilitation suggests that in high-pressure situations, relatively simple tasks can be impaired because arousal levels can be too high. The theory does not only relate to the presence of audiences; it also relates to the presence of anyone else. Therefore, when you work with others your performance can increase. This is known as the co-action effect.

Home advantage

Home advantage suggests that a team playing at home will have a far better chance of winning a game than when playing away from home. There is a body of research that strongly supports this idea, claiming that home advantage is greater in indoor sports than outdoor sports.

Home advantage has sometimes been referred to as away disadvantage, because the focus is normally on how the crowd negatively affects the away team, rather than how it positively affects the home team.

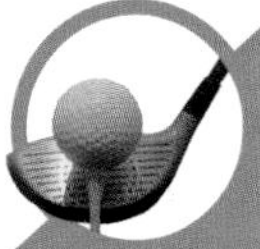

Think it over

Think about when you have observed or attended a game at your team's ground or court. How much time have you spent whistling, booing and jeering opposition players in an attempt to put them off rather than cheering on your own team?

A number of reasons have been suggested to try to explain home advantage. Some of these reasons are physical (e.g. related to the location of the event) and some are psychological (e.g. players choking under the pressure of fans).

As the importance of the game increases, home advantage has been shown to decrease in certain sports. In play-offs and championship games, the home team is less likely to win in certain sports due to performance errors that occur with the increased pressure. For example, as a basketball game becomes more important, the away team's performance has been shown to remain fairly constant but the home team's performance usually decreases in certain areas such as free-throw shooting.

Taking it further

Look at a copy of one of the sports papers that has all of the results of the games at the weekend for a range of sports. It is a good idea to do this activity for your local area and then to repeat it with one of the national papers.

- Draw a table with three columns: win, lose and draw.
- Look at all of the results from a particular sport.
- Use tally charts to record whether the home team has won or lost in a range of sports.
- Is there a big difference between home wins, draws or losses?

Assessment practice

Watch a sporting event of your choice to observe they way the group interacts with each other. It will be better if you do this with a group you are all familiar with, so that you can observe them in more detail, but don't tell the group you are observing them.

Produce a report of your observations that includes the following information.

1 Describe the four factors that affect cohesion (environmental, personal, leadership and team). 

2 Explain each factor. 

Think it over

Think about when you have played a sport inside in front of other people, and then think about when you have played a sport outside in front of others. How did you feel in each situation? Did you feel differently? If so, why do you think you felt this way? How do you think the two situations could affect an away team?

grading tips

Grading Tip 

Male sure you discuss four factors that can affect cohesion.

Grading Tip M4

Use sporting examples to explain how each factor can affect team cohesion and performance.

■ Drive theory

Zajonc's drive theory of social facilitation (1965) suggests that there is an apparently random way in which some people perform better and some perform worse in the presence of others. This is known as the audience effect (see page 111).

Activity

1 Imagine you are a golf coach working with a novice player who is learning the new skill of driving the ball from the tee. How does drive theory influence how you set up your training environment?

2 The England football team has lost on penalty shoot-outs in five out of six major tournaments since 1990. Many of the missed penalties were down to player error on the part of the penalty taker. Using drive theory, try to explain why this could be the case.

3.4 Understand psychological factors that affect people in exercise environments

With health issues such as obesity and mental health being key areas of interest in society, physical activity and exercise are becoming increasingly significant. Health professionals, such as fitness instructors, occupational therapists and physiotherapists, all need to have a detailed understanding of factors that can affect people in exercise environments.

Exercise adherence

One of the key factors that affects people in exercise environments is their ability to maintain exercise or physical activity for a period of time.

Think it over

When people start a programme of exercise or physical activity, they do it with the best of intentions. However, within a period of six months, around half of them have stopped. Why do you think that is?

Reasons why people exercise

There are a number of reasons why people take part in exercise, including health benefits, enjoyment, self-esteem and social reasons.

- Health benefits: the main health reasons for taking part in exercise relate to weight management, cardiovascular risk and mental health issues.
- Weight management: people like to look and feel good, and weight management is a key aspect of that. People take part in exercise because they know that it can help prevent conditions such as obesity. Weight control and the benefits of the physical appearance that go along with it are more frequently cited by women as reasons for taking part in exercise.
- Cardiovascular risk: coronary heart disease is one of the biggest killers worldwide. A main benefit of exercise is that it reduces the risk of mortality related to cardiovascular diseases.
- Mental health issues: regular exercise is beneficial in reducing conditions such as stress, anxiety and depression. The psychological benefits of exercise will be discussed in more detail on page 117.
- Enjoyment: many people begin exercise programmes to gain the health benefits from taking part, but for them to carry on exercising they need to have fun! Enjoyment is a main reason at all levels for taking part in exercise, but women and young people are more likely to report enjoyment as an important factor.
- Self-esteem: regular exercise also plays an important role in building an individual's self-confidence and self-esteem. These feelings normally come as a result of achieving exercise goals (e.g. managing to walk around the block, lifting a target weight). Examples of how exercise can build self-esteem include personal development, fitness, competition (all reported mainly by males) and independence (reported mainly by older exercisers).
- Social reasons: people often start exercise programmes as an opportunity to meet new people and socialise with others. Most people who exercise tend to do so with a partner, and the social opportunities offered are often a big reason why they attend group-based exercise sessions, such as aerobics and group walks.

Case study

Starting an exercise programme

Becky is 21 years old and wants to get into regular exercise. She wants to change her body shape and lose a little weight in order to feel better about herself around others. She finds attending the gym on her own a bit daunting, so asks one of her friends to go with her. Becky starts to have a good time with her friend at the gym and they start to set each other weight-loss targets, which they go on to achieve.

1. **What reasons does Becky give for starting the exercise programme?**
2. **How likely is it that Becky will stick to the exercise programme? Justify your answer.**
3. **How do you think the exercise programme will benefit Becky?**

Reasons for not exercising and barriers to exercise

Reasons for not exercising and barriers to exercise can be classified under five main headings: physical, emotional, motivational, time and availability. This links to the psychological factors affecting exercise environments because people believe these five barriers can prevent them from exercising, whether they actually stop them or not. Most of these barriers can be overcome by planning or education.

- Physical: individuals regularly report physical barriers to some degree as barriers to exercise. The most common forms of physical barriers referred to relate to injuries or disabilities, health, age (e.g. 'I'm too old') and weight (e.g. 'I'm too fat'). Generally, men give physical reasons more than women do for not taking part in exercise.
- Emotional: these relate to some form of fear relating to health (e.g. 'I might get injured', 'It may damage my health"), being too shy to take part, being too embarrassed to take part and considering themselves not the sporty type. Generally, women give emotional reasons for not taking part in exercise more than men.
- Motivational: not having the commitment to maintain an exercise programme or physical activity programme due to other factors is known as a motivational barrier. It is easy to allow factors such as work, friends, family and energy to affect motivation to exercise. The most common motivational barriers are needing time to relax, needing rest in spare time, not having any energy, not enjoying physical activity and not thinking the exercise programme would last (e.g. 'I'd never stick to it', 'I'd never keep it up'). Both men and women give motivational reasons for not taking part in exercise.
- Time: this is argued to be the most important barrier to exercise, but lack of time is more often a perceived barrier than an actual one. The most common time factors relate to not having time because of work or family commitments (e.g. having to look after children), or just generally not having the time. However, people usually have enough time to watch television or socialise with friends, so time can be down to an individual's priorities. Time-related

Case study

Barriers to participation

Nicki is a single mother who has been thinking about starting an exercise programme. However, whenever someone talks to her about it, she says it is too expensive to join a gym, she has to look after her children and she doesn't think she is the type of person who could use a gym.

1. **What reasons does Nicki give for not wanting to take part in exercise?**
2. **What type of barrier would each be classed as?**
3. **If Nicki started an exercise programme with her current thoughts on exercise, do you think she would adhere to it? Explain your answer.**

reasons are given by both men and women most often when discussing why they don't take part in exercise.

- Availability: availability barriers relate to finances, facilities, equipment and other individuals to exercise with. Common reasons for not exercising relating to availability are 'I can't afford it', 'I don't have the right kit', 'There aren't any facilities nearby' or 'There is no one to do it with.'

Problems with exercise adherence

The main problem with exercise adherence is that within six months of starting a programme, half the participants drop out. Exercisers often have lapses that can last for up to three months. The reasons for these lapses include injury, work constraints, lack of time or interest, unsuitable weather or family demands. The most frequently used reason is injury.

Activity

1. Think about a time when you had planned to do something but did not end up doing it. The activity doesn't have to be sports related – it can be anything.
2. Make a list of all of the reasons you gave for not following through your intentions.
3. Say which type of barrier each of these reasons were.

Models of behaviour change

Researchers have tried to explain many of the issues relating to exercise behaviours using models of behaviour change such as the transtheoretical model (or stages of change model), social cognitive theory and the health belief model.

Transtheoretical model (stages of change)

The transtheoretical model (or stages of change) was developed by Prochaska and DiClemente. It suggests that in order to change behaviour, individuals go through a series of stages and this process is a dynamic (ever-changing) one. It is often the case that people move through the different stages several times while trying to change their behaviour. A final stage is often added to the model (as shown here) which is known as relapse. When people fall back from their current stage, relapse occurs. Relapse can happen at any stage and individuals begin the cycle again from the stage before.

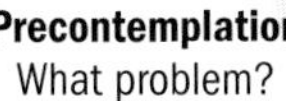

Precontemplation
What problem? Oh – *that*. I'd rather not go there right now
1 The individual has no intention of becoming active in the next six months

Contemplation
I'm thinking about it
2 The individual is thinking about becoming more active in the next six months

Preparation
I've made up my mind and I'm ready
3 The individual has a plan to start exercising, or has started to exercise on an irregular basis

Action
I'm committed
4 The individual has become a regular exerciser, but only within the past six months

Maintenance
I made it and I'm going to maintain the change
5 The individual has achieved regular exercise status for longer than six months

The transtheoretical model (stages of change): 1992

Assessment practice

Identify which stage of the transtheoretical model each of the following people are at and explain your answers. **P8 M5**

1 Someone who has joined a gym but not yet attended.

2 Someone who has been riding their bike to work every day for the past year.

3 Someone who thinks they weigh too much and wants to start exercising.

4 Someone who thinks they weigh too much and wants to start exercising but cannot be bothered.

5 Someone who has joined a gym and has attended three times a week for the last three months.

■ Social cognitive theory (Bandura)

Bandura's social cognitive theory says that personal, behavioural and situational factors will interact with each other and actually be determinants of each other. This means that the situation could affect behaviour, just as someone's behaviour could affect the situation they are in. Different personal factors (such as thoughts, beliefs and emotions) can affect behaviours in different situations.

This theory relates to exercise behaviours. It says that if a person believes they are going to be able to successfully perform a behaviour (e.g. take part in exercise), then it is more likely that they will attempt that behaviour (e.g. they will take part in exercise). This theory states that self-efficacy is a good predictor of behaviour.

Key Term

Self-efficacy Believing you can perform a task or behaviour successfully.

Case study

Social cognitive theory

Joan is a 45-year-old, obese, divorced, single woman. She knows that starting an exercise programme will benefit her health conditions and may offer her the chance of meeting new people if she attended some form of group-based activity. However, Joan doesn't think she will be able to take part in any of the activities without feeling bad about herself.

Using only social cognitive theory to support your answer, say whether you think Joan will start an exercise programme or not.

Health belief model

The health belief model argues that someone is likely to take part in exercise if they can see the health benefits of taking part. If someone sees that there is the potential to prevent serious illnesses and can weigh up the advantages and disadvantages, they are more likely to take part in the programme.

Theory into practice

A man is suffering from coronary heart disease. He recognises the severity of the illness and understands the potential benefits of taking part in exercise as a method of reducing the symptoms of the disease and reducing the risks to his health. He realises that there may be some costs associated with taking part in regular exercise, but understands that the pros (the health benefits) are more important than the cons (the cost). Would the health belief model claim he is more likely to take part in exercise?

Exercise and well-being

Mental health issues are serious public health issues. It was estimated that, by 1999, 4 out of 10 leading causes of disability were mental health issues. It is predicted that by 2020 mental health issues will be a bigger global killer than cancer.

Psychological benefits of exercise

No controlled study has ever found exercise to be an ineffective primary or complementary treatment for psychological disorders. Exercise has been shown to:

- decrease the symptoms of depression
- bring about small to moderate decreases in the symptoms of anxiety
- offer small decreases in panic disorders
- bring about small to moderate increases in self-esteem
- reduce or lower the symptoms of stress.

In 1988, Morgan and O'Connor suggested four hypotheses to try to explain how exercise benefits different mental health issues.

- Monoamine hypothesis: this suggests that exercise benefits psychological well-being by altering levels of brain chemicals such as serotonin, dopamine and noradrenaline. This helps to regulate and enhance mood. This hypothesis has not been proven.
- Thermogenic hypothesis: this suggests that exercise benefits psychological well-being by increasing your overall body temperature. This exposure to increased heat leaves you in a more relaxed frame of mind and feeling generally more pleasant. This hypothesis is less likely to account for long-term changes in psychological well-being and more research is needed to firmly support this theory.
- Endorphin hypothesis: this suggests that exercise benefits psychological well-being because it releases extra endorphins. Endorphins are chemicals in the brain that create a sense of euphoria and mastery. This sense of euphoria is commonly referred to as the 'runner's high' (see page 119).

Key Term

Endorphins Proteins in the brain that act as the body's natural pain reliever.

- Distraction hypothesis: this is different from the other three theories as it is not based on physiology or biochemistry. The hypothesis suggests that exercise benefits psychological well-being because it diverts attention from negative thoughts, emotions and behaviours. Think about when you have been in a bad mood and you have started exercising. During the session, the things that were bothering you were probably erased from your mind. The distraction hypothesis suggests that this happens because your body is distracted through exertion, and your mind is distracted through concentrating on other activities. This theory is not proven and more work is needed to provide extra support for it.

Case study

The four hypotheses

Frank is 48 years old and has been diagnosed with clinical depression. He has recently started an exercise programme with one of his friends and has noticed that when he is exercising he doesn't think too much about the things that have been getting him down. He has noticed that he starts to get comfortably warm at the start of his exercise sessions, which has motivated him to try harder because he takes this as a sign he is ready for exercise. As he has got fitter, he feels a little more like he has accomplished something and finds his exercise sessions more enjoyable because of this.

Using Morgan and O'Connor's four hypotheses, explain how Frank's exercise sessions may be benefiting his psychological well-being.

Activity

Which of the four hypotheses do you think is the most likely to explain the effects of exercise on psychological well-being? Justify your answer.

Exercise in treating anxiety and depression

Temporary reductions in state anxiety have been shown after short-term exercise, and prolonged exercise can result in long-term reductions. Significant reductions in anxiety symptoms are shown with aerobic exercise, but it could be argued that this is because most anxiety research has looked at the benefits of aerobic exercise rather than anaerobic exercise. If exercise is stopped, anxiety levels might return to pre-exercise levels within 24 hours.

The long-term benefits of exercise on anxiety are due to a number of reasons and happen regardless of age or gender. Long-term exercise has been shown to decrease levels of muscle tension (somatic anxiety), but it has also been argued that exercise benefits anxiety simply because it takes your attention away from what is causing the anxiety (e.g. day-to-day hassles, such as work).

Depression is the most common mental health condition and one of the most treatable using exercise. There is a substantial amount of evidence to suggest that exercise can cause a moderate decrease in depression, but how it does this is unclear. Significant long-term improvements in depression can be seen after exercising three times a week for five weeks, and the gains can remain in place for up to a year, but mood improvements linked with reducing depression are evident after just one exercise session. There is a causal link between exercise and decreased depression, which means that research has shown it is the exercise that has benefited the depression.

For exercise to be effective in treating depression, choose enjoyable, moderate-intensity exercise activities. Activities such as walking, jogging, swimming, stretching and weight training all benefit depression, and no form of exercise has been shown to be better than any other. If possible, exercising in groups and in outdoor settings are particularly good. Trees, grass and natural light, can all benefit depression by benefiting mood, especially when exercise is built into your normal routine.

Assessment practice

Imagine you are working in a fitness centre. Your manager has asked you to produce a report that will help her to increase the revenue for the centre. She wants to be able to identify why people may not want to take part in exercise and wants to have a big mental health push aimed at business clients.

Produce a short report for your manager that includes the following information:

- an explanation of the barriers to exercise
- an explanation of the psychological benefits of exercise. **P8 M5**

Exercise and mood control

Regular exercise or physical activity can help to improve mood. Thirty minutes of activity have been shown to elevate mood by reducing muscle tension, increasing heart rate and helping you to feel more in control.

Secondary characteristics of the menopause include mood swings, tiredness, sleeplessness, weight gain and frequent headaches. Exercise has been shown to elevate mood in this group because it reduces some of these symptoms. However, the problem is that menopausal women are less likely to start an exercise programme than other people.

Exercise and quality of life

Regular exercise or physical activity has also been shown to improve quality of life. It can do this by:

- increasing independence in older participants
- reducing secondary characteristics of the menopause
- preventing osteoporosis
- improving mental health
- benefiting cardiovascular health (e.g. lowers blood pressure, reduces the risk of coronary heart disease)
- reducing muscle tension
- increasing feelings of alertness.

Key Term

Osteoporosis A condition involving a decrease in bone mass, making bones more fragile.

Release of endorphins

When a person is physically active or exercises for a certain period of time (about 20 minutes or longer) the body releases endorphins, which are chemicals in the brain that act as the body's natural pain reliever. When endorphins are released, a person may experience a feeling of euphoria. Many people enjoy this feeling and look forward to the natural high they get from keeping physically fit.

The runner's high

During a long run, some runners gradually lose the ability to feel pain and experience a thrill as their bodies are filled with exhilarating energy. This is called a runner's high. Some experts believe a runner's high is caused by the surge of endorphins distance runners feel during a difficult workout.

Knowledge check

1. Is there a link between personality and sports participation and performance? Justify your answer.
2. What do the terms intrinsic, extrinsic and amotivation mean?
3. What are the different factors that affect motivation?
4. What are Gill's criteria for aggression?
5. What are the different types of aggression?
6. What is the difference between aggression and assertion?
7. What are the different theories that have been suggested to explain the relationship between arousal and performance?
8. What is stress and what are the different factors that can cause stress in sporting environments?
9. What is anxiety and what are the causes, symptoms and effects of anxiety?
10. What are the four main factors that can affect team cohesion according to Carron's conceptual model of cohesion?
11. What do the terms 'social loafing' and the 'Ringlemann effect' mean?
12. What are the different leadership styles?
13. What are the three main models of behaviour change in exercise psychology?
14. What are Morgan and O'Connor's theories to explain the benefits of exercise on psychological well-being?
15. What effect does exercise have on the different psychological variables such as depression, anxiety, mood, quality of life and self-esteem?

End of Unit assessment

Preparation for assessment

1 Sports psychology is a relatively new area within sport. Some people are still resistant to using sport psychologists because they don't really understand any of the concepts within sports psychology. Your task is to produce an illustrated leaflet that can be used as an educational tool for coaches. Your leaflet needs to be split into four sections.

- *Section 1 – Personality*: say what personality is and whether it can affect sports participation and performance. Use different theories to analyse how personality can affect sports performance. P1 M1 D1
- *Section 2 – Motivation*: say what motivation is and discuss the different ways people are motivated. P2

grading tips

Grading Tip P2 

Make sure you define motivation and the different types of motivation. Look at how both intrinsic and extrinsic motivation can affect sports performance.

- *Section 3 – Aggression*: define aggression and the different types of aggression. Explain how people can become aggressive in three different sports situations of your choice. P3 M2

grading tips

Grading Tip P1

Give a brief outline to say whether personality affects sport behaviour or not.

Grading Tip M1 

Make it clear how personality affects behaviour in a sports setting, if at all.

Grading Tip D1 

When you are asked to analyse something, make sure you look at both the positive and negative aspects. For example, if you are analysing the effects of personality on sports performance, look at arguments that say personality can determine sports performance as well as arguments that say personality doesn't affect sports performance.

grading tips

Grading Tip P3 

Make sure you define aggression and the different types of aggression.

Grading Tip M2 

You need to cover three different sporting environments for this criterion.

- *Section 4 – Arousal, stress and anxiety*: describe arousal, stress and anxiety and their causes. Explain the symptoms of arousal and anxiety. Explain the positive and negative effects of arousal and anxiety on sports performance using different theories. Name and explain different sources of stress. P4 P5 P6 M3 D2

grading tips

Grading Tip 

When explaining concepts such as arousal, refer to the different theories that are used. Using diagrams is also a good idea.

Grading Tip 

Define stress and include a range of sources of stress.

Grading Tip 

Define anxiety and include a range of sources of anxiety. Describe its symptoms, causes and effects.

Grading Tip M3

Use all the theories to explain how arousal affects performance, then say which is most likely to explain the relationship between arousal and performance. Make sure you discuss how arousal can be both positive and negative.

Grading Tip D2

You need to say how arousal affects sports performance.

grading tips

Grading Tip 

Describe the different group dynamics such as leadership, group processes and cohesion.

Grading Tip 

Say how each factor contributes to the psychology of group dynamics.

- *Section 5 – Group dynamics*: define groups and teams. Discuss how a group becomes a team. Explain at least four different factors that can affect how the team functions. P7 M4

2 When you work in exercise psychology, you will be expected to work with different client groups with a range of issues and conditions.

Wendy is 50 years old and lives on her own. Her children have left home and she has few friends. She has recently been diagnosed with clinical depression. She has a poor lifestyle and she drinks frequently and smokes, and refers to herself as a bit of a 'slug' (she has very low self-esteem). Wendy understands the benefits of regular exercise but she does not take part in any physical activity. She says she has no intention of doing so, as she does not feel she would be able to take part in it effectively.

Using your knowledge of exercise psychology and the benefits of exercise, produce an exercise psychology intervention that will help to get Wendy into regular exercise. Your intervention should be presented in the form of a ten-minute PowerPoint® presentation with accompanying handouts and visual aids. Include the following information in your presentation.

a An introduction to Wendy that discusses her conditions and issues, and the stage of the transtheoretical model she is currently at (with a justification of your choice).

b Details on any other behaviour change models that you think may be relevant in this case. P8

c A suggested physical activity intervention that would benefit Wendy.

d A justification of your intervention that says how exercise can benefit Wendy's specific issues and conditions. M5

grading tips

Grading Tip 

Say what psychological factors Wendy presents with and how they can influence her exercise participation.

Grading Tip 

Relate the proposed benefits of the intervention you have selected to the specific conditions that Wendy presents.

Grading criteria

To achieve a pass grade the evidence must show that the learner is able to:	To achieve a merit grade the evidence must show that, in addition to the pass criteria, the learner is able to:	To achieve a distinction grade the evidence must show that, in addition to the pass and merit criteria, the learner is able to:
P1 describe the efforts of personality on behaviour in sports environments **Assessment practice page 87**	**M1** explain the effects of personality on behaviour in sports environments **Assessment practice page 87**	**D1** analyse the effects of personality on behaviour in sports environments **Assessment practice page 87**
P2 describe the factors which affect the motivation of athletes **Assessment practice page 88**		
P3 describe the types and causes of aggressive behaviour in three different sports environments **Assessment practice pages 90, 92, 94**	**M2** explain the types and causes of aggressive behaviour in three different sports environments **Assessment practice pages 90, 92, 94**	
P4 describe the causes of arousal and its effects on sports performance **Assessment practice page 98**	**M3** explain the causes of arousal and its effects on sports performance **Assessment practice page 98**	**D2** analyse the effects on sports performance **Assessment practice page 98**
P5 describe factors that can cause stress in sporting environments **Assessment practice page 100**		
P6 describe anxiety, and its symptoms, causes and effects **Assessment practice page 103**		

Grading criteria

To achieve a pass grade the evidence must show that the learner is able to:	To achieve a merit grade the evidence must show that, in addition to the pass criteria, the learner is able to:	To achieve a distinction grade the evidence must show that, in addition to the pass and merit criteria, the learner is able to:
P7 describe four different factors which contribute to the psychology of group dynamics **Assessment practice page 112**	**M4** explain the four different factors which contribute to the psychology of group dynamics **Assessment practice page 112**	
P8 describe the psychological factors that affect people in exercise **Assessment practice pages 116, 118**	**M5** explain the psychological benefits of exercise **Assessment practice pages 116, 118**	

Research methods for sport and exercise sciences

Introduction

This unit explains the key techniques that are used in both qualitative and quantitative research methods in sport and exercise sciences.

Sport and exercise scientists play a key role in the development of research and they need to have a detailed understanding of various research techniques to be able to do this. Research in sport and exercise sciences means collecting and analysing data. This unit will help you to learn how to collect and analyse data effectively.

We will start by looking at key issues in research methods. We then move on to looking at ways you can acquire key skills in both qualitative and quantitative research, including questionnaire design, interview skills and statistical skills. You will then be shown ways in which you can practise these skills in real-life situations with a view to developing your practical skills in research methods.

After completing this unit you should be able to achieve the following outcomes:

- understand key issues in research methods for the sport and exercise sciences
- understand data collection techniques for the sport and exercise sciences
- understand qualitative data analysis techniques for the sport and exercise sciences
- understand quantitative data analysis techniques for the sport and exercise sciences.

Think it over

Think about some of the following questions.

- How do you think we are able to explain how David Beckham managed to bend a football around a wall the way he does?
- How did we manage to find out how athletes react to high-level competition?
- What was behind the government's recommendations for physical activity to reduce obesity?
- How do we know what attracts people to different types of sports?

Research is at the heart of everything we currently do or have ever done in sport and exercise science. It affects, benefits and provides recommendations for the improvement of performance in all areas. Without it, athletes would not be able to perform in the way they do, and we would not be able to come up with ways of reducing the incidence and effects of diseases and illnesses such as obesity, diabetes, depression and cancer. Research is more than people in white coats sticking needles into small animals or dropping things into Petri dishes!

4.1 Understand key issues in research methods for the sport and exercise sciences

Research

'Research is a systematic process of discovery and advancement of human knowledge.'

(Gratton and Jones, 2004)

Before starting to conduct research, you need to consider which type of research would be best to answer your research problem. There are two main types of research: quantitative and qualitative.

Quantitative research

Quantitative research is a formal, objective, systematic process in which numerical data are used to obtain information. It normally involves testing a hypothesis or trying to find out relationships.

- It is generally deductive research (this means that a scientist would start from a hypothesis and then begin observations to prove the hypothesis).
- It is designed to establish differences, relationships or causality (does one thing cause another?).

Key Terms

Hypothesis A hypothesis is a testable prediction of what will happen through your research project.

Deductive research Research that tests a hypothesis.

Causality When you can identify that something has caused something else.

Qualitative research

Qualitative research, on the other hand, is generally subjective and involves words rather than data. It looks at feelings, opinions, emotions and sentiments and is more concerned with trying to explain Why…? rather than What…? or How many…?.

- It tends to be inductive, which means it develops a hypothesis.
- It tries to explain differences, relationships or causality. (Note that qualitative data can sometimes be handled in such a way as to produce quantitative data.)

Remember!

There is no single 'best' approach to research. You just need to make sure that you choose the correct one for the research project you are wanting to carry out and the research question you are trying to answer. In some cases you may combine the approaches.

Key Terms

Inductive research Research that develops a hypothesis through the research process that can then be tested at a later time.

Null hypothesis is a prediction that there is no relationship.

Activity

Think about when you are watching a football game. You are concentrating on the number of times a striker keeps missing chances on goal of every variety. We've all seen it – they miss one-on-ones with the goalkeeper, missing both long and close shots. As a sports scientist, you might want to find out a couple of things in this situation.

- How many chances did the striker miss?
- Why did the striker miss those chances?

Assessment practice

Imagine the British Association of Sport and Exercise Sciences (BASES) has asked you to help explain to a group of new members the differences between qualitative and quantitative research. The organisation would like you to present something at the next BASES student conference by using a poster presentation. You have been given the following guidance.

1 Produce an A3-size poster that describes, compares and contrasts qualitative and quantitative research.
2 Use a range of presentation methods (e.g. tables, images, diagrams, examples of each type of research).
3 Make your poster eye-catching.
4 Make your poster clear enough to be read from a short-distance away. P1 M1

grading tips

Grading Tip 

Make sure that you say in detail what both types of research are.

Grading Tip 

Make sure you say what both types of research are and highlight the similarities and differences in a suitable format.

Key issues

Validity

Validity is a key issue in research because it relates to whether you are actually measuring what you planned to measure.

There are a number of different types of validity. To be able to achieve criteria P2 and M2, you need to be able to explain what the different types of validity are and give examples of them.

- Internal validity: relates to whether the results of the study can be attributed to the different treatments in the study. This means that for your research to claim internal validity, you need to make sure you have controlled everything that could affect the results of the study.
- External validity: relates to whether or not the results of the study can be applied to the real world.

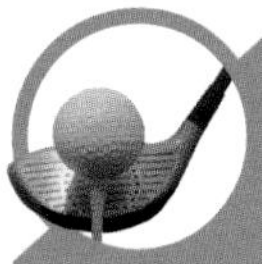

Think it over

It can be difficult to achieve both internal and external validity at the same time. Internal validity requires you to control everything that could affect the results of your study, so that you know you are measuring only the effects of your treatment. However, in a sporting- or exercise-related real-world environment, how can you control everything that can affect performance?

- Face validity: refers to whether or not the method you have selected measures what it is supposed to measure. You can achieve face validity by asking other researchers or participants what they think of the project. (This type of validity is also known as logical validity.)
- Construct validity: is the most rigorous form of validity. This type of validity can be claimed if the data you have collected agrees or correlates with other data. For example, if you did a piece of research asking people whether they participated in sport or not, would the results you found correlate with other measures such as playing matches?
- Predictive validity: would allow your measures to predict future behaviour. For example, if you interviewed people about their attitudes towards exercise, would you be able to predict exercise habits from the results of your interviews?

Case study

Title

A basketball coach wants to measure the overall flexibility of the team's players and has decided to use the sit-and-reach test to measure this. However, although this test is a measure of flexibility, it would not be valid.

1. **Explain to the coach why the sit-and-reach test is not a valid measure of overall flexibility.**
2. **The coach needs some advice about fitness testing with his players. He has come to you for some advice. Your job is to suggest a more appropriate method of testing the players' overall flexibility. Make sure you can explain why your suggestions will increase the validity of testing.**

Reliability

Reliability relates to whether, if you carried out the research again, you would get the same results. However, reliability can be claimed without the results being correct. For example, if you always ask the wrong questions in research, you would always get the same wrong answers. This would mean the test would be reliable because you have received the *same* wrong answers, even though they are not the ones you have been wanting.

In quantitative research, reliability can be one researcher conducting the same test on the same individual on a number of occasions, and getting the same (or similar) results. Alternatively, it can be different researchers conducting the same test on the same individual and getting the same (or similar) results.

In qualitative research, reliability relates to the same researcher placing results into the same categories on a number of different occasions, or different researchers placing results into the same or similar categories.

Remember!

You need to be careful, as reliability can be claimed without the results being correct!

There are certain factors you need to take into account that can affect reliability. For example:

- errors can happen when researchers don't know how to use the equipment correctly
- the equipment is poorly maintained
- the wrong type of equipment is selected.

There are two main types of reliability.

- Inter-researcher reliability: This looks at whether different researchers in the same situation would get the same (or similar) results. An example of when inter-researcher reliability is a problem comes through body composition assessment. When people are learning to use the skinfold calliper technique (see page 129) of assessing body composition, it is sometimes difficult to take accurate measurements from the correct sites. Researchers often come up with different values. When this happens, you cannot claim to have achieved inter-researcher reliability.
- Test-retest reliability: This relates to doing the same test on a number of different occasions and getting the same (or similar) results. An example of a test-retest reliability issue in sport or exercise research is the measurement of heart rate. Heart rate can be affected by a number of factors, such as temperature, time of day, diet, sleep patterns, physical activity levels and alcohol. Therefore, if you were to measure heart rate on the same person at the same time of day, but on different days, it is likely you would get different measurements.

Assessment practice

A newly-qualified fitness instructor has been asked to measure the body fat percentage of a client. They are a little unsure of how to use the skinfold callipers, but take the measurements anyway. However, they take the measurements in the wrong places and record the results. The results of the tests are shown below.

Site	Measurement 1 (mm)	Measurement 2 (mm)	Measurement 3 (mm)	Mean (mm)
Biceps	7	7	7	7.0
Triceps	7	6	7	6.6
Subscapular	8	11	6	8.3
Suprailiac	13	6	7	8.6
				30.5

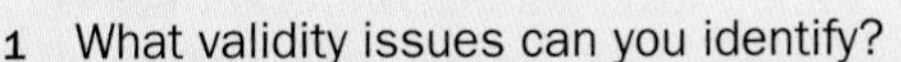

1 What validity issues can you identify?  P2
2 What reliability issues can you identify?  P2
3 Which results in the table do you think are unreliable? Explain your answer.  M2

grading tips

Grading Tip  P2

Say how you know when something is not valid or reliable.

Grading Tip M2

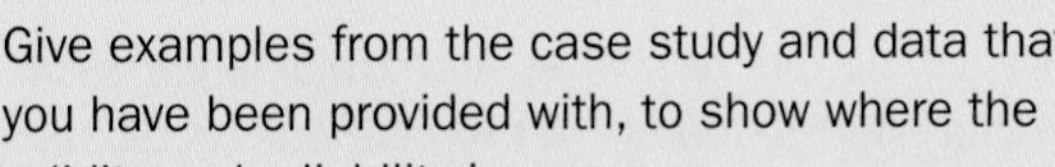

Give examples from the case study and data that you have been provided with, to show where the validity and reliability issues are.

Think it over

Can something be valid without being reliable? Can something be reliable without being valid?

Accuracy

Accuracy relates to how close your measurement is to the 'gold standard', or what you are actually intending to measure. Imagine you are looking at the weight of a boxer before a fight. If the boxer had an actual weight of 100 kg and your weighing device showed him to weigh 100.1 kg, you could say this is accurate. However, if the measuring device showed him to weigh 103 kg, you would say this is not accurate as it is not close to their actual body weight.

Key Term

Gold standard The norm value closest to what you are actually intending to measure. For example, in darts if you wanted to hit the bulls eye, the gold standard would be hitting the bulls eye.

Precision

When working in a research setting, any measurement you take will have some unpredictability about it. This degree of unpredictability relates to the amount of precision the tool selected for measurement has. Precision is related to the refinement of the measuring process. It is mainly concerned with how fine or small a difference the measuring device can detect. Precision is closely related to repeatability/reliability (see page 128).

An example involves measuring the bowling speed of Steve Harmison in the Ashes series using a speed gun and light gates. The speed gun gives you three speeds, all to the nearest mile per hour (e.g. 80mph, 81mph,

81mph). The light gates give you three speeds to the nearest tenth of a mile per hour (e.g. 79.9mph, 80.0mph, 79.9mph). Therefore, the light gates are more precise as they can detect a finer difference between values.

An easy way to get to grips with accuracy and precision is to think about target sports, such as archery. If you were to hit the bull's eye on the archery board with all of your arrows, you would say that you have been both accurate and precise. However, if you were to miss the board completely in all different directions with your arrows, you would say that you had been neither accurate nor precise.

Remember!

- For something to be precise, it does not have to be accurate.
- For something to be accurate, it does not have to be precise.
- Something can be both accurate and precise.
- Something can be neither accurate nor precise.

Assessment practice

1 Here is a sample data set from a baseball pitching investigation that looked at assessing the pitch speed of a baseball.

Pitcher	Speed recorded using a speed gun (mph)			Speed recorded using light gates (mph)		
A	89	90	92	90.1	90.2	90.1
B	94	97	96	95.2	95.4	95.3

Which method of recording speed is more precise? Explain why. **P2 M2**

2 Look at the table below. Your task is to explain why each diagram has been classified in this way. **P2 M2**

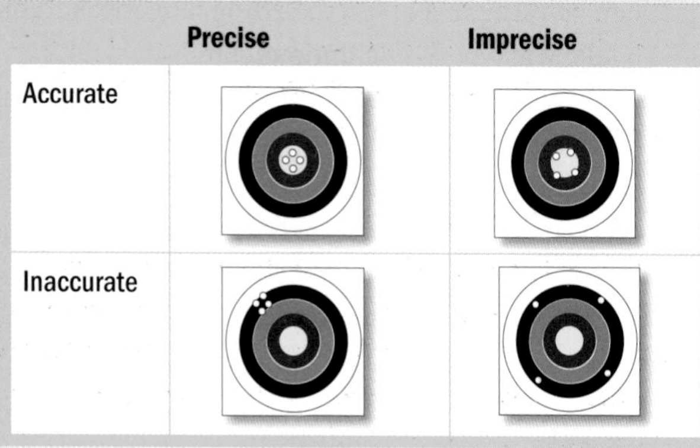

3 Produce a ten-minute PowerPoint® presentation with accompanying handouts, that looks at what research is and explains some of the key issues of research. Make sure you include the following details.

- A definition of research. **P1**
- A slide that describes, compares and contrasts qualitative and quantitative research. **P1 M1**
- A slide that describes and explains validity and the different types of validity using sport research- or exercise research-based examples. **P2 M2**
- A slide that describes and explains reliability and the different types of reliability using sport research- or exercise research-based examples. **P2 M2**
- A slide that describes and explains accuracy using sport research- or exercise research-based examples. **P2 M2**
- A slide that describes and explains precision using sport research- or exercise research-based examples. **P2 M2**

grading tips

Grading Tip

To achieve the higher grades, you need to include practical sport research- or exercise research-based examples to explain the different key issues in research methods.

Data

Primary

Primary data are data that you collect yourself through questionnaires, interviews, observations, etc. and which you use to investigate your research problem.

Secondary

Secondary data are previously published data that can be found in books, journals, government publications, websites and other forms of media. Secondary data are used to form rationale for your research and also to support or counter-argue your research findings.

Classifications of data

Discrete

Discrete data are a form of data where only separate, isolated or opposite values can be achieved (e.g. male/female, win/lose, yes/no).

Nominal data are sometimes referred to as discrete data, but there is an important difference between them. For nominal data, a number is assigned to a category and the number has no numerical value at all. It is simply assigned to that category for identification purposes.

For example:

- Discrete data: asking a simple question such as 'Do you take part in exercise?' Answer yes or no.
- Nominal data: recording male and female athletes in a table, allocating men the identification code 1 and women the identification code 2.

Ordinal

Ordinal data are ranked data that give no indication of the difference between levels. This type of data provides more information than nominal data, as they allow us to say who is best and second best, but they do not tell us the difference between the two. This type of data provides the researcher with a rank order, but they do not give an exact value. For example, on a table tennis ladder the person at the top is assigned a score of 1, the person second down is awarded a score of 2, the third person is awarded a score of 3, and so on. There is nothing to say that the person at the top of the ladder is three times as good as the person in third place on the ladder.

Continuous

Continuous data are data that can have any numerical value with any number of decimal places. Ratio and interval data are forms of continuous data. For example, lap times in a Formula One race can be classed as continuous data because of the values they are given (1 minute, 24.76 seconds).

Interval

Interval data are based on a scale that has equal intervals of measurement with equal intervals between each score. For example, in a figure skating scoring scale there is the same difference between scoring 5 and 5.5 as there is between scoring 5.5 and 6.

Ratio

Ratio data have proportional equal units of measurement. Ratio scales range from zero upwards and cannot have negative scores. For example, if a rugby team scores 40 points, it is worth twice as much as their opponents who have scored 20 points.

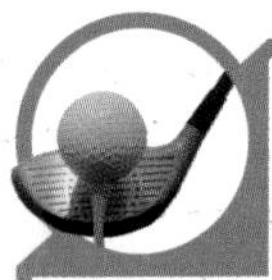

Think it over

Both interval and ratio data can be converted to ordinal or nominal data. How do you think this can be done?

Assessment practice

Produce an applied report that explains each of the types and classifications of data. Make sure you use practical sporting or exercise-related examples from a research setting to explain each type and classification. **P3**

grading tips

Grading Tip **P3**

Don't define only the different types and classifications of data – make sure you provide appropriate examples of each type and classification. It would be good if you could think of examples from both the sport and exercise domains.

Ethical and legal issues in research

British Association of Sport and Exercise Sciences (BASES) code of conduct

The British Association of Sport and Exercise Sciences (BASES) has produced a code of conduct that governs the way in which sport and exercise scientists work, both when working as practitioners and as researchers. The code of conduct outlines ethical and legal issues that are key to safe research within the sport and exercise sciences.

Key Term

BASES (The British Association of Sport and Exercise Sciences). BASES is the UK professional body for all those with an interest in the science of sport and exercise.

Ethical clearance

When conducting research, you need to make sure that you are working both ethically and legally. One of the first things you have to do before you can actually start is to gain ethical clearance from an appropriate body.

If you conduct any research as part of your course, ethical clearance will come from your tutor, college or school ethics committee. An ethics committee is an organisation that looks at your research proposal and says whether the project is safe and ethical. It will confirm whether you can start work on your project.

If you conduct research with athletes or sports teams, you may need to gain ethical clearance from an appropriate body such as BASES.

Informed consent

Once you have gained ethical approval for your research project, you need to get informed consent from your participants. This is both an ethical and a legal requirement of research. It can be verbal but it is safer for both you and your participant if you obtain it in writing. When you are seeking written informed consent from your client, you need to get them to read and sign a document (or have the document signed on their behalf in the case of children or vulnerable adults). The document normally includes:

- a description of the investigation
- details of the procedure to be followed
- details of any risks to the participant
- details of the potential benefits of taking part in the research
- a section that offers to answer any questions and confirms that any questions asked have been answered fully
- an indication that the participant is free to withdraw at any time without penalty
- a section that explains that any information collected about the participant will remain confidential.

An example of a blank informed consent form is shown on page 180.

Confidentiality/Data protection

Where confidentiality is concerned, you may disclose only information that is pertinent to the study you are conducting.

Any data you collect is protected under the terms of the Data Protection Act (1998). No data that makes the participants personally identifiable should be included in your research project. Data collected should be stored in a locked filing cabinet that is accessible only by you and your research supervisor.

Remember!

You should not store electronic versions of your data anywhere that is publicly accessible, nor should any data that make the participant personally identifiable be publicly displayed.

Activity

For a fitness test of your choice, produce an informed consent form.

Safety of the participants

When conducting research, the key concern is the safety of the participants. The researcher must maintain the highest professional standards so as not to endanger the participants or themselves. It is important that the researcher treats all participants equally and only works within their own area of competence.

Acting with due regard for equality and impartiality

In order to preserve the reputation of sport and exercise science, you must make sure that you remain totally unbiased in your actions and practices when you are working within sport and exercise science. This means that you cannot let factors such as race, age or gender affect the way you work with clients, you must not exploit personal relationships for personal gain, and you must make sure that any decisions you make are completely objective, (i.e. based purely on the facts presented to you rather than on your own opinions).;

Importance of ethical and legal issues

Ensure the welfare and safety of participants and the researcher

The ethical and legal guidelines are in place to maintain the safety of the participants and the researcher.

Ensure that researchers only work within area of expertise

If you think about some of the dangers that participants could be placed in through some areas of research, you will understand why the ethical and legal issues need to be in place so that researchers work only within their own areas of competence. For example, someone who had never used a syringe should not be allowed to take blood from participants.

Preserving and developing the reputation of the sport and exercise sciences

The guidelines also exist to promote excellence in sport and exercise sciences. This means that someone who works in a research capacity must be able to maintain the reputation of sport and exercise sciences by following the procedures.

Implications of not working within ethical and legal guidelines

The implications of not working within the ethical and legal procedures can be severe. The most obvious implication is that you are putting your participants' welfare and safety at risk. When working in a professional setting, if you do this there are a number of restrictions that can be placed on you.

Tribunals

If you do not work within ethical and legal guidelines, you could be subject to a tribunal which could lead to a fine, a written warning or you not being allowed to conduct research again.

Legal or civil action

If you work without due regard for ethical and legal issues within sport and exercise science, you are leaving yourself open to legal or civil action should something go wrong. You need to make sure that you follow the code of conduct to the letter when working in an applied setting, to ensure that you are not leaving yourself open to this type of action.

Measures to stop future research

When you are working as a member of BASES, you are subject to the BASES disciplinary procedure should you not work ethically and legally. You could be called before a tribunal where a group of BASES officers and the chair of BASES will review your particular case to find out if you have been working ethically and legally. From this tribunal, significant measures can be put in place to stop research temporarily or permanently, such as temporary suspension or permanent expulsion from BASES.

- Temporary suspension: you could be suspended from working under BASES for a fixed period of time as a result of the outcome of your tribunal. This means that you would not be able to function as a BASES accredited sport and exercise scientist for a period of time, with the opportunity for re-acceptance or a review after that time.
- Permanent expulsion: you could also be permanently excluded from working under BASES as a result of the outcome of your tribunal. This means that you will no longer be able to work as a BASES accredited sport and exercise scientist.

In both cases, you have a right of appeal against the decision made, within 14 days, to the BASES executive committee. The potential outcome of the appeal are a reduction of the punishment, confirmation of the punishment or an increase in the punishment.

Assessment practice

1. Go to the BASES website at www.bases.org.uk. Search for the BASES code of conduct and print a copy. Highlight all of the ethical and legal issues that you can identify. **P4**
2. Describe at least two ethical and legal issues. **P4**
3. Explain what could happen if you do not adhere to these guidelines in sport and exercise research. **M3**

4.2 Understand data collection techniques for the sport and exercise sciences

Qualitative techniques

Four main types of data collection are involved with qualitative research:

- interviews
- focus groups
- observation
- questionnaires (can be used in both qualitative and quantitative research – see page 139).

Each type of data collection method has its advantages and disadvantages. Read the text relating to each specific method for more information.

Interviews

An interview is a conversation that has a purpose. There are four main types of interview: structured, unstructured, semi-structured and focus groups.

Key Terms

Unstructured interview An interview with little structure. This type of interview could be a start question and you go from there. Generally, the direction of this type of interview comes from the way the conversation is going.

Semi-structured interview This is when there is a guide to follow, but there is an opportunity for the researcher to explore different issues that come up from the answers received (known as 'probing'). This is a good technique as it allows you to ensure that you get the information you want, as well as giving the participant the opportunity to discuss any relevant issues from questions that may arise.

Structured interview A set interview guide that you stick to without making any changes in the light of the participant's responses.

Focus group A group-based interview where the group interaction is an essential aspect of data collection. Focus groups, by the nature of the task, tend to be semi-structured.

No one type of interview is ideal, it needs to be matched to the situation or participant. Interviews are used frequently in qualitative research because they are a useful way for researchers to understand the beliefs, opinions, emotions and understandings of participants. They are particularly useful because the researcher gets a view of what the participant thinks in the participant's own words. This gives the researcher a greater understanding of the meanings that the participants can attach to their experiences of various events.

Interviews are used often within qualitative research as they are a good way to get a lot of information about a specific topic quickly, but this only works if you have developed your interview skills. In interviews, you will only ever get answers to the questions you ask. Therefore, if you ask the wrong questions, or the wrong types of questions, you will never find out what you want.

If you want to get the most out of an interview, you should first establish some form of relationship with your participant. You could do this by setting the tone of the interview by having a friendly chat before you start. Another way is to break the ice with more general questions at the start of the interview, which don't require too much thought or effort to answer. If you can do this and then progress to more specific questions, you are more likely to get more detailed responses.

In order to get the most out of an interview, guide the conversation around your research problem. Gently probe the participant further, and try to get them to provide you with examples of things they have actually experienced, rather than hypothetical examples.

A summary of the pros and cons of using interviews is shown in the table on page 136.

Remember!

Make sure you ask both open and closed questions in your interviews.

Key Terms

Open question A question that allows participants to answer in their own words, which makes them feel more confident and gives an option to use examples. Open questions are often put at the beginning of an interview or questionnaire in order to warm up participants.

Closed question A question with a limited number of logical answers (e.g. Yes or No).

Think it over

A leading question is when you try to guide your participant towards the answer you want to hear. If you guide a participant towards the answer you want, you are getting them to give your answer, instead of their own. What validity and reliability issues are there in leading questions?

Advantages	Disadvantages
Participants can express their views in their own words	Require more resources and are more time-consuming than using questionnaires
Participants can provide information from their own perspective	Tend to use small sample sizes as interviews are time-consuming
Unexpected data may come out in the interview	The participant can take the interview off in a number of directions
Body language, tone and pitch of voice, and speed of speech can be assessed	Data analysis is more difficult and takes longer than using questionnaires
The researcher can establish a rapport with the participant and investigate target groups	Quality of data is dependent on the quality of the questioning and quality of responses

Advantages and disadvantages of interviews

Transcribing interviews

You need to record the interview process. There are a number of ways of doing this, including recording key points on paper, recording the interview using some form of audio recording (e.g. dictaphone, mini-disc player) or using some form of visual recorder (e.g. video camcorder, DVD camcorder). A benefit of using a visual recorder over an audio recorder is that you can also record when the participant's body language changes throughout the interview. Unfortunately, when you use a visual recorder any changes in body language can be because of the presence of the recorder rather than the importance of what the participant is saying.

Informed consent and data protection are important, particularly with visual and audio recorders. To record the interview, you must have the permission of the participant and you must have planned a way to protect your data.

When transcribing the interview, it is best to do this word for word, including any pauses. You could also make notes about any changes in body language, which can help you to investigate further the meaning behind statements made.

Interview techniques

When interviewing, a three-stage technique is often used in research.

1. The researcher asks the main guiding question (e.g. 'What motivates you to...?'). This 'gets the ball rolling'.
2. This is followed up with probe questions (e.g. 'Can you give me a specific example of…?'). This clarifies or deepens understanding or knowledge.
3. The final aspect is a follow-up question (e.g. 'So, am I correct in saying that…?'). This gives the researcher the opportunity to ensure they have understood what the participant has said and that it is taken in the correct context.

The listening part of interviews is just as important as the speaking part. A good interviewer knows when to keep quiet and listen and when to speak. Make sure you do not interrupt the participant when they are speaking as this can prevent them from wanting to answer further questions.

Theory into practice

Work with a partner. Ask them to talk to you for two minutes about something they have done recently that is of interest to them. Listen to what they say, without taking any notes, and then repeat the story back in as much detail as you can. Ask them to highlight any points you missed.

Remember!

Listening is just as important as speaking during interviews. Make sure you listen to what your participant is saying and pick up as many details as you can.

Activity

Produce an interview guide about any sport- or exercise-related topic you are interested in. Try to include a range of questions (e.g. open and closed) and structure the interview how you like (e.g. unstructured, semi-structured or structured). At the end of your interview guide, produce an analysis of why the type of interview you have chosen was suitable, giving reasons why it was better than the other options.

Focus groups

Focus groups are similar to interviews, but they involve more than one participant at the same time. There are usually between 6 and 12 participants and the researcher acts as a discussion facilitator rather than an interviewer. In this context, your role as the researcher is to make sure that the focus group stays on topic and isn't allowed to wander.

Focus groups are more effective if everyone has a say in the discussion. They can provide you with a better quality of data because the discussion can get deeper as the group develops ideas. They are a good way of finding out opinions and ideas.

■ Transcribing focus groups

Focus groups are harder to record than interviews. When you record focus groups, try to video record them rather than just using audio, as this will allow you to see which member has contributed which comments. You could also have an assistant with you who can take notes during the focus group. They will be able to concentrate on the key points that come out through the research.

To transcribe the recordings, the techniques are similar to interviews (see page 136). However, you need to make sure you say which member is making each comment.

Activity

Produce a focus group guide about any sport- or exercise-related topic you are interested in. Run a focus group based on that particular topic. Get six of your friends to be participants in the focus group. Ask another friend to act as your research assistant, taking down any key points in relation to the topic.

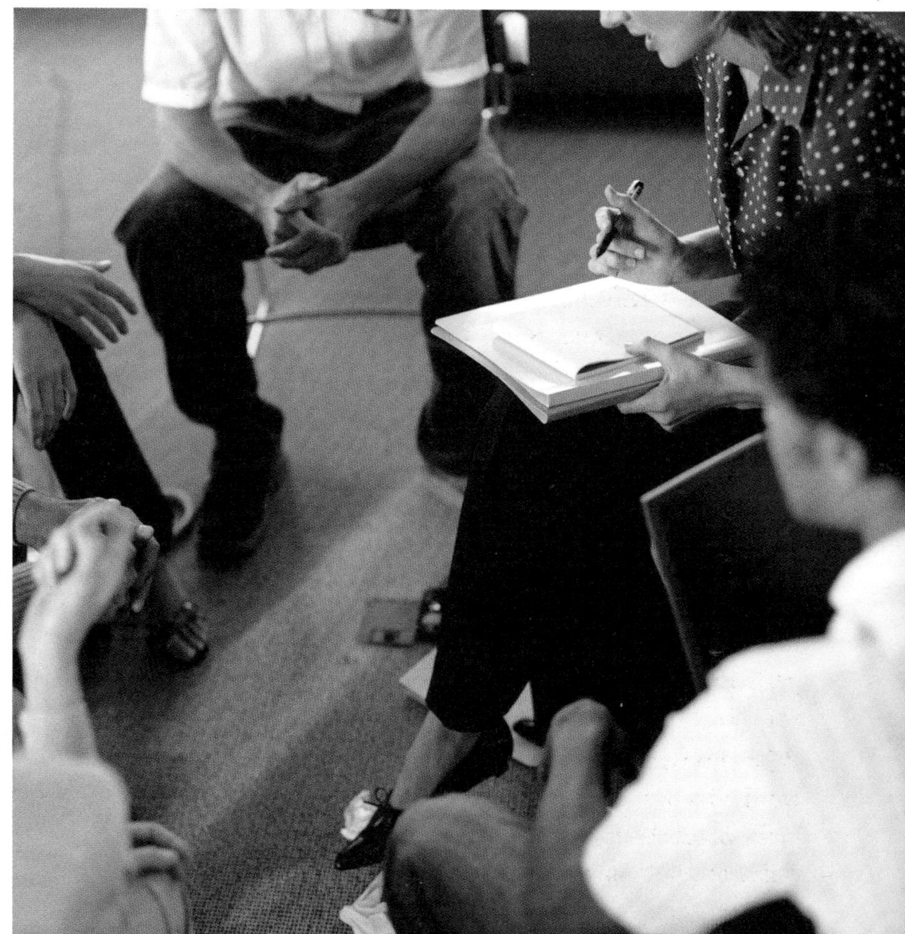

Focus groups are a good way of doing group-based interviews to find opinions and ideas ▶

Observation

Two main types of observation are used in qualitative research: participant and non-participant.

■ Participant observation

Participant observation means that the researcher is actively involved in the topic they are researching. For example, if a researcher was studying team cohesion in rugby, they could go and join a rugby team, so that they can observe 'from the inside' and gain their own experiences of cohesion as a player. Data would then be recorded in the form of field notes, with the researcher recording their own thoughts, feelings, opinions, emotions and experiences. This method is useful when trying to discover the more delicate aspects of group behaviour that are not easy to see from the outside.

■ Non-participant observation

Non-participant observation is more simple than participant observation. It involves the researcher observing 'from the outside'. There is no interaction with either the individuals or the activity the researcher is observing.

For example, if someone wanted to look at basketball match attendances, they could watch how many people entered the arena and record the numbers on an appropriate data recording sheet.

A summary of the advantages and disadvantages of observation is shown below.

■ Recording observational data

Observation checklists and field notes are methods of recording data in observational research.

Observation checklists are used more frequently in quantitative research, or in qualitative research for observing more simple forms of data. For example, if you were observing a young developing footballer while researching two-footedness in football, you could use an observation checklist similar to the one below.

Tick the box each time the behaviour occurred

Player number						
Controlled ball left foot						
Controlled ball right foot						
Passed ball left foot						
Passed ball right foot						
Shot left foot						
Shot right foot						
Shifted ball from left foot to right foot						
Shifted ball from right foot to left foot						

Field notes are more commonly used in qualitative data collection than in quantitative data collection. They allow the researcher to record observations they make. They are more flexible than observation checklists and allow

Advantages	Disadvantages
Observations can be 'Here and now' rather than being dependent on recall	Potential for the researcher to misunderstand what they are seeing
They can take place in natural settings rather than research settings	Difficult to identify and record the correct type of data
They allow for the identification of behaviours that may not be apparent to the person and may not have been discovered through interviews	Hawthorne effect: If the person knows they are the subject of research, they will act differently and invalidate the whole project – the researcher must be very careful exactly how they approach the people in observation research
They allow for the identification of behaviours that the person may not wish to disclose	

Advantages and disadvantages of observations

Activity

1 Using the above observation checklist as a guide (page 138), produce a checklist of your own so that you can complete an observation of your chosen sport. Remember that you need to decide on exactly what you want to observe before you can produce your checklist.

2 When you have produced your checklist, conduct an observation of your sport and assess the usefulness of your observation checklist.

you to collect more complex data. Field notes should include the following:

- Descriptive notes that tell you about the setting the research is taking place in, the participants that are the subject of research and how they behave in a particular setting.
- Detailed notes to help you remember certain details over time.
- Reflective notes (a key to successful observational research) should contain the researcher's thoughts, opinions, beliefs, evaluations and experiences and form an integral aspect of the data analysis.

Remember!

It is important that your notes are detailed enough in case you forget some of the information before data analysis.

Benefits and limitations of each type of data collection method

Each method of data collection has advantages and disadvantages (see the information above about each method for more details).

Quantitative techniques

Several data collection techniques can be used for quantitative data collection. We have already discussed how observations (see page 138) can be used in both qualitative and quantitative research, so don't forget about this technique when you are thinking about quantitative research.

Other types of technique that are used in quantitative research include questionnaires, field-based data collection and laboratory-based data collection.

Questionnaires

Questionnaires are generally suitable when you are trying to collect a large amount of data from large groups. They are suitable when the data you want to collect is not too in-depth. If you do need to obtain more in-depth information, questionnaires would not be suitable on their own. However, they could be effective if they are used in conjunction with other qualitative methods of data collection (such as interviews). When you start to design your questionnaire, you need to consider a number of factors.

- You need to decide what you want to find out.
- You need to decide on your sample, as this will affect how you will write your questionnaire.
- You need to bear in mind the length and appearance of your questionnaire when you design it, and try not to make it too long or difficult to answer.
- You need to decide how and when you are going to give out your questionnaire. If you are going to distribute it by hand, it is often best to wait for it to be completed rather than going away and returning later. Another way you can distribute your questionnaire is by post or email, but this can reduce the chances of it being returned. Include a return address and a covering letter to explain why your questionnaire is being sent out.
- You need to decide on the best way to analyse the results. The following table outlines the benefits and limitations of using questionnaires.

Advantages	Disadvantages
They are people-friendly if the form is designed correctly	Questions can be too complex if the form is designed incorrectly
They are an opportunity to reduce participant bias	There are control issues
The participant can be anonymous	There is no opportunity for probing questions
The data are structured	There is a potential for a low response rate
They are usually accessible to most people	

Advantages and disadvantages of questionnaires

Types of questionnaire

Open questions

Open questions are usually used more in qualitative research than in quantitative research. They allow people to express ideas, opinions and sentiments in words. They are also used when you are asking questions that could lead to more complex or in-depth answers, or if you are unsure of what the answers to the question could be. Open questions can take a lot longer to answer than closed questions, so you need to make sure that you plan your research effectively to account for this. Here are some examples:

- What do you think makes a good football player?
- What are your thoughts on the promotion of disability sport within the UK?
- How do you feel about the way female athletes are portrayed in the media?

Closed questions

Closed questions are usually used when a specific response is required and answers generally involve ranking, scales or categories. These questions are used more in quantitative data collection as they generate numbers for you to analyse using statistical methods. The participants respond to a set of answers that the researcher has included on the questionnaire. The responses are usually in less depth than those from open questions. Here are some examples:

- Do you like playing rugby? Yes/No
- Which of the following do you prefer? Running in the park/Road running/Running on a treadmill
- How many times do you exercise per week?

Questionnaire design

Remember!

When writing your questionnaire, bear in mind that people usually don't enjoy filling them in! So you need to make sure your questionnaire is attractive enough to hold your participants' attention.

You need to make sure that all questions have a purpose, and you are not asking for information you don't need.

If your questionnaire looks poorly organised and unprofessional, it will probably be thrown away, particularly if you decide to post them. If it looks well organised and purposeful, you have a better chance of it being completed.

The use of coloured paper, artistic designs, dotted lines and tick boxes are all recommended, but make sure that your design is geared towards the audience it is aimed at. For example, make it easy and simple to use for young children.

When designing your questionnaire, remember that if it is more than one page long it is much less likely to be filled in – so don't make it longer than it needs to be.

Always consider why you are asking a particular question. This will prevent you from including unnecessary questions and the quality of your questionnaire will increase as its validity increases. Then decide which format would be most appropriate for the question you want to ask. Should it be an open question or a closed question?

Remember!

1 Make sure the first questions are straightforward and ask for facts.
2 Don't put questions that require lengthy answers at the start.
3 Leave personal or potentially sensitive questions to the end.
4 Group questions with a similar theme or topic together.
5 Don't ask leading questions.
6 Don't include questions that ask for responses on two different topics (these are known as 'double-barrelled' questions).
7 Be simple and clear – don't use over-complex wording.
8 Use appropriate paper and colours to make it attractive to your audience.
9 Use tick boxes to make it easy to fill in.
10 Don't make the questionnaire too long.

Activity

1 Produce a questionnaire that allows you to find out what people feel prevents them from being physically active.
2 Include questions on the design of the questionnaire as well.
3 Give out your questionnaire.
4 Look at the responses to the questions and comments regarding the design of the questionnaire.
5 Redesign your questionnaire, taking into account the comments given by your participants.

Laboratory-based data collection

Laboratory-based data collection involves collecting data in an environment where all of the conditions are controlled, so that you are only measuring the variables in question.

Key Terms

Construct validity This is when you are able to relate the results to some form of behaviour after measuring some form of theoretical construct.

Logical validity You can claim logical validity (sometimes known as face validity) when your research obviously measures what it intends to measure, without being affected by outside influences.

Ecological validity This is when your research can be applied to real-world settings because of the way the data are collected.

This type of data collection has less ecological validity than field-based data collection, because the data are not being collected in a situation that reflects the situation in which the activity is performed.

However, you could claim more construct validity and logical validity because you have made sure that you have isolated the variables you are measuring.

Laboratory-based data collection normally requires the use of expensive or technical equipment to collect data.

For example, if you wanted to measure the VO_2 maximum of an athlete, you could do this using field-based or laboratory-based data collection methods. If you wanted to measure VO_2 maximum in a field-based way, you could do this indirectly using a multi-stage fitness test to get an indirect prediction of VO_2 maximum.

On the other hand, if you wanted to test in a laboratory setting, you could use a Douglas Bag and gas analysis system to collect the athlete's expired air. This air could then be analysed and the results used to calculate VO_2 maximum rather than relying on a (field-based) prediction.

Field-based data collection

Field-based data collection is data that are collected in the environment that simulates the one in which the sport is played.

For example, if you wanted to investigate the effects of imagery on football penalty shooting, you could collect the data on a football pitch outside, regardless of the conditions (e.g. if it were windy and raining you would still collect your data because sometimes when you play football it is windy and rainy).

You might also want to an audience present to match a real-life situation. This would allow you to say that your research had more ecological (real-world) validity, because you have collected the data in an environment that replicates the match situation. This type of data collection is less controlled than laboratory-based data collection.

Research designs

A number of research designs are used within sport and exercise sciences. Some of the most common that you will need to have an understanding of in the early stages of your research careers are experimental research, cross-sectional research, case study research, longitudinal research and comparative research.

Experimental

The aim of experimental research is to look at the effects of an independent variable on a dependent variable.

For example, an athletics coach wants to find out if her lower back flexibility training is benefiting the athlete's high jump performance. She has asked you to research the topic for her.

In order to investigate the effects of flexibility, you need to identify which is the independent variable and which is the dependent variable.

The independent variable affects the dependent variable. As the coach wants to find out if flexibility affects performance, flexibility is the independent variable and performance is the dependent variable.

Therefore, you would ask the athlete to complete some form of task (e.g. high jump performance). He would then complete a specific lower-back flexibility training programme and follow this up with a repeat of the initial task. You would then be able to see if the results were significantly different after the flexibility training programme using an appropriate method of statistical analysis such as the Wilcoxen matched pairs signed ranks test.

Key Term

Variable This is something you measure.

Remember!

The **independent** variable affects the **dependent** variable.

For example, when looking at the effects of the amount of game experience a young developing basketball player has on their confidence in new games situations, confidence would be the dependent variable and game experience would be the independent variable – game experience affects confidence.

Cross-sectional

Cross-sectional research involves using a range of participants with different backgrounds, ages, and genders from the overall population.

After you have sampled your participants, you would conduct your data collection, usually through survey-type questionnaires or interviews.

You would then conduct data analysis and form conclusions that can then be related back to the general population.

For example, if you want to look at preferences for team sports or individual sports in people in the UK, cross-sectional research would be useful. This would allow you to obtain opinions from a range of people. You would send your participants a survey-type questionnaire that would allow them to say which type of sport they preferred. Then you would be able to produce some descriptive statistics for the results of the study (e.g. 73 per cent of men prefer team sports, 20 per cent of men prefer individual sports and 7 per cent of men had no preference).

Case study

Case study research is where you investigate a particular phenomenon (i.e. an individual or team) over a long period of time. Case study research takes into account both the development of the area of investigation over time and the environment in which the research resides.

For example, to investigate the psychological effects of injury at different stages of injury and recovery, a case study design would be suitable. It allows you to investigate one person over a period of time and at different times throughout the stages of injury. This means you can draw conclusions relating to that particular individual and then suggest these conclusions as directions for future research on a larger scale.

Longitudinal

Longitudinal research involves measuring the same variables over a long period of time.

It can take years to complete and sometimes requires greater resources than other types of research, so you need to be careful when approaching this design. Longitudinal research is useful if you want to examine the developmental characteristics of a group.

For example, to investigate factors associated with talent development in a particular sport, longitudinal research would be a good way of doing this. It would allow you to focus completely on developmental issues over an extended period of time.

For example, a popular topic within sport sciences is to look at factors that affect talent development in different sports. A good way to investigate this would be by using longitudinal research covering the development of the athlete (e.g. from the ages of 3–16 years old).

Follow-up studies would be used at intervals (e.g. ages 5, 7, 9, 11, 13 and 15) to investigate the factors that have been shown to influence development, such as the influence of parents and maturation factors.

Key Term

Longitudinal This means that you research your topic, subject or group of interest over a long period of time, which can range from several months to many years.

Comparative

In comparative research, the researcher compares two or more things with the aim of finding something about one of or all of the things being compared.

This technique often uses multiple disciplines in one study and this approach can often make comparative research very flexible.

Assessment practice

For the following research problems, identify an appropriate research design and analyse your choices.

1 The effects of imagery training on basketball free-throw shooting performance.

2 Gender differences in team and individual sporting participation.

3 The influence of parents on player development in ice hockey. M4 M5 D1 D2

grading tips

Grading Tip 

You need to say why the research design you have chosen is suitable. Then discuss why the design you have selected is better than others that you could have used.

4.3 Understand qualitative data analysis techniques for the sport and exercise sciences

Stages of data analysis

Although there is no single accepted method of analysing qualitative data, data analysis in qualitative research follows three procedures.

- Reducing the data into manageable sizes: this is something that should start as soon as your first batch of data is collected. It involves reducing the large amounts of data that you could potentially have through qualitative research into more manageable chunks. At this stage, you develop codes for your data and get rid of any data that you see as irrelevant.
- Displaying your data: this is where you start to draw your initial conclusion on the data you have collected using tables, charts and diagrams.
- Drawing conclusions and verifying data: this is where you finalise your data analysis and draw your conclusions of the research. Your conclusions can then be checked for validity. Once this process has been completed, your data analysis is finished.

Data reduction

The most common form of data analysis in the data reduction stage is coding. If you choose to conduct a qualitative research project, you will be expected to effectively code your data as part of your data analysis. Coding is when you organise raw data (sentences, phrases or words from your questionnaires or interviews) into various categories. The categories are given a valid heading and must have a rule for inclusion.

Having a rule for inclusion helps to guide which data you place in each category. For example, if you were researching 'factors affecting talent development in football', you could have a category called 'importance of parental tangible support'. Your rule for inclusion could be 'statement made refers to concrete support given to player from parent (e.g. the purchase of playing kit or transport to matches) being either a positive or negative influence on the player's development'.

Key Term

Categories Raw data are placed into categories. The easiest way to think of a category is that it is a like a file into which you put all of the words, sentences or phrases from your data collection that are related to each other.

Remember!

You should have a rule for inclusion for all of the categories that you use.

■ Coding

Coding techniques are simple to use when you get used to them. When you are coding data, all you are doing is breaking it all down into manageable chunks. You then put it back together in parts that relate to each other, before making sure that all of your categories are valid. Coding involves the line-by-line analysis of data in minute detail and is used to generate categories. Coding involves three stages: open coding, axial coding and selective coding.

Open coding

In open coding, data are broken down and examined. Your aim is to identify all of the key statements made in the interviews that relate to the aims of your research and your research problem. After you have identified all of the key statements, you can start to put some of the key points that relate to each other into categories, but you will need to give each category a suitable heading to be able to do this. When you start to organise your data under different categories, you have started the coding process.

Axial coding

After the open coding stage, the next stage is to start to put the data back together again. Part of this process means rereading the data you have collected because the idea is that you begin to make more precise explanations about your particular area of interest. To do this, you need to be able to refine the categories that you started to create during open coding. During this stage you may also develop new categories. To allow you to refine your codes at this stage, start asking more questions about the categories (and thus the codes) you have created. Some questions you may want to consider are:

- Can I relate certain codes together under a more general code?
- Can I place codes into a particular order?
- Can I identify any relationships between different codes?

Selective coding

Selective coding is the final stage of coding. This stage involves aiming to finalise your categories (and codes) so that you can start to group them together. When you group them together, you will produce different diagrams to show how your categories link together. The key part of this is to select a main category, which will form the centre of your diagram. You also need to try to look for data that contradict previous research, rather than data that supports it. This will help you to make good arguments in your discussion section of the research project and draw more conclusions based on your data.

Your aim through your data collection and data analysis in qualitative research is to achieve a condition known as data saturation.

Key Term

Data saturation This occurs when new data collected does not give you any new information. This is something to be aimed for during qualitative research, as this is the point where you know you don't need to collect any more data.

Other techniques

■ Non-numerical unstructured data indexing, searching and theorising (NVivo7, ATLAS/ti)

Other qualitative data analysis techniques include non-numerical unstructured data indexing, searching and theorising (NVivo7) and ATLAS/ti, which are electronic programmes designed to analyse data. It is unlikely that you will need to use these at this early stage in your research career – it is better for you to learn the skills of manual data handling, so that you can understand how to analyse your data.

NVivo7 and ATLAS/ti can deal with textual data, graphical data, audio data, video data and photographs. They can allow the data that you have collected to be analysed quickly, but there are a number of issues relating to the use of this type of electronic-data analysis systems.

- First, it is important to learn how to handle data manually. If you use only electronic data analysis programmes, you will not get a 'feel' for your data – an important part of the learning process.
- Another problem is that they do not contextualise the data (as you do through manual data analysis).
- Finally, these data analysis programmes can be complicated. They can take a lot of time to learn how to use – often longer than manually conducting the data analysis.

Key Terms

Textual data Written data in the form of words, phrases and sentences.

Graphical data Non-written data in the form of graphs and charts.

Audio data Sound recordings of qualitative data.

Video data Video recordings of qualitative data.

Contextualise To contextualise something, you apply a meaning to it, possibly by placing it into a particular setting using examples.

Activity

Using the interview guide you planned as part of the activity on page 137, conduct your interview with a friend who is interested in that topic. When you have completed the interview, transcribe and code your interview using the coding techniques outlined one page 145. This will take some time – don't worry if you think it is taking a while!

Displaying data

Network diagrams

These can be used to display your information. It is important that you select the appropriate type of diagram to get across your argument effectively. If you use the wrong diagram, you could be saying one thing with your words and something else with your diagram.

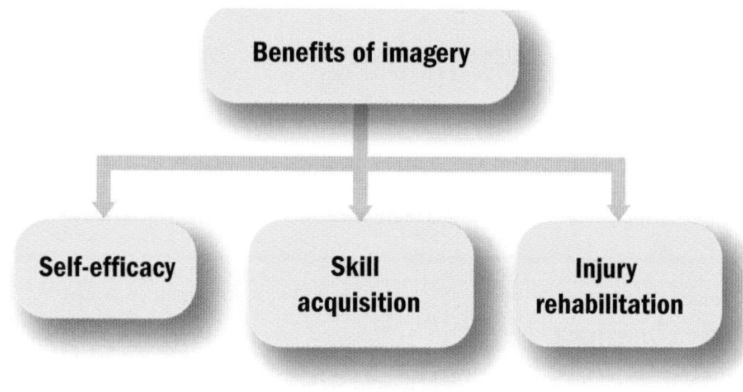

▲ A network diagram

Venn diagrams

Venn diagrams are made up of two or more overlapping circles. They show how different topics relate to each other. In the example below, you can see how the different disciplines within the sport and exercise sciences interact to make up the overall discipline.

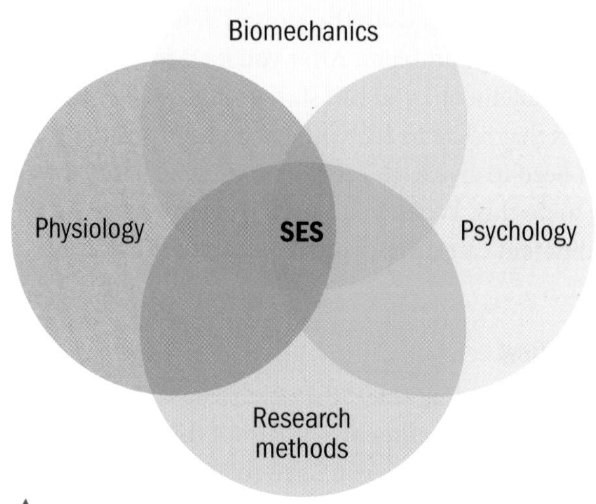

▲ A Venn diagram

Radial diagrams

A radial diagram (or spider diagram) illustrates a relationship where each item is linked to a central item. This diagram can be thought of as a simple organisation chart that starts from the centre rather than the top. These diagrams are useful for showing items in relation to a core element. A radial diagram flows from the outside in or the inside out.

▲ A radial diagram (or spider diagram)

Cycle diagrams

A cycle diagram is used to show the stages in a process with a continuous cycle. The process is shown as a circle, with a break at each stage, with an arrowhead to show the direction of the process. In the example below, the diagram shows that team cohesion affects team performance, which in turn affects team cohesion further, and so on.

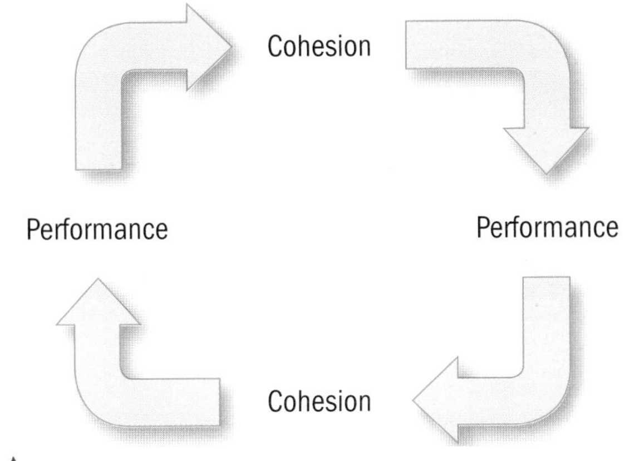

▲ A cycle diagram

Activity

Using the data analysis you conducted as part of the activity on page 141, produce suitable diagrams to display your conclusions. You are not limited on the number of diagrams you can use, but make sure that you plan exactly how and why you will be using the type of diagram you have selected.

Drawing conclusions and verifying data

In qualitative research, there are many ways to ensure the data you collect is valid and reliable. The most commonly-used methods are triangulation and member checking.

Triangulation

Triangulation refers to combining several different methods of inquiry and data collection in a single study. The rationale is that each method reveals different aspects of empirical data, and serves as a check for internal validity (see page 127). Triangulation helps to avoid errors linked to a particular method by using multiple methods in which different types of data can be used to provide cross-validity.

Key Term

Empirical data Based on experiment and observation or practical experience, not on a theory.

Triangulation can be achieved by using different sources of data, such as a combination of interviews, participant observation and questionnaires. Alternatively, several researchers could be employed to draw their own conclusions on the same set of data. If the data collected through the different sources create the same findings, or if multiple researchers draw the same (or similar) conclusions, the research can claim to be valid.

Triangulation may sound easy to achieve, for example combining data collected in fieldwork interviews with focus groups. In practice, however, it can be difficult to combine data collected using different methods.

■ Member checking

For member checking (or member validation), the researcher completes the data analysis and draws out the final conclusions relating to the aims of the study. The researcher then shows the analysis to the participants who took part in the research. Their reactions to the analysis are then incorporated into the study findings.

The purpose of showing the conclusions to the participants is that they can check to make sure that the researcher has correctly interpreted the collected data with reference to the aims. If they decide that the researcher's analysis is correct, the researcher can claim that the data is valid.

Assessment practice

Imagine you want to conduct a qualitative study into different psychological factors involved with talent development in sport. Ideally, you would like to look at this across a range of sports, over an extended period of time, and with a variety of age ranges and experience.

1 Describe the three main data collection techniques used for qualitative research. **P5**

2 For the project outlined above, justify which data collection technique (or techniques) you think would be useful and explain why. **M4**

3 Say which research design you think would be most suitable for this project and explain why. **D1**

4 Describe the three main stages of data analysis in qualitative research. Say which you feel would be appropriate for this particular study. It may also be useful for you to look at how you will make sure the data you collect are valid and reliable. **P7**

grading tips

Grading Tip 

Make sure you discuss all the different data collection techniques (e.g. interviews, focus groups, questionnaires, observations).

Grading Tip M4

Make sure that you use details from the project to justify why the data collection techniques you have selected are suitable.

Grading Tip 

Say why and how the research methods you have selected are suitable for the project.

Grading Tip 

Describe all three stages of data analysis (data reduction, displaying data, and drawing conclusions and verifying data) using the different research methods that are used at each stage.

4.4 Understand quantitative data analysis techniques for the sport and exercise sciences

Statistics can be a frightening prospect, however, they are more time-consuming than difficult, and it is likely you have seen and done some of these methods before. A good tip is to change all the letters in the formula into the numbers you will be working with, and then rewrite the equation using the numbers There are two types of statistics: descriptive and inferential.

Key Terms

Descriptive statistics These are used to simply to describe what is going on in your data. They describe the basic features of the data in a study. They provide simple summaries about the sample and the measures. Together with simple graphics analysis, they form the basis of virtually every quantitative analysis of data.

Inferential statistics We use inferential statistics to make inferences from our data to more general conditions. For example, we use inferential statistics to try to infer from the sample data what the population might think.

Organising data

Range

Range is a simple method of organising your data. It is simply the distance in numerical value from the highest to the lowest value collected. You calculate the range by subtracting the lowest number from the highest number.

Activity

A fitness instructor has assessed 15 people on the one-minute press up test. Using the raw data below, calculate the range of scores.

23, 26, 31, 29, 20, 33, 39, 41, 22, 28, 27, 35, 32, 30, 31

Rank order distribution

Rank order distribution means placing your data into an ordered list in a single column. Rank order distribution is used when the total number of participants is less than or equal to 20 ($n \leq 20$). In order to use rank order distribution, you place all your raw data in numerical order from the lowest to the highest in a single column, making sure you include all of the scores.

Activity

A fitness instructor has assessed 12 people on the sit-and-reach test. Using the raw data below, produce a rank order distribution list of the scores.

17.2, 16.3, 15.8, 17.9, 15.2, 16.4, 16.8, 17.0, 15.1, 16.1, 16.5, 15.7

Simple frequency distribution

This technique is known as simple frequency distribution because it is less complex than grouped frequency distribution.

At times, the amount of data collected will be too large to place into rank order distribution. Simple frequency distribution is used when the total number of participants is greater than 20 ($n > 20$) and when the range is less than or equal to 20 ($r \leq 20$).

You use simple frequency distribution with a table that has two columns, one for raw data scores (X) and one for frequency scores (f). The frequency column is the number of times that particular score was achieved.

Here is an example of how to lay out your data. A basketball coach is looking at the number of free throws missed in each game over a season. He has 25 games to assess ($n > 20$) and the number of missed shots per game ranges from 1 to 7 ($r \leq 20$), so simple frequency distribution is suitable. The data are set out as shown below.

Number of missed shots (X)	Frequency (f)
7	3
6	5
5	14
3	2
1	1
	n = 25

Basketball shots missed throughout the season

Grouped frequency distribution

In quantitative research, it is common to work with ranges greater than 21 ($r > 21$) and more than 20 participants ($n > 20$). This is when grouped frequency distribution is used.

The table has two columns. The X column is for groups of scores and the f column is for frequency. In order to keep your data on a single sheet of paper, you normally have between 10 and 20 groups of scores – the ideal number is 15. You also need to decide on the interval size for each group, which is calculated using the formula i = range ÷ 15.

Here is an example. An athletics coach is looking at the times recorded (in seconds) by her trialists wanting to represent the college at 5,000m. She has 30 times to look at ranging from 900 seconds to 1,094 seconds. Grouped frequency distribution is a suitable method because both $r > 21$ and $n > 20$. The interval size for group is 13 seconds (r = 194 seconds; 193 ÷ 15 = 12.93 seconds, which is rounded up to 13). The data are shown above.

Time (X)	Frequency (f)
1,082–1,094	1
1,068–1,081	1
1,054–1,067	1
1,040–1,053	1
1,026–1,039	5
1,012–1,025	8
998–1,011	3
984–997	2
970–983	2
956–969	1
942–955	1
928–941	1
914–927	1
900–913	2
	n = 30

5,000m run times (seconds)

Professional football clubs use statistics to judge how well players have performed and to help to decide whether they should be selected for games

Although using grouped frequency distribution is a useful way of organising large amounts of data, some information is lost through this process. Once scores have been placed into groups, it is impossible to say which athlete has achieved which score. For example, if you look at the 1,012–1,025 seconds row in the table, it is only possible to identify that eight athletes fell within that range, rather than the individual scores achieved.

Displaying data

There are a number of ways you can display your data and it is your choice on which methods you select.

Graphs

A graph or chart is a visual display of data. They are used in quantitative research methods to compare two sets of data. The minimum information you need on a graph or a chart is a title, an *x* axis and a *y* axis. You normally put the scores on the *x* axis (the line along the bottom) and the frequency of those scores on the y axis (the line up the side). On the *x* axis, the data should range from the lowest score on the left-hand side of the line to the highest score on the right-hand side of the line. On the *y* axis, the smallest frequency goes at the bottom of the line and the highest frequency goes at the top of the line.

Histograms

A histogram is a vertical block graph with no spaces between the blocks. It is used to represent frequency distribution data. The range of the variable is divided into class intervals, for which the frequency of occurrence is represented by a rectangular column. The height of the column is proportional to the frequency of observations within the interval.

The histogram below is based on the data in the table on page 150.

Bar charts

A bar chart is a chart that shows the interrelation of two or more sets of data using bars. The bars can be either vertical or horizontal, and 2D or 3D.

Remember!

When using bar charts, the highest value is not always the best score. For example, a sprinter whose speeds produce the biggest bar on a chart will actually have the slowest time.

▼ **A histogram**

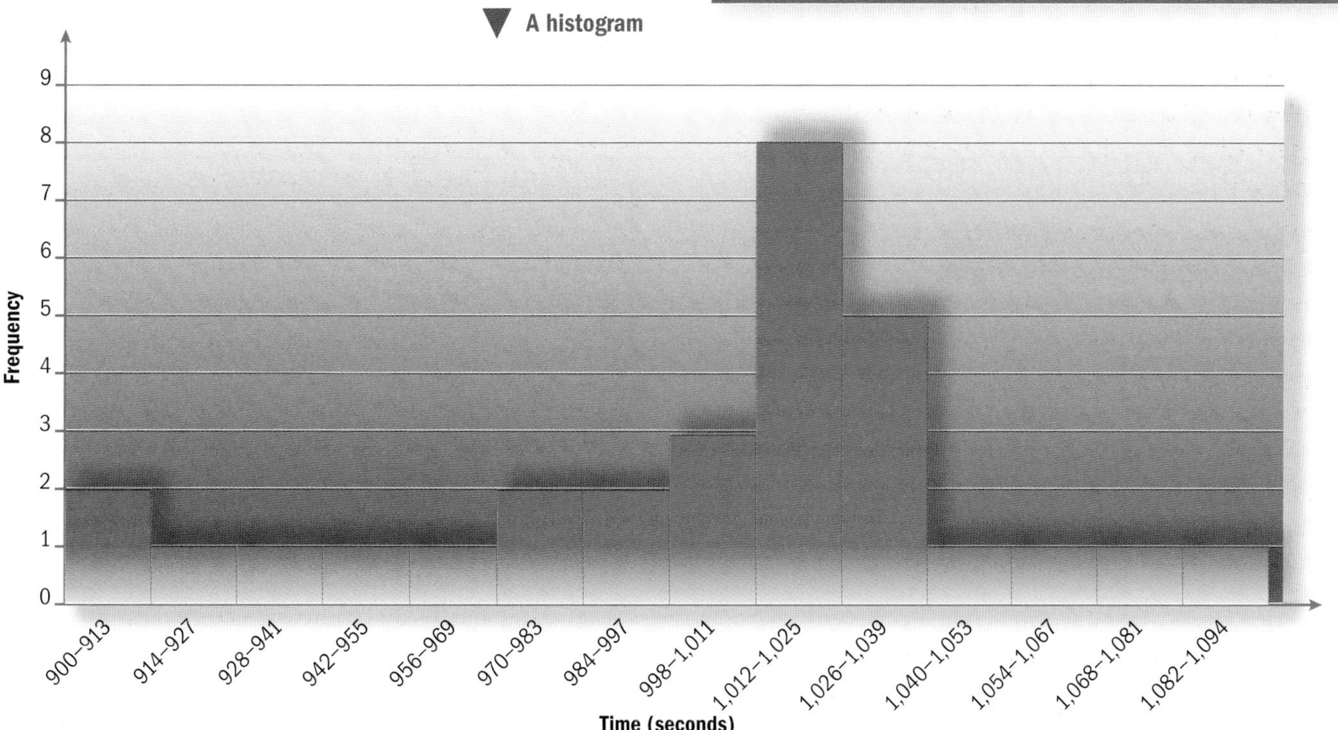

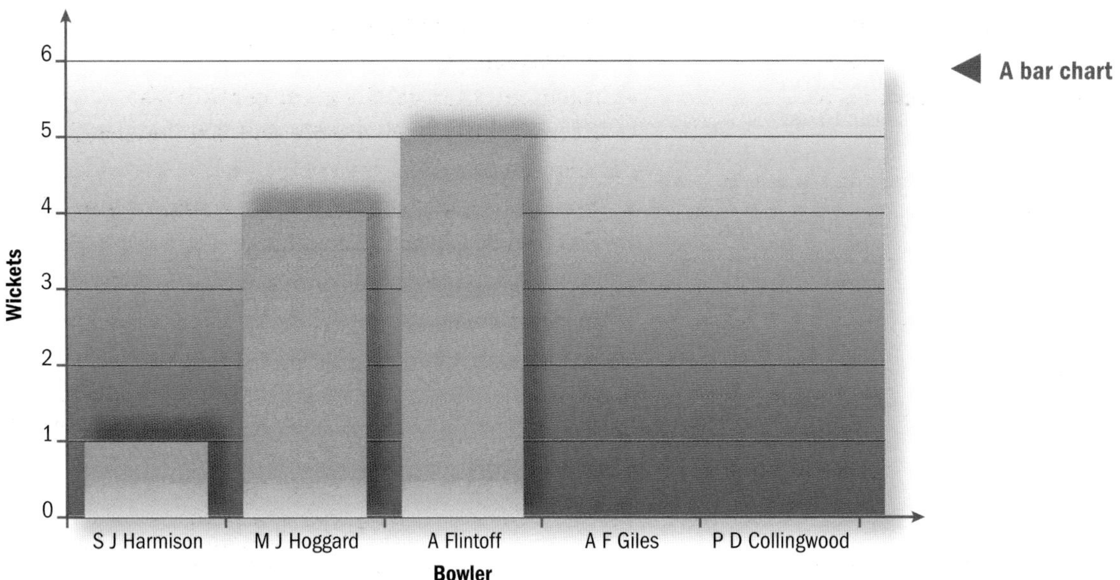

A bar chart

The table below shows the number of wickets taken by England bowlers during the last match of the 2005 Ashes series. The bar chart above allows you to quickly compare the wickets taken.

Bowler	Wickets
S J Harmison	1
M J Hoggard	4
A Flintoff	5
A F Giles	0
P D Collingwood	0

Wickets during the last match of the 2005 Ashes series

Cumulative frequency graphs

Cumulative frequency graphs show the cumulative totals of a set of values up to each of the points on the graph. The scores are plotted along the *x* axis, and the number of subjects who scored at or below a given score are plotted on the *y* axis.

Look at the table, which shows the results of sit-up tests for 50 participants. The results ranged from 10–42 sit-ups, and these scores have been sorted into 11 groups. The data are displayed in a table with three columns. Column *X* gives the groups, which are listed from the lowest to the highest numerical value. The next column *f* gives frequency scores. The final column gives the cumulative frequency.

No. of sit-ups (*X*)	Frequency (*f*)	Cumulative frequency
10–12	1	1
13–15	5	6
16–18	2	8
19–21	5	13
22–24	7	20
25–27	10	30
28–30	6	36
31–33	3	39
34–36	5	44
37–39	4	48
40–42	2	50

Sit-up test results from 50 test participants

Here is how to calculate the cumulative frequency.

- First, add the number from the frequency column to the previous row. For example, for 10–12 sit-ups, we have only one observation and no previous row. The cumulative frequency is one.

$$1 + 0 = 1$$

- However, for 13–15 sit-ups, there are five observations. Add these five to the previous cumulative frequency (1), and the result is 6.

  $1 + 5 = 6$
- Continue these calculations until you have added up all of the numbers in the frequency column.
- Record the results in the cumulative frequency column.

The final cumulative frequency value will be equal to the total number of participants.

Remember!

Ensure the cumulative frequency graph is always plotted using the correct axes, i.e. cumulative frequency is always plotted on the vertical axis.

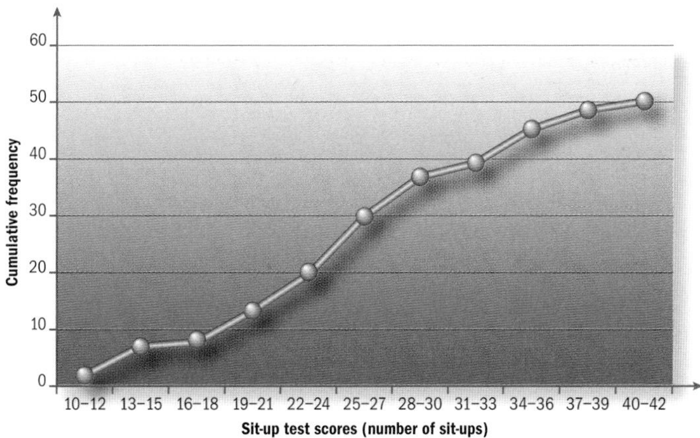

Cumulative frequency graph for sit-up scores

Normal distribution

There are three types of curve:

- normal
- positively skewed
- negatively skewed.

A normal distribution of data means that most of the examples in a set of data are close to the 'average', while a few examples are at one extreme or the other. Normal distribution graphs have these characteristics:

- the curve has a single peak
- it is bell-shaped
- the mean (average) lies at the centre of the distribution and the distribution is symmetrical around the mean
- the two 'tails' of the distribution extend indefinitely and never touch the *x* axis
- the shape of the distribution is determined by its mean and standard deviation (see page 155).

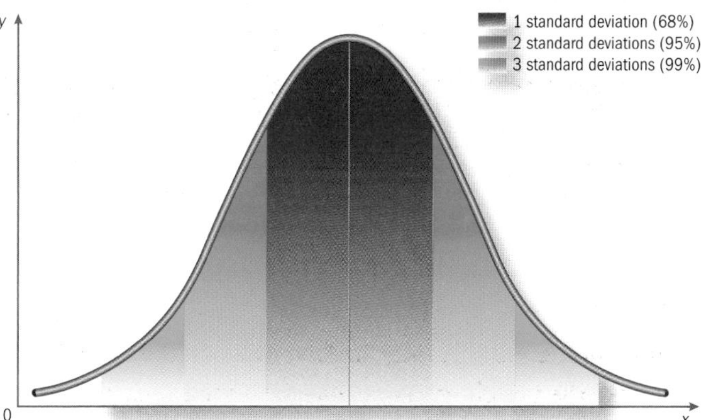

A normal distribution graph

Not all sets of data will have graphs that look this perfect. Some will have relatively flat curves, others will be steeper. Sometimes the mean will lean a little bit to one side or the other. However, all normally-distributed data will have something like this bell-shaped curve.

Generally speaking, if you go right or left one standard deviation from the mean, you will include about 68 per cent of the scores in the distribution. One standard deviation away from the mean in either direction on the *x* axis (the red area on the graph) accounts for around 68 per cent of the scores in this group. Two standard deviations away from the mean (the red and green areas) account for about 95 per cent of the scores. Three standard deviations (the red, green and blue areas) account for about 99 per cent of the scores.

Standard deviation tells you how tightly all the various examples are clustered around the mean in a set of data. When the examples are tightly bunched together and the bell-shaped curve is steep, the standard deviation is small. When the examples are spread apart and the bell curve is flat, this tells you that you have a relatively large standard deviation.

Positively skewed curves and negatively skewed curves

If the shape of the curve is asymmetrical, your data are not distributed normally and they are said to be either positively or negatively skewed.

(a)

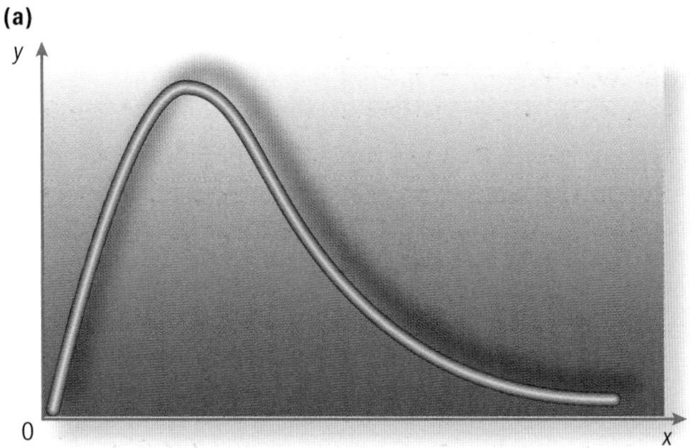

(b)

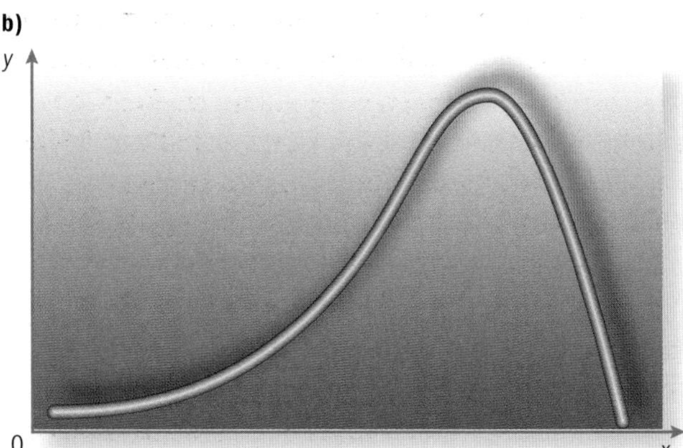

▲ (a) A positively skewed graph and (b) a negatively skewed graph

- Positively skewed means the longer tail of the curve points to the positive (higher) end of the scale and the scores are bunched to the left of the centre.
- Negatively skewed means the longer tail of the curve points to the negative (lower) end of the scale and the scores are bunched to the right of the centre.

Measures of central tendency and variability

Measures of central tendency are numbers that describe what is average or typical of the distribution. These measures include the mean, median and mode.

Key Terms

Mean The measure of central tendency calculated by adding all the values and dividing the sum by the number of values. It is also called the average.

Median The middle value in a series of numbers.

Mode The value of the score that occurs most frequently.

Mean

The mean is the centre of normal distributions. To calculate the mean, take all the scores, add them up and divide the sum by the total number of scores in the sample.

Here is an example. To work out the mean of the following data, add them all up and divide the total by 11 (there are 11 numbers).

Data set: 3, 7, 60, 72, 9, 18, 22, 24, 39, 44, 16.

Therefore,

$3 + 7 + 60 + 72 + 9 + 18 + 22 + 24 + 39 + 44 + 16 = 314$

$314 \div 11 = 28.55$

The mean is 28.55.

Median

The median is the value of the score that divides the distribution in half, with 50 per cent of the scores above the median and 50 per cent below the median.

To calculate the median, use the formula $(n + 1) \div 2$, where n is the number of values in the distribution. When n is an odd number, the formula tells you which value in the numerically ordered distribution corresponds to the median location.

Here is an example. First arrange the data into numerical order.

Data set: 3, 7, 60, 72, 9, 18, 22, 24, 39, 44, 16.

Therefore, numerical order is

3, 7, 9, 16, 18, 22, 24, 39, 44, 60, 72.

The median location is $(11 + 1) \div 2 = 6$. This means it is in the sixth place in the row of numbers. So the value 22 is the median, with 5 scores above and 5 below.

Here is an example when n is an even number.

Data set: 3, 7, 60, 72, 9, 16, 18, 22, 24, 39.

Therefore, numerical order is

3, 7, 9, 16, 18, 22, 24, 39, 60, 72.

The median location is $(10 + 1) \div 2 = 5.5$. In this case, the median is halfway between the fifth and the sixth scores (18 and 22), i.e. 20.

Activity

Imagine you have been employed as a statistician. You have been provided with the league scoring charts for a rugby season. Your task is to conduct simple descriptive data analysis on the scoring charts. You need to calculate the mean, the median and the mode, and provide feedback.

Team	Points
St Helens	48
Bradford	44
Leeds	38
Hull	32
Wigan	32
Huddersfield	30
Wakefield	26
Harlequins	22
Castleford	20
Salford	20
Warrington	18
Les Catalans	10

Mode

The mode of a data sample is the value that occurs most often in the distribution. For example, the mode of the sample 1, 3, 6, 6, 6, 6, 7, 7, 12, 12, 17 is 6. There can be more than one mode (such as 1, 1, 2, 4, 4,).

Key Term

Outlier A result that differs greatly from what you would expect.

Identification of outliers

A result that differs greatly from what you would consider 'normal' is known as an 'outlier'. Except for extremely small samples, the median is totally insensitive to outliers (such as occasional, rare, false experimental readings). The mode is also very robust in the presence of outliers, while the mean is rather sensitive. Statistics derived from data sets that include outliers can be misleading.

In most samples, some data points will be further away from their expected values than what is deemed reasonable. This can be due to systematic errors, faults in the theory that generated the expected values, or because some observations happen to be a long way from the centre of the data. Outliers can therefore indicate faulty data and incorrect procedures, or areas where a certain theory might not be valid. However, a small number of outliers are expected in normal distributions.

Standard deviation

The most common way of measuring variability is known as standard deviation. This is a number that indicates how much each of the values in the distribution deviate from the mean (or centre) of the distribution. If the data points are all close to the mean, then the standard deviation is close to zero. If many data points are far from the mean, then the standard deviation is far from zero. If all the data values are equal, then the standard deviation is zero.

The formula for calculating standard deviation (sd) is as follows:

$$sd = \sqrt{\frac{\Sigma(X - M)^2}{n - 1}}$$

where:

sd = standard deviation
Σ = sum of
X = individual score
M = mean
n = number of participants

Here is how to calculate standard deviation:

- calculate the mean
- subtract the mean from each subject's score $(X - M)$
- square the answer $(X - M)^2$
- sum the squared scores $\Sigma(X - M)^2$
- divide by the number of participants minus 1 $(n - 1)$
- take the square root of the answer.

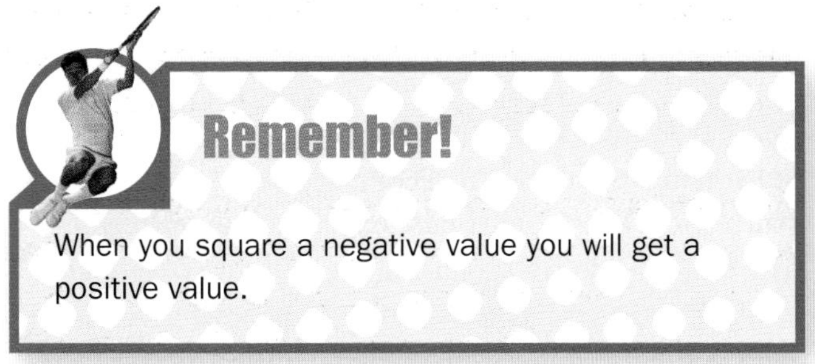

Remember!

When you square a negative value you will get a positive value.

Tests

There are two types of statistical tests within inferential statistics: parametric tests and non-parametric tests.

Key Terms

Parametric tests These use interval or ratio data, assume that data is drawn from a normal distribution (data is not skewed) and has the same variance.

Non-parametric tests These are used with ordinal (ranked) or nominal data.

It is important to be able to interpret the results of the test. Although choosing the correct test and performing that test correctly are essential skills in statistics, greater importance lies in being able to understand and explain what the results mean.

Parametric and non-parametric tests can be broken down further into two categories: tests of association or tests of difference (see the key to the diagram).

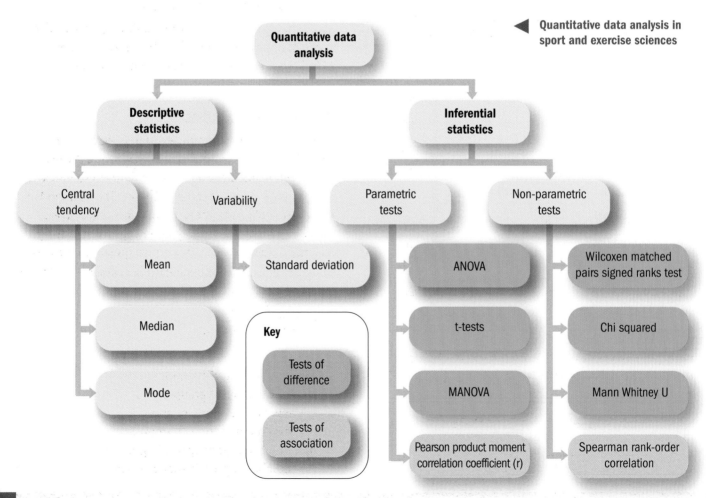

Quantitative data analysis
Descriptive statistics
Inferential statistics
Central tendency
Variability
Parametric tests
Non-parametric tests
Mean
Median
Mode
Standard deviation
ANOVA
t-tests
MANOVA
Pearson product moment correlation coefficient (r)
Wilcoxen matched pairs signed ranks test
Chi squared
Mann Whitney U
Spearman rank-order correlation
Key
Tests of difference
Tests of association

Quantitative data analysis in sport and exercise sciences

Parametric tests

The most common t-tests are the dependent t-test (also known as the paired samples t-test) and the independent t-test.

Dependent t-test

The dependent (paired samples) t-test looks at whether the mean score of one group is different when measured at different times.

The test is calculated using the formula below:

$$t = \frac{\Sigma D}{\sqrt{[n\Sigma D^2 - (\Sigma D)^2] \div (n-1)}}$$

where:

D = difference between before and after
n = number of paired scores
Σ = sum of

Here is an example of how to use the test using figures in the table below.

Subject	Pre-training height (cm)	Post-training height (cm)	D (post-training minus pre-training)	D^2
1	176	179	3	9
2	169	172	3	9
3	171	175	4	16
4	173	177	4	16
5	164	166	2	4
6	170	171	1	1
7	161	168	7	49
8	159	169	10	100
9	163	166	3	9
10	170	176	6	36
n = 10			$\Sigma D = 43$	$D^2 = 249$

Investigating the effects of a 12-week plyometric training programme on high jump performance.

$$t = \frac{43}{\sqrt{[2490 - 1849] \div 9}} \qquad t = \frac{43}{\sqrt{641 \div 9}}$$

$$t = \frac{43}{\sqrt{71.22}} \qquad t = \frac{43}{8.44} \qquad t = 5.09$$

Key Term

Degree of freedom Used as a correction factor for bias and to limit the effects of outliers, and based on the number of participants you have.

You need to calculate the degree of freedom (*df*) to assess the relationship between the two values. For the dependent t-test, you use the formula $df = n - 1$. In the example above, $df = 9$.

After you have calculated your *t* value, you would need to compare your result to the values in the significance table. In sport and exercise science, the level of significance is usually 0.05. Therefore, find your *df* value (in this case 9), then go across and see if your result is greater than or equal to the number in the column below the 0.05 level.

If the value achieved for your t-test is equal to or greater than the number shown, your results are significant to that level. If *df* is equal to or greater than 120 ($df \geq 120$), use the infinity column (∞) at the end of the table.

Using the example we have worked through, the *t* value calculated (5.09) is greater than the critical value of *t* (2.262), meaning our result is significant to the 0.05 level.

Independent t-test

The independent t-test is the most frequently used t-test. It is used when you have two groups and you are trying to find out if the mean scores of two groups can be considered to be significantly different. The independent t-test is suitable when the data you have collected are interval or ratio data, when your groups are randomly assigned, and when the variance (or spread) in the two groups is equal. The independent t-test is calculated using the formula below:

$$t = \frac{M_1 - M_2}{\sqrt{s_1^2 \div n_1 + s_2^2 \div n_2}}$$

where:

M_1 = mean value of group 1
M_2 = mean value of group 2
s_1 = standard deviation of group 1
s_2 = standard deviation of group 2
n_1 = number of participants in group 1
n_2 = number of participants in group 2

Key Term

Standard deviation A statistic that indicates the amount of variability in a group of scores.

Pearson product moment correlation coefficient (r)

A correlation is the value of the relationship between two or more variables, which can be positive or negative. Whether it is positive or negative depends on the direction of the line when the results are plotted on a graph. The graphs below show examples of perfect positive and perfect negative correlations, but it is rare to record such correlations during data analysis.

The Pearson product moment correlation coefficient is a parametric test that is suitable for use when you have interval or ratio data and when you are trying to identify a relationship between two variables. It is also a test of association, which means it looks at whether two or more variables are related.

The test can be used in one of two ways. Either you can try to find out a relationship between two variables or you can try to predict one score from another. In a simple correlation that is trying to find out a relationship between two variables, it doesn't matter which variable is assigned *X* and which *Y*. If you are trying to predict one score from another, then *X* is the independent variable and *Y* is the dependent variable.

There are three stages to using the Pearson product moment correlation:

1 Summing each set of scores.
2 Squaring and summing each set of scores.
3 Multiplying each pair of scores and obtaining the cumulative sum of these products.

The formula for the is outlined below:

$$r = \frac{n\Sigma XY - (\Sigma X)(\Sigma Y)}{\left[\sqrt{n\Sigma X^2 - (\Sigma X)^2}\right]\left[\sqrt{n\Sigma Y^2 - (\Sigma Y)^2}\right]}$$

where:

n = number of paired scores
Σ = sum of
X = scores for one variable
Y = scores for the other variable
$(\Sigma X)^2$ = sum of raw scores for X, squared
$(\Sigma Y)^2$ = sum of raw scores for Y, squared
ΣX^2 = sum of all of the X^2 scores
ΣY^2 = sum of all of the Y^2 scores

To interpret the significance of your *r* value, select your level of significance (remember that in sport and exercise science this is normally 0.05) and find your degree of freedom (*df*) for your test. For this test, use the formula $df = n - 2$ and compare your *r* value to the table of significance to find whether your results are significant.

Taking it further

Two other parametric tests that you might use are known as ANOVA and MANOVA. Find out more about these tests and answer the following questions.

1 a What does ANOVA stand for?
  b What is the formula for ANOVA?
  c When would you use ANOVA?
2 a What does MANOVA stand for?
  b What is the formula for MANOVA?
  c When would you use MANOVA?

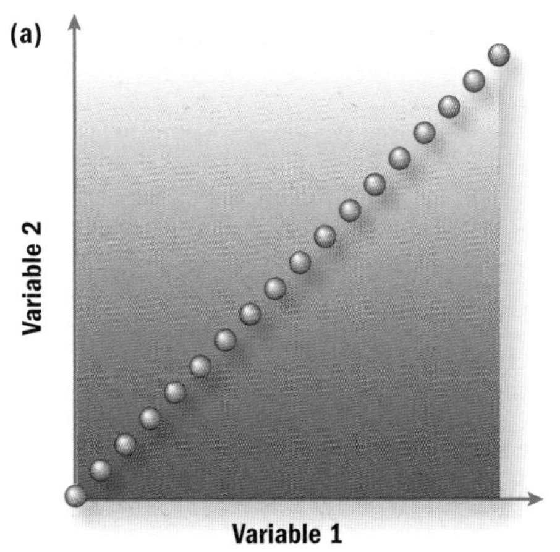

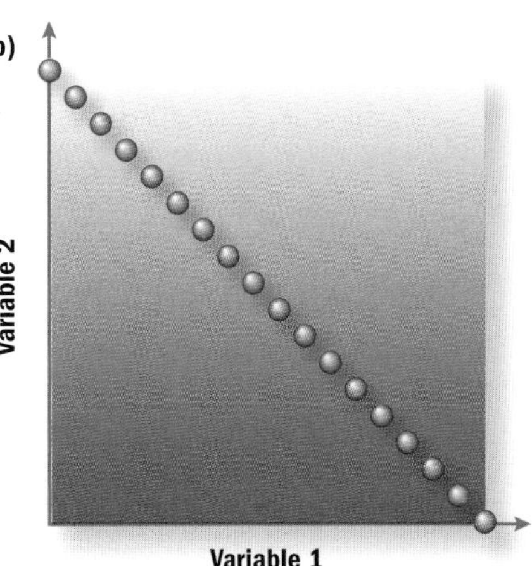

(a) Perfect positive correlation and (b) perfect negative correlation

Non-parametric tests

If the data are non-parametric, t-tests cannot be used. In this case, the Wilcoxen matched pairs signed ranks test is used in place of the dependent t-test, and the Mann Whitney U test is used in place of the independent t-test.

Wilcoxen matched pairs signed ranks test

The Wilcoxen matched pairs signed ranks test is used when you are trying to find out if there is a significant difference between two scores that are taken from the same participant (or from matched participants). It is used when the data are ordinal (ranked).

To do the test:

1 Disregard any results for participants who scored the same in both conditions, then count up the number of paired scores left. This is your *n* score.
2 Calculate the difference between the two scores of each participant, assigning plus or minus signs (*d*).
3 Rank the differences, giving the smallest a rank of 1 (ignoring plus or minus signs, i.e. +2 is of the same value as –2).When two scores are tied, each is given the mean of the two ranks and the next rank is missed out, (for example, if two participants are in level sixth place, they would both be given the rank of 6.5 and the next place would be given a rank of 8).
4 Add up the ranks of all the minus scores.
5 Add up the ranks of all the plus scores.
6 Take the smaller of the two figures calculated in points 4 and 5 to gain your *T* value.
7 Look up your value for *T* in the significance table. If it is equal to or less than the figure in the 0.05 column, the result is significant at that level.

Chi squared

The Chi squared test is used to assess the significance of the discrepancy between results that were actually achieved and the results that were expected. The formula for calculating the Chi square is given below:

$$x^2 = \Sigma[(O - E)^2 \div E]$$

where:

Σ = sum of
O = observed frequency
E = expected frequency

The degree of freedom (*df*) is calculated using the formula $df = c - 1$, where c is the number of cells (see table on page 160).

Activity

A squash coach is a believer in luck, karma and fate. One of his main players plays on four courts on a regular basis and the coach believes that one of the courts is an unlucky court for the player. He believes the player loses more on that court than on any of the others. The coach aims to prove his point by comparing the number of losses on each of the four courts. The player has lost a total of 40 matches over the course of the season. From this, it could be expected that the player would lose an equal number of matches on each court (i.e. 10).

Using the Chi squared test, find out whether there is a significant difference between observed and expected losses. In this example, *df* = 4 – 1, as there are four courts.

Use the following table to work out your answer.

	Court number				
	1	2	3	4	Total
Observed losses (O)	7	8	11	14	40
Expected losses (E)	10	10	10	10	40
(O – E)					
$(O - E)^2$					
$(O - E)^2 \div E$					
$\Sigma[(O - E)^2 \div E]$					

Degree of freedom (*df*)	.10	.05	.02	.01	.001
1	2.71	3.84	5.41	6.64	10.83
2	4.60	5.99	7.82	9.21	13.82
3	6.25	7.82	9.84	11.34	16.27
4	7.78	9.49	11.67	13.28	18.46
5	9.24	11.07	13.39	15.09	20.52
6	10.64	12.59	15.03	16.81	22.46
7	12.02	14.07	16.62	18.48	24.32
8	13.36	15.51	18.17	20.09	26.12
9	14.68	16.92	19.68	21.67	27.88
10	15.99	18.31	21.16	23.21	29.59
11	17.28	19.68	22.62	24.72	31.26
12	18.55	21.03	24.05	26.22	32.91
13	19.81	22.36	25.47	27.69	34.53
14	21.06	23.68	26.87	29.14	26.12
15	22.31	25.00	28.26	30.58	37.70

Degree of freedom (*df*)	.10	.05	.02	.01	.001
16	23.54	26.30	29.63	32.00	39.29
17	24.77	27.59	31.00	33.41	40.75
18	25.99	28.87	32.35	34.80	42.31
19	27.20	30.14	33.69	36.19	43.82
20	28.41	31.41	35.02	37.57	45.32
21	29.62	32.67	36.34	38.93	46.80
22	30.81	33.92	37.66	40.29	48.27
23	32.01	35.17	38.97	41.64	49.73
24	33.20	36.42	40.27	42.98	51.18
25	34.38	37.65	41.57	44.31	52.62
26	35.56	38.88	42.86	45.64	54.05
27	36.74	40.11	44.14	46.96	55.48
28	37.92	41.34	45.42	48.28	56.89
29	39.09	42.56	46.69	49.59	58.30
30	40.26	43.77	47.96	50.89	59.70

Table of significance for the Chi squared test

■ Mann Whitney U

This test is used when your data are ordinal (ranked). It is used to find out if the ranks of two groups are significantly different. The U value that you achieve tells you whether one of the ranks (group 1) is significantly higher than the other (group 2). The version of the Mann Whitney U test described here is suitable for group sizes up to and including 20 participants.

To conduct the Mann Whitney U test, the group scores are ranked. This means that the person who achieves the highest scores out of both groups is ranked number 1, the second highest number 2, and so on. After you have done this, you need to add up the ranks of both groups (so that you can see if the rank scores of both groups can be considered significantly different). It does not matter which of your subject groups you label as group 1 or group 2.

In this test, you will calculate two U values. You will compare the smaller U value that you calculate to the critical values of U in a table called initial values of u, in order to see if it is significant.

The formulae used to complete the Mann Whitney U test are shown below:

$$U_1 = n_1 n_2 + \left(\frac{n_1(n_1 + 1)}{2}\right) - \Sigma R_1$$

$$U_2 = n_1 n_2 - U_1$$

where:

n_1 = number of participants in group 1
n_2 = number of participants in group 2
ΣR_1 = sum of ranks for group 1
ΣR_2 = sum of ranks for group 2

Activity

Mann Whitney U Activity:

Using the data set below, find out if there is a significant difference between the ranks of players and non-players Baketball Free Throw shooting success.

- Remember the formula for the Mann Whitney U test.

Basketball Free Throw Shooting

Players	Non-Players
1	3
2	5
4	6
7	14
8	15
9	16
10	17
11	18
12	19
13	20
$ER_1 = 77$	$ER_2 = 133$

	N_2											
N_1	9	10	11	12	13	14	15	16	17	18	19	**20**
1											0	0
2	1	1	1	2	2	2	3	3	3	4	4	4
3	3	4	5	5	6	7	7	8	9	9	10	11
4	6	7	8	9	10	11	12	14	15	16	17	18
5	9	11	12	13	15	16	18	19	20	22	23	25
6	12	14	16	17	19	21	23	25	26	28	30	32
7	15	17	19	21	24	26	28	30	33	35	37	39
8	18	20	23	26	28	31	33	36	39	41	44	47
9	21	24	27	30	33	36	39	42	45	48	51	54
10	24	27	31	34	37	41	44	48	51	55	58	62
11	27	31	34	38	42	46	50	54	57	61	65	69
12	30	34	38	42	47	51	55	60	64	68	72	77
13	33	37	42	47	51	56	61	65	70	75	80	84
14	36	41	46	51	56	61	66	71	77	82	87	92
15	39	44	50	55	61	66	72	77	83	88	94	100
16	42	48	54	60	65	71	77	83	89	95	101	107
17	45	51	57	64	70	77	83	89	96	102	109	115
18	48	55	61	68	75	82	88	95	102	109	116	123
19	51	58	65	72	80	87	94	101	109	116	123	130
20	54	62	69	77	84	92	100	107	115	123	130	138

Critical values of U (p = 0.5 one tailed)
Adapted from Vincent (1999)

	N_2											
N_1	9	10	11	12	13	14	15	16	17	18	19	20
1											0	0
2	0	0	1	1	1	1	1	1	2	2	2	2
3	2	3	3	4	4	5	5	6	6	7	7	8
4	4	5	6	7	8	9	10	11	11	12	13	13
5	7	8	9	11	12	13	14	15	17	18	19	20
6	10	11	13	14	16	17	19	21	22	24	25	27
7	12	14	16	18	20	22	24	26	28	30	32	34
8	15	17	19	22	24	26	29	31	34	36	38	41
9	17	20	23	26	28	31	34	37	39	42	45	48
10	20	23	26	29	33	36	39	42	45	48	52	55
11	23	26	30	33	37	40	44	47	51	55	58	62
12	26	29	33	37	41	45	49	53	57	61	65	69
13	28	33	37	41	45	50	54	59	63	67	72	76
14	31	36	40	45	50	55	59	64	67	74	78	83
15	34	39	44	49	54	59	64	70	75	80	85	90
16	37	42	47	53	59	64	70	75	81	86	92	98
17	39	45	51	57	63	67	75	81	87	93	99	105
18	42	48	55	61	67	74	80	86	93	99	106	112
19	45	52	58	65	72	78	85	92	99	106	113	119
20	48	55	62	69	76	83	90	98	105	112	119	127

Critical Values of U (p= .05 two tailed)
Adapted from Vincent (1999)

Spearman rank-order correlation

The Spearman rank-order correlation test is similar to the Pearson product moment correlation coefficient in its purpose. However, it is a non-parametric equivalent and is used when your data are ordinal (ranked). This test should be used when you want to find a relationship between two sets of ordinal data (e.g. goals scored and final league position in football, serving accuracy and final ladder position in badminton, golf driving distance and final leader board position).

The first step is to rank your data (goals scored/serving accuracy/golf swing accuracy) from highest to lowest, with 1 being the highest. After this, determine the difference between your data and the place in the tournament. This must be squared and then summed.

Remember!

When two scores are tied, each is given the mean of the two ranks and the next rank is missed out. For example, if two participants are in level fourth place, they would both be given the rank of 4.5 and the next place would be given a rank of 6.

The formula used for the test is shown below:

$$r_2 = 1 - \frac{6(\Sigma D^2)}{n(n^2 - 1)}$$

where:

n = number of ranked pairs

D = difference between each pair

In order to interpret the significance of your r_s value, select the level of significance (0.05) and calculate the degree of freedom (*df*) for your test. For the Spearman rank-order correlation test, this is calculated using the formula $n - 2$. Compare your value to the table of significance to find whether your results are significant.

Selecting tests

It is important to select the correct test when conducting statistical analysis. Your choice of statistical test will depend on whether your data you have collected is interval, ratio, ordinal or nominal.

Degrees of freedom

The degree of freedom is a measure of how much precision an estimate of variation has. A general rule is that the degree of freedom decreases when we have to estimate more parameters.

ICT-based techniques

It is common to use ICT-based techniques to conduct your statistical analysis. However, at this early stage in your research careers, we strongly recommend conducting your statistical analysis by hand so that you become familiar with data handling.

When you are comfortable with manual data handling, the two main ICT programmes you could use for your data analysis are the Statistical Package for Social Sciences (SPSS) and Microsoft Excel®.

You will not be judged on the way you have conducted your statistical analysis, more on whether you have done it right and how you interpret the results.

Remember!

Whether you conduct your statistical analysis by hand or using ICT, you should get the same results – proving you have done it right!

Statistical Package for Social Sciences (SPSS)

SPSS is probably more commonly used in a research setting. It is a user-friendly software package that allows you to work with large data sets and conduct a range of statistical tests. It also produces a wide range of graphs and charts. For those of you thinking of entering into higher education, it may be worthwhile finding out how SPSS works, as this statistics package is used on a number of sport and exercise science-based degree courses.

■ Microsoft Excel®

Microsoft Excel® is a spreadsheet-based program that allows you to conduct a range of statistical tests on large data sets. You can produce graphs and charts to display your results. It is user-friendly and easy to follow once you become familiar with it. It is worthwhile using the Help function or the advice of your tutor to get to know how to conduct different aspects of data analysis once you have got to grips with manual data analysis.

Assessment practice

Imagine you are working as a statistician for a football league. You have been asked to find out if there is a relationship between goals scored and the FA premier league position. This project will involve you looking at the league table, ranking the teams in terms of goals scored (so your data will be ordinal) and then seeing if there is a relationship between the rank of goals scored and the league position. You need to put together a proposal for how you plan to collect and analyse the data. You need to provide the following information.

1. A description of three quantitative data collection techniques. **P6**
2. A description of one of the three quantitative data collection techniques that you feel is the most appropriate for the study and your reasons why you feel it is the most appropriate. **P8**
3. An appropriate research design for the study, with your analysis on why you feel it is the most appropriate. **D2**
4. A description of two contrasting methods of quantitative data analysis (e.g. one parametric and one non-parametric) that could be used for this type of project. **P8**
5. A selection of one of the two methods you have described above, justifying why it is more appropriate than the other. **M5**

grading tips

Grading Tip 

To describe something, you need to give a detailed account in words of the topic, which could include definitions of the topic.

Grading Tip 

To justify something, you need to say why it is suitable for the intended purpose.

Grading Tip **D2**

To analyse something, you need to take your justifications further by not only saying why something is suitable for the intended purpose but progress by saying why it is more suitable than the other options that could be used in the same situation.

Knowledge check

1. What is research?
2. What are qualitative and quantitative research?
3. What are the differences between qualitative and quantitative research?
4. What do the terms 'validity', 'reliability', 'accuracy' and 'precision' mean?
5. What are the different types and classifications of data that are common in research?
6. What are the common ethical and legal issues associated with research?
7. What can happen if you don't work ethically and legally?
8. Name and describe three types of data collection in qualitative research.
9. Name and describe three types of data collection in quantitative research.
10. What are the three stages of qualitative data analysis and which analysis tools are used at each stage?
11. What is a parametric test? Give two examples.
12. What is a non-parametric test? Give two examples.
13. What does the term 'descriptive statistics' mean?
14. What does the term 'inferential statistics' mean?

Preparation for assessment

1 Imagine you have been asked to go around colleges and universities promoting research in sport and exercise science. You need to produce an imaginative and lively poster presentation that will introduce students to research and some of the key issues within research. You need to include following information in the poster.

a A description and comparison of qualitative and quantitative research. **P1 M1**

b A description and explanation (with examples) of validity, reliability, accuracy and precision. **P2 M2**

c A description (with examples) of the different types and classifications of data. Include primary and secondary data, discrete, ordinal, continuous, interval and ratio classifications. **P3**

d A description of two ethical and legal issues that affect how we conduct research in sport and exercise science. **P4**

e An explanation of the implications of not working ethically and legally in sport and exercise research. **M3**

2 Imagine you want to conduct a qualitative study into different coping strategies that are used with cricket players. The study will look at which coping strategies are considered to be the most effective. You would like to do a really focused study looking at just one player to start off with, with a view to providing recommendations for future research of this nature.

a Describe the three main data collection techniques used within qualitative research. **P5**

b For the project outlined above, justify which data collection technique (or techniques) you think would be useful and explain why. **M4**

c For the project outlined above, say which research design you think would be most suitable and say why. **D1**

d Describe the three main stages of data analysis within qualitative research, then say which you feel would be appropriate for this particular study. It may also be useful for you to look at how you will make sure the data you collect is valid and reliable. **P7**

3 Imagine you are working as a statistician. You have been asked to find out if there is a relationship between goals scored and league position. This project will involve you looking at the league table, ranking the teams in terms of goals scored (so your data will be ordinal) and then seeing if there is a relationship between the rank of goals scored and the league position. You need to put together a proposal for how you plan to collect and analyse the data. You need to provide the following information.

a A description of three quantitative data collection techniques. **P6**

b An appropriate research design for the study, with your analysis on why you feel it is the most appropriate. **D2**

c A description of two contrasting methods of quantitative data analysis (e.g. one parametric and one non-parametric) that could be used for this type of project. **P8**

d A selection of one of the two methods you have described above, saying why it is more appropriate than the other. **M5**

grading tips

Grading Tip 

Make sure you use all the appropriate technical terminology and give research-based examples.

Grading Tip 

To describe something, you need to give a detailed account in words of the topic, which could include definitions of the topic.

Grading Tip 

To justify something, you need to say why it is suitable for the intended purpose.

Grading Tip 

To analyse something, you need to take your justifications further by not only saying why something is suitable for the intended purpose, but by saying why it is more suitable than the other options that could be used in the same situation.

Grading criteria

To achieve a pass grade the evidence must show that the learner is able to:	To achieve a merit grade the evidence must show that, in addition to the pass criteria, the learner is able to:	To achieve a distinction grade the evidence must show that, in addition to the pass and merit criteria, the learner is able to:
P1 describe qualitative and quantitative research **Assessment practice pages 127, 130**	**M1** compare and contrast qualitative and quantitative research **Assessment practice pages 127, 130**	
P2 describe the key issues that affect research in sport and exercise sciences **Assessment practice pages 129, 130**	**M2** explain the key issues that affect research in sport and exercise sciences **Assessment practice pages 129, 130**	
P3 describe the types and classifications of data that are common in research in the sport and exercise sciences **Assessment practice pages 132**		

Grading criteria		
To achieve a pass grade the evidence must show that the learner is able to:	**To achieve a merit grade the evidence must show that, in addition to the pass criteria, the learner is able to:**	**To achieve a distinction grade the evidence must show that, in addition to the pass and merit criteria, the learner is able to:**
P4 describe two ethical and legal issues associated with research in sport and exercise sciences **Assessment practice page 134**	**M3** explain the implications of not working both ethically and legally when conducting research in the sport and exercise sciences **Assessment practice page 134**	
P5 describe three data collection techniques in qualitative research in the sport and exercise sciences **Assessment practice page 148**	**M4** for a selected research-based example, justify the most appropriate research design and techniques for qualitative data collection and data analysis **Assessment practice pages 144, 148**	**D1** analyse why the selected research design and techniques for qualitative data collection and data analysis are most appropriate for the selected research-based example **Assessment practice pages 144, 148**
P6 describe three data collection techniques in quantitative research in the sport and exercise sciences **Assessment practice page 162**	**M5** for a selected research-based example, justify the most appropriate research design and techniques for quantitative data collection and data analysis **Assessment practice pages 144, 163**	**D2** analyse why the selected research design and techniques for quantitative data collection and data analysis are most appropriate for the selected research-based example **Assessment practice pages 144, 163**
P7 describe the three main stages of qualitative data analysis in the sport and exercise sciences **Assessment practice page 148**		
P8 describe two contrasting quantitative data analysis techniques used in the sport and exercise sciences **Assessment practice page 163**		

Research project in sport and exercise sciences

Introduction

Why do people take part in sport? Why do some people not take part in exercise? How does a talented athlete become an elite athlete?

These are just some of the areas of research that have taken place in sport and exercise sciences. However, there is still much to learn about the different disciplines within sport and exercise sciences. It is the role of research to bridge the gap in knowledge, and it is the role of sport and exercise scientists to conduct this research.

The work of sport and exercise scientists, in a research-based setting, involves the ability to plan to collect data effectively, collect and analyse data, communicate research findings with others and use key aspects of reflective practice to evaluate the research undertaken.

This unit will help you to learn how to conduct all of these aspects of the research process so that you can effectively plan, conduct, produce and evaluate your research.

After completing this unit you should be able to achieve the following outcomes:

- be able to plan a sport science- or exercise science-based research project
- be able to conduct a sport science- or exercise science-based research project
- be able to produce a sport science- or exercise science-based research project
- be able to evaluate a sport science- or exercise science-based research project.

Think it over

When people talk about 'research', you might think of a number of things.

You might start to think about looking things up in books, newspapers or on the Internet. At other times, you might have images of animals in laboratories, people hooked up to expensive equipment with wires everywhere, or scientists in white coats pouring things into test tubes.

All of these are different types of research. To get you thinking of what the term 'research' means to you and how it will influence your achievement in this unit, think about the following questions:

- What are you interested in with regard to sport and exercise sciences?
- What things do you want to find out about in these areas?
- Why are you interested in these things?
- How could you go about researching them?

5.1 Be able to plan a sport science- or exercise science-based research project

To achieve the first learning outcome for this unit, you need to plan and produce a proposal for a research project that you would like to conduct. This diagram shows the stages you will go through when you develop the plan for your project and produce your proposal.

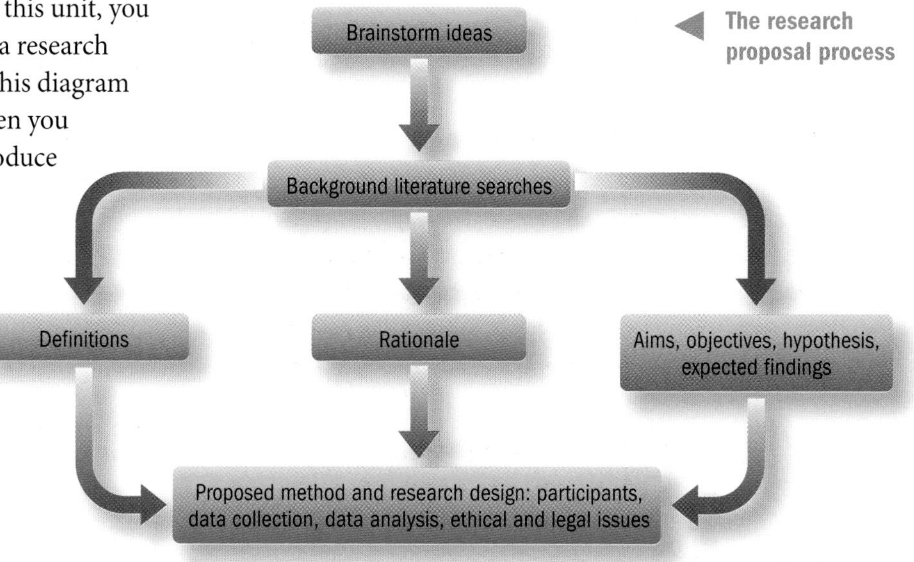

The research proposal process

Plan

When thinking about starting a research project, the first thing you need to do is to decide on a topic that you would like to study. Although this is the first stage in the research process, it is important. If you think carefully about the topic you want to study, your project will be far easier to complete than if you just come up with an idea from the top of your head and run with it.

When you start to think about what you want to research, you might think that if your idea isn't original, it isn't any good – but this isn't true! Any research that you will do at this level will be based on something that has been done before and will use current knowledge. There is nothing wrong with this at all.

Focus

You might not be able to identify a focused research project straight away, so here are some guidelines to help you decide on a suitable topic.

- Think about what you are interested in and what you know something about. If you choose a research project that is based on a topic you are interested in and know something about it will make your project easier for you to complete. You will also find it more interesting and you are likely to be more motivated to complete it.
- Use existing literature as this will provide you with a range of ideas that you may want to develop further. This will help you to form a rationale for your project. When you present your research proposal, you should include a mini-review of the literature that demonstrates your rationale.
- Think about current popular issues that might be worth researching, such as obesity in children. You may be able to get ideas for current popular issues by looking on a range of Internet sites or through magazines and newspapers.
- You might also want to think about some of the social issues that affect sport or exercise, such as football hooliganism.
- Go over some ideas with friends. Talk about any ideas you have with others in your group and perhaps mind map some of these thoughts, to develop your ideas further.
- Speak to your tutor. Your tutor will be able to help guide you with your ideas.

Key Term

Rationale A reasoned argument made to justify a particular course of action.

Remember!

Your tutor will help you to decide on a suitable topic for your research project. However, it is not their job to decide on the topic for you – you need to do this for yourself.

When looking at whether your research project is worth reading, some people may ask 'So what?' Your rationale for the project is your way of answering this question – your reason for doing the project. It should be based on some form of problem that has been identified or a current 'hot' topic.

After you have decided on the basis for your project, you may find that you cannot complete it because the project is not feasible. The CAFÉ principle can help you decide whether or not a project is feasible.

- Complexity: your topic might be very complicated and you will have to work out whether you think you can complete the project or not.
- Access: you need to think how easy it will be to collect your data. Will you have access to participants to collect data? Will you be able to collect the right type of data?
- Facilities and resources: will you have access to the right type of facilities and will you have access to sufficient resources? You need to think about the demands of your research when answering this question.
- Expertise: there is nothing wrong with being ambitious or enjoying a challenge, but you need to consider your own knowledge and experience when deciding on the type of topic you want to study.

From M. Clarke et al, *Researching and Writing Dissertations in Hospitality and Tourism*, 1998

Title

After you have decided on the focus of your project, you can start to look at the title. Your title does not have to be a question, but it must clearly demonstrate the problem you are trying to solve and say what the project is about. It can be a 'writing title' – you can improve on it as you progress with your project.

Activity

Here are some examples of project titles, which show the style you could use when deciding on your title.

- An examination of the psychological factors associated with life-span talent development in basketball.
- Gender differences in VO_2 max levels of elite endurance swimmers.
- How does creatine supplementation benefit weight-lifting performance?
- How do levels of two-footedness change across football developmental stages?
- Is there an optimal point of release for javelin throwing?

Can you think of other examples of project titles and write them in this style?

Theory into practice

1. In small groups, discuss which aspects of sport and exercise sciences you are interested in and which ones you feel you know a lot about.
2. Create a mind map for each aspect to show:
   - a the aspect you are interested in
   - b why you are interested in this area
   - c how you think you could research the topic
   - d why you think the topic is important.

   Do this for two or three different topics.
3. Select the topic you are most interested in and make sure it is realistic. Try to produce a research question based on this topic.

Aims

The aims of your project are what you want to achieve through your research. They provide a clear statement of what you want to achieve and guide the internal coherence of your research (see page 197 for more on internal coherence.)

Research is used at all levels of sport, even at the highest level

Objectives

The objectives are what you need to do in order to achieve your aims. They identify measurable tasks that need to be done in order to complete the project.

Here is an example of how you could set out the title, aims and objectives for a particular research problem.

> ***Title:*** How successful was the management of the England national football team during the 2006 FIFA World Cup?
>
> ***Aims:*** To assess the success of the management of the England national football team during the 2006 FIFA World Cup.
>
> ***Objectives:***
>
> 1. Find out what the management strategies of the management team were (e.g. team decisions and squad selection, coaching styles and set up).
> 2. Decide on a way of measuring the team's success (e.g. did they win the World Cup? Did the team play well?)
> 3. Use secondary data to analyse the management strategies effectiveness
> 4. Provide recommendations for future management strategies for future competitions

Hypothesis/Null hypothesis/expected findings

A hypothesis is the predicted relationship between two variables. A null hypothesis is the prediction that there will not be a relationship between the two variables. When you are writing the hypothesis and null hypothesis, be careful to not write two separate hypotheses. This is easily done, so you need to be careful about how you phrase your sentences.

Here is an example of a hypothesis and a null hypothesis.

> - Hypothesis: Females will have greater levels of flexibility than males.
> - Null hypothesis: Females will not have greater flexibility levels than males.

In this example, it would be an easy mistake to say that your null hypothesis is 'Males will have greater levels of flexibility than females', but these are actually two different hypotheses as you would be suggesting two different relationships.

In some cases, it may not be appropriate to report a hypothesis and null hypothesis, so you should report expected findings instead.

In the example above, we identified a research problem of 'How successful was the management of the England national football team during the 2006 FIFA World Cup?'

In this case, it would not be appropriate to report a hypothesis or null hypothesis, but it would be appropriate to suggest that the expected findings of the study would be that the management of the England national team during the 2006 FIFA World Cup was ineffective due to the team's failure to progress past the quarter final stage.

Generally speaking, you will provide a hypothesis and null hypothesis when you are conducting quantitative research and you will provide an expected findings statement for qualitative research (see page 184 for more information on quantitative and qualitative data).

Scope

Your plan should indicate the scope of the project. This means who the research could be applicable to, whether the study is large or small scale, and the expectations of the research.

For example, if you conduct a research project with ten elite male rugby players that was expected to find out their levels of flexibility, you would not then be able to claim that your results could be applied to all athletic populations when discussing flexibility levels, because your sample size is too small and your sample type is too focused.

Here is an example of how you could write the scope of research using the details in the section above.

> ***Scope:*** The proposed study is a small-scale study that will examine the flexibility levels of elite male rugby players. The results will be able to be applied to male populations playing sports with similar demands to rugby, but further research would be needed to examine the results against other populations.

Design

In Unit 4, we discussed different research designs that can be applied to research projects. Look back at this unit if you need a reminder about which research designs are suitable for different projects.

As part of your proposal, you need to report the research design that you will use and say why you will use it. In your research design section, it is also good practice to say what your variables are.

> ### Key Terms
>
> **Variables** Things you measure.
>
> **Dependent variable** A variable that is affected by the independent variable.
>
> **Independent variable** A variable that the researcher can manipulate to assess its effect on the dependent variable.

If you were conducting an experimental research project into the effects of imagery on golf putting performance, here is an example of how you could present the information.

> ***Design:*** The proposed project will adopt an experimental research design because the aim is to identify whether the independent variable has an effect on the dependent variable. In the proposed project, the aim is to find out if imagery (the independent variable) will have an effect on golf putting performance (the dependent variable).

Sample

After you have decided on your research project area and the design that you are going to use, you then need to discuss your participants in the project. In Unit 4, we looked at different types of sampling and when you would use them.

In this section of your proposal, you need to say what sampling techniques you will use, why you have chosen this particular type of sampling and go on to discuss the

Mario Lemieux would be an ideal participant for the research project discussed here. However, with his sporting commitments, do you think it would be within the scope of your study to be able to get him to take part?

details of your participants in the study. When you are writing about the people you would like to include in the study, you should discuss gender, age, level of training, level of performance and any special population details. For the research projects you will conduct, you will probably want to consider using your class mates, local sports teams or friends as participants.

The people you choose as participants will depend on the type of project you want to conduct, but as a general idea you need to get people who are easy to contact and who will help you to answer the research problem.

Here is an example of how you could write about your proposed sample.

> ***Participants:*** For this study, 45 males ranging in age from 21 to 25 will be randomly selected from the overall available population (n = 100) of elite ice hockey players who have played at an elite level for at least three years. After this, participants will be randomly assigned to one of three groups (n = 15).

Data collection and analysis

How you will collect and analyse your data is one of the most important aspects of the proposal. This is because it shows that you have given the project careful thought and have planned the kind of information you need to collect to achieve the results you want. If you fail to plan your data collection and analysis sections, you may find that you end up with data that will not help you to answer your research problem and will effectively make the whole process a waste of time.

When planning data collection and analysis, it is important to write about what you have chosen to do. You also need to say why you have chosen to collect and analyse your data in that way and how you have planned specifically to make sure any data you collect is valid and reliable. The best research proposals incorporate each of these areas. The weakest proposals tend to miss out why the data collection and analysis methods have been chosen, and how the data collected will be valid and reliable.

When you are looking at which data collection methods and data analysis methods you could use, look again at Unit 4. The more detail you can apply here, the better your proposal will be.

Ethical and legal considerations

The next aspect of your proposal should show that you have considered the ethical and legal issues as laid out by the British Association of Sport and Exercise Sciences (BASES) code of conduct. In Unit 4, we discussed a range of ethical and legal issues (e.g. informed consent, confidentiality, data protection, ethical clearance, working competently) that you need to consider and you should include these in your proposal.

Web links

Visit the BASES website at www.bases.org.uk to find out more about its work.

Validity and reliability considerations

Whenever you conduct research, you need to ensure your data are valid and reliable. In research there are a number of ways this can be achieved. Here are some possibilities for you to consider.

Pilot studies are smaller versions of your study that you use to test the research methods you have selected, before you start to conduct your research. They allow you to identify any problems with the research methods and correct any mistakes that could affect the validity and reliability of the data collected.

Repeated measures are when data are collected from the same individual or groups over a period of time on more than one occasion to help you to assess the reliability of your data. If you collect data that is the same or similar when all the test conditions are the same, you can say that you have achieved reliability. For example, a fitness centre wanted to test the benefits of three protein drinks so that it could decide which product should be marketed to clients. The centre conducted a research project that looked at each of the drinks, and found all the drinks to be useful. To make sure the results were not down to chance, the centre conducted the research project four more times. Coke drink was more beneficial than the

People in sport and exercise are always interested in additional information that may benefit performance. Through research, we can provide them with valid and reliable information

Activity

If you wanted to assess students' opinions of their National Diploma in Sport and Exercise Sciences course, you could give them a questionnaire. In order to make sure that the questionnaire was suitable, you would give it to a small group of students, ask them to fill it in and check whether you have been able to find out the information you wanted from it. You would also ask them to make any comments about the overall design of the questionnaire and see if they had any suggestions on how to improve the design before it is used in your final project.

What factors do you think are important in designing this questionnaire?

others and the same results were produced on a number of occasions but the results for the other two drinks varied greatly. The repeated measures increased the validity of the research because the fitness centre found out which drink was the most beneficial. The results were reliable because they were repeated on a number of occasions.

Triangulation is the use of a range of research methods, sources of data or a number of researchers to try to increase the validity of the data you collect. If you were to use a range of methods and the range of methods used allowed you to draw the same conclusions, you would be able to say you had increased the validity of your research. For example, triangulation was used in a study investigating factors associated with talent development in football. The initial data collection method required participants to complete a questionnaire relating to which factors they thought were important in the life span development of football players. Then an additional research method of semi-structured interviews was used with a sample of the participants. This allowed the researcher to get more in-depth information about why the players thought the different factors they had identified were important. This increased the quality of the data collected and helped the researcher to form more in-depth conclusions, thus increasing the validity of the research.

Member checking: this is a method of using interviews and questionnaires to verify any conclusions you have made about the data collected. Member checking happens at the final stage of data analysis (drawing conclusions and verifying data – see Unit 4 for a reminder) and involves giving the conclusions you have made back to the participants in the study to make sure you have interpreted what they have said correctly, thus increasing the validity of the research.

Assessment practice

For an area of your choice from either sport science or exercise science, produce a proposal for a research project that you would like to complete. Use all of the information in this section to help you to produce your proposal. Try to write about 1,000 words and use following headings in your research proposal.

a *Title*

b *Background*
Introduction
Aims
Objectives
Hypothesis/null hypothesis/expected findings

c *Proposed method*
Research design
Participants
Data collection
Data analysis
Benefits and limitations
Ethical and legal issues
Validity and reliability considerations   

grading tips

Grading Tip 

Here is a suggested format for completing your research proposal, which you can use to help you write your proposal. Your proposal will generally be divided into three main areas after your title: background, proposed method, and benefits and limitations. Each main area should include a number of sub-sections.

- **Background**: discuss your particular area of study and include definitions. For example, if you are conducting a research project to investigate coping mechanisms used by elite cricketers, you would be expected to provide a definition of 'coping' and 'elite'. State the problem you are investigating and produce a literature review that demonstrates a rationale for conducting the project. Following on from your literature review, state your aims, objectives, hypothesis and null hypothesis or expected findings (where appropriate).
- **Proposed method**: within your proposed method, you need to discuss all the factors relating to data collection and analysis. The first thing you need to write about is the research design as you need to select and justify an appropriate design.

  Next, write about your proposed participant information, including the number of participants, age, gender, performance level (e.g. grass-roots or elite), particular sports (e.g. football, rugby, basketball, cycling), sampling details and how groups will be separated (where applicable). Describe the methods to be used. If any in-depth methods are followed, it is best to describe them in full in the appendix.

  When completing this section, consider the following points:
  - What data collection techniques will you use?
  - What data analysis techniques will you use?
  - Include information on instruments, apparatus and equipment to be used, including model numbers.
  - Say how you planned your methods to ensure the data collected are valid and reliable (e.g. pilot study, triangulation, member checking) and discuss why the selected method are appropriate.
  - Identify any ethical or legal issues that are important (e.g. explain that you will not let people take part in the research without completing informed consent forms; explain how you will make sure you maintain confidentiality).
  - Include a proposed timescale for the research project to help to guide you when you come to conduct the research project.
- **Benefits and limitations:** this section helps you to further justify your research by:
  - explaining why it will be useful
  - who your results will be applicable to or aimed at (or if they could be generalised)
  - explaining any of your own areas for improvement (e.g. will you have to learn how to use new equipment to complete the project?)
  - identifying and describing any ethical and legal issues that are important in your project.

Grading Tip M1

When writing the research design and proposed methods sections, include as much detail as you can.

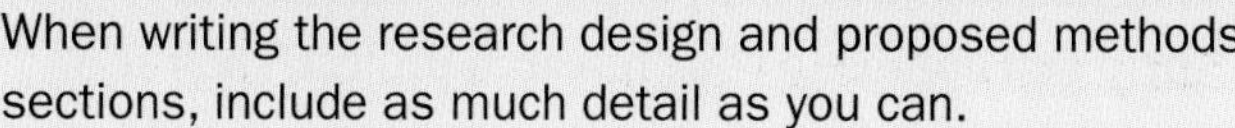

Grading Tip D1

You need to say not only which research methods you are going to use but also why you are going to use them. Make sure you discuss how you have planned your research so that the data collected will be both valid and reliable.

Grading Tip P1 M1 D1

For your plan to be effective, make sure you write it in the future tense and in the third person (for example, 'data will be collected using questionnaires with follow-up semi-structured interviews'). This will benefit you later when it comes to writing up your project because you will be able to use a lot of the information from your proposal (but changed into the past tense).

5.2 Be able to conduct a sport science- or exercise science-based research project

When you are conducting research, there are a number of things that you need to take into account to be able to research effectively. These include resources required, any ethical and legal issues arising, data issues and the use of a research diary.

Resources

Resources needed

The first aspects you need to think about are the types of resources you need to complete your project. There are three main types of resources: physical, human and fiscal.

- Physical resources are what you need to help you to complete your research, such as any equipment you need.
- Human resources are people who you need to help you complete your research project, such as a supervisor, participants and research assistants.
- Fiscal resources are any economic or financial resources you need to complete your project, such as the money needed to buy supplements if you are carrying out a nutrition project. If you need to buy various things to be able to conduct your project, how will you find the money to pay for them? Where will the money come from?

Your tutor usually acts as your research supervisor. You have only one project to complete but your supervisor will have a number of students to work with, so you need to plan your time effectively to make the most of your supervisor.

You need to think of ways you can commit your participants to the study as you need to make sure they will complete the project so that your research is not worthless. You may find that you would like to use research assistants. These are people who help you to collect your data, organise equipment, etc. Your friends can be really useful for this purpose, so why not ask some of them to help you set up your equipment? You can act as their research assistant in return, which makes the whole research process easier for everyone.

Key Terms

Physical resources Items you need to undertake your research, such as any equipment or tools.

Human resources People you need to help you with your research.

Fiscal resources Money you need to buy things for your research.

Remember!

You need to plan effectively to make sure your tutor has made the time to see you by arranging appointments with them in advance.

Considerations

Think about how you will access the resources you need and how they will be used.

Availability and booking

You need to make sure that the resources you need are available. There is nothing worse than going to start your research project and finding out that the resources you need are not available. Once you have listed all the resources that you require for your research project, make sure that you book them. For example, you will probably be conducting your research project at the same time as several other students in your class and you may all need to use your sports hall (a physical resource) at roughly the same time. To make sure that you actually get to use the sports hall, you will need to arrange to use it.

Arranging

Ensure your participants and colleagues know what the arrangements are, where they should go and at what time, and what they will be expected to do.

Familiarity with research techniques

You need to make sure you are familiar with all the techniques you have selected for your research project. According to the British Association of Sport and Exercise Sciences (BASES) code of conduct, you may not work within research if you are not able to work in a professional manner. A key part of working in a professional way is knowing what you are doing and how all the techniques work.

Familiarity with research equipment

As well as making sure you are familiar with the data collection techniques, you need to know how to use all the equipment that you require to complete your research project. You need to ask your tutor for help, use your class notes, use instruction manuals for equipment, and practise using the equipment to make sure you are familiar with how everything works.

Recording thoughts and feelings regarding the research process

It is important that you record your thoughts and feelings regarding the progress you are making. Try to do this throughout your research project, as this will help when you come to write your 'future recommendations' section. It will also enable you to write a good conclusion and it will make it easier for you to conduct an overall evaluation of your project at the end. (See Research diary on page 187.)

Ethical and legal issues

Whenever you conduct research, you need to be able to conduct your research both ethically and legally. In order to conduct research in this way, there are a number of things you need to do before and during research.

Informed consent and confidentiality

Informed consent is obtained by asking participants to read and sign a document setting out all of the information relevant to the proposed project. The document should include:

- a description of the investigation and its objectives
- the procedures to be followed
- an outline of any possible risks and benefits to the participants
- an offer to answer any questions that the participants may have
- an instruction that the participants are free to withdraw at any point without penalty.

At the end of the document, you should include an explanation saying how you will maintain the confidentiality of the participants' personal details, followed by a section where the participants sign to say they are happy to take part in the research.

Remember!

All the information that you get from the participants for this particular section of research must be stored in a locked filing cabinet (or some other form of secure storage) accessible only by you and your research supervisor.

Key Term

Informed consent This is the knowing permission or agreement of your participants (or legal representative in the case of a child) to take part in the research as you have described it to them. The agreement must be willing and the participant should not be unfairly persuaded into taking part.

An example of an informed consent form

Name	

Age [ ] Date of Birth [ ] Gender Male / Female

Name of Test	
Protocol to be followed	
Details of Protocol	
Potential Risks / Benefits	

Participant to read and sign

- The details of the test have been explained to me fully. I have read and fully understand all of the procedures that are to be used in the test and have had the potential benefits and risks associated with the tests explained to me fully.
- All questions that I have about the tests and my involvement in the tests have been answered.
- I am aware that I am free to cease participation in the test at any time.
- I am aware that my test results and any information that makes me personally identifiable will remain confidential and will be protected under the Data Protection Act (1998).

Signature of Participant		Date
Signature of Parent / Guardian (if under 18)		Date

Investigator to read and sign

- I have explained the test procedure fully and have answered any questions the participant had regarding the test and their involvement in the project.

Signature of Investigator		Date

Assessment practice

Produce an informed consent form for the research project you have planned. After you have produced your informed consent form, show it to your tutor for approval. Once your form has been approved by your tutor, give copies of it to your participants. Make sure you receive the signed copies back, to go with your research records. **P2**

Health screening

As part of your research project, you may need to conduct health screening with your participants, for example, if you are investigating any form of physiological testing. If you do need to carry out health screening, this must be done before any research is started and stored away securely with your signed informed consent forms.

Within sport and exercise sciences research, health and medical screening is conducted to ensure the health and safety of the participants by identifying any contraindications to the research they will be taking part in. These contraindications are:

- disease
- illness
- injury.

The information on the health screening form generally falls under three sections.

- demographic information (name, age/date of birth, gender)
- lifestyle information (diet, alcohol intake, smoking/ drug use, current physical activity/exercise level)
- medical/health information (disease, recent illnesses, recent injuries, family history, current medication).

After you have asked all of the questions, it is the norm to include a section that allows the participant to confirm that they have understood all aspects of the questionnaire, that they have raised any questions and that they have answered everything truthfully. There should also be a section where you sign to say that you have answered any questions the participant had.

The following example (on page 182) shows how you can incorporate this information into a questionnaire.

Use Internet search engines such as Google to research physical activity readiness questionnaires (PAR-Qs). This will help you with your questionnaire design and analysis. You may also find the following websites useful: www.healthstatus.com, www.self.com/calculators.

Unit 6 gives further information on how to conduct health screening with different participants.

Assessment practice

Produce a health screening form for the research project that you have planned. After you have produced your health screening form, show it to your tutor for approval. Once your form has been approved, give a copy to each of your participants. Make sure you receive signed copies back to go with your research records. **P2**

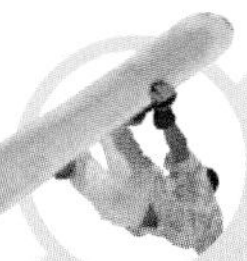

grading tip

Grading Tip 

You need to provide evidence that you have taken ethical and legal issues into consideration. This could be achieved by providing sample informed consent and health screening forms.

Data protection

Any data you collect is protected under the terms of the Data Protection Act (1998). No data that makes the participants personally identifiable should be included in

An example of a health screening form ▼

Name ☐ D.O.B ☐ Male / Female

Address ☐

Height ☐ Weight ☐

Home telephone ☐

Mobile telephone ☐

Email ☐

Lifestyle Information

Do you currently, or have you ever smoked? Yes / No If yes, how many per day ☐

On average how many glasses of beer, wine, spirits or other alcoholic drinks do you consume in a week?

Beer ☐ Wine ☐ Spirits ☐ Other ☐

Do you currently use any other form of non-medical drug? Yes / No

If yes, please specify ____

Which of the following do you regularly eat?

Breakfast ☐ Mid-morning snack ☐ Lunch ☐ Mid-afternoon snack☐ Dinner / Evening meal☐ Supper ☐

How many times per week do you eat fried foods? ☐

How many times per week do you eat salty foods? ☐

Do you eat meals whilst taking part in other activities (e.g. watching T.V, working, etc)? Yes / No

Would you consider yourself to be physically active? (By physically active we mean active for at least 30 minutes per day for at least 5 days per week) Yes / No

What activities do you regularly take part in?

Walking, jogging or running ☐ Swimming ☐ Cycling ☐ Aerobics ☐ Gardening ☐ Walking the dog ☐

Competitive sport ☐ Please specify ____

Other activities ☐ Please specify ____

Medical Information

Has your doctor ever said that you have a heart condition and that you should only do physical activity recommended by a doctor? Yes / No

Do you feel pain in your chest when you do physical activity? Yes / No

In the past month, have you had chest pain when you were not doing physical activity? Yes / No

1

your research project. Data collected should be stored in a locked filing cabinet that is accessible only by you and your research supervisor. You should not store electronic versions of your data anywhere that is publicly accessible, nor should any data that make the participant personally identifiable be publicly displayed.

Ensuring the welfare and safety of the client throughout the research process

It is important that you ensure the welfare and safety of your participants throughout the research process. All participants have the right to expect the highest standards of professionalism, consideration and respect from you when you are conducting research. The safety and welfare of your participants should always be your main concern throughout the research process.

Child protection

You must never harass or abuse in any way any children that you are working with as part of your research. Abuse can fall under one of four headings: physical abuse, sexual abuse, emotional abuse and neglect.

- Physical abuse is when somebody physically hurts or injures someone. Physical abuse can also come about by not reporting current signs of physical abuse to appropriate individuals.
- Sexual abuse is where somebody uses children to meet their own sexual needs, ranging from explicit conversations to full sexual intercourse. Due to the nature of some research techniques, it is possible that there is some degree of physical contact with children. It is your responsibility to make sure that any contact you have with children during your research is appropriate and used only where completely necessary.
- Emotional abuse is the persistent emotional ill treatment of a child, which is likely to cause severe and lasting adverse effects on their emotional development. Putting children under consistent pressure to perform to unrealistically high standards is also a form of emotional abuse, as are criticism, name-calling, and bullying. You must make sure you do not partake in any such activities while working with children.
- Neglect arises if you do not ensure children under your care are safe while you are conducting your research. If you expose children to undue cold or heat, or place them under unnecessary risk of injury, you are also neglecting them while they are in your care.

CRB checking

If you are going to work with children or vulnerable adults, you may be asked to apply for a Criminal Records Bureau (CRB) check. This is a check that will help to show (in this context) if you are able to work with children or vulnerable adults, or if there is any reason why you should not. You can refuse to complete a CRB check if you wish, but this will limit certain types of research you can conduct.

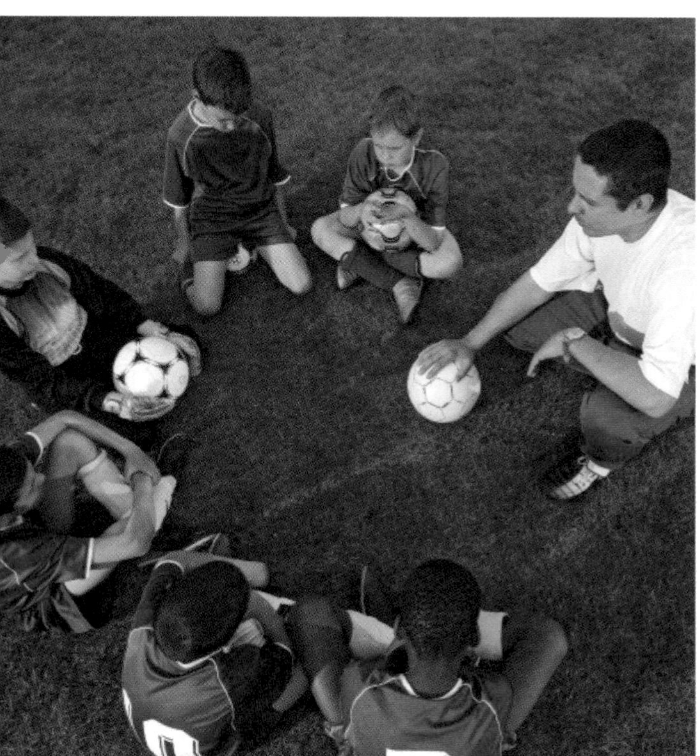

There are a number of factors that you need to consider when you are working with children to make sure that you are working ethically and legally

Web links

For more information on CRB checking, go to www.crb.gov.uk.

Knowledge of operating equipment

In research, you always need to think about protecting the welfare of your participants. Therefore, you must not practise or work when you are not fit to work in a professional manner – this includes knowing how all of your equipment, and works and what procedures you should follow. It is important that you recognise your level of competence when working with new equipment, and you must work within your limits. If you are working with something new, ask your tutor to show you how it works before you attempt to use it yourself. If you try to work with participants without first doing this, you may jeopardise their safety by not working responsibly.

Ethical clearance for the project

When you have written your research proposal, you need to show it to your tutor for approval. Whenever you plan research, you need to have it approved by an ethics committee. An ethics committee is an organisation that looks at your research proposal and says whether the project is safe and ethical. It will confirm whether you can start work on your project. There will usually be an ethics committee at your college (or it may be your tutor).

Data

When conducting your sport or exercise research project, you need to consider three things regarding your data: how you will collect it, how you will record it and how you will store it.

Collecting

By the time you come to conduct your research project, you will have already decided on the data collection methods you will be using. You need to be able to use the data collection methods you have selected to make sure you get the best quality of data possible. Whether your data are qualitative or quantitative in nature, whether you are using field-based or laboratory-based methods or whether you are using interviews, questionnaires, surveys or observations, you must always aim to collect data that are valid and reliable.

Key Terms

Qualitative data Non-numerical data that focuses on thoughts, opinions, feelings, experiences and beliefs about a particular topic. It is based on words and descriptions rather than statistical analysis.

Quantitative data Numerical data that are analysed using statistical techniques.

Precision

In Unit 4, we looked at the idea of precision. You need to make sure your data collection is precise. This means that your data collection should produce the same or similar values or results.

Field-based

Field-based data collection is data that are collected in the environment that simulates the one in which the sport is played.

For example, if you wanted to investigate the effects of imagery on American football goal kicking, you could collect the data on an American football pitch outside, regardless of the conditions (e.g. if it were windy and rainy you would still collect your data because sometimes when you play American football it is windy and rainy). This would allow you to say that your research had more ecological (real-world) validity because you have collected the data in an environment that replicates the match situation. This type of data collection is less controlled than laboratory-based data collection.

Laboratory-based

Laboratory-based data collection involves collecting data in an environment where all of the conditions are controlled, so that you are only measuring the variables in question.

Key Terms

Construct validity When you are able to compare the results to some form of behaviour.

Logical validity You can claim logical validity (sometimes known as face validity) when your research obviously measures what it intends to measure, without being affected by outside influences.

Ecological validity When your research can be applied to real-world settings.

This type of data collection has less ecological validity than field-based data collection because the data are not being collected in a situation that reflects the situation in which the activity is performed. However, you could claim more construct validity and logical validity because you have made sure that you have isolated the variables you are measuring. Laboratory-based data collection normally requires the use of expensive or technical equipment to collect your data.

Use of spreadsheets or databases

When collecting data, it is the norm to collate your quantitative data using ICT in the form of word-processed tables, spreadsheets or databases.

- A table can be used during collection. However, you cannot sort the information or perform complex calculations in a word-processed table – you can only view and display the data.
- A spreadsheet can be used to display and view your data, as well as performing statistical calculations. Spreadsheets are easy to use and can make initial data analysis straightforward.
- A database can be used to store large amounts of data easily. The database can be used to view, sort and search the stored data.

It is more secure to collect and store your data using an ICT-based method than it is to collect the data by hand. However, always make sure that, whichever method you use, you print a hard copy of the data as well.

Interviews, questionnaires, surveys, participant observation

In Unit 4 we looked at how to use different data collection techniques (such as interviews, questionnaires, surveys and participant observation). You need to make sure you know how to use each of these techniques correctly. (If you need a reminder of how each of these data collection techniques can be used, look back at Unit 4.)

Recording

In Unit 4, we looked at various ways you can record your data (including rank order, frequency, cumulative frequency and range). Use the information you have on these methods, together with your preferred methods of data collection (tables, spreadsheets or databases, or a combination of all three), to decide on the best methods of recording your data.

Rank order

Rank order distribution means placing your data into one list in a single column. This method of recording data is used when the total number of participants is less than or equal to 20 ($n \leq 20$).

Frequency

There are two types of frequency distribution.

- Simple frequency distribution: at times, the amount of data collected will be too large to place into rank order distribution. Simple frequency distribution is used when *the total number of participants is greater than 20* ($n > 20$) and when the range is less than or equal to 20 ($r \leq 20$).
- Grouped frequency distribution: in quantitative research, it is not uncommon for you to be working with data ranges greater than 20 and with data sets greater than 20. Grouped frequency distribution is used when both the total number of participants and the range are greater than 20 ($n > 20$, $r > 20$).

Cumulative frequency

This is obtained by adding up the frequencies as you go along to give a running total.

Cumulative frequency graphs are always plotted using the highest value in each group of data, and the cumulative frequency is always plotted vertically on a graph, never horizontally.

A cumulative frequency graph has a characteristic S-shape.

Range

Range is a simple method of organising your data. It is the distance in numerical value from your highest to your lowest value collected.

Transcribing, audio recording, video recording

When you have recorded your interviews, you need to transcribe them. Transcribing can be time-consuming, so you need to plan for this.

When you transcribe your interviews, always try to transcribe them 'verbatim'. This means that you transcribe the interview in exactly the same words as used by the participant, including any pauses.

You should also try to show any changes in body language throughout the interview, as this can give you an indication of the meanings behind some of the words the participant may have used.

Use of ICT

Many methods of collecting and recording data are based on the use of ICT. This has the advantage of being easy to use, and it allows you to conduct data analysis quickly and efficiently.

Although it is recommended that you use ICT to record your data in its final draft form, do not discount the old-fashioned paper and pen method of collecting your data if you are in a field-based or laboratory-based setting. Aside from the fact that there is the practical issue of not usually having a computer in the field, the advantage of using both methods is that you already have a back up copy of your data should anything go wrong with your computer. It is vital that you keep electronic back ups of all of your data and store them in a safe place.

Storage

Secure storage

You have a responsibility to maintain the confidentiality of all participants in the project, unless they have given you prior written consent that you can include such details where they are personally identifiable.

You are bound by the terms of the Data Protection Act to make sure that this is the case. You need to make sure that you organise a safe place for you and your tutor to store the information you collect throughout your project.

It is best if the data are stored in a locked filing cabinet that only you and your research supervisor have access to.

Ongoing evaluation of the research project

It is important that you write down any problems you have had while completing your research project.

You should explain how you dealt with these problems, or how you would change things in the future were you to carry out the project again.

Opportunity to conduct manual data analysis

Your data analysis should start as soon as possible. This is normally after the first round of data collection has been completed.

When you start your data analysis you will be able to see how it is progressing and look at any themes that are emerging.

Making initial conclusions regarding analysed data

Just as you should start analysing your data as soon as you have finished your first round of data collection, you should start drawing your first conclusions as soon as you have finished your first round of data analysis.

Research diary

A research diary is something that you use to record the information about your project as you go through the research process.

You should record everything that is important about your research process, concentrating on the following areas: ongoing evaluation of data, opportunity to conduct manual data analysis, initial conclusions, and recording your thoughts and feelings regarding the research process.

You should record your thoughts and feelings regarding the progress you are making throughout the project, because if you can get into the habit of doing this, you will be able to produce a better 'future recommendations' section and a better 'conclusion'. It will also make it easier for you to conduct an overall evaluation of your project at the end.

You should record minutes of meetings with your supervisors, so that you do not forget the guidance they have given you. In your supervisory meetings, it is likely that you will get a lot of information in a short space of time, so putting the key points in your research diary will help.

You can also record ideas about your project as you go along, such as if you read something or see something in the news that might be useful. Think about all the times you have seen something on television and the next day thought to yourself, 'Where did I hear that again?'

It is important that you write down any problems you have had while completing your research project aswell, and how you either dealt with them or how you would change things in the future should you do the project again. This can be part of your evaluation.

Assessment practice

Conduct the research project that you planned earlier in this unit. Remember to take into account all the factors throughout this section that relate to conducting a research project.

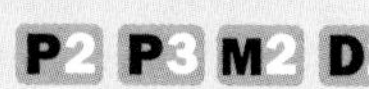

grading tips

Grading Tip P2 P3 M2 D2

If you decide not to keep a research diary while conducting your research project, you will not be able to achieve a distinction grade for the unit overall. You should conduct your initial data analysis in the research diary and draw initial conclusions about the data in there as well.

5.3 Be able to produce a sport science- or exercise science-based research project

The purpose of conducting research is to in some way benefit a particular area of knowledge. This is done by communicating what you have found with others,who may be interested.

Conducting your research can be time-consuming and you may need to invest a lot of time and effort into completing it, so the last thing you want to do is let yourself down by producing a poor report. Follow the guidelines in this section and they will help you. Here are some points to get you started.

- It is likely that you will not be able to write your report 'off the bat' first time around. You will probably need to draft and redraft it several times. To make this easier, do not leave this task to the last minute. Make sure that you plan how you will write the report and leave time for this.

Remember!

You can start to write some of your research report before you finished your project (e.g. acknowledgements, introduction, literature review and method sections), so get on with it as soon as you can.

- You must make sure you back up your work regularly. This is probably the longest assessment you will complete as part of your course, so the last thing you want to do is have to start it all over again. Print out the work you have done on a regular basis so that you have a hard copy in your file. This will also help you with proofreading and editing your work.
- Proofread and edit your work yourself – do not rely on the computer's spell checking function. The spell checker is useful if you have spelt something incorrectly, but it will not detect other mistakes such as 'too' instead of 'two' or 'one' instead of 'won'. Check for cases where the writing is in the first person; your project should be written in the third person and the past tense. For example, 'I noticed that' should be changed to 'It was noted that'.
- Make use of your research diary to help you write your report. You will get ideas as you go through the research process that you will want to include in your project write up. Make notes as you go along in your research diary because you will almost certainly be unable to remember them when you come to your write up.
- It is very important that you read the assessment criteria for your project report. If you do not use the assessment criteria to guide your writing, you will not be able to do as well as you could have. This means it is unlikely you will receive the high grade you are capable of.

Scientific structure of the research report

When writing your project, try to make the report as readable as you can for your audience – one of the main things is to make it interesting.

It is likely you will be conducting your research project in a topic that you are interested in. You need to demonstrate this level of interest through your writing because that will keep your readers interested.

When students start to produce a research report, they sometimes fall into one of these traps.

- They make the report overly-complicated, long-winded and full of complex technical terms because they think that this will impress the reader. However, this will not impress anyone.
- They make the report too 'chatty' and avoid using technical terms because they are worried that the audience will not understand it or because they do not understand it themselves. This style often lacks any real form of academic rigour.

What you need to try to do is find a happy medium between these writing styles. Try to demonstrate your enthusiasm for the topic in an academic manner, using appropriate terminology (such as key terms at relevant times), while at the same time showing your opinions, thoughts and arguments.

Remember!

The report should be written in the third person using the past tense.

There is an accepted format for research reports within sport and exercise sciences that should be followed. This section outlines what the format is and what you should put in each section.

Title page

Your title page should include the following information, usually in this order:

- project title
- your name
- your course (include qualification and level)
- the unit title
- the date when the project is due to be handed in.

Abstract

The abstract is a short summary of your research. It is normally about 150–200 words long at this level, but it may be a little more the further you go in education. This is an important section because it is the first thing people will look at and so it often determines whether they want to carry on reading or not.

The abstract should include a brief description of your topic, aims, objectives, hypothesis and null hypothesis, rationale, a brief description of your method, and a summary of the main results and conclusions.

General contents page

The contents page should show the layout of the report and say what is in each section. Each aspect of the contents should be given a specific heading and the page number recorded next to it. Any major sub-divisions of each section should also be shown in the general contents page in the same way.

Contents page for figures and tables

This should show the table or figure number, the title of each item and the page location within the report, so that it can be sourced easily should the reader need to refer to it.

Case study

Writing an abstract

Writing the abstract is the part many students struggle with (or forget about), so reading and analysing other abstracts will help you to get into the habit of writing good copy. Here is an example of an abstract:

'This investigation employed Smith's (1996) model of performance-related anxiety to examine links between perfectionism, achievement goals and the temporal patterning of multidimensional state anxiety in 119 high-school runners. Instruments assessed achievement goals (Roberts and Balague, 1989), perfectionism (Frost, Marten, Lahart and Rosenblate, 1990) and multidimensional state anxiety (Martens, Burton and Vealey, 1990) on four occasions prior to a cross-country meet. Regression analysis indicated that perfectionism was a consistent, significant predictor of cognitive anxiety. Perceived ability was a consistent predictor of confidence, and ego and task goals contributed to the prediction of cognitive anxiety and confidence respectively. Concern over mistakes, doubts about action, and personal standards were consistent predictors of cognitive anxiety, somatic anxiety and confidence respectively. The findings help further develop Smith's (1996) model and suggest that the appraisal process underlying multidimensional state anxiety is influenced by individual differences in a number of achievement related constructs.'

From H. K. Hall et al, 'Precompetitive Anxiety in Sport: the Contribution of Achievement Goals and Perfectionism', *Journal of Sport and Exercise Psychology*, Vol. 20, 1998.

1. **What is the topic of this investigation?**
2. **What were the authors aiming to find out?**
3. **Which method was used?**
4. **What are the main conclusions?**
5. **Are there any aspects missing from the abstract?**

Contents page for appendices

As for the general contents page, and for figures and tables, you need to have a section that shows the content of your appendices. This should give the appendix number and the content of the appendix.

Acknowledgements

In this section, you should acknowledge all the people without whom it would not have been possible to complete the research. This could include those who have given you information, such as your tutor, and the participants in the study.

Introduction

The introduction should describe your topic and give the rationale for conducting the project. It should identify and explain your research question, your aims and objectives and the hypothesis and null hypothesis. It should also define any key terms used in the project. You will have done this already in your proposal, so the key terms can often be transferred from your proposal (after changing from future tense to past tense). Alternatively, they may need to be altered slightly before being included in the introduction. If the area you are looking at has more than one definition from a number of people, you need to choose the definition that you are going to use for your project. This is known as the operational definition.

Key Term

Operational definition Quite often in sport and exercise sciences, terms have a number of different definitions that have been offered by different people. The operational definition is the definition of the topic that you are going to use for your research project.

It is also good practice to include a purpose statement in your introduction. There are different types of purpose statements for qualitative and quantitative research. The table below summarises the two types of purpose statement.

Quantitative purpose statements	Qualitative purpose statements
Words like 'test' or 'measure'	Words like 'understand'
Research design and variables	Research design
Who/what you are testing or measuring	Data collection methods
The theory or model that is the basis of research (where applicable)	The area being researched

Examples of quantitative and qualitative purpose statements

The purpose statements for both qualitative and quantitative research need to include the information in the table, but the details do not need to be in the same order.

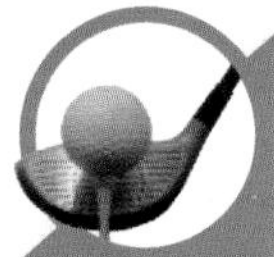

Think it over

Here is an example of a quantitative purpose statement: 'The following quantitative experimental research project will test whether or not the use of internal imagery can improve basketball free-throw shooting accuracy in adolescent male and female basketball players. The results of the project will be discussed with reference to the psychoneuromuscular theory.'

Here is an example of qualitative purpose statement: 'The current research project is a longitudinal study that aims to develop an understanding of children's perceptions of the roles of luck and ability in successful sport performance.'

Why is one quantitive and the other qualitative?

Theory into practice

Using the quantitative and qualitative purpose statements in the table on page 190, identify each of the criteria in terms of your research project. For example, can you identify the theory or model that is the basis of your research?

Literature review

In the literature review you start to think about arguments that have been made in previous research. A common mistake with literature reviews is that students simply list a lot of research from other areas and leave it at that. However, this does not make up a literature review.

For your literature review, you need to include a list of all the literature you have studied and give important details about that literature. You also need to discuss strengths and areas for improvement from previous research, and highlight key arguments from previous research and say how they apply to your project. You should allow the literature to set the scene for your project. The literature you use should relate to the aims, objectives and research problem in your study, otherwise you will not be able to produce an internally coherent research project report (see page 197).

One of the best ways to learn how to write a literature review is to read others and see how they have been written. Until you have written a literature review, the prospect may seem quite daunting.

A literature review has three main components: the introduction, the main body, and the summary and conclusion sections.

- The introduction to the literature review should explain why the literature review has been set out in the way it is.
- The main body is where you discuss the important arguments and concepts in the literature. This will be the longest section and you need to make sure that you follow the three Cs: the text needs to be clear, concise and coherent.
- The summary and conclusions section should summarise the main arguments and indicate how they have influenced your project.

Method

The purpose of the method section is for you to set out how you achieved your research objectives. As with the introduction and literature review, there will be aspects of the method section that you can reuse from your proposal (and you will simply need to change from future tense to past tense). This section will be the focal point of your project write up because it tells the reader exactly what you did, how you did it and why you chose to do it that way.

For your method to be an effective one, it must be in enough detail for somebody to be able to pick up your report, read your method and reproduce your study in exactly the same way as you. Your method should be written in the third person, past tense and continuous prose. For example, instead of writing 'I collected data from 20 participants and then I analysed it using Spearman's rank order correlation' you should say 'Data were collected from 20 participants and analysed using Spearman's rank order correlation.' The method section should be split into three main parts: participants, data collection and data analysis.

- Participants: this section needs to provide all the important details about your sample, as discussed on page 174. The style of writing needs to be in the past tense and you need to take into account any changes to your participants since the planning stage. Other than that, this section will be almost identical to the participants section of your proposal. The main difference is that you will now know all of the participants' details, so you will be able to include all the mean and standard deviation data in the method section. Here is an example of how you could write about your proposed sample.

> ***Participants:*** For this study, 45 males ranging in age from 21 to 25 were randomly selected from the overall available population (*n* = 100) of ice hockey players who have played at an elite level for at least three years (*m* = 4.1 ± 0.7). After this, participants were randomly assigned to one of three groups (*n* = 15).

- Data collection: in this section of your method there are a number of details you need to include, such as research design, the methods you used (e.g. interviews) and the data collection procedures.
- Research design: this section should identify and explain the choice of research design. For example, 'The experimental design aimed to investigate the effects of the independent variable (coaching technique) on the dependent variable (performance).'
- Methods used: this section should explain your choice of research methods (instruments, apparatus, etc.) and outline any design issues where appropriate. This section also needs to include information on any pre-test methods you used. For example:

> Before research was started, a pilot study was conducted and necessary alterations were made to the design of the questionnaire. Informed consent was obtained from each of the participants before any aspect research was conducted. Questionnaires were used as the primary data collection tool. The questionnaires consisted of a range of open and closed questions because... Interviews were then used as a follow-up data collection tool. Semi-structured interviews were selected because...

Again, much of this section can come from your proposal and be changed from future tense to past tense.

- Data collection procedures: this section needs to provide details of how the research was actually carried out, what data were collected, how many times data were collected, how long the data collection took, etc. Finally, you need to report any ethical or legal considerations important to this stage. For example:

> A total of 100 questionnaires were given out by hand to the participants. These were completed in the presence of the researcher. From this, 10 follow-up semi-structured interviews were completed, ranging from 40 minutes to 60 minutes (*m* = 47 ± 4.6) and then transcribed. Interviews were conducted in a setting familiar to the participants to ensure they were comfortable with the research process and to increase the quality of response from each participant. Ethical approval for the overall test procedure was obtained before research started and all data collected were kept confidential, with no details that made the participants personally identifiable included.'

- Data analysis: the analysis section needs to outline all the methods you used that contributed to the overall analysis of your data, along with an explanation for why you used those methods. This section should also include any aspects of the data analysis that you used. For example, 'Data were analysed using the independent test because the aim of the study was to find out if there was a significant difference between the mean scores of the two groups and the data collected were ratio in nature.'

Results

The next section is the results section. This is probably the most important part of your research project because it shows what you found through your research. A common mistake is to report every single finding you have and let your reader find their way through it. What you need to do is report the results that are important to the aims of your study in a concise, well-organised way. The overall aim of data analysis in your research project is to provide the reader with a coherent and logical development of answers to all the questions you raised in their minds throughout the introduction and literature review. The last thing you want to do is to spoil this by reporting everything regardless of its relevance because you think it looks good.

There are some items that should always be reported in the results sections, including the descriptive statistics you calculated such as the mean and standard deviation data. These results are important because they give the reader an easy way to evaluate the results and, if possible, the data should be presented in one table.

You must present the results in a way that is easy to understand and not daunting, but without using too many colours, fonts and special effects. The correct combination of tables and figures will make your data analysis easy to follow, and less detail is usually more beneficial to the reader. Therefore, a simple graph or chart in black and white is preferable to a three-dimensional graph in a multitude of colours. Make sure you describe the key aspects of figures and tables in the results section too; do not include them without saying what they show. Say what the tables show, but do not repeat the information in them as this is a waste of time.

Another important part of the results section is to consider how you should report quantitative data analysis and qualitative data analysis. Although the principles are largely the same, the technical aspects are different.

- Quantitative data: as with the general principles of completing the results sections, when reporting your statistics a general guide is: the easier something is to understand, the better. Tutors are not looking to be blinded with statistics; they are looking for you to correctly analyse your data in the best way to suit your project. Make sure you report only the relevant data analysis, always include the level of significance and report your data using the appropriate number of decimal places. If you can place your results into an appropriate context, this will also benefit the overall quality of the results section.
- Qualitative data: just as with the use of statistics where you report only the relevant numbers, with qualitative data analysis you report only the relevant words, phrases or quotes. Select the correct type of organisational diagram or chart to make sure that you are not saying one thing with your quotes but another with your diagrams. For example, do not report results that show an interaction between different concepts and then use a radial diagram instead of a Venn diagram.

Discussion and conclusion

The discussion gives you the opportunity to discuss the implications of your results (i.e. what your results mean). You get to discuss whether your results were the same or different from the results of previous research and why this may be the case. One common mistake is to discuss only your own results and not in relation to other research.

The discussion should make reference to the aims and objectives of your study, and whether they were achieved or not (including any evidence to support this). However, be careful when discussing the implications of your results – this is where the scope of your research comes in. If you are conducting a relatively small-scale study, report your results as such. Do not claim the results can find the answer to every problem in the sport and exercise area you are looking at, when really the results have made a very small contribution to one area. In your discussion you should try to generalise your results as much as possible, but you do not want to make unsupported claims as this will actually detract from the quality of the arguments you make.

Remember!

Write your discussion in language you understand. Base it around how the results of your project link to your aims and objectives, and also how your results are similar to or different from previous research.

When writing the discussion, do not feel you have to use a thesaurus to write every word, in the hope that it will make the text sound more technical and detailed. The best discussion you can write is based on your observations and analysis of the results and written in such a way that you understand them. If you complete your discussion in this way, your arguments should be effective and convincing.

The table below gives some examples of how a perfectly good argument can be changed into an overly complex sentence (or, in some cases, paragraph) that makes far less sense.

What they said	What they meant
There is a large body of experimental evidence which clearly indicates that smaller members of the genus Mus tend to engage in recreational activities while the feline is remote from the locale	While the cat's away, the mice will play.
From time immemorial, it has been known that the ingestion of an 'apple' (i.e. the pome fruit of any tree of the genus Malus, said fruit being usually round in shape and red, yellow or greenish in colour) on a diurnal basis will with absolute certainty keep a primary member of the healthcare establishment from one's local environment	An apple a day keeps the doctor away
Even with the most sophisticated experimental protocol, it is highly unlikely that you can instil in a superannuated canine the capacity to perform novel feats of legerdemain	You can't teach an old dog new tricks

Examples of complex sentences

A final point to consider in your discussion is the use of secondary sources to discuss your results. To be able to achieve a distinction for your research project, you need to show that you have compared your results to secondary sources, and that you have made some conclusions in your research diary that relate your initial data analysis to secondary sources.

Use this checklist to make sure you have written a good discussion section.

- Have you interpreted your results?
- Have you said whether the results are similar to or different from previous research or what you would have expected?
- Have you discussed your results and related them back to your aims, hypothesis, rationale, introduction and literature review?

Remember!

The literature in your literature review is also used to discuss your findings.

The conclusion and future recommendations section is the last section that will discuss your research project, its successes or its shortfalls. The conclusion should be drawn from the discussion you have just finished writing and the future recommendations should be based on the overall research process. This section is key to you showing that you can evaluate your research project and reflect on what you have done.

The conclusion should relate directly to your overall aims of the project. You should repeat your aims and hypothesis/null hypothesis and say if they were achieved and supported respectively. It should finish with a statement that summarises the main findings of the project.

Remember!

Remember that the introduction sets the scene for the overall project and asks initial questions, while the conclusion provides the overall definitive answer.

To make sure you have written a good conclusion section, when you have finished writing your first draft of the research project report, read the introduction and then read the conclusion without anything else in between. If you have written both of these sections correctly, they should make perfect sense without reading anything else.

The future recommendations should be based on what you see as the areas for improvement for your project.

Some questions to ask yourself when writing this section are as follows.

- What could you have done differently to make this project better?
- What went well with the project that could be developed in the future?
- What else would you have liked to have found out from the research project?

Remember!

Your conclusion should summarise the main finding (s) of your project with reference to the aims and hypothesis; and your future recommendations should evaluate your project and say how it could be improved in the future.

Harvard reference section and appendices

The reference section is where you list all of the authors whose work you have used in the text. It is a list of the sources you have used, written in alphabetical order of the lead author's surname (the author that is first on the front of the book) and is produced using a technique known as the Harvard reference system.

The reference section is sometimes confused with the bibliography, but there are some distinct differences between them. The bibliography contains all of the information you have used to help you complete the project but you may not have mentioned in text, whereas the reference section lists work you have directly quoted from in your own work.

It can be useful to write both a reference section and a bibliography, but it is best to ask your tutor if you should include both. You will usually be required to include only a reference section because you need to show which work is your own and which you have used from others.

If you try to say work is your own when you have taken it from other areas, this makes your research unethical. You could put your work at risk, because you would be doing something known as plagiarism.

Start to produce your reference list as soon as you start to write your research project report. Every time you put a reference in the text, make sure you add the full source to your reference list. Doing this is the easiest way to make sure you include all of your authors in the list and will save you a long job at the end.

You will use a range of sources in your research project, all of which should be referenced in your text. You will take direct quotes from some of the sources, while others will be paraphrased.

Remember!

When referencing work you have paraphrased, you need to give the author and the year of publication, such as: 'Côté (1999) suggests there are three distinct phases of sport participation from an early age through to adolescence.'

Remember!

When using a direct quote, the page number is also required and the quote must be placed in quotation marks, such as: 'A collaborative effort among coaches, athletic trainers, parents, physicians and athletes is optimal for recognising, preventing and treating eating disorders in athletes' (Sundgot-Borgen and Torstveit, 2004. p.25).

If you need to reference work with more than two authors, the first time you reference the work you need to include all the authors' surnames, then each subsequent time you can give just the first author's name and the other authors are replaced with the term 'et al.', which means 'and co-authors'.

Remember!

When referencing more than two authors, give all the surnames the first time but use 'et al.' thereafter: Martin, Moritz and Hall (1999) proposed a model of imagery use. Martin et al. (1999) suggested four stages in their model for imagery use.

When you write the reference list, there are slightly different techniques for referencing work from different sources.

- To reference a book: author's surname, author's initials, year, title of book, place of publication, publisher.

Remember!

Here is an example of how to reference a book. This format should be followed carefully.

Thomas, J. R., Nelson, J. K. and Silverman, S. J. (2005) *Research Methods in Physical Activity* (5th edn), Champaign, IL, Human Kinetics.

- To reference a chapter in an edited book: author's surname, author's initials, year, title of chapter, editor(s) of book, book title, pages of chapter, place of publication, publisher.

Remember!

Here is an example of how to reference a chapter in an edited book:

Griffin, P. and Hemplin, T. J. (1989) 'An overview of qualitative research', in P. W. Darst, D. B. Zakrajsek and V. H. Mancini (eds.) *Analysing physical education and sport instruction* (2nd edn., pp.399–410), Champaign, IL, Human Kinetics.

- To reference a journal article: author's surname, author's initials, year, title of journal article, title of journal, volume number, pages.

Remember!

Here is an example of how to reference a journal article:

Eccles, D. W. (2006) 'Thinking outside the box: the role of environmental adaptation in the acquisition of skilled and expert performance', *Sport and Exercise Sciences*, 24, 1103–1114.

- To reference an Internet source: author (if known) or title of article, full website address of Internet site, date accessed.

Remember!

Here is an example of how to reference an Internet article:

FA Structural Review Update, www.thefa.com/TheFA/NewsFromTheFA/Postings/2006/10/StructuralReview.htm (accessed 29/10/2006).

The appendix section is where you insert any information that helps to provide support for anything you have said or done in your report. Pieces of information that are found in the appendices include: sample questionnaires or interview guides, sample informed consent forms and detailed protocols about the calibration of equipment. Any appendices that you include should be referenced in the text. For example, 'The gas analysis testing equipment was calibrated prior to each data collection session (for full details of the calibration protocol followed, see Appendix 1).'

Appendices do not normally count towards your word count, so check with your tutor to find out if they are included in your suggested word count for the assessment.

Purpose and structure of each of the sections of a well-structured research project

The purpose and structure of each of the sections of a well-structured report is to make the report easy to navigate, with clear signposts in the text for the readers to follow. There is an accepted format for research reports, which should be followed.

Use of ICT

You need to produce the research project report using appropriate ICT. Think about using word processing packages such as Microsoft Word® to produce the text and tables within your project; Microsoft Excel® to produce graphs, charts and spreadsheets; and Microsoft Access™ for databases.

Remember!

Make sure you match the ICT program to the task you are working on. if you use the wrong program, your project may suffer because it will not look as professional as possible.

Internal coherence

One important concept you need to demonstrate throughout your writing is known as internal coherence. This means that you report everything with reference to the aims of the project, relating your arguments to those aims.

Remember when we said in the discussion and conclusion section on page 194 that you should be able to read your introduction and then read your conclusion straight after and the two should be related and make sense? If you can do that, you have achieved internal coherence.

Here are some questions that you can use as an internal coherence checklist.

- Are your literature review and the literature reported based on the aims of the project?
- Are the arguments that you have made in your discussion section related to the aims of the project?
- Have your conclusions made it clear whether the aims were achieved and whether the hypothesis can be accepted or rejected?

Reporting literature with reference to the aims of the project

Make sure the literature you report relates to the aim of the project. For example, if you are looking at the effects of imagery in football, it would be really useful to include as much literature as you can about how imagery can benefit football and sports similar to football. This will help you to ensure that your project has levels of internal coherence.

Making arguments in the discussion section that are related specifically to the aims of the project

The arguments you make in your discussion section should relate to the aims of the project. This will help you to ensure that you produce an internally coherent report. A good discussion also uses the literature you have reported to further relate your arguments to the aims of the project.

Drawing valid conclusions based on the aims of the project

Your conclusions should say clearly whether or not you have achieved your aims.

Assessment practice

Write a research report for the research project you have conducted. To complete a good, detailed research report you will probably want to aim for about 3,000 words in total (not including items that do not count towards the word count, such as appendices). Use a standard scientific structure and make sure you achieve internal coherence.

grading tips

Grading Tip 

Your research report must demonstrate high levels of internal coherence to achieve the highest grades.

Grading Tip 

To get the highest grades for your research project, you need to make sure you use a range of sources in your literature review from a combination of books, periodicals and Internet-based sources.

Grading Tip 

Make sure you follow the structure of a research report section so that you know in which order your sections need to go and what needs to be in each section.

5.4 Be able to evaluate a sport science- or exercise science-based research project

Evaluation

When you conduct a research project, you need to evaluate the project and provide future recommendations. We have looked at future recommendations as part of the research report on page 199, because they are sometimes reported in the conclusion and future recommendations section of your research project.

When you have finished the project, you might be asked to complete an oral or written evaluation of it. This section will help you to produce a more in-depth evaluation and provide future recommendations based on the evaluation.

The overall evaluation aspect of the research process has two aspects and can be completed by answering two questions:

- What were the strengths of the research project and what evidence do you have to support this?
- What were the areas of the research project that you needed to improve on and what evidence do you have to support this?

The main areas you will discuss when you are completing this aspect of the research process are validity and reliability of data and whether the aims of the project were achieved.

Remember!

You have to provide evidence to support the arguments you make. Simply stating 'Yes' or 'No' does not count as an evaluation.

To produce a more detailed evaluation of your project and your research report, you need to look at your report section by section and ask specific questions of each one. If you answer the questions honestly and in detail, you will be able to produce a good evaluation. Some questions to ask about each section and some overall questions are outlined below.

Strengths and weaknesses

When you are evaluating your research project, you need to identify strengths and weaknesses of the research project as a whole. An evaluation of your project is not a simple 'Yes' or 'No' answer to the question: was your project successful?

Evidence

You should provide evidence of the strengths and weaknesses of your project. This evidence needs to relate to validity, reliability and aims of the project (i.e. was it valid or reliable, and which aspects of validity and reliability did you achieve and why? See unit 4.)

Examples

The best evaluations are supported by evidence from your project. For example, if you were saying that your research could claim test/retest reliability, you would be expected to say that you had achieved this through completing a repeated measures study.

Future recommendations

If the project was to be completed again, what would be changed with the project and why?

A key part to reflecting on the research process is to develop the strengths and weaknesses you have identified, and to provide evidence and examples of directions for future research. For example, you might identify through your 'strengths and weaknesses' section that you did not have enough time to complete you study. As a result, you were not able to analyse developmental issues over a long period of time, which in turn affected the validity and reliability of your study. You would then be expected to be able to say that a suggestion for future research would be to adopt a longitudinal research design.

Benefits of suggested changes

This section follows on from your previous suggested changes, and allows you to justify why you would make them. Using the example above, you could suggest that your use of a longitudinal study would be beneficial because it would allow you to plan your research over a longer time frame, allowing you to investigate developmental issues more closely.

Knowledge check

1. What is the process you have to go through to plan your research project?
2. What factors do you need to take into consideration when planning your research project?
3. What factors do you need to take into account when looking at the resources required for your research project?
4. How can you make sure that you are working ethically and legally when you are conducting your research project?
5. What headings and subheadings should you use when structuring your research proposal?
6. How can you make sure you record your data in an appropriate manner?
7. How can you make sure you analyse your data correctly?
8. What does it mean when you are asked to compare your results to secondary sources and how could you do this?
9. What is the accepted scientific structure of a research report?
10. What does the term 'internal coherence' mean?
11. What criteria do you need to consider when you evaluate a research project?

Assessment practice

1 Use the following questions to evaluate your research project. Produce a written evaluation of your project using the sub-headings given for each set of questions. Try to write a good quality paragraph for each section and do not forget to give as much supporting evidence as you can. **P5 M4**

a *General evaluation*
Were the data you collected valid and reliable?
Were the aims of the project achieved?
Is your report internally coherent?
Have you written fluently in the third person?

b *Evaluation of abstract*
Have you shown what the report is about?
Have you shown your aims and objectives?
Have you indicated the methods used?
Have you discussed the main results?
Have you reported the overall conclusions?

c *Evaluation of introduction*
Have you put the project into context for the person reading the report?
Have you clearly shown aims, objectives and hypothesis?
Have you clearly defined all the key terms for the project?
Have you provided a clear rationale for the project?

d *Evaluation of literature review*
Have you used a range of secondary sources rather then being dependent on one?
Have you analysed enough in your literature review and made sure that you have not just described things?
Have you looked at literature that supports and argues against the point you are trying to make?
Have you made your literature review clear, coherent and concise?

e *Evaluation of method*
If somebody picked up your method, would they be able to replicate your study exactly as you did it?
Is your choice of research design clear?
Is it clear why you chose that research design?
Did you choose the best methods for data collection and data analysis?
Is it clear why you chose your data collection and data analysis methods?
Have you included all the information needed about your participants?

f *Evaluation of results*
Are your results clear and easy to follow?
Have you included all of the necessary results?
Have you included any results that are not important to your arguments?
Are your graphs, charts and tables easy to follow?

g *Evaluation of discussion*
Have you interpreted your results correctly?
Have you related your results to the previous literature or have you just discussed your results without any reference to secondary sources?
Is your discussion clearly written and easy to follow?

h *Evaluation of conclusion*
Have you made reference to the aims and hypothesis?
Are your conclusions based on what you found?

i *Evaluation of future recommendations*
Have you provided suggestions for changes if projects of this nature were to be completed again?
Have you justified these changes by saying how they would benefit future projects like this?

j *Evaluation of reference section*
Have you correctly used the Harvard reference system?

2 Produce a ten-minute oral presentation to be presented to a small group of your class mates, which evaluates your research project. Create a new slide to evaluate each of the different sections of your research report, and one slide for a general evaluation that looks at validity, reliability and whether or not you achieved your aims. **P5**

grading tips

Grading Tip P5 M4

A good evaluation will describe strengths, areas for improvement and future recommendations for the research project.

Grading Tip P5 M4

You need to provide evidence for the strengths and areas for improvement you have identified.

Grading Tip M4

To achieve a higher grade for your evaluation, you need to analyse whether or not you have achieved your aims. Your evidence for this could come through relating the conclusions from the project to the aims.

Grading criteria

To achieve a pass grade the evidence must show that the learner is able to:	To achieve a merit grade the evidence must show that, in addition to the pass criteria, the learner is able to:	To achieve a distinction grade the evidence must show that, in addition to the pass and merit criteria, the learner is able to:
P1 plan a sport- or exercise science-based research project **Assessment practice page 176**	**M1** Describe the proposed research design of the project and research methods to be used to complete the project. **Assessment practice page 176**	**D1** Explain how the selected research design and research methods will ensure that data collection and analysis is valid and reliable **Assessment practice page 176**
P2 conduct a sport- or exercise science-based research project, considering use of resources and ethical and legal issues **Assessment practice pages 181, 187**		
P3 collect and record data from the research project conducted **Assessment practice page 187**	**M2** correctly analyse collected data **Assessment practice page 187**	**D2** compare the analysed data to appropriate secondary sources and draw valid conclusions **Assessment practice pages 187, 197**
P4 produce a full research report using a standard scientific structure and ensuring internal coherence **Assessment practice page 197**	**M3** produce a coherent research project that clearly states the conclusions of the project and provides evidence of use of a combination of books, periodicals and internet-based sources **Assessment practice page 197**	
P5 evaluate the research project conducted, describing strengths, areas for improvement and future recommendations **Assessment practice page 200**	**M4** analyse the success of the project, relating the conclusions of the project to the initial aims of the project **Assessment practice page 200**	

Sports biomechanics in action

Introduction

Biomechanics is the study of the mechanics of life forms – in this case, the human athlete. Over the last few decades, biomechanics has concentrated on the role of forces within the athletic body and their influence on performance. Typical investigations may have centred on how a hammer thrower releases the hammer. More recently, there has been a move towards sports biomechanics.

Sports biomechanics looks at an individual player's and a team's performance through notational analysis. For example, sports biomechanics may consider the shooting accuracy in football of the striker, or the team as a whole. Within this unit you will explore the principles of sports biomechanics through a variety of sporting activities. You will be able to develop meaningful explanations in relation to the sports that interest you. In the future, you may wish to use the experience gained in this unit in careers ranging from coaching to fitness training.

After completing this unit you should be able to achieve the following outcomes:

- be able to perform notational analysis for sport
- be able to compare a numerical model to sporting performance
- be able to compare a technical model to sporting performance
- be able to provide feedback on performance to an athlete or team.

Think it over

Over the last few years, professional sports teams, especially international teams, have employed sports biomechanists to help them improve their performance and ultimately become successful. For example, the England National Cricket Team used sports biomechanists to improve their performance in bowling and batting.

The following examples should demonstrate the importance to performance of sports biomechanics in action.

Discuss the importance and advantage to a team of a sports biomechanists in each case:

- as a cricket player, you are poor at playing the hook shot and have been caught out five times recently playing this shot
- in football, you conceded a high number of goals in the last ten minutes of a match
- in rugby, you threw the ball to the third player in the lineout 80 per cent of the time.

Look at the photo. Hockey, as with other team sports, involves a number of important performance criteria, for example cleanly striking the ball.

In groups, use the photo as a starting point to draw up a list of the possible performance criteria a sports biomechanist might be interested in when analysing the performance of a hockey player.

Hopefully you will have produced a list that contains some important performance criteria. You may have included criteria such as passing and shot accuracy.

6.1 Be able to perform notational analysis for sport

In this section you will analyse the performance criteria of a sport of your own choice.

Performance criteria, put simply, are the separate parts of the performance which, if performed well, should lead to success for the athlete or team. For example, if you are interested in netball you could analyse the passing, interception rates and shooting accuracy as three examples of performance criteria of a particular player or team. Part of this analysis centres on data evaluation, for which you will need to use statistics (for example, calculation of the mean), and you will be expected to display this data accordingly (for example, by using a pie chart).

In the past, coaches have observed their athletes' performances and have tried to draw valid conclusions. However, these observations have been found to be unreliable and also inaccurate. This is because the coach cannot view all of the relevant information and mistakes are made when recalling the information. This is where notational analysis can help.

Key Term

Notational analysis A method used by sports biomechanists to analyse the performance of an individual or team. It is an emerging method used in professional sports to gain a competitive advantage over opponents.

Performance is analysed by recording data from teams and players, and by looking at tactics and techniques. This data or information can then be used in following matches to improve performance or gain an advantage over the opposition.

For example, by monitoring a game of football, the notational analyst can obtain data showing how much distance has been covered by each player, how much of this distance involves sprinting, jogging or walking, and even how many tackles, jumps, headers and correct passes they have made. Therefore, they can identify strengths and areas for improvement.

Taking it further

In small groups, perform some basic research into the uses of notational analysis. Look for information about sports that use notational analysis and then how they use this information. Once you have your research, discuss your findings with the rest of the group.

Performance criteria

Each sport, whether individual or team based, will have a different performance criteria profile. Criteria is simply a list of the factors (e.g. shot accuracy, saves, headers, dribbling) that are key for the sporting performance. Some sports, if simple in nature (such as snooker), may have only a few performance criteria (such as safety success). In comparison, more technical sports (such as hockey) will have a more exhaustive list, to include factors such as tackle success.

Remember!

Even within a team sport (such as rugby union) a specific position (for example, a hooker), will possess a different performance criteria profile in comparison to another one (for example, a winger) because of the demands placed on the player.

For example, the performance criteria of a squash player are:

- winner
- error
- stroke
- let.

Unforced errors

An unforced error is an error that comes from your own actions (and not as a direct consequence of what an opponent does).

If an athlete (for example, a squash player) can reduce the number of unforced errors they make in a match, then this should increase the chances of success in the match.

Activity

1 In pairs, choose two different sports you are familiar with. Identify the reasons why unforced errors in each sport occur (for example, loss of concentration). You should consider reasons not related to sport and exercise science as well in your answer.

2 Discuss the similarities and differences of enforced errors in each sport.

When analysing unforced errors in sporting performance, you could simply count the number made during a match. You could repeat this over a number of performances to see if there is a trend forming. However, you could dig deeper into this performance criteria by categorising the unforced errors. For example, in squash you may consider whether the unforced errors are on the serve or from backhand shots, etc.

Forced errors

Forced errors are as a direct result of the actions of your opponent. In tennis, a player is likely to make many forced errors because the other player is more powerful in their shots or is using uncontrollable spin on the ball. By getting your opponent to make many forced errors, you are more likely to win the match.

Remember!

In tennis, great players like Roger Federer make their opponents play many forced errors. This makes them successful.

When analysing unforced and forced errors you need to determine which one is which. If you are interested in tennis, you could record a match to watch specific points again to clarify which category the shot falls into.

Remember!

The difference between unforced and forced errors is that unforced errors are caused by yourself, whereas forced errors are brought on by your opponent.

Shot success/failure

There is a wide range of individual and team sports that rely on shot success to determine the match outcome. If you consider football as an example, many teams in the past have had plenty of goal-scoring opportunities but lost the match. This is because they cannot convert their chances, whereas the opposition may convert their only chance in the game. If you are interested in shot success, you could consider splitting the criteria into other areas. For example, in football you could analyse:

- each striker individually
- every player in the team
- left-footed shots
- right-footed shots
- shots inside the box
- shots outside the box.

You could also split this criteria even further. For example, in snooker you may analyse:

- long pots
- short pots
- pots to a specific pocket

- pots where positional play is required
- other pots such as colour, etc.

Taking it further

Choose a sport that requires an element of shot success and research into the technique required for success. You should try to describe the key coaching points. For example, in football you should look at the goal, not the ball. This research may help you later when you consider the feedback you want to give to the athlete or players.

Shot accuracy

You might think it would be easy to assess shot accuracy because you could just look at shots on and off target. However, in some team sports a shot on target can be saved, whereas a shot off target can take a deflection and go in.

Crosses

A cross in team-based sports such as football or hockey is another key performance criterion. Crossing can be analysed either from a defensive or an attacking perspective. You should decide which aspect of crossing you are interested in. If you want to analyse defending crosses, you need to look at issues beyond simply clearing the cross. This is because the defender (in hockey) may clear the cross initially, but this may lead to:

- another cross
- a shot on target
- a goal
- a penalty
- other negative outcomes for the defending teams.

It is suggested that you look at the number of crosses cleared first, and then look at the overall outcome (as above).

This type of analysis will allow the coach to identify areas of strength and areas for improvement

Remember!

To avoid producing too much data in relation to crosses you should either look at the defensive or attacking aspect.

Catches/interception rates

In terms of cricket you may have heard the phrase that 'catches win matches'. This is also important for many other team sports such as netball, rugby and basketball.

One form of analysis that you could use with catching is field or court position, where ball possession was lost or gained. Field position can be used with other performance criteria such as passing. Look at the following diagram of a netball court. It shows where possession was lost (or gained) through catching (interception rates).

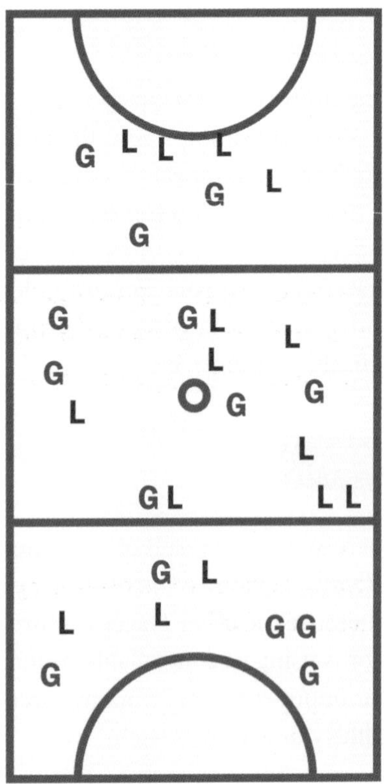

From the diagram we can consider the position on the court and the number of times possession was gained or lost.

To take this analysis further, we may add another code (for example, WA) to show that the wing attack was involved in a particular incident.

Remember!

By using the outline of a pitch or court you can add another dimension to your analysis, namely position. It also provides a useful aid for visual feedback.

Passing

One of the key elements that is central to a team's performance is its ability to pass. Here is a list of the key sports that you may be interested in analysing in relation to passing:

- football
- rugby
- hockey
- basketball
- netball
- water polo.

Within the performance criteria of passing there is a wide range of types you may want to analyse, these being:

- short passing/long passing (sports specific)
- backwards
- forwards
- square
- consecutive
- passing between particular players (e.g. goal shooter and goal attack in netball).

Remember!

When considering performance criteria such as passing, catching, etc. you also need to look at the outcome, because each pass or catch should be productive to the team.

Saves

As with catches, you could use an outline (of a goal) to represent and collect your raw data. You can just count the number of shots saved and missed (e.g. in hockey), but a coach may need more detailed information than this. This diagram of a hockey goal captures more information.

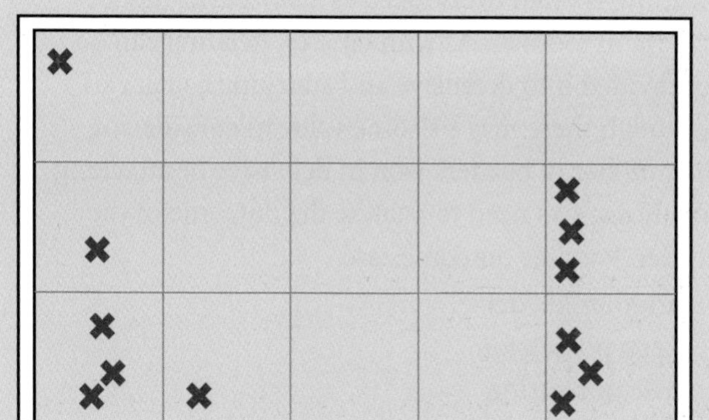

Data generated using this approach could lead to flexibility or agility training for the keeper

By dividing the hockey goal into different segments, you could identify the part of the goal where the keeper fails to save shots (marked X on the diagram) on a regular basis. From this, the coach would be able to concentrate on coaching a specific skill (for example, saving shots in the bottom right-hand corner).

Tackles

Tackling is another performance criteria you may consider using in relation to team sports.

Taking it further

In small groups, prepare and present a presentation based on the performance criteria of tackling. You should cover:

- the sports where tackling is important
- the correct technique of tackling
- the importance of tackling to levels of performance
- the method of recording tackles in a match
- a possible method of displaying your raw data
- the data analysis you may use to analyse your raw data.

Headers

Heading is often overlooked as a key performance criteria in football. As with crosses, heading can be subdivided into defensive and attacking categories. Although there may be some value in considering the number of headers won in defensive or attacking situations, you need to analyse the outcome of the header. Possible outcomes are:

- another header
- keep possession
- lose possession
- foul the opposition
- header off target
- header on target
- goal
- corner kick.

Dribbling

Dribbling involves a player trying to take the ball around an opposition player or players with the aim of gaining an advantage.

Dribbling is a key component in a number of team-based sports (for example hockey, football and basketball).

▲ **Dribbling the ball in basketball is often risky play because the player may lose control of the ball and give it to the opposition**

When dribbling the ball it is important that the end product of the dribble is a positive one. This means that it leads to:

- a shot at the target
- successfully passing the ball to a team member
- drawing a foul from the opposition
- gaining field advantage.

For example, you may record that a basketball player made 34 dribbles in the match. However, only 17 led to an end product. Therefore, you can calculate that:

$$\frac{\textit{17 successes}}{\textit{34 dribbles}} \times 100$$

= 50% success rate

Assessment practice

1 Choose an individual or team-based sport. Work in pairs to produce a list (or a flow chart) of the performance criteria that is key for sporting success. **P1**

2 Describe five relevant performance criteria (e.g. unforced errors, catching, passing, shooting, breaking of laws). You may include criteria not covered in this unit if you feel it is important (for example, in snooker you may consider safety play as being relevant). **P1**

Think it over

Most of the discussion has centred on team-based sports (although you can analyse the performance of one individual). Discuss within your group the performance criteria for an individual sport such as judo, snooker, golf, etc.

Notational analysis

Movement

Notational analysis can help a sports scientist, coach or fitness instructor to improve an athlete's or team's performance in most sports. We have looked at a wide range of sports in relation to many performance criteria such as passing or crossing. This section will concentrate on other key criteria:

- work rate
- positional play
- distance covered
- movement patterns
- breaking of rules/laws.

Work rate

From a biomechanical and physiological perspective, assessing an athlete's work rate is traditionally difficult to perform. There are many key factors to consider. For example, was the outcome of this work productive? Did the opposition have an influence on the work rate because of their style of play? It is not an easy performance criterion to consider.

However, you could use a heart rate monitor to calculate work rate. The heart rate monitor (attached to the player) will give you a great deal of feedback after the performance because you can upload the information onto a computer.

Activity

Investigate the work rate (heart rate) of two squash players during a match. Use two heart rate monitors (one per player) to collect your data. If you prefer, you can use the traditional method of recording heart rate in beats per minute (recording for 15 seconds and multiplying by 4). Record their heart rate at one-minute intervals for 20 minutes in total.

1 Plot the heart rate for both players against time using a line graph.

2 Describe the data on the line graph, looking for similarities and differences between the players.

3 Discuss whether the work rate corresponds to the performance of the players during the match.

Positional play

A manager of a team may be interested in one particular player and their positional play within a match. For example, in football, a manager may be interested in signing a new right back, but wants to know how much attacking the player performs during a match. This is because the manager wants to make sure that the player will fit into the team's style of play. As a sports biomechanist, you can perform some basic analysis to assist them.

Remember!

When analysing positional play you should try to record the match, because it will be difficult to log all the data at the time of play at once.

Case study

Champions League Final

When analysing positional play you may want to use this approach, which logs the amount of runs made, the distance and the direction using an arrow system. This diagram represents a ten-minute sample taken from the Champions League Final between Barcelona and Arsenal on 17 May 2006, which Barcelona won 2–1.

1. **In relation to the diagram, give a basic description of the positional play of the right back.**
2. **Describe how you could transfer this information into numerical data.**
3. **Explain how you could analyse this data.**
4. **Describe the advantages and disadvantages of using this style of analysis.**

▼ When working with elite performers, these types of movement would be tracked by sophisticated computer software

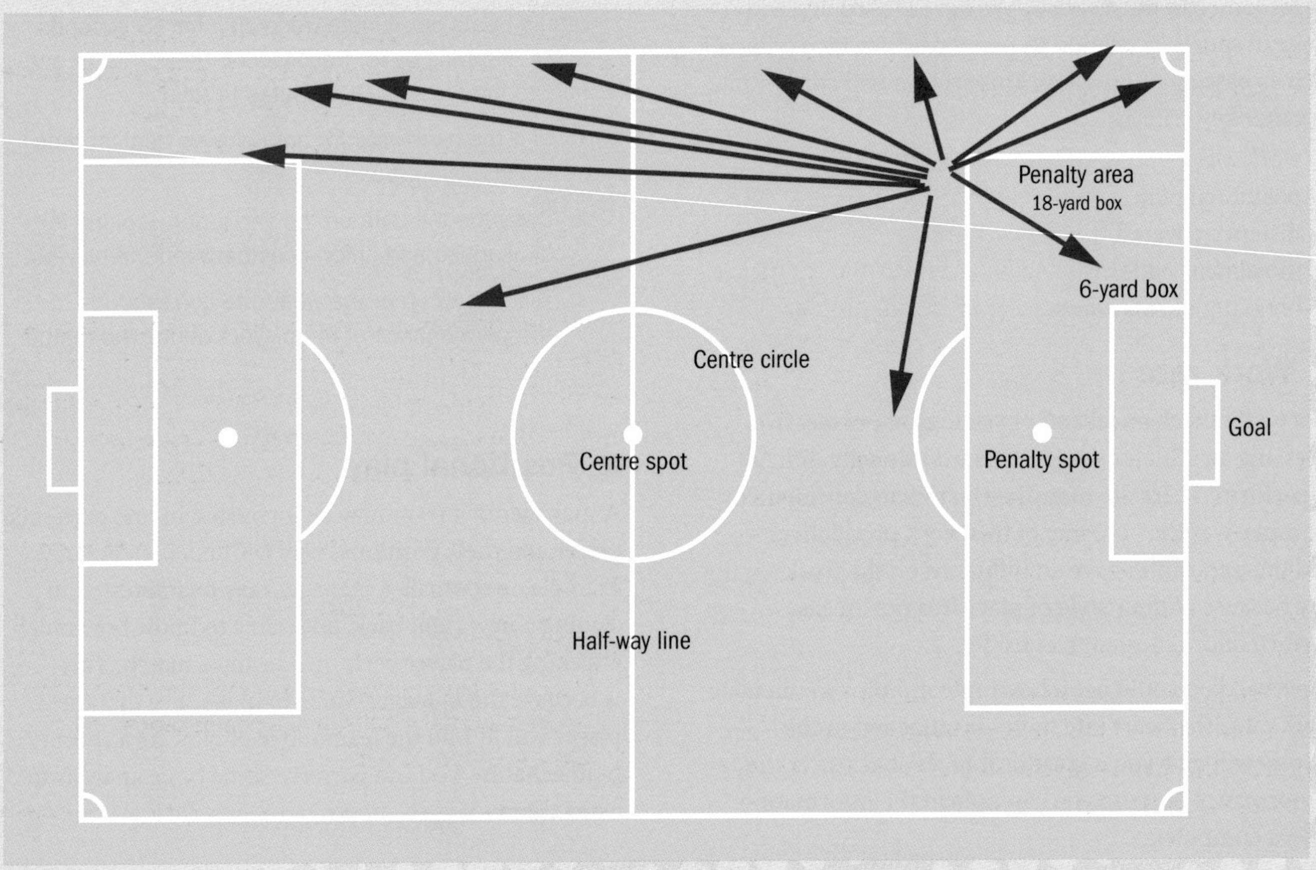

Distance covered including sprinting

In some sports (for example, rugby union) it is important for a player to cover as much distance as possible. However, this distance must be productive. Therefore, in rugby union, you may log the distance covered with the ball in metres for the number 8. This is because if the player can make some big runs and break the gain line, then it can bring other players into the game and is a clear advantage. As a sports biomechanist, you should record the distance covered with the ball and also log the outcome of the carry, such as a try or pass.

Movement patterns

In many respects the basics of movement patterns are similar to positional play (which has already been discussed). However, a movement pattern is a series of movements made by an athlete; therefore you are looking at a sequence of movements. If you are interested in basketball, you could analyse the movement patterns of players. For example, by looking at a recording of the match in the feedback session, you may note that when attacking as a team most of your attacks come down the left side of the court. This may be viewed as a weakness if the coach wants variety by attacking the left, central and right areas.

Breaking of rules/laws

When playing sports it is inevitable that the athletes will break the rules or make an illegal move (for example, punching below the belt in boxing). This rule breaking may be unintentional (for example, in football you may foul an opponent through a mistimed tackle).

In comparison, an athlete may break a rule on purpose with the aim of gaining an advantage over the opposition. For example, a hockey player may touch the ball with their foot on purpose to concede a foul. This will then allow their team to regain their position when trying to defend.

From an analysis point of view it is important to record how many times an athlete breaks the rules because, generally, this has a negative influence on the athlete's or team's performance.

Activity

Choose a sport you are interested in. Research and note the key rules or laws that could be used for data collection. In addition, identify the key illegal moves or plays made by a sports performer.

As a follow on, you may also consider the outcome of these illegal moves. A break of the rules may lead to:

- nothing, as the opposition fails to take advantage
- booking
- sending off
- suspension
- the sin bin
- goal/score/points for the opposition
- loss of field advantage
- the breakdown of own team's play
- other outcomes specific to your sport, e.g. in snooker conceding the frame or match.

Performance criteria

A central part of notational analysis is selecting the performance criteria to assess the sporting performance (such as passing). For a full review of the key performance criteria see pages 104–111.

Statistics

A central component of sports biomechanics is the use of statistics (see Unit 4). The statistics you may have to use are fairly simple in nature, such as median or mean. This section explains the key statistical measures you may have to use with the data you have collected.

Remember!

Using statistics allows us to interpret the raw data, understand the results, make comparisons and draw valid conclusions.

Mean

The mean is the sum of a series of measurements divided by the number of those measurements. The mean is also known as the average (although there are other statistical techniques which are different types of averages) and is often used by sports and exercise scientists when trying to analyse raw data.

Standard deviation

The standard deviation is the average distance of a set of scores from the mean. It is the most frequently calculated measure of variability. Knowing the standard deviation helps to create a more accurate picture of the distribution along the normal curve.

A smaller standard deviation is where scores are very close in value to the mean (a smaller range.) A data set with a larger standard deviation has scores with more variance (a larger range). For example, if the average score on a test was 80 and the standard deviation was 2, the scores would be more clustered around the mean than if the standard deviation was 10.

Mode

The mode represents the most popular reoccurring value in your set of data and is another measure of average.

Consider the following scores given to a gymnast by the judges after a floor routine:

9.8   9.7   9.8   9.6   9.8   9.7

The mode in this set of data would be 9.8 because it appears three times. It is possible to have more than one mode if two scores appear the same number of times. You may use the mode in target sports such as archery to determine the most popular score obtained by the archer (to compare with another archer or past performances of the same archer).

The major drawback of the mode is that it changes very quickly.

Look at the following example taken from cricket.

Runs scored by the opening batsman for Lancashire Second X1 team: 1, 1, 16, 23, 45 and 100

The mode = 1 (representing a poor run of form)

Case study

Blackpool Bullets versus Preston Pirates

Look at this example taken from netball (points scored per game in a tournament).

1. **Calculate the mean points for the Preston Pirates.**
2. **Comment on the usefulness of the information in this table.**
3. **Explain what other performance criteria from the tournament the coach may want to analyse and why.**
4. **Through your own understanding and research, comment on the advantages and disadvantages of using the mean when analysing data.**

Game number	Blackpool Bullets	Preston Pirates
1	65	56
2	43	55
3	56	43
4	32	58
5	56	40
6	65	39
7	44	62
	Mean = 361 ÷ 7 = 51.57 points	

If we change a 1 to a 100: 1, 16, 23, 45, 100 and 100

The mode = 100 (representing a good run of form)

This shows that a change in one value can have a dramatic influence on the mode average.

Median

The median is the value in the centre of a set of values. To obtain the median (another average) you need to arrange the values in order (lowest to highest). These values are a snooker player's breaks in a local competition. The middle value is the median.

Raw data: 60, 55, 48, 56, 73, 120 and 63

Lowest to highest: 48, 55, 56, **60**, 63, 73 and 120

The median = 60

Where there is an even set of values, we take the two central values and find the point between them.

Raw data: 60, 55, 48, 56, 73, 66, 120 and 63

Lowest to highest: 48, 55, 56, **60**, **63**, 66, 73 and 120

The median = 61.5

When working with your raw data, you need to consider the amount of information you have. To calculate the median with a hundred or so sets of values can be very time consuming. On the positive side, the median is less influenced by extreme values (such as the 120 points in the example). In comparison, the mean for the second example for the snooker player would be 67.63 points. This is larger than six of the values because of the inclusion of the 120 points. A median of 61.5 gives a true representation of the data.

Range

To calculate the range, take the lowest value away from the highest value.

For example you may be interested in the driving distances of two local golfers in relation to their driving woods. You have recorded the following:

Golfer A (yards)	Golfer B (yards)
179	222
201	213
194	179
200	201
213	217
178	192
203	211

Activity

1 Calculate the range for both golfers. Comment on your results.

2 Calculate the mean for both golfers. Comment on your results.

3 Using ICT, calculate the standard deviation. Comment on your results.

4 Explain briefly how using these statistics may inform the golfer of their performance.

5 If you were analysing the golfers' driving performance, what other information may you need to take into account?

Percentages

You could express your results as a percentage depending on the data you have. For example, in tennis you may be interested in the percentage split of the shots played by the tennis player.

Case study

Arthur Glenn

Let's look at the following raw data obtained for the under 17s Scottish Champion Arthur Glenn in his quarterfinal match.

Shot	Shots played	Points won	Points lost
Serve	98	5 (Ace)	12*
Lob	8	3	3
Volley	23	8	9
Smash	6	5	0
Backhand drive	143	21	7
Forehand drive	124	25	13
Chip	5	1	1
Drive volley	2	2	0

Note: * represents points lost directly after a serve was made (return of serve).

The data from the volley does not add up to 23 (8 and 9) because the other six shots were in the middle of a rally and were neither winning nor losing shots. This is the same for the other shots.

If we were interested in calculating the percentage of winning volleys, we would calculate:

$$\frac{\textit{8 winning volleys}}{\textit{23 shots played}} \times 100$$

= 35% (rounded up)

1 **Calculate the percentages won for each shot played (you need the information from the second column only).**

2 **Calculate Arthur's most successful and unsuccessful shot in terms of the percentages.**

3 **What concerns from a performance analysis perspective do you have with the results you have generated?**

4 **How would you represent this percentage data in graphical form and why?**

5 **As a coach, how could you use this data to aid the player in the future?**

Data analysis

A central component for sports biomechanics is data analysis. Once you have collected your data you will be expected to perform some data analysis. The reason for this is that data analysis allows us to:

- organise and examine the collected data
- present the information using narrative linked to charts, graphs and tables
- process the relevant information and draw conclusions.

Remember!

Data analysis is an important tool as it allows the sports biomechanist to analyse the data in a scientific manner and draw valid conclusions.

■ Correlation test

Correlation is a statistical technique that can show whether pairs of variables (sets of data) are related and, if so, how strongly. For example, height and success at the high jump are related, as taller people tend to be better than shorter people. However, there is never a golden rule that covers every athlete. Some smaller athletes will be very good at the long jump, but the general rule considers that taller athletes will have an advantage.

Remember!

The most common correlation test is called the Pearson, or product-moment, correlation test.

The Pearson correlation test produces a value that ranges from –1 to 1. A negative value means there is a negative relationship between the two sets of data. The table below will help you with a positive value.

Value	Correlation
0–0.20	None to weak
0.21–0.40	Weak to moderate
0.41–0.60	Moderate to good
0.61–0.80	Good to strong
0.81–1	Strong to perfect

Positive correlation

Like all statistical techniques, correlation is only appropriate for certain kinds of data. It works for data in which the numbers are meaningful (usually quantities of some sort).

Data representation

It is important to put results of your investigations into graphs, charts and tables. First, it is a visual way to look at the data and see what happened and make interpretations. Second, it is usually the best way to show the data to others. Reading lots of numbers in the text puts people to sleep and does little to convey information. The following section will highlight the key issues relating to data representation.

Databases

A database defines a structure for storing information. Databases are typically organised into tables that are collections of related items. You can think of a table as a grid of columns and rows. A column defines one piece of data stored in all rows of the table. A row contains one item from each column in the table.

For example, a table might contain the football player's name, position, tackles made and other performance criteria (see example below). Each row, called a data record, corresponds to one player:

Player's name	Position	Tackles made	Completed short passes	Completed long passes	Shots on target
R. Gray	R Midfield	12	23	4	2

Activity

1. Using a spreadsheet (*fx*-key in Microsoft Excel®), calculate the Pearson's correlation value from the following data. The table represents the hours of practice performed by penalty kickers in rugby league and the conversion rate in Super League matches.
2. Using your value, interpret the correlation between the two sets of scores.
3. What other factors would you need to consider when analysing the data in terms of assessing performance?

Player	Hours of practice per week on kicking	Conversion rate in matches (%)
1	6	87
2	2	77
3	1	65
4	5	80
5	5	69
6	3	78
7	3	74
8	2	71

Hours of practice and conversion rate

Key Term

Database A collection of related information stored in a structured format.

The benefits of using an electronic database are as follows:

- can store large amounts of data
- easily stored and retrieved
- easy to update
- can generate tables and graphs using stored data.

Spreadsheets

A spreadsheet, also known as a worksheet, contains rows and columns and is used to record and compare numerical biomechanical data. Originally, spreadsheets only existed in paper format, but now they are most likely created and maintained through a software program that displays the numerical information in rows and columns.

Computerised spreadsheets are similar to a paper spreadsheet. The advantage of using computerised spreadsheets is their ability to update data and perform mathematical calculations extremely quickly. On a computerised spreadsheet, the intersection of a row and a column is called a cell. Rows are generally identified by numbers (1, 2, 3 and so on) and columns are identified by letters (A, B, C and so on). The cell is a combination of a letter and a number to identify a particular location within the spreadsheet (for example A3).

To manoeuvre around the spreadsheet you use the mouse or tab key. When the contents of one cell are changed, any other affected cell is automatically recalculated according to the formula in use. A formula is the calculation to be performed on the data. Formulas can be simple, such as sum or average, or they can be very complex. To use simple formulas like the sum or average (mean) in Microsoft Excel® you will need to use the *fx* button.

Tables

You will need to use a table to display your raw data. It is important to understand that you may not display all of your raw data. However, it should be displayed in a table that makes the data easy to view and understand. In basic terms, the table will include a number of rows (horizontal) and columns (vertical).

Tally charts

A tally chart is a great way of recording your raw data, when trying to count certain performance criteria in a real-life sporting performance. A simple tally chart will look like the one on the next page and represents the types of shots played by a tennis player.

Activity

(1) 71	(9) 53	(17) 4
(2) 59	(10) 23	(18) 41
(3) 112	(11) 78	(19) 23
(4) 34	(12) 25	(20) 64
(5) 7	(13) 13	(21) 36
(6) 4	(14) 13	(22) 34
(7) 77	(15) 98	(23) 13
(8) 109	(16) 41	(24) 10

This table gives the highest breaks obtained by a snooker player (frame numbers in brackets).

1. Calculate the sum, mean and standard deviation using a spreadsheet for the above data.
2. Produce a tally chart using the information from the table and put the data into appropriate categories.
3. Produce a bar chart using the information you have gathered from your tally chart.
4. Write an interpretation of the calculations and charts you have made in relation to snooker. Therefore you are answering the question – what have we discovered?

Shot	Tally	Total
Backhand drive	𝍸 𝍸 𝍸 |	16
Drop shot	|||	3
Smash	𝍸 |	6
Lob	||	2

Remember!

When collecting data, it is vital that you have your data collection sheets ready before the start of the match, so that you can easily record the information.

Activity

1 Devise a tally chart that includes five performance criteria for the sport or activity of your choice.

2 Watch a live performance (on television is fine) and fill in your tally chart. You can use the tally chart on either the team or one individual.

3 Produce a pie chart to show your raw data in graphical form.

4 Briefly discuss your findings with members of your group.

Graphical representation

When working with athletes and analysing their performance you will gather lots of data. This data needs to be represented in graphical form, for example:

- pie chart
- bar chart
- line graph.

It is important that you represent the data in the correct style of chart or graph because it makes the information more manageable and easier to analyse. Your choice depends on the data you generate.

Pie charts

Sports biomechanists often display data in a pie chart. It displays data that is based on percentages. The pie chart allows you to look at the various parts and make comparisons in relation to size. For example, the following data from a boxing match is displayed as a pie chart in relation to the types of punches thrown.

▼ **A pie chart is ideal for showing proportions and can easily be understood by the athlete**

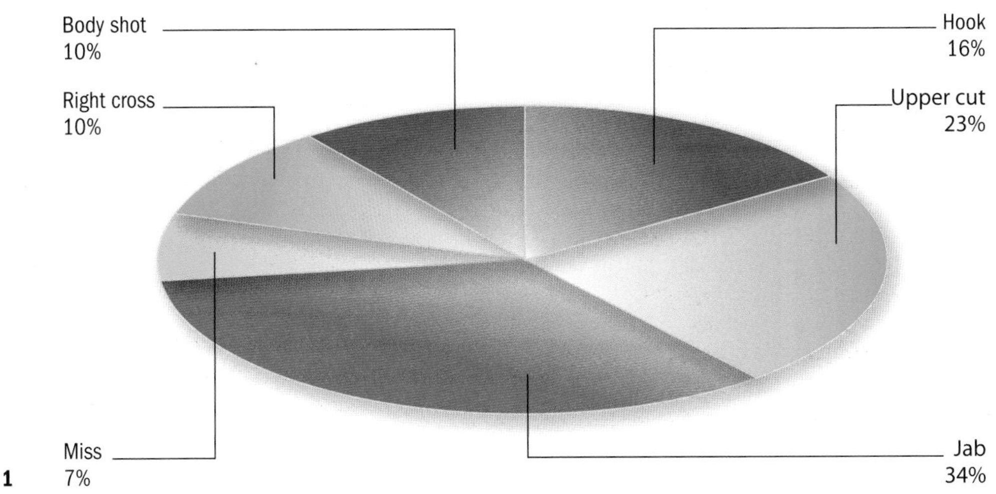

Activity

1. Produce a pie chart to represent the following data for Boxer B in round 1: hook 6 per cent; upper cut 13 per cent; jab 35 per cent; miss 17 per cent; right cross 19 per cent; and body shot 10 per cent.
2. Why might a trainer need this type of information when training a boxer?
3. From a technical perspective, what performance criteria might you be interested in?
4. Which other sport may lend itself to producing data that can be displayed in a pie chart?

Bar charts

A bar chart is a way of summarising a set of categorical data. (For example, backhand in tennis would be classed as a category.) It displays the data using a number of rectangles of the same width, each of which represents a particular category. The length of each bar shows the data in each category. Bar charts can be displayed horizontally or vertically and they are often drawn with a gap between the bars (rectangles).

A histogram is similar to a bar chart, except that the area of the bar represents the data (rather than the length) and the bars are drawn immediately next to each other.

Line graphs

A line graph allows you to study information over a specific time period. Therefore you are able to look for trends (either positive or negative) or specific points of interest (extreme high or low values). The most common type of line graph that you may generate using your raw data will be based on data in relation to time. The line graph below represents the finishing place in the championship for a UK Racing team over the last ten years.

Taking it further

1. Study the line graph below. Describe the trend shown over the last five years.
2. Offer suggestions for any high or low points as shown by the line graph.
3. Explain in your own words how you think the team will do over the next three years based on the information you have been given.
4. What factors in your opinion may have influenced these results over the last ten years in relation to Formula One racing?

You can identify short-term or long-term trends using line graphs

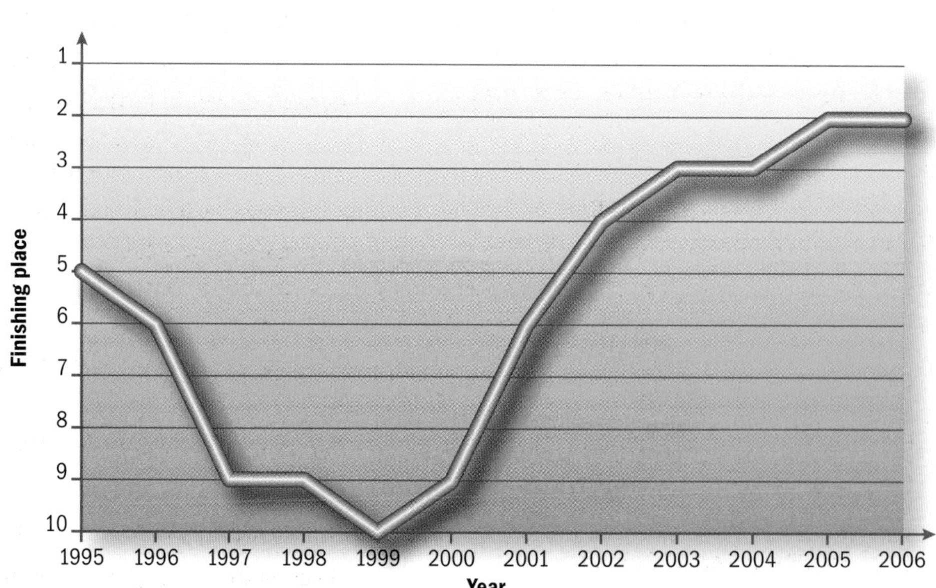

Finishing place in the championship for a UK Racing team.

Assessment practice

1 Carry out a case study in which you perform two notational analyses on your chosen sport. Within the case study you will need to:

- clearly show that you have performed two separate analyses on the same athlete or team on two separate occasions (for example, you could analyse the goal shooter in one netball team that is playing against the Stockport Sabres this week, and against the Sale Snakes next week)
- include your raw data (for example, a handwritten table of passes made)
- show evidence of statistical work (for example, you may calculate the percentage of shot success against shots in the match)
- represent your data (which could include a series of tally charts that are then used to produce a number of pie charts)
- analyse three components of the sporting performance (for example, success and failure rates – for catching, shooting and intercepting – for the goal shooter in netball). **P2**

2 Extend the work within your case study to show that you have compared the performances. The comparison can be based on looking at the data and data representation of the performances. **M1**

3 Evaluate your findings in the case study, commenting on their influence on performance within the chosen sport. **D1**

6.2 Be able to compare a numerical model to sporting performance

In this section you will research and produce a numerical model (numerical means the inclusion of numbers, such as that the velocity of a sprinter needs to be above nine metres per second). Your model will either come from literature, an elite-level athlete, or a specific athlete you have access to. For example, if interested in the shot putter, you will need to consider three components: velocity of release, height of release and angle of release.

Once you have designed your model, you will then assess a real-life sporting performance and compare it to your model. This should allow you to identify strengths and areas for improvement as feedback for the athlete.

In the past, another word used to describe the term 'numerical' would have been 'quantitative' (meaning some quantity). If we can produce a model, then when we assess our sports performer we have something solid to compare against and make valid conclusions. Here is an example of a basic numerical model (using three performance criteria).

Performance criteria	Value	Source	Reference
Run-up speed	$8 m/s^{-1}$	Journal	Smith and Carter (2004)
Take-off angle	22°	Internet	www...
Stride length	1.40m	Book	Jones (2007)

Key Term

Numerical model Involves a number of key performance criteria and has quantifiable information, for example speed of $6.5 m/s^{-1}$.

From this example we can identify some golden rules.

1 You do not have to cover all the performance criteria of a sport.
2 Only cover the ones that you think are important and can justify using them.
3 Using a combination approach is fine (journal, Internet and book, etc.).
4 Give references for your sources because other sources may say something else.

Think it over

It is important that the information you use is valid, reliable and up to date. Working in small groups, list the advantages and disadvantages of using the information sources opposite. Once you have completed this list, discuss the points within the group.

Numerical model production

To produce a model that you can use to assess against the sporting performance of your athlete or team, you will need to carry out some research. The model should come from:

- the literature available to you
- an elite-level athlete
- a specific athlete (e.g. previous performances)
- a combination of all these approaches.

The following section will briefly outline these approaches.

Literature based

As sport and exercise science has now become an established area for scientific study, there is a lot of research that has taken place in the context of the sports performance. You will be able to find information from the following:

- key textbooks
- Internet
- scientific journals (e.g. *The Journal of Sport and Exercise Science*)
- magazine articles
- coaching manuals
- fact sheets
- newspapers.

Elite-level athlete based

Part of your model may come from an elite-level athlete. For example, if you are interested in golf, you may use Tiger Woods' swing as a model for performance. However, you are not trying to find the 'perfect' swing, just a successful swing – so there are a number of good swings you may consider using from other elite golfers.

Specific-athlete based

Another option would be to use the athlete you are analysing as the model. They may have been successful in the past, but have had a number of poor performances recently. By using the previous model, you can assess why the performances are now different.

For example, a tennis player may not be tossing the ball as high as they used to during the serve. Therefore, they need to return to their previous technique.

Combination approach

The final option open to you is to use a combination approach. You could select some information from a textbook and link this together with the performance of an elite-level athlete.

Remember!

A numerical model can be generated through using different approaches.

Numerical component

Mathematical principles are fairly integral to sports biomechanics. We have previously mentioned fairly general performance criteria, such as crossing or tackling. The following performance criteria are based around numerical principles and can be used to analyse the sporting performance.

Linear motion

All sporting movement is classed as being based on linear, angular (involves rotational movement, for example during a somersault), or a combination of these two. Linear motion, also known as translation, is motion where the athlete or object (sports equipment) moves the same distance in the same time in the same direction. There are very few types of movement in sport that are purely based on linear motion. An athlete sprinting 100m is said to be in linear motion (sprinting in a straight line). Although, from your experience, you will realise that you do not run in a purely linear motion, as you tend to move side to side when sprinting down the track.

Key Term

Linear motion Also known as translation, linear motion is where the athlete or object (sports equipment) moves the same distance in the same time in the same direction, for example a 100m sprinter.

In terms of analysing linear motion as a sports biomechanist, you may be interested in calculating displacement, speed, linear velocity and linear acceleration.

Taking it further

Some sporting motion is said to rectilinear and curvilinear in nature.

1 Through your research, define, explain and provide sporting examples of these types of movements.

2 Describe the difference between the two types of motion.

Linear displacement

When an object (e.g. a snooker ball) changes its position, regardless of the direction of movement, linear displacement has taken place. As you can see from the diagram on page 222, the ball has moved from position A to position B and, therefore, has been displaced from its original position.

Linear displacement such as the 100m sprinter is measured in metres.

Speed

In everyday language we use the terms 'speed' and 'velocity' interchangeably because we believe them to be the same thing. However, from a biomechanical point of view they are different. Speed is the rate of change of distance with respect to time and is measured inm/s^{-1} (metres per second is classed as an SI unit). The formula for calculating speed is:

$$\frac{d}{t}$$

where:

d = distance in metres

t = time in seconds

Therefore, if a sprinter ran the 100m in 11.29 seconds, we would need the following calculation:

$$\frac{100}{11.29}$$

$$= 8.86\text{m/s}^{-1}$$

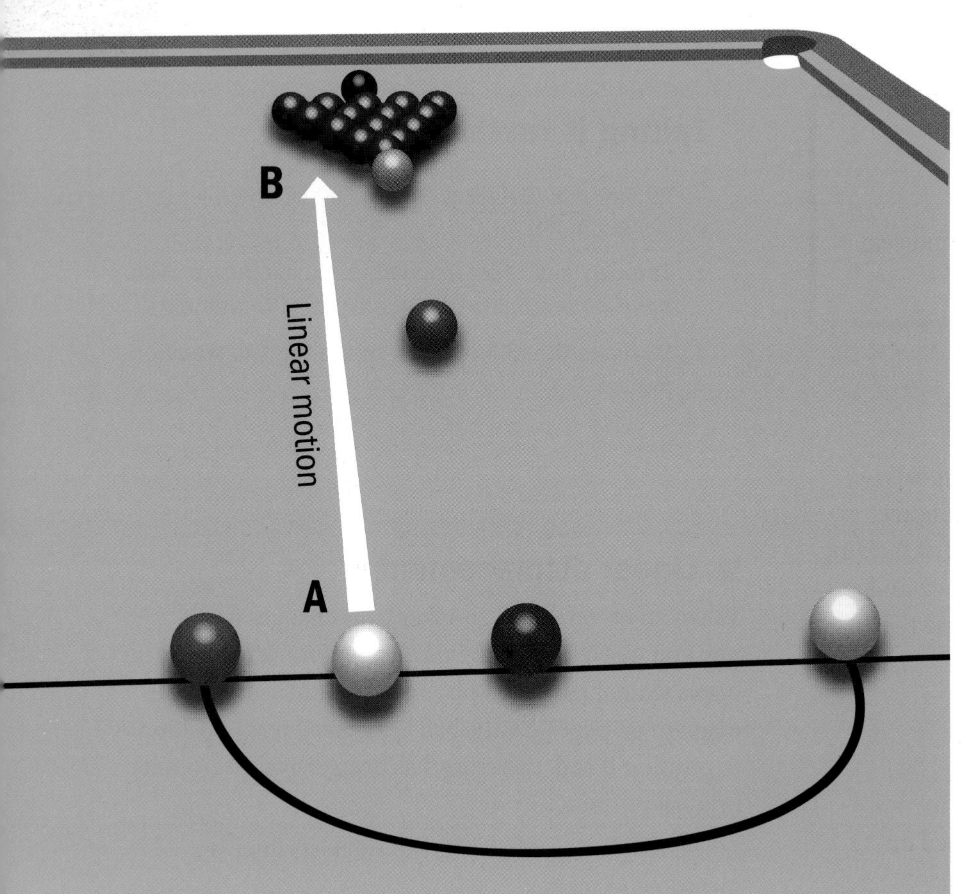

True linear motion is difficult to ascertain due to external factors such as swerve

Taking it further

1. Find the current world records for the 100, 200, 400 and 800m (both men and women) in athletics.
2. Calculate the speed of the athletes.
3. Write a brief discussion on your findings in terms of the differences between the distances and genders.

Remember!

Numerical components of performance (for example, speed), are given a specific SI unit such asm/s^{-1}. An SI unit is internationally recognised as being the correct unit to use for a specific measurement.

We can say that the average speed was 8.86m/s^{-1}. However, this does not give us much information. This is because the athlete at the start will be going slower due to starting from a stationary position.

Although the information calculated for the speed of an athlete is rather basic, this may be a numerical performance criterion that you consider using for your assessment.

Linear velocity

In contrast to speed, linear velocity is the rate of change of displacement (in metres) with respect to a specific time period (measured in seconds). The unit of measurement for linear velocity is alsom/s^{-1}. We have already mentioned the key disadvantage with calculating the average speed. However, there is some merit in calculating the linear velocity at a specific time period. Here is the formula to use:

$$\frac{\textit{change in displacement (m)}}{\textit{specific time period (s)}}$$

Let's look at the following example. A 100m sprinter was at the 50 metre-point after 5.78 seconds and then at the 60 metre-point after 7.12 seconds. Therefore at that stage:

$$\frac{10}{1.34}$$

$= 7.46\text{m/s}^{-1}$

Remember!

When reporting figures you should look to report to two decimal places, as this is good scientific practice.

Key Term

Linear acceleration The rate of change of velocity with respect to time and is measured inm/s^{-2} (metres per second).

In relation to the example shown previously, hopefully you can see that this provides more useful information because we can look at the velocity at different stages of the performance. We should be able to identify areas for improvement for the athlete. We may discover that the sprinter's linear velocity decreases dramatically after 70m. This finding should alert the coach, who should then concentrate on training the sprinter to maintain their power during the full performance, not just the first 70m.

■ Linear acceleration

Once you know the linear velocity of an athlete or object, then you can calculate the linear acceleration.

Therefore, if the athlete's velocity is increasing, they will have a positive acceleration value. In comparison, an athlete who is slowing down will have a negative acceleration value. If we consider the 100m sprinter again, we can show how to calculate the linear acceleration of the athlete:

Velocity at 20m = 3.45m/s^{-1}

Velocity at 30m = 4.56m/s^{-1}

Therefore, the change in velocity between 20m and 30m was 1.11m/s^{-2} (this being linear acceleration).

To pull this together, if you were interested in producing a numerical model for the 100m sprinter, you may consider calculating the velocity and acceleration of the

Case study

Investigation into 100m linear sprint velocities

The following displacement data was taken from a 100m sprinter at the county under-13s trials.

1. **Calculate the linear velocities for each 10m interval, for example between 20m and 30m.**
2. **Using graph paper, produce a velocity time curve showing displacement on the *x* axis and velocity on the *y* axis. You will need to display a line of best fit for your curve.**
3. **Based on your curve, interpret the line of best fit in context of the velocities and the 100m sprinter.**
4. **Describe how a coach could use this information for future coaching sessions.**

Displacement (m)	Time (s)
0	0
10	1.78
20	3.23
30	4.54
40	5.84
50	7.02
60	8.22
70	9.56
80	11.00
90	12.60
100	14.55

sprinter coupled with the knee angle joint in degrees (measurements of joint angles will be discussed later).

Angular motion

Angular motion is present in all athletic movements. Angular motion can be expressed within the human body in a body segment – for example, the arm moving around a joint (shoulder) as with the cricket bowler, where rotation is taking place.

We can also witness angular motion when watching a gymnast who performs a somersault. The gymnast is rotating around an imaginary axis of rotation.

The calculations for angular motion are more complex than those of linear motion.

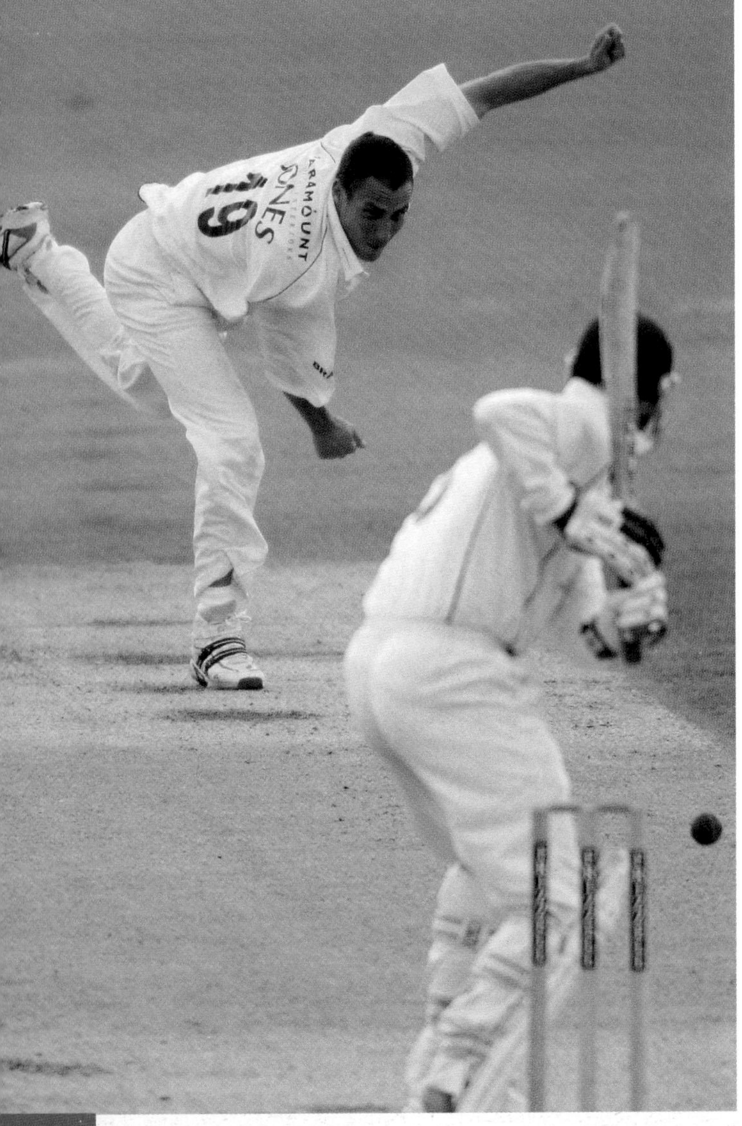

Rotation, thereby angular motion, is taking place at the shoulder joint as the cricketer bowls the ball

Key Term

Angular motion Rotation that takes place when a body moves along a circular path.

Angular displacement

Angular displacement is the angle that a rotating body goes through.

For example, if a skater skates in a circle around the centre of the rink, stopping and starting at the same place, the angular displacement would be 360 degrees. The direction of the rotation is important: a counter-clockwise circle is a positive 360-degree displacement. However, a clockwise circle is a negative 360-degree displacement. If a skater were to switch directions and skate half a circle counter-clockwise, turn around and skate back clockwise, the displacement is a positive 180 degrees and then negative 180 degrees, for a total displacement of zero.

Angular displacement is measured in radians (SI units) or degrees. One radian is equal to 57.3 degrees with 30 degrees being 0.5236 radians.

Angular velocity

Angular velocity is the rate of change of angular displacement and can be described as the speed of rotation. The units of angular velocity are most conveniently given in radians/sec, but can also be expressed in degrees/sec. This formula is used to calculate angular velocity is:

$$\frac{\textit{angle in radians turned through}}{\textit{time taken}}$$

Angular acceleration

Angular acceleration is the rate of change of angular velocity and is measured in radians/sec/sec, but can also be expressed in degrees/sec/sec. To calculate the angular acceleration, you need the following formula:

$$\frac{v}{t}$$

where:

v = change in angular velocity

t = time taken

Activity

1 The following raw data has been taken from a gymnast performing a somersault. Using the examples in the table, fill in the missing raw data that you will need to calculate the angular velocity.

Angle in degrees	Time on the film (s)	Elapsed time	Angle in radians	Time for previous 30° or 0.5236r
0	25.70	0.00		
30	25.90	0.20	0.5236	0.20
60	26.10	0.40	1.0572	0.20
90	26.20			
120	26.25			
150	26.30			
180	26.35			
210	26.40			
240	26.50			
270	26.60			
300	26.70			
330	26.90			
360				

2 Using the data you have calculated in the table above, calculate the angular velocity and average time at each segment in the table below.

Segment of tumble°	Angular velocity/rs^{-1}	Average time at segment/s
0–30	2.618	0.100
30–60	2.618	0.300
60–90		
90–120		
120–150		
150–180		
180–210		
210–240		
240–270		
270–300		
300–330		
330–360		

Projectile motion

Human athletes (such as high jumpers) or sports equipment (such as javelins) that are launched into the air are called projectiles.

Key Term

Projectiles Subject only to the forces of gravity and air resistance.

Activity

In groups, identify 20 sports that involve projectile motion.

It is important that you understand the mechanical principles that are involved in the flight path or trajectory of the projectile. For some projectile objects, such as a shot put, air resistance and lift effects are very limited. However, in comparison, aerodynamic forces (air resistance and lift effects) play an important role in the performance of the discus. Within this section we will concentrate on objects that are not affected by aerodynamic forces. The three key parameters that you need to be aware of are:

- angle of release
- height of release
- velocity of release.

Angle of release

The angle of release is defined as the angle between the projectile's velocity vector and the horizontal at the instant of release or take off. Different sports require different angles of release. Sports that require maximum horizontal distance, such as the long jump, have smaller angles. In comparison, in sports like the high jump where height is key, then the angle is larger.

Taking it further

Through your research you should answer the following questions. These will extend your knowledge of the projectile motion.

1. What is the optimum angle of release for the shot put and the long jump?
2. Name three ways in which an athlete can improve their performance during the long jump.
3. What does the term 'parabolic shape of flight' mean?
4. Draw a parabolic shape and explain the relationship with gravity.

Height of release

If the angle and velocity of release are the same for two shot putters, the athlete who has a greater height of release will have a longer flight time and, therefore, record a greater distance. Based on this principle, taller athletes will generally have an advantage over shorter athletes (although technique, power, etc. also play an important role in performance).

Key Term

Height of release The distance from the ground (in metres) that the implement leaves the thrower.

Velocity of release

The velocity of release is recorded at the instance of release (e.g. when the longer jumper leaves the take-off board). During the flight phase, the projectile will show constant horizontal velocity (excluding air resistance as discussed).

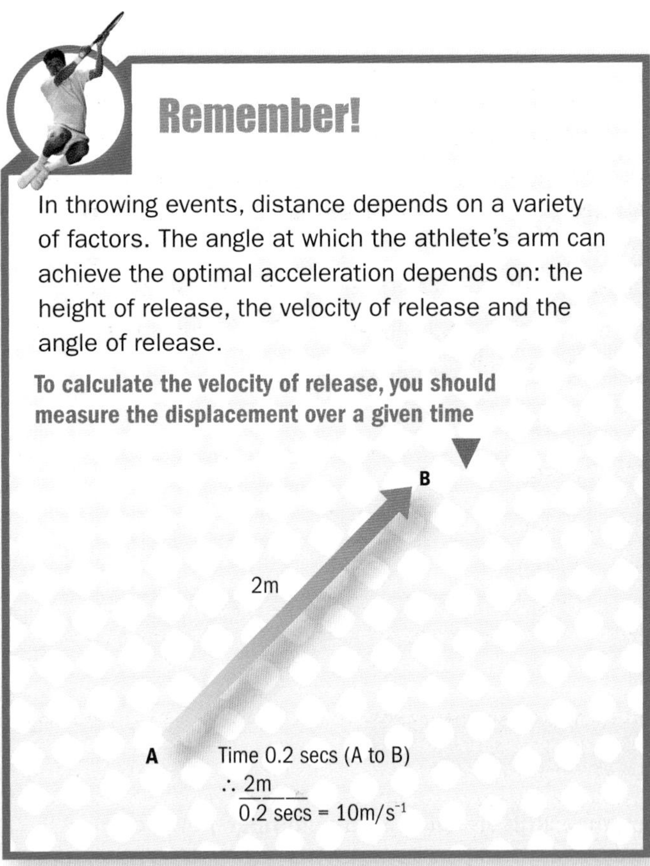

Remember!
In throwing events, distance depends on a variety of factors. The angle at which the athlete's arm can achieve the optimal acceleration depends on: the height of release, the velocity of release and the angle of release.
To calculate the velocity of release, you should measure the displacement over a given time
B
2m
A
Time 0.2 secs (A to B)
∴ 2m / 0.2 secs = 10m/s-1

Angle of attack

The angle of attack is the difference between the path of flight of the javelin's centre of mass, and the angle of the javelin to the ground (see diagram on the next page).

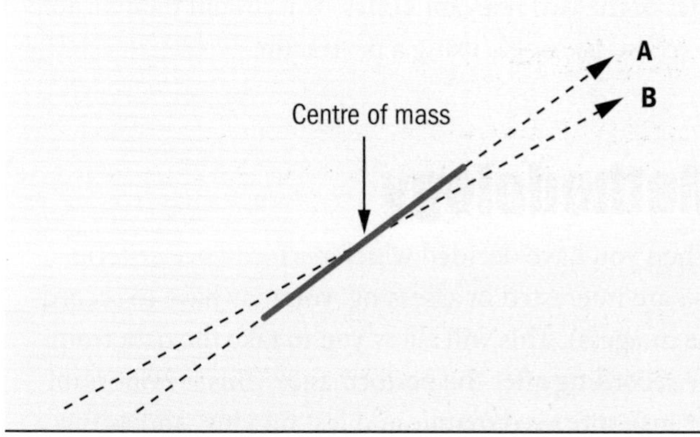

▲ **The lift, which is caused by the angle of attack, is a projectile motion variable along with gravity and air resistance**

A large angle of attack means the javelin will stall in the air and fall vertically. Studies have shown that javelins are best launched at about 30° to the horizontal with an 'angle of attack' of about 7° – in other words, the javelin is tilted 7° more steeply than the direction traced by its centre of mass, to maximise performance. The angle of attack influences both the javelin's 'lift', which acts perpendicularly to its direction of motion, and the drag, which acts parallel to it.

Remember!

The angle of attack is the difference between the path of flight of the centre of mass and the angle of the javelin to the ground.

Measurement of movement

When we measure the athlete's or equipment's movement it is important to use the correct measurements of movement (for example, linear velocity is measured in metres/second).

Activity

Using your research, complete the following table. You can refer to this table in the future to ensure you are using the correct measurement of movement.

Performance criteria	Unit of measurement
Linear displacement	
Linear velocity	
Angular displacement	
Angular velocity	
Angle of release	
Angle of attack	
Height of release	
Velocity of release	

Range of movement

Successful technique and, therefore, performance is based on an athlete performing the correct movements at specific joints (for example, flexion and extension). As a sports biomechanist, you can analyse the range (in degrees) of the movement during the performance. For example, you may consider:

- elbow extension during the shot put
- knee extension during a shot in football
- hip rotation during the golf swing.

Centre of gravity

The centre of gravity is an imaginary point at which the weight of an object (e.g. the athlete) can be considered to act.

Key Term

Centre of gravity The 'balance point' of any object and is the point in the object about which its weight is evenly distributed.

Limb angles and goniometry

Direct measurement of joint angles can be made using a goniometer. It is normally plastic or metal and comes in different sizes depending on the joint which requires assessment. The range of motion at a joint is measured by planning the centre of the goniometer at the axis of rotation of the joint. The arms of the goniometer (similar to a basic ruler) are lined up with the long axis of the specified bones. After the athlete has made the movement, the change in position is recorded by measuring the angle in degrees on the goniometer. Although this method can provide a precise reading in terms of degrees, it is difficult for the tester to determine the axis of rotation or joint centre.

You may want to use this type of measuring when you are looking at specific joint angles for technical activities such as:

- knee joint during the golf swing
- shoulder joint during the tennis serve
- elbow joint when playing a snooker shot.

Another method to measure a joint angle (although this is not as accurate) is to record the image and then take the reading off the display. The angle, in basic terms, can be seen by using an acetate and marker pen to draw the lines of the two relevant bones. You should then be able to record the angle using a protractor.

Methodology

When you have decided which performance criteria you are interested in assessing, you may have to record the image(s). This will allow you to take the data from the recording after the performance. This is important because sport is dynamic and fast moving, and as the tester, you will not always be able to record all the data at once.

If you are using a digital camera or a camera that takes still photographs, there are some basic fundamentals to filming that you must be aware of, and these are discussed in the text that follows.

Recording

Two dimensional (2D)

It is more than likely that you will be recording your athlete using two-dimensional filming in your school or

Remember!

It is important you consider issues relating to recording images such as scaling because failure to do so will cause you to generate inaccurate data.

Most sports are dynamic and fast and need recording so you can generate the raw data after the performance college. In comparison to three-dimensional filming two-dimensional filming is:

- quicker at recording the images
- faster to extract the relevant data from the images
- requires less sophisticated software
- requires less technical and mathematical knowledge.

Two-dimensional filming allows you to film the athlete with consideration of the width and height of the image, but not the depth.

To get the most accurate and valid images, it is important that you consider issues such as scaling your image (see opposite). First, here is a checklist to help you with the filming.

- ☐ Book your camera with the appropriate person in college/school well in advance of needing it.
- ☐ Make sure you have a fully charged battery, spare battery (if possible) or external power supply (if you can access a power socket), and the instruction booklet for the camera.
- ☐ Check that you have all the fittings to attach your camera to the tripod.
- ☐ Be sure that you will not erase anybody else's film from the tape.
- ☐ Remember the label on your film cassette so you can find it later.
- ☐ Set the shutter speed to at least 1/1000s.
- ☐ Use auto focus with the subject in the plane of movement and then switch to manual focus so that it doesn't change during the movement.
- ☐ Be sure that your camera is firmly on the tripod and doesn't move at all during filming or between filming and calibrating.
- ☐ Switch off the camera when not in use to save batteries.
- ☐ Make sure you view your film to make sure it is there before packing up.

Digital images

Over the last five years there has been a significant change in technology with the introduction of digital technology. Within sports biomechanics, if you are recording an athlete's performance, you are likely to be producing digital images by using either a digital camera or digital camcorder.

Key Term

Digital image A picture made up of pixels and recorded as data.

Measuring

Horizontal scaling

Before you start filming it is vital that you scale the field of view. The field of view is the area that will be filmed that contains the sporting action.

In the case of a long jumper, we are simply interested in the run up. Before you film, you will need to record a tester by holding a one-metre rule in the field of view to scale the image.

Remember!

Don't forget to film your scaling in the same plane as the movement after you have switched to manual focus.

Once you have scaled your image, do not move the camera or use the manual focus as the scaling will be incorrect and will lead to invalid data. The scaling will allow you to take measurements off the playback and convert them to real-life measurements. For example, if we are interested in the stride length of the long jumper, we can calculate that: 1m (real life) = 2cm on screen. Therefore if we have recorded that the stride length on screen is 2.5cm, using the scaling process means the real-life stride length was 1.25m.

Vertical reference

The principle of vertical reference is the same as horizontal scaling. The vertical plane may be useful in activities based around vertical movement (for example, the high jump).

Perspective error

When filming your athlete there is always a chance that your recording may have an element of perspective error because you are filming a dynamic action. This is best explained through consideration of the 100m sprinter. We may be interested in recording the time at ten-metre intervals, with the camera positioned at the 50m point.

As you can see in the diagram below, we would need to film the athlete going through all the points at ten-metre intervals. However, for example at the 80m point the camera is not in a direct line with the athlete. Therefore, it is very difficult to say exactly when the athlete reaches the 80m point. In this case, it is hard to resolve the problem unless you have more sophisticated equipment (an automated mobile camera that runs alongside the sprinter). Therefore, it is important that you keep the dynamic action in your field of view and only take a sample of the performance.

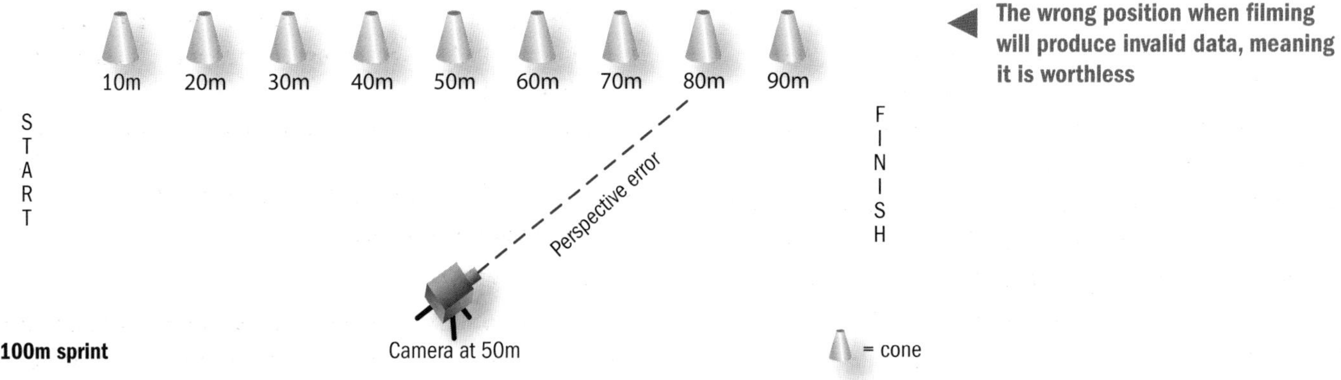

100m sprint

The wrong position when filming will produce invalid data, meaning it is worthless

Assessment practice

The local coach who works with the county shot putter has asked you to analyse the performance of the shot putter, as there has been a decrease in performance recently. The coach wants you to analyse the following performance criteria:

- height of release
- angle of release
- angle of joint (elbow) on release.

1 You are to produce a small report that includes the following sections:
   - evidence from the literature that details the optimum height of release, angle of release and elbow joint angle
   - outline of basic methodology to collect raw data
   - raw data results
   - comparison of performance with evidence from the literature.

You will need to use either a local shot putter for data collection or another group member.  P3

2 To expand your knowledge, include the following section within the report:
   - an explanation and justification of the methodology you used to collect the data from the shot putter.

   You will need to consider issues such as horizontal scaling.  M2

6.3 Be able to compare a technical model to sporting performance

There are clear similarities between this learning outcome, which looks at technical modelling, and the previous numerical-based learning outcome in terms of the way you gather your raw data. As with the previous learning outcome, you will need to produce a model. However, this will be from a technical perspective. Although there will be some numerical elements within this learning outcome, the central element is based around the technique of the performance.

You will need to produce a four-component technical model. For example, if your sport is cricket, you may look at the technical aspects of balance, grip, stance and striking of the ball (if your specialist area is batting). As before, you will need to identify strengths and areas for improvement for athletes, and provide them with relevant feedback.

Technical model production

The key concepts of model production from a technical perspective are the same as numerical modelling. However, the key difference is the type of information you are seeking to discover. You are looking at the technique used by the athlete and, in most cases, do not consider numerical aspects. For example, you may investigate components such as:

- balance
- footwork
- stance.

To recap, you will need to produce a model for your assessment and can generate evidence from the following sources of information:

- literature
- elite-level athlete
- specific athlete (e.g. past performances)
- combination approach.

For more details see page 220.

Remember!

As with previous criteria within this unit, we will look at the technical performance criteria using a variety of sports. It is important to remember that principles highlighted in this section can be used for a number of sports.

Within your assessment you will need to produce and use a technical component using four performance criteria. For example, in boxing they may be:

- balance
- stance
- coordination
- body position.

Qualitative biomechanics

Within your research you are likely to come across the term 'qualitative'. This term is used in conjunction with the technical aspects of the performance and is not based on numerical information. Here are some qualitative statements.

- When taking the shot the golfer used too much rotation around the trunk causing the ball to hook.
- In the flight phase of the long jump there was too much forward rotation, which reduced the distance jumped.
- When serving in tennis the player is striking the ball cleanly at the sweet spot of the racket.

Key Term

Qualitative biomechanics This term is descriptive and subjective in nature and is generally not based on numerical information.

Descriptive

When you are analysing the sports performance within the technical perspective you will need to describe the sporting performance, based on either strengths or areas for improvement.

Activity

Using your research, provide a description of five key technical aspects of performance for one of the following movements:

- tennis serve
- golf shot
- catching technique in cricket
- shooting technique in netball.

Subjective

When assessing performance based on the athlete's technique you will be, in most cases, giving your subjective opinion.

Key Term

Subjective Within this context, subjective means that the analysis is based on opinions rather than numerical information.

This is same approach that a coach may use to comment on the performance of an athlete. For example, a football coach may inform a player that they should keep their head down when shooting. Although there is no statistical data to support this, the coach has years of experience, which can provide valid information. As a sports biomechanist, the more you analyse performance the easier you will find it to make subjective comments.

Key performance criteria

The following section will now highlight key performance criteria you may use when producing your technical model.

Body position

One of the most important aspects from a technical perspective is the body position of the athlete. If you consider the golf swing, it is paramount that every stage is coordinated and executed in the correct manner.

Theory into practice

In small groups, design a leaflet that demonstrates the correct body position of a sporting movement of your choice. You should look to:

- include relevant diagrams
- use technical language
- break the sporting movement down into smaller logical movements
- use your anatomy knowledge to describe the key body parts used in the movement.

Footwork

The way a tennis player moves on the court is very important. Tennis performance depends on quick bursts of speed interspersed with variations of fast lateral and side-to-side movements. It also depends on the player's ability to make necessary adjustments as they get to the ball so as to maintain balance throughout the stroke. Statistics have shown that 70 per cent of missed or poorly hit shots are due to poor footwork. In tennis it's not necessarily how fast you are that is important, but how fast you are relative to the ball. The following components are important for footwork in tennis and can be analysed using descriptive terms:

- starting position when ball is struck
- acceleration to the ball
- agility
- balance
- stride length
- stride frequency.

For a discussion on stride length and frequency see page 238.

Balance

Balance is one of the key basic skills needed in practically every sport and exercise activity. From football to cricket, changing your centre of gravity to match your moves is the key to shot/move execution.

Balance is very important for another component of fitness, namely agility. Agility is what allows us to move gracefully and maintain the correct body shape, wasting little energy. It allows our joints to move through the full range of motion smoothly.

There are two types of balance that we may be interested in – static balance and dynamic balance.

Key Terms

Static balance When the athlete is still, for example during the hold stage of the handstand.

Dynamic balance Required for all movements within sport and, for example, stops a rugby player falling over when they side step the opposition.

When assessing balance you should carry out an observational assessment. For example, if assessing a tennis player, you should look at their coordination and balance when making difficult shots, such as the smash or volley.

Grip

In some sports, one important technical aspect that may influence the performance of the athlete is the grip. For example, the grip is important for the golfer and the javelin thrower.

The importance of placing the hands in the correct position on the golf club cannot be over exaggerated. There is no such thing as the perfect grip, but there are certain factors when holding the club in an orthodox way that have proved to be successful for the majority of players.

It is important that a V is formed on the right hand by the thumb and lower section of the forefinger, pointing between the chin and the right shoulder, and only two knuckles are visible on the left hand to the player.

Activity

In groups, identify six sports other than golf where grip is an important performance criterion. Explain why.

Taking it further

One of the sports you chose may have been tennis. Within tennis there are different types of grips. Through research, describe the similarities and differences between the following grips:

- full eastern backhand
- eastern backhand
- continental
- semi-western forehand
- western forehand.

Stance

In martial arts such as Judo and combat sports such as boxing, the stance (position of the body, particularly the feet) of the athlete is paramount. These types of sports require good balance and coordination, combined with the optimal stance. Failure to do this will result in a loss of balance, which will give the opponent a big advantage. Within boxing, the most important factor when considering the stance is perfect balance, enabling the boxer to move quickly and smoothly, to shift the weight constantly from one leg to another and, thus, punch effectively.

The stance recommended is flexible and allows a boxer to attack or defend, move in or out, lead or counter punch. The key elements are as follows.

1. The left foot is flat on the floor and turned inwards slightly.
2. Both legs are bent slightly – the left is relatively straight, but the knee is not locked.
3. The right foot should be offset to the right of the midline of the body to afford a firm base.
4. The right heel is raised with the right knee bent and weight taken on the ball of the foot.
5. The left side of the body forms an approximate straight line with the left leg. Trunk should be kept as upright as possible to allow the hips and shoulders to pivot when punching.
6. The body weight is evenly distributed between both feet and acts through an imaginary line running through the centre of the trunk, which acts as the pivot.
7. The left hand is carried, loosely clenched about shoulder height in front of the body, the distance from the body is entirely personal, and the elbow is tucked in comfortably.
8. The right hand is carried with the palm open towards the opponent at shoulder height, directly in front of the right shoulder.
9. Elbows should be tucked in comfortably to offer protection to the ribs.
10. The chin is dropped towards the chest; the opponent should be watched through the eyebrows.

As the boxer tires, you can see changes in the technique, which will be detrimental to performance

Passing

Although passing is a general technical term, each sport will use a different action to complete a pass. For example, a pass in football is very different from one in rugby.

Activity

To support your own knowledge, within the sport of your choice research the passing technique. Look to support your research notes with simple diagrams that will aid you in the future. Make sure you have the technical points included in your research.

Kicking

The following six key stages detail a kicking action, which is general in nature to football, rugby league and union, plus many others. Within each sport, a variety of kicking styles has evolved to suit different ball types, game rules and the part that kicking plays in the game. We can break the kick action into six stages:

- the approach
- planting of standing foot
- start of movement (kicking foot)
- hip flexion and knee extension (kicking foot)
- foot contact with ball
- follow-through.

Theory into practice

In your group, produce an information booklet on kicking technique for a coach to use in a coaching session. The booklet is to be six pages long, with each page representing one of the six stages of the kick. Divide into pairs, with each pair producing one page.

For each stage you should have the following pieces of information:

- diagram of the stage
- body part (for example, trunk)
- action (for example, flexion)
- muscles used (for example, hamstrings)
- technical information (for example, head over ball).

Shooting

In netball, unlike other sports, only two players are allowed to shoot at the basket. It is a very specialist position that requires a good level of technical ability to shoot. The key technical points are as follows.

- Keep your balance, find your aim and use your whole body to make the shot.
- Stay focused: do not let the crowd or opposition put you off.
- Have a clear view of the ring.
- Stand with your feet shoulder width apart and keep your body straight.
- Balance the ball on the fingertips of one hand (similar to basketball) and use your other hand to steady it.
- Bend your knees.
- Keep your back straight and your head up. As you prepare to release the ball, drop your hands back behind your head.
- Try to focus on a point at the back rather than the front of the ring, and let the ball go at the same time as you straighten your legs.
- Move your arms as little as possible when you release the ball.
- End your shot standing on tiptoes with your arms following through towards the ring.

Throwing

Throwing is a central component for many sports (such as cricket, American football, football, etc.). Due to the differences in the type of ball being thrown (in addition to the reason for throwing), there are different techniques required for the varying sports. Within cricket, throwing is a key aspect of fielding and leads to run outs, and can also save runs for the fielding side.

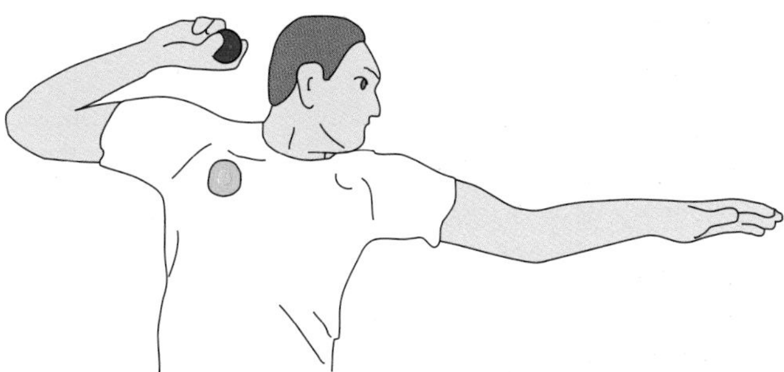

▲ **When assessing throwing technique you should also consider the accuracy and speed of the throw**

The technical basics for throwing the ball in cricket are as follows.

- Once the ball is in your throwing hand, stand sideways to the wickets.
- Pull the throwing hand so it is behind your head.
- Aim your non-throwing hand at the wickets.
- Push the throwing arm through, keeping the elbow joint at a similar height as the shoulder joint.
- Turn the chest to the target and release the ball from a firm standing position.

Catching

Catching a ball can often be a difficult task due to a variety of factors.

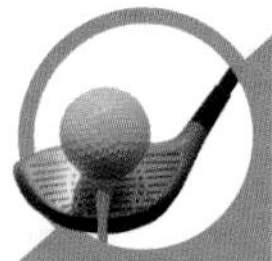

Think it over

In your group, try to produce a list of the factors that make catching a ball difficult.

You have hopefully produced a list that has a variety of factors, ranging from lack of experience to weather conditions. However, if you have the correct technique, regardless of these factors, you will increase your chance of success.

One of the most difficult balls to catch in sport is the high kick in rugby. It is an important skill every rugby player should learn.

As it is likely that the opposition will be surrounding you, you will need to catch the ball in the air. Before you leave the ground you should take a look at the surrounding area so that you are aware of what is going on. You should bear in mind the following technical points.

- Call for the ball so that another player from your team does not jump for it.
- Get into a direct line with the ball's path (this will be difficult when the wind is blowing).
- Start to reach out your arms towards the direction of the ball.
- Bend your elbows slightly – to ready yourself for the impact of the ball.
- Make sure you are side on – to soften the blow from an oncoming tackle.
- Catch the ball at or above eye level, then bring the ball into your hands, then your body – so that it is less likely to be knocked from your body (when back on the ground).

Remember!

The key element in catching any ball is to keep your eyes on the ball at all times.

Fielding

In cricket, when fielding it is important that you 'attack' the ball (you come to the ball if it is hit towards you, rather than standing still and waiting for it). If you can do this, it puts more doubt in the batsman's mind.

- As the bowler is running in about to bowl, you as the fielder should start walking in from a few steps behind your original fielding position.
- When the bowler releases the ball, a good idea is to stop and 'spring' with your knees. This allows you to transfer your weight off either foot, enabling you to react to the left or the right.
- The main technique used to stop balls along the ground is called the 'long barrier'. This occurs when your body forms a 'barrier' behind the ball, giving you the best chance of stopping the ball. Make sure you keep your eye on the ball right up until the point it reaches you, as it could be costly. The long barrier is demonstrated below.

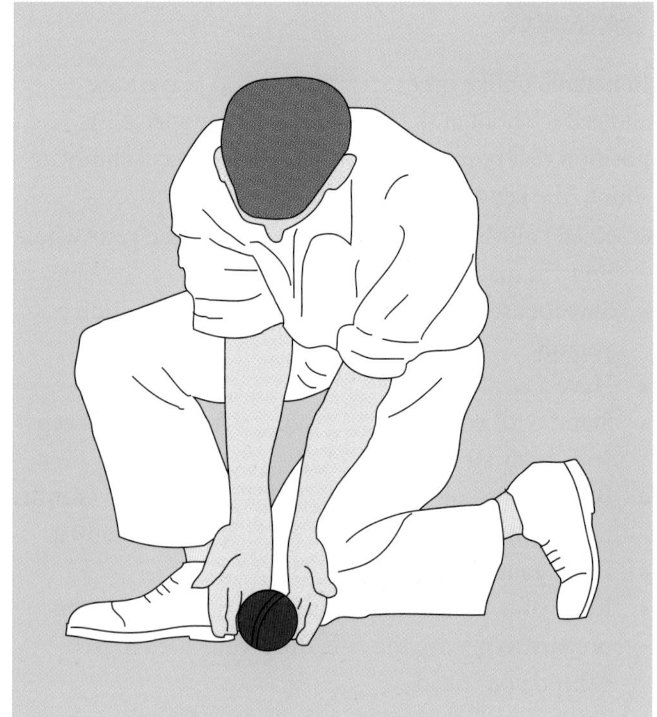

▲ **Often overlooked, fielding is just as important as batting and bowling in determining success or failure**

Batting

In cricket, there are many shots that require a high level of technical ability. For example, in a forward defensive shot the aim is to put the bat in front of the wicket, so as to stop the ball from hitting the wicket. This shot has no strength behind it, usually played with a light or soft bottom-hand grip and merely stops the ball moving towards the wicket. The basic technical points are as follows.

- The head and front shoulder should lean into the line of the ball.
- The front leg should stride towards the pitch of the ball, bending to take the weight.
- The back leg remains straight.

▲ As with many sporting activities, the head position in batting is a vital technical component

- The bat should swing down and make contact with the ball beneath the eyes.
- The face of the bat should be angled towards the ground.

Activity

In pairs, design an A3 poster that illustrates four cricket shots. Explain in basic terms the correct technique (see the forward defensive shot discussed opposite). This poster could be displayed in your sports hall to help beginners with their technique for either indoor or outdoor cricket.

Striking

The term 'striking' tends to relate to sports such as rounders or baseball. The player usually strikes the ball as far as possible (however, sometimes it is to a specific area of the field of play to gain an advantage). Striking the ball with a bat requires good hand–eye coordination.

Taking it further

In small groups, carry out some research to answer the following.

1. Describe the correct technique for striking a ball in rounders or baseball.
2. Identify other sports that require good hand–eye coordination.
3. Describe how an athlete can improve their hand–eye coordination.
4. Explain how your hand–eye coordination decreases with age.

Dribbling

In dribbling, there must be an end product, for example a shot at the goal or basket depending on the sport. From a technical perspective, the key elements for dribbling in basketball are as follows.

- Spread your fingers evenly and cup your hand over the basketball (it's almost like you are trying to palm the basketball, although your palm does not touch the basketball).
- The only parts of your hand that touch the basketball are the bases and seams of the fingers.
- As you dribble the basketball, keep your upper body fairly steady while moving your forearm up and down as you push the basketball to the floor with a wrist snap.
- Dribble the basketball by pushing it down to the floor, then lower your hand to receive the basketball (suck it off the floor).
- When the basketball touches your hand, raise your forearm slightly to absorb the dribbling pressure. Release the basketball as you push it down again.
- Move forward on the balls of your feet and bend your knees to maintain your balance.
- Keeping your body over the ball will help to shield it from your opponents.

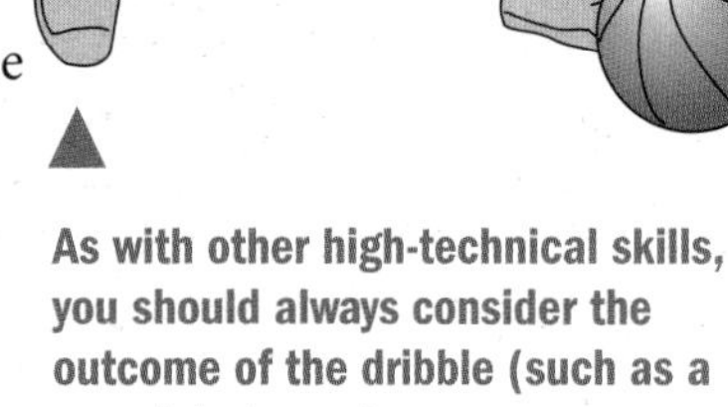

As with other high-technical skills, you should always consider the outcome of the dribble (such as a completed pass)

Stride length and frequency

Two key elements in the spring technique are stride length and stride frequency. Stride length is defined as the distance the athlete covers with each stride (measured in metres). In comparison, stride frequency is the number of strides made in a specific time (one second). The case study opposite illustrates this.

Case study

Relationship between stride length and stride frequency with athletic performance

Millie (aged 19) has recently been selected to join a national squad for athletics in her discipline of 100m. As part of the whole training package, a sports biomechanist working with a coach has calculated her speed. The results are as follows:

stride length × stride frequency = average speed

1.45 × 6 = 8.70 metres per second

1 **Calculate Millie's total time for the 100m.**

2 **Based on her coach's instructions, Millie now sprints the 100m using a stride length of 1.25m but her stride frequency is 7. Calculate Millie's new average speed.**

3 **How has this changed Millie's overall time?**

4 **What are the possible problems of changing Millie's technique in terms of stride length?**

6 **Based on your knowledge of sport and exercise science, what other areas could Millie's coach consider in trying to improve her performance?**

Theory into practice

In groups, use a video or digital camera at your college or school to calculate the stride length and stride frequency of six 100m athletes. Then calculate their average speed and total time (with a stopwatch).

Based on your data, does there seem to be an optimal stride length or stride frequency for performance? Discuss your findings within your group.

Run up

In track and field, there are a number of jumping events (such as the long, triple, high jump and the pole vault) where there are five clear phases to the performance. These five phases are:

- run up
- take off
- flight phase
- landing phase
- recovery phase.

To make the performance successful, the athlete must execute all five phases correctly with a good level of transition between the stages. These events are described as being highly technical, since if the athlete has a poor technique in one phase, it can have a knock-on effect with the other stages.

We will only discuss the long jump in relation to the five phases we have identified. However, you should be aware that the key elements described are also applicable to the other events (for example, body position at take off). The key aim for the long jump is to obtain the greatest horizontal distance possible without making a foul jump. This section will now discuss the key technical aspects (highlighting numerical factors where possible).

In the long jump, it would be fair to say that the athlete with the greatest sprinting speed would have a huge advantage in the run up. Yet, this is not always the case because the run up depends on other factors. As the sports biomechanist, you may consider the run-up speed (refer back to page 221 explaining how to calculate this).

Remember!

Although some events like the high jump are technical in nature, they can also contain numerical information (for example, run-up speed).

From a technical perspective you should look for:

- stride consistency during the sprinting stage (excluding the last three to four strides)
- a trunk which is brought upright (or close to upright) during these last three to four strides
- a lowered centre of gravity in the final few strides (see the discussion for centre of gravity on page 227)
- increased stride length of the second to last stride (numerical)
- a decreased stride on the last stride (numerical)
- accuracy at take-off (numerical).

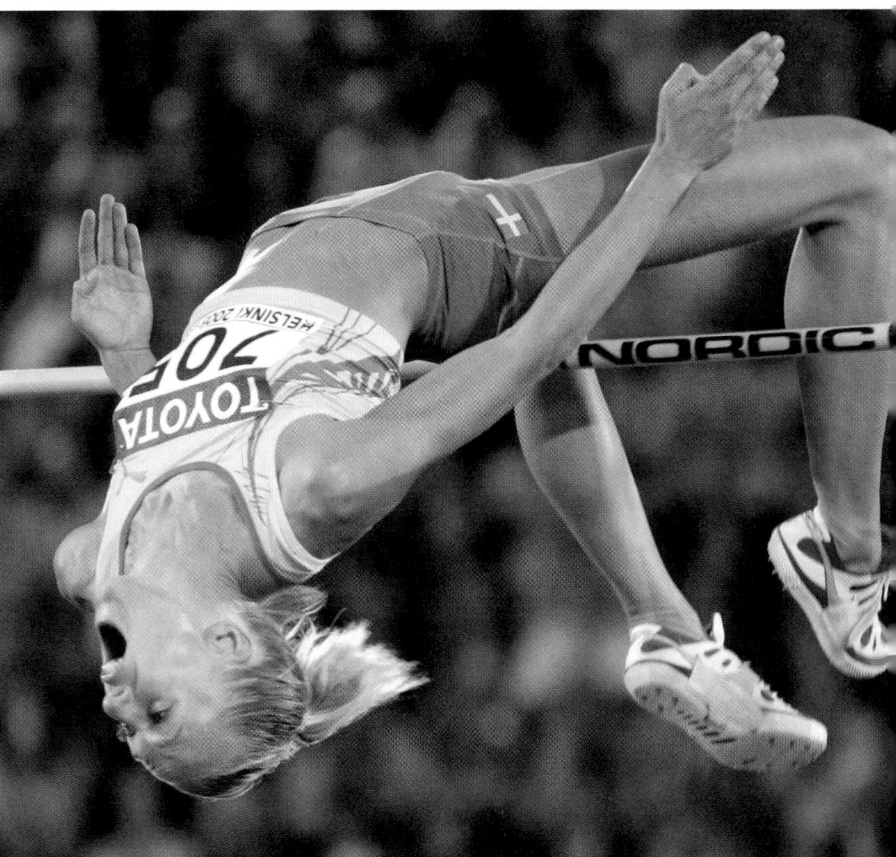

The five phases of the high jump can also be used in conjunction with the triple jump

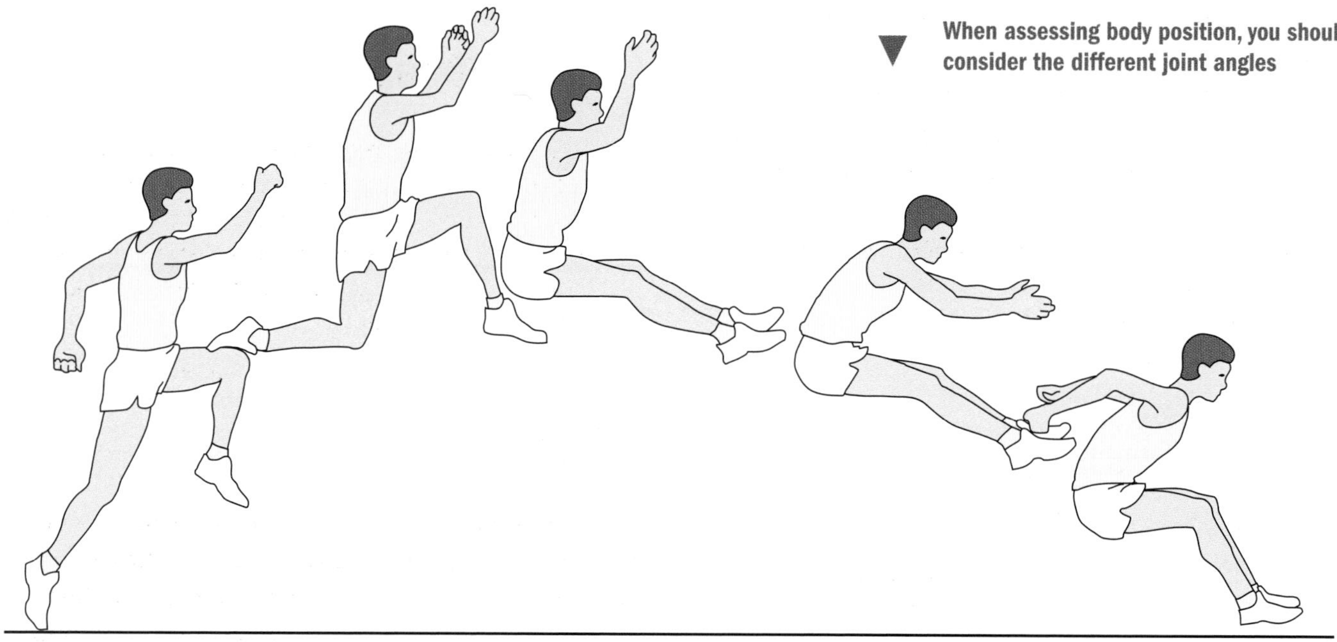

When assessing body position, you should consider the different joint angles

Taking it further

1 In small groups, research the run-up requirements for a triple jumper by identifying the key elements.

2 After the research, present your findings to the rest of the group. Try to draw on any similarities or differences with the long jump technique.

Sprinting

Sprinting is a key aspect of many team sports (for example, the football winger who sprints after the ball to make a cross). However, the technique for sprinting in athletics (100m, 200m, etc.) is completely different and requires special consideration. The sprinting technique can be split into seven separate phases.

1 Pre-race start (block position).
2 On your marks (fingers behind the line).
3 Set position (eyes focused on the track).
4 Go (driving of the arms).
5 Acceleration (face and neck muscles relaxed).
6 Drive (on the balls of your feet).
7 Finish (dip for the line at the appropriate point).

Within the seven phases there are key technical features (as you can see from the examples).

Activity

1 In small groups, use your research to produce a technique checklist for each phase (each phase should have a least four performance criteria).

2 Record a 100m sprinter and compare their performance with your checklist. Once you have the comparison, produce a list of strengths and areas of weakness, and provide feedback to the athlete.

Take off

In take off, the athlete wants to gain vertical lift while retaining as much as possible the vertical speed, has generated during the run up stage. When looking to assess the performance, you should look for the following points at the take off stage:

- the take-off foot should be a heel strike (for most athletes)
- the take-off leg should show some flexion at the hip, knee and ankle joints for cushioning the high impact
- centre of gravity should move from behind to over the take-off point
- lead leg, coupled with the arms at take off, should drive in an explosive upward motion
- height of take off (numerical)
- angle of take off (numerical)
- speed at take off (numerical).

Release phase and flight

During this key phase it is vital that the athlete maintains the optimum body position. Due to the take-off or release phase (released from the take-off board) the athlete, to some extent, will be fighting forward rotation. The forward rotation will have the effect of bringing the legs back underneath the athlete and therefore, when landing, will reduce the horizontal distance.

▲ The take off is vital for power generation and ultimately the final distance

As with other track and field events, there are different techniques that the athlete may use to maximise performance during the flight phase. These are the sail, hitch kick and the hang.

Activity

Design an A3 poster to be displayed at your local athletics club. Using pictures and simple text, demonstrate the differences between the three flight techniques. In your poster, you should try to identify the key biomechanical performance criteria that you may be interested in assessing.

Landing

As in most sports, the difference between winning and losing is very small and, in this case, centimetres make the difference. A few centimetres can be gained or lost due to the landing phase. When considering the landing phase you should look for the following:

- in the last stages of the flight phase, the athlete should lean forward as this raises the legs
- knee flexion at the landing point for shock absorption
- after landing, the athlete should push their head forward to aid forward rotation (so they do not fall backwards into the pit).

Recovery phase

It is important the athlete is aware of the importance of the recovery process although it is a small phase in terms of importance in comparison to the other four phases. After landing has taken place, the athlete should leave the pit without making a mark (before the landing mark). The rules state that if the athlete falls back into the pit towards the take-off board, then the mark made would be recorded as the final distance.

Motion of centre of gravity

Objects with a low centre of gravity seem to have better balance and are more difficult to tip over. In sports, a low centre of gravity will help an athlete to stay upright.

The 'balance point' of any object is its centre of gravity. The centre of gravity is the point in the object about which its weight is evenly distributed.

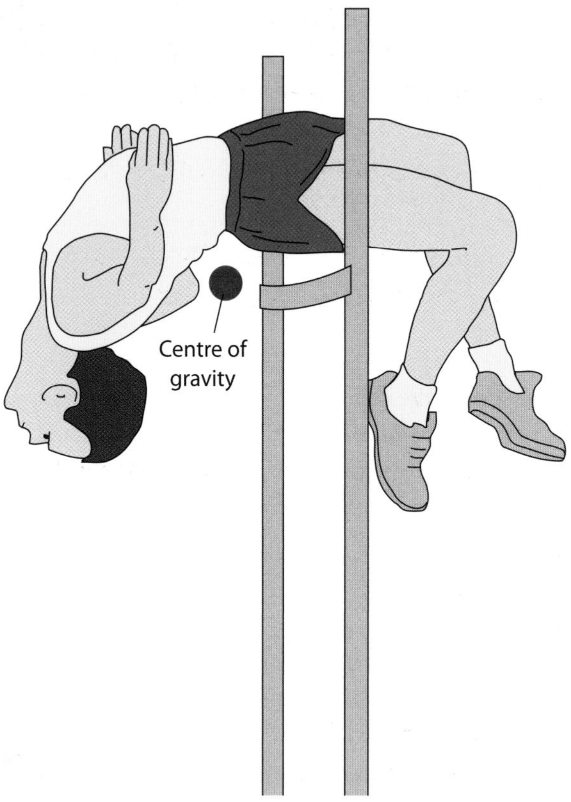

▲ **Mathematically, it is difficult to calculate the centre of gravity; however, you can estimate its position**

When studying the motion of any object, we can assume that it acts as if all its weight were concentrated at its centre of gravity.

Taking it further

Using your knowledge combined with research, answer the following questions.

1 Explain why Formula 1 cars are designed to have a low centre of gravity.

2 Explain why rugby wingers benefit from having a lower centre of gravity when opponents are trying to tackle them.

3 Explain why 100m sprinters should try to minimise the vertical motion of their centre of gravity.

Assessment practice

You are to produce an A3 poster that shows the correct techniques required for netball.

1 On the poster, include the performance criteria of passing, shooting, catching and balance. The poster will need to include both diagrams and supporting text. You should then film a netball player and compare their technical performance with your poster. You should include your findings on your poster. **P4**

2 On the back of the poster, to expand your knowledge, you may wish to include an explanation and justification of the methodology you used to collect the data from the netball. You will need to consider issues such as horizontal scaling and the choice of performance criteria. **M2**

6.4 Be able to provide feedback on performance to an athlete or team

This last learning outcome aims to pull together all the key components of the unit. The focus is centred on the feedback you provide to the athlete, and addresses issues such as confidentiality and clarity of information. To complete the analysis with the athlete, or team, which you have performed in the other learning outcomes, you will consider the future action required to improve performance. Within this future action you will need to set goals and consider specific training techniques.

Regardless of the quality of the biomechanical testing or notational analysis you have carried out, it is the quality of the feedback that you provide that will determine the usefulness of your investigations.

Remember!

The feedback is the most important aspect to the coach or athlete, as it allows them to set appropriate goals for the future.

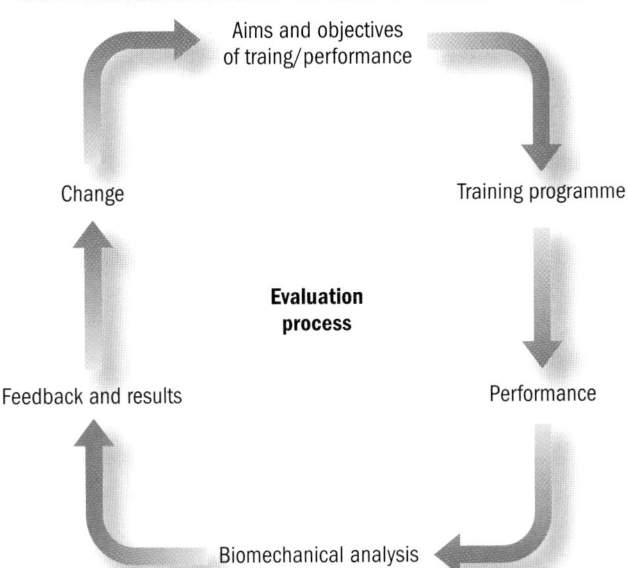

Many athletes never improve their performance because they do not complete the evaluation process

The diagram opposite shows the role of feedback in the whole coaching or training process.

This section will now discuss the key elements to the process of preparing and delivering feedback.

Feedback

The feedback that you provide to the athlete or coach can take a number of forms, these being:

- verbal
- written
- text based
- numerical
- tabular
- graphical or chart based
- linked to supporting literature.

It is also paramount to understand that some feedback may be presented immediately after the performance and some at the next training session.

Confidentiality

Those involved in collecting data have a duty of confidentiality to their athletes. They should ensure any personal information such as test results is stored in a secure place. This information (for example, mean calculation of shot success) should remain confidential and should not be discussed with other athletes. It is also recommended that when working in a sports biomechanics environment, data collectors should have a policy on confidentiality included in their contract of employment.

Activity

As the data collector, you will hold a great deal of client information (such as home phone numbers) which must be kept safe and confidential.

In small groups, produce a list of the types of information you must keep confidential.

Under the Data Protection Act 1998 your athlete has a right to have inaccurate data corrected, destroyed, blocked or erased, and may seek compensation for any damage or distress caused by you by such inaccuracy. Inaccurate data means information that is incorrect or misleading about any matter of fact.

The Act also governs the way in which you may use the personal information given to you, and your athlete has the right to require you to stop (or not to begin), using their personal information for direct marketing purposes.

Appropriate language

When you are providing feedback to the athlete, whether written or verbal, it is important you use appropriate feedback.

Remember!

Don't baffle the client with science or technical jargon – unless they understand these terms – as this is likely to confuse the issue. For example, say 'most popular' rather than 'mode'.

Strengths

When providing the feedback to the athlete or coach, you will need to make a distinction between strengths and areas for improvement (weaknesses). When identifying the strengths you must always consider:

- past performances (look for a pattern or profile)
- the influences on performance (such as motivation)
- separating the individual's strengths from the team's strengths
- the ability of the athlete and competition.

Areas for improvement

You need to consider the same points above for areas for improvement. However, you will need to consider which ones need to be addressed first because they have the biggest influence in performance.

Positive and negative feedback

An integral part of providing feedback is that there will be positive and negative elements. When providing verbal positive and negative feedback you should consider the following golden rules.

Positive feedback

- [ ] Give it straight away whenever possible – to maximise the effect.
- [ ] Be specific – for example, don't say 'You did well'; say 'Your shot accuracy improved on the previous performance'.
- [ ] Follow it up with written feedback, adding more detail.

Negative feedback

- [ ] Find a private place so that the discussion is not made public.
- [ ] Once again, make it specific to cover actual performance criteria.
- [ ] You create an immediate barrier when you criticise the person. Focus instead on what you want to change. Focus on their performance.
- [ ] Follow it up with written feedback, which includes an action plan so the athlete feels they can move forward.

Clarity of information

In your analysis you will be producing a great deal of information, which you will need to pass on to the athlete or coach. It is important that the information you produce is clear. You should avoid using large amounts of text because the key features will not be clear. You should look to use:

- tables
- charts
- bullets points
- graphs
- diagrams
- headings.

Written

Written feedback to athletes can be produced in a number of formats. However, as with verbal feedback, it must remain simple and easy to understand and be applicable to the specific athlete or team. You can show a comparison of the athlete's data against other athletes' data (if permission has been given), either in a graph or a table. Graphs and tables can be generated through a computer program, which will then provide a results profile for the athlete/team to show strengths and weaknesses.

Remember!

When providing written feedback that include statistics, it is important you describe what the statistics mean to the athlete. Numbers alone can mean nothing without interpretation.

Verbal

The information you have gained from the data collection should be given to the athlete as either verbal or written feedback. There are a few basic guidelines to follow when giving verbal feedback.

- Ensure the feedback is given in a quiet environment with no distractions, as some information may be confidential and personal.
- Don't baffle the client with science or technical jargon – unless they understand these terms – as this is likely to confuse the issue. For example, say 'most popular' rather than 'mode'.
- Remember to link the results of your data collection to any factors that may have influenced them (for example, time of day).
- If the athlete is part of a team, it is important that you not only discuss the results based on the individual, but also mention the links to team performance.
- If the results are poor, be ready to suggest other ways of improving performance. For example, suggest possible coaching points they may want to consider.

Assessment practice

Based on the results you have obtained previously, deliver feedback verbally to a fellow member of your group taking into account the above guidance points. The person receiving the feedback should write down some strengths and weaknesses to aid both of you in the future. **P5**

Evidence based

When you have analysed your results, either using quantitative methods (statistics) or qualitative methods (description of performance), you will need to make your conclusions evidence based. It is important that you base your information on valid information, to support the athlete in their future coaching sessions or performances. Your job is to link the results to relevant evidence that may come from:

- scientific journals
- biomechanical/coaching textbooks
- valid Internet sites
- previous performances from your athlete
- data from elite-level athletes.

Athlete/coach friendly

When providing feedback to the athlete or coach, it is important that you make the information friendly and easy to understand. Therefore, you should consider the following points.

- Consider the use of language – avoid using over-technical points unless the athlete and coach are used to this level of technicality.
- Provide the feedback in stages and break it down – avoid too much information in one session.
- Avoid excessive amounts of text and numbers – use sparingly by using the key information only.
- Avoid an over reliance on tables, charts, etc. as too many can lead to confusion.
- Provide a report after verbal feedback to allow for reflection at a later date.

Acknowledgement of biomechanical limitations

As with other subjects within sport and exercise science (such as sports psychology and exercise physiology), sports biomechanics has limitations that you must be aware of in respect of feedback given to athletes and coaches. In your feedback and consideration of the results, it is important you give real thought to these biomechanical limitations. These limitations include:

- lack of scientific equipment and support
- lack of detailed biomechanical knowledge
- lack of time to consider all the performance criteria
- factors which influence biomechanical performance.

It is also important to understand that most of the issues raised are outside of your control. This is because the school or college you attend will be unable to provide the expensive scientific equipment and support. This type of equipment is more available at a university. In respect of the detailed biomechanical knowledge, this is because the National in Sport and Exercise Science, which you are studying, only requires you to study at a certain level. Therefore, if you take biomechanics as an option at university you will be learning more in-depth issues and concepts.

Factors influencing performance

Theory into practice

In groups, produce a list of the possible factors that may influence the performance of the athlete. Try to explain briefly how these factors may affect the biomechanical performance criteria.

All athletes, regardless of their level, will have training or competition days when their performance levels will drop. There is a variety of factors that may influence their performance and thereby your biomechanical investigation.

It is important that you consider these factors in relation to your evaluation of the test results and the feedback to the athlete or coach. The possible factors that may influence performance are as follows.

■ Age

Special consideration needs to be given to children when testing them from a biomechanical perspective.

When working with children, it is important that you do not treat them like small adults because they are growing, so their skeletal and muscular systems are constantly changing. Due to changes brought on by puberty, the teenage athlete may experience a dip in their performance level.

From a biomechanical point of view, the change in their body will often lead to decreased balance and coordination. An athlete may experience poor performance, especially in technical sports (for example, golf) for a long period of time due to the biological adaptations. However, after a while the body will adapt and performances should show an improvement.

Remember!

An older athlete due to the aging process is likely to show a reduction in their coordination, balance, power, mobility, plus other key components to performance. Therefore, you must consider these points when analysing their biomechanical performance.

Health

The performance of an athlete can be highly influenced by either short-term conditions (e.g. a cold) or more long-term conditions (e.g. shin splints). If we consider a football player who suffers from a mild form of asthma, then this may influence their performance during a match that you are performing notational analysis on. As the player may have a reduced aerobic capacity (due to the asthma) this may influence their:

- work rate
- positional play
- tackling ability
- position-specific performance criteria.

Activity

Design a leaflet (based on a sport of your choice) to inform people about the importance of full health and fitness when competing. Identify four health issues on the poster that may influence sporting performance (use the example of a football player and asthma as a guideline). Highlight which performance criteria is affected by each health issue.

Diet

There are numerous key dietary factors that you may need to consider when assessing your results:

- eating too close to a performance can cause digestive discomfort and lead to poor performance
- lack of specific carbohydrates can reduce glycogen stores and cause the onset of fatigue at an early stage
- poor levels of sodium, potassium plus other minerals can influence muscle contraction
- lack of fluids can lead to dehydration, which can influence temperature regulation (overheating) during exercise and events requiring aerobic endurance.

When considering the role of diet on performance you may want to use a diet sheet to highlight possible issues.

Previous training

You will need to consider the previous training of the athlete from two perspectives:

- in the short term – for example, training a day before the performance can cause fatigue and decrease the performance
- in the long term – increased training over six weeks (for example, in a specific skill or drill) will lead to an increase in performance; but decreased training over recent weeks (possibly due to an injury or lack of motivation) will reduce the performance potential.

Motivation

One of the most powerful factors for influencing performance is the athlete's motivation. Regardless of the level of the athlete, any decrease in motivation will have a detrimental effect on performance (and vice versa). As a sports biomechanist, you may or may not be aware of this change in motivation, but you will certainly be aware of the decrease in biomechanical performance.

Key Term

Motivation Drives us to play sport and makes us perform in a certain way (positively or negatively).

Case study

The role of motivation in determining performance levels

You have been analysing Amy (aged 15), the captain of the school hockey team, for her defensive duties in the team as she plays in the back line. You have recorded that there has been a severe decrease in performance over the last two matches. In conversation, Amy comments that she can't be bothered at the moment.

1. **Identify possible reasons for Amy's decrease in motivation.**
2. **List three performance criteria that you may use to assess Amy for.**
3. **Apart from having a brief conversation, how else could you gain more information from Amy?**
4. **What is the difference between intrinsic and extrinsic motivation?**
5. **Describe the possible effect on the team in terms of group cohesion due to Amy's current behaviour state.**

Confidence

In many respects, confidence is just as important to performance as motivation. Self-confidence is based on expectations an athlete has in terms of success or failure. These expectations can change quickly within a game. For example, a football striker who has not scored for six games and then scores in a match and the team goes on to score four goals in three games, will increase in confidence. Confidence can be influenced by a whole host of reasons, such as anxiety or stress.

Ability level

You are likely to be working with athletes who possess differing ability levels. These may range from beginners to experienced athletes who perform at a high level.

When working with beginners, you will be able to identify many areas for improvement because they will possess little technical ability. It is important you can identify the basic skills that they need to improve on, such as striking the ball to aid progression of performance.

When working with experienced athletes ,you will need to concentrate on how they can improve the more technical aspects of performance, which may be harder to identify. (These athletes will already possess the technical ability if it can be produced on a regular basis.)

Group dynamics and group cohesion

Your analysis could concentrate on a particular team or group of players such as a hockey or cricket team. Within the team there should be communication between players, and they should, in theory, get on with each other. They should have accepted values that they are all working to within shared objectives (for example, winning the league title). If the team has good cohesion and group dynamics, they should perform at their best and produce positive results. There are two types cohesion as follows.

Key Terms

Task cohesion The degree to which all group members work together to achieve agreed goals.

Social cohesion The degree to which group members like each other and support each other.

There are a number of key factors that influence group cohesion:

- time (increased time aids stability)
- size of the group (small groups tend to work better because all members can interact with each other)
- type of sport (if a player relies on others, as in football, this will produce greater cohesion)
- success (success for the team will forge cohesion – for example, winning three matches in a row)

Remember!

Positive group cohesion will improve performance of the team and individuals. However, negative feelings and poor cohesion will be detrimental to performance.

- external factors (the threat of relegation may increase cohesion to avoid relegation).

It is vital that when you analyse the team's performance you consider group cohesion because this may have influenced the results. Your observations on this should be included in any feedback to the team or specific athlete.

Temperature

You may need to consider the temperature in which the performance takes place. For example, the rugby league season is played during the summer and is often played in hot temperatures. Extreme hot or cold environments can influence the athlete's body. For example:

- hot conditions in team sports, such as rugby league, may cause a reduction in distance covered due to the need to conserve energy
- cold conditions may be experienced by a sprinter in winter as part of their training cycle, and will affect certain physiological factors. For example, the sprinter will not sprint as fast as the cold can affect the tension produced in the muscle fibres.

Time of day

The time of day when the performance took place is important. The human body has a daily biological clock that has clear circadian rhythms (meaning about a day). The circadian clock regulates many aspects of metabolism, physiology and behaviour in the athlete. Therefore, from a sports perspective, there are certain times of day when it is better to perform certain exercises.

- Balance activities are suited to the morning, such as those required for gymnastics.
- Flexibility, strength and power peak in the early evening, due to daily maximum of body temperature.
- Heart-rate based tests (submaximal) show better results in the morning.

Future action for strengths and weaknesses

To make sure the evaluation process is complete, it is important that an action plan is put in place. This future action should be based on sound principles (such as goal setting) and will normally be devised in conjunction with the coach who can provided specialist technical support. This section will highlight some of the key issues for planning for future action.

Goals

It is highly likely that the athlete will have a few areas of improvement. However, it is important to categorise them into short-, medium- and long-term goals. Examples of these are shown below from netball.

Short term

Decrease number of fouls in the next match.

Medium term

Increase catching success for entire team to 95 per cent within eight weeks.

Long term

Integrate new defensive system to reduce the number of opposition goals at the start of next season.

Targets

When providing feedback to the athlete it is important that you set goals that are based on SMART targets. SMART means the following.

Specific

They say exactly what you mean (to improve shooting success in netball by the goal shooter).

Measurable

You can prove that you've reached them (increase shot success to 78 per cent from 56 per cent).

Achievable

You can reach them in the next few weeks (the increase in shot success must be manageable – 100 per cent success rate is not achievable).

Realistic

They are about action you can take (you can practise and improve this skill through coaching).

Time-bound

They have deadlines (to reach the target within six weeks).

Recommendations

Part of the role of the sports biomechanist is to provide possible recommendations to the athlete and coach in terms of the following.

Priority of future coaching and training

As part of the feedback process, you will need to prioritise future coaching and training sessions. You must be realistic. You will not be able to coach or train all the areas for improvement at once, and so you must base your decisions on:

- competition schedule
- access to coaches and training facilities
- current fitness status
- identification of key performance criteria
- individual and team-based performance criteria.

Team skills and drills

Within this unit we have considered the key performance criteria for a variety of sports. Within these performance criteria there are basic sports skills (such as catching, passing, etc.). You may have identified how the influence of these basic sports skills has affected team skills and drills (for example, how to defend a corner in football). Future action for the team could concentrate on improving these team skills and drills.

Individual skills training

Many sports require a number of very precise movements, which require good coordination and application of force. It is important that an athlete's training programme is specific and involves movements that are similar or identical to those performed in competition. The concept of matching training to performance is known as movement pattern specificity.

For example, the tennis serve; it involves all of the body at some point in the movement. Precise training for the speed, power, flexibility, coordination and balance required will train the player to make the serve effective. This type of movement pattern training also trains the muscle groups that will be used in competition.

Theory into practice

In pairs, produce a four-page coaching booklet to highlight the key skills and drills for a sport of your choice. (For example, you may choose to just concentrate on attacking plays within your sport.) To make the coaching booklet useful and interesting, use diagrams to represent the team skills and drills.

Fitness training for specific components of fitness

One key factor, which may help the athlete improve their biomechanical performance, is to train a specific component of fitness. Fitness can be divided into two key parts, namely health-related fitness and skill-related fitness.

There are various types of training you may recommend to your athlete for each component of fitness. For example, aerobic fitness can be improved through using various training methods such as steady state, interval and Fartlek training.

Taking it further

In pairs, use your research to produce a list and brief description of the different types of training you can recommend to the athlete, taking into account both health-related and skill-related fitness.

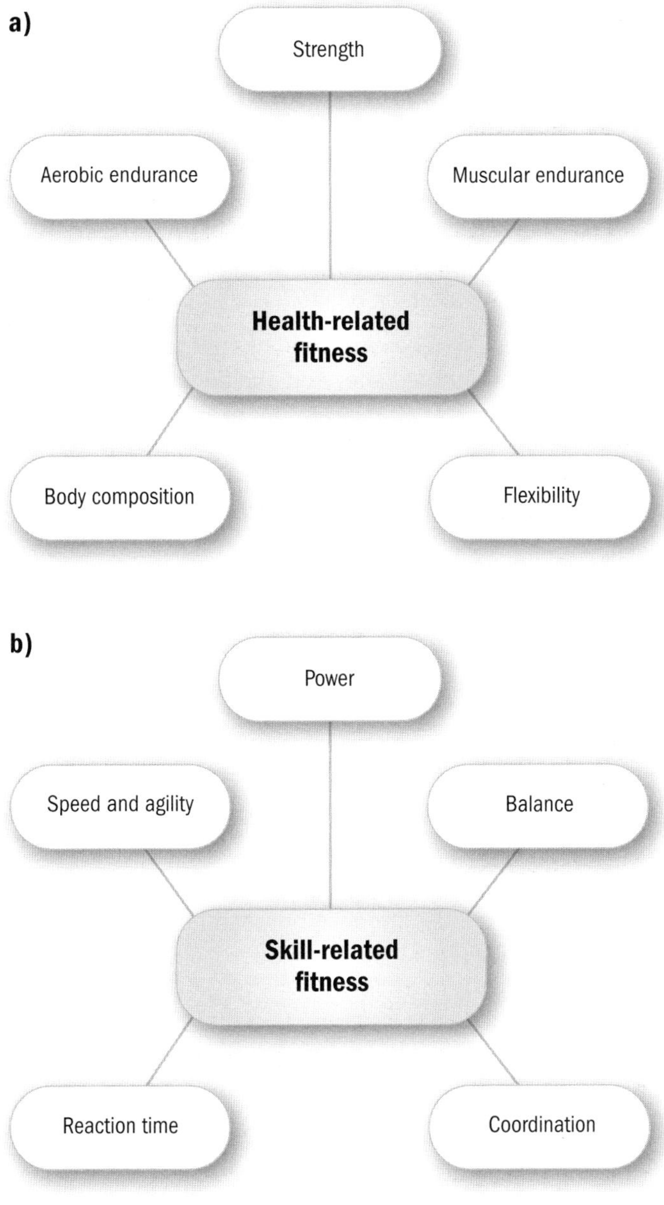

▲ **Health-related fitness and skill-related fitness**

Another important aspect to consider is metabolic specificity. Metabolic specificity relates to specific energy systems used by the athlete to produce a particular movement. The training programme should be matched to a specific energy system being used when the athlete is in competition. For example, a rugby player uses predominantly anaerobic energy to make repeated sprints. Therefore, the training programme should centre on exercises that use the anaerobic energy system, such as hill sprints.

■ Technique coaching specific to movement

A coach who has specialist knowledge within a given sport should be able to improve the athlete's performance from a technical perspective. It is the role of the sports biomechanist to work with the coach in identifying strengths and areas for improvement. The sports biomechanist should continue to work with the coach on a regular basis providing specialist support to maximise the athlete's performance.

Assessment practice

1 Using the poster you produced on page 242, which analysed the performance of a netball player, provide feedback to the player. You will need to provide verbal (through video evidence) and written feedback (two-page summary report). Within the feedback you will need to include:

- strengths
- areas for improvement
- evidence supporting your findings
- factors influencing performance
- goal setting
- recommendations for future training. 

2 Discuss a range of factors influencing performance and set short-, medium- and long-term goals based on SMART targets. Your recommendations will need to consider individual skills training, fitness training and specific coaching points. M3

3 Justify the recommendations that you have made to the athlete. Add additional evidence to support your choices, (for example, a quote from a book). D2

Knowledge check

1 In your own words, describe what notational analysis is.

2 What type of data would you use in conjunction with a line graph? Explain why.

3 List the key performance criteria for a sport of your choice and explain why you have included them.

4 Why is it important to produce a numerical model when making a comparison with a sporting performance?

5 Describe the advantages and disadvantages of using the mean when analysing your data.

6 Describe the reason for horizontal scaling when filming your athlete.

7 Describe how age may influence the biomechanical performance of an athlete.

8 What is the difference between height of release and angle of release?

9 Explain how goniometry works.

10 Why is goal setting important for future training plans?

11 Describe the five phases of a long jump.

12 Describe the reasons why an athlete may be suffering from poor motivation and, thereby, influencing their biomechanical performance.

Preparation for assessment

1 You have been given an interview for a coaching position, which is open to you on a local coaching scheme. As part of the interview, you will need to show that you have a solid biomechanical understanding of performance. On an individual basis, you are to plan and present a five-minute presentation based on the title 'Performance criteria for …' (name of sport).

- Choose a team/individual-based sport depending on your own interest or area of expertise.
- You need to cover five performance criteria that are relevant for your sport. It is possible for another group member to present the same sport with different performance criteria. This is acceptable as long as both can show it is relevant.
- You can choose to describe a particular player in a team (for example, a goal shooter in netball) rather than the team as a whole. However, you may decide to pick an individual-based sport such as snooker.
- Consider using pictures of your chosen performance criteria to demonstrate your point and also make the presentation interesting. **P1**

2 The interview went well and you have been appointed a role within the scheme, with a dual role of sports coach and performance analyst. Your boss, the performance director, asks you to carry out two notational analyses on a sports player/team of your choice to show your expertise. The performance director has asked you to provide a report on your findings.

Here are some helpful hints.

- You could approach your school's/college's sports teams to gain access to the athletes/players. Alternatively, you could use the club that you are attached to either during evenings or at weekends.
- If this is not possible, you could always analyse televised events.
- As you will need to produce a fair amount of raw data, you should record the performances, if possible, so you can review them at a later date (recording may also help to provide evidence for your work).
- The report must include the performance criteria, the use of statistics, data representation, raw data results and key findings. **P2**

To help you meet the M1 and D1 criteria you should read the following M1 and D1grading tips. **M1** **D1**

Grading Tip **M1**

To meet the M1 grading criteria you will need to take the data you have generated for P2 and compare the performances to draw out strengths and areas for improvement of the two performances. This comparison can be made through the use of statistics, for example comparison of percentages (look at the percentage differences). You should also make comparison through data representation (for example, you could put the two sets of data on the same line graph to make the comparison easier to see). Your findings should be supported by relevant information or data taken from the literature. For example, if your goal shooter in football only catches 65 per cent of the passes, you may use data from the Internet, as a comparison, which states the goal shooter at a recent competition catches 96 per cent of the passes. This supports your analysis that this is an area for improvement for your goal shooter you have analysed.

3 The performance director is pleased with your work and wants to extend your role within the scheme. In conversation with the performance director, you mention that you can compare sporting performance to a numerical model. The performance director asks you to carry out a numerical investigation into a local sports performer. You are asked to produce an A2 poster to be displayed in the local sports centre to demonstrate the work you can do. Within the poster you will need to show:

- the three performance criteria (model) you investigated
- references from the literature, which helped you produce the model
- a basic methodology (for example, camera position)
- your results, including any numerical calculations or equations used
- findings and implications for the athlete or team. **P3**

To help you meet the M2 criteria you should read the following M2 grading tip. **M2**

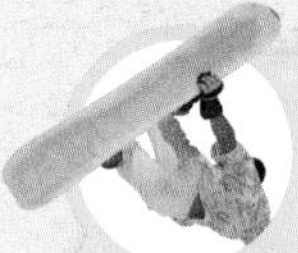

Grading Tip  **M2**

You will need to provide an explanation and justification of the methodology you used to collect the data from your athlete used in the poster. Therefore, you will need to consider issues such as horizontal scaling and camera position. In addition, you should explain and justify why you have included the three performance criteria you have used in the investigation. Therefore, if you can find supporting quotes and statistics that, for example, explain why you used the height of release in the javelin, this will help.

4 Within the coaching scheme another performance analyst is struggling to produce a technical investigation into a hockey player's performance. The performance director has asked you to produce a case study that you can give to the performance analyst to aid their understanding of the process. Therefore, within the case study (based on a sport of your choice) you are to include:

- the four performance criteria (model) you investigated
- references from the literature, which helped you produce the model
- a basic methodology (for example, camera position)
- your results, including any numerical calculations or equations used
- findings and implications for the athlete or team. **P4**

5 Despite your good work, the performance director is concerned that the athletes you have investigated have not received feedback regarding their performances. You are to produce a written report that details the feedback you have given. This report can be either based on the notational analysis (P2), numerical investigation (P3) or technical investigation (P4) you have carried out. Within the report you should include:

- strengths
- areas for improvement
- evidence supporting your findings
- factors influencing performance
- goal setting
- recommendations for future training. **P5**

To meet the M3 and D2 criteria please refer to the following M3 and D2 grading tips. **M3** **D2**

Grading Tip 

To provide detailed feedback the report will also need to include statistics (where appropriate) and data representation. You will also need to discuss a range of factors influencing performance and set short-, medium- and long-term goals based on SMART targets. The recommendations will need to consider individual skills training, fitness training and specific coaching points. In relation to recommendations, you should consider using diagrams to explain the specific training to be used by the athlete.

Grading Tip 

As with other elements of the assessment criteria you can choose to meet D1 grading criteria through extending your work in either the notational analyses, numerical or technical investigation. Therefore, you must evaluate your findings in only one of these areas. Based on your results, you will need to consider how they influence the sporting performance. For example, you may consider the following.

- What was the influence on the overall performance for the individual?
- Was it a key performance criterion in terms of the overall performance?
- Did it influence the team as a whole (if applicable)?
- Did it influence the opposition's performance?
- What will be the possible consequences for future performances?
- What other performance criteria may you investigate in the future?

Grading Tip 

Once again, you can choose to meet D2 grading criteria through extending your work in either the notational analyses, numerical or technical investigation. This extension work requires you to link biomechanical and sporting theory to your feedback. Therefore, evidence for your recommendations may come from:

- biomechanical journals
- coaching manuals
- fitness guidelines
- training books
- Internet.

Grading criteria

To achieve a pass grade the evidence must show that the learner is able to:	To achieve a merit grade the evidence must show that, in addition to the pass criteria, the learner is able to:	To achieve a distinction grade the evidence must show that, in addition to the pass and merit criteria, the learner is able to:
P1 describe five relevant performance criteria for an individual or team-based sport **Assessment practice pages 209, 253**		
P2 perform two notational analyses on a chosen sport, with some support **Assessment practice pages 219, 253**	**M1** compare the two notational analyses, using statistics, data representation and literature to explain the strengths and areas for improvement **Assessment practice page 219**	**D1** evaluate findings for either the notational analyses, numerical or technical models commenting on their influence on performance within the chosen sport **Assessment practice page 219**
P3 produce a numerical model, using three numerical components, and compare it to a sporting performance, with some support **Assessment practice pages 230, 254**	**M2** explain and justify the methodology for either the numerical or technical models **Assessment practice page 230**	
P4 produce a technical model, using four technical components, and compare it to a sports performance, with some support **Assessment practice pages 242, 254**	**M2** explain and justify the methodology used to collect the data **Assessment practice page 242**	
P5 provide feedback on performance, to an athlete or team, using information gathered from one of the analyses performed, prescribing future action, with support **Assessment practice pages 245, 252, 254**	**M3** provide detailed feedback and prescribe future action for the athlete or team from either the notational analyses, numerical or technical models **Assessment practice page 252**	**D2** justify the prescribed future actions for either the notational analyses, numerical or technical models **Assessment practice page 252**

Exercise, health and lifestyle

Introduction

Good health helps you to achieve your maximum potential. Regular exercise and physical activity should make you feel fitter, look better, and provide you with vitality and energy to go about your daily tasks with ease. Numerous other health benefits are gained from regular exercise, such as weight management; a reduced risk of chronic diseases such as coronary heart disease, diabetes and osteoporosis; maintenance of physical work capacity with ageing; and a reduced feeling of depression and anxiety. The importance of regular exercise and physical activity in promoting good health is a common feature in policy initiatives to improve the nation's health and well-being, but general lack of exercise and physical activity remains a serious public health concern.

After completing this unit you should be able to achieve the following outcomes:

- understand the importance of lifestyle factors in the maintenance of health and well-being
- be able to assess the lifestyle of a selected individual
- be able to provide advice on lifestyle improvement
- be able to plan a health-related physical activity programme for a selected individual.

Think it over

Take five minutes to think about all the factors that might influence your health and well-being. Now consider the range of health-related topics that have featured in the news in the past two weeks? Are there any themes that emerge from these topics?

Take a look at a range of health, fitness and sport-related magazines. Scan them for health-related features and advertisements. How many are there? What kind of topics do they focus on?

7.1 Understand the importance of lifestyle factors in the maintenance of health and well-being

Evidence suggests that adhering to a healthy lifestyle by following a sensible diet, taking regular physical activity, maintaining a healthy body weight and avoiding smoking, excessive alcohol consumption and stress is important to health and longevity.

Key Terms

Health Defined by the World Health Organization as a state of complete physical, mental and social well-being and not merely the absence of disease and infirmity.

Wellness This can be viewed as our approach to personal health that emphasises individual responsibility for well-being through the practice of health-promoting lifestyle behaviours. These include regular physical activity, a healthy diet, and the maintenance of good emotional and spiritual health.

Lifestyle Refers to the way a person lives and typically reflects an individual's attitudes, values and behaviours.

Lifestyle factors

There are five lifestyle factors that appear to be of significance in the maintenance of health and well-being:

- physical activity
- avoiding excessive alcohol
- not smoking
- avoiding excessive stress
- healthy diet.

Physical activity

Physical activity can be considered as any bodily movement produced by your skeletal muscles that increases your energy expenditure above resting levels. It may include planned activities such as walking, cycling, running and playing sport, as well as daily activities such as those carried out at work or in the home.

Recommendations and guidelines

To gain health benefits the Department of Health recommends that we do least 30 minutes of moderate exercise on five, if not all, days of the week.

This 30-minute-a-day recommendation should probably be viewed as the minimum required to achieve health benefits, but the good news is that it does not have to be achieved in a single bout. Several short bursts of activity can count towards your total. This approach may make it easier for some individuals to meet their daily physical activity target.

Greater benefits will be gained from increasing the amount to 40–60 minutes each day, especially for those who are at risk of weight gain and the diseases associated with this.

The same recommendations apply to older people, dependent on ability, but children are encouraged to achieve at least one hour every day of moderate intensity activity. 'Moderate' means that you must get a little warmer and slightly out of breath. The more vigorous the activity, the greater the gains in terms of cardiovascular health.

In terms of type, it can be anything that raises your energy expenditure above resting level, enough to expend about 200 calories, and brings about the symptoms already described, for example: brisk walking, swimming, cycling, jogging, dancing, heavy housework and gardening.

Current activity guidelines for health promotion encourage the daily accumulation of lifestyle activities, such as walking and stair climbing.

Remember!

Physical activity is any activity that increases energy expenditure above resting level. Physical activity undertaken for health benefits would be targeted at avoiding disease and delaying death.

Exercise is physical activity that is structured and undertaken usually for fitness gains. Exercise undertaken for fitness benefits would be targeted at improving one or more components of health-related fitness.

Activity

Consider all the benefits a regular programme of physical activity and exercise can bring. Group the benefits you have identified into the following categories:

- physical
- social
- psychological
- economic
- environmental.

Health benefits

Individuals who lead active lives are less likely to die early or suffer from chronic disease such as coronary heart disease and diabetes, and are better able to cope with stress.

In the 1950s, researchers studying workers on London's double-decker buses found that 30 per cent fewer conductors had heart disease compared with their fellow bus drivers. The proposed argument for this was that the conductors were much more active in their jobs, moving between the decks to collect fares and issue tickets. American studies in the early 1980s showed that men who expended more than 2,000 calories a week by regular walking also had a much lower risk of heart disease.

These early studies, and many more since, have demonstrated numerous health benefits of physical activity and exercise.

With the boom in the private health and fitness industry, it would be easy for people to think that exercising for health and well-being requires a considerable amount of special equipment, clothing and money. However, this is not necessarily the case. There are many types of exercise accessible to those on a limited budget – walking being an excellent example. It is also important to remember that whatever your age regular exercise offers many health benefits, both short and long term.

The highly mechanised environment that we live in today has significantly reduced the number of opportunities open to us to incorporate moderate intensity physical activity into our daily living, but exercise has a crucial role to play in weight loss and maintenance.

Increased physical activity elevates total daily energy expenditure, helping to maintain a higher energy output. In the case of initiating weight loss, it can assist in achieving a negative energy balance. Regular

The physical benefits of regular physical Activity

endurance-type exercise improves the ability of our muscles to burn fat as a fuel.

Resistance-type exercise can help to combat the loss of lean body mass that often occurs as a result of dieting. Gains in lean body mass contributing to an increase in resting metabolic rate, can further aid weight loss and maintenance by increasing energy requirements even at rest.

The best approach to weight loss is to undertake a combined programme of progressive aerobic and resistance training in which training sessions should aim to expend at least 250 kilocalories. A lifelong commitment to regular exercise is essential to facilitate weight maintenance.

Psychological benefits

The psychological benefits of exercise should not be overlooked. Studies have shown that exercise brings about both short- and long-term psychological benefits to health and well-being. Regular physical activity can enhance mood and the way you feel about yourself, improving self-confidence and body image. Researchers have found that regular physical activity reduces depression and anxiety, and makes you better able to manage stress and tension. It is also possible to improve concentration.

Remember!

Physical activity enhances mood, reduces anxiety and raises self-esteem and confidence. This is a growing area of scientific research, but surveys suggest that physically active individuals feel happier with life – even single bouts of activity can improve mood and energy.

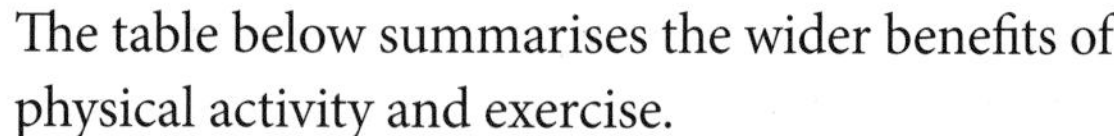

The table below summarises the wider benefits of physical activity and exercise.

Social	Economic
• Encourages 'connectedness' • Improves social skills • Reduces isolation • Enhances self-esteem and confidence	• Reduces health costs • Creates employment • Supports local businesses • Reduces absenteeism • Enhances productivity

The wider social and economic benefits of physical activity and exercise

As you can see from the table above, when we consider the health and well-being of the nation there are wider social and economic benefits to an active lifestyle. At an individual level, we can take a closer look at short- and long-term benefits of physical activity in maintaining health and well-being.

- It provides an opportunity for fun and enjoyment.
- It relaxes and revitalises the body, reducing muscular and mental tension.
- It boosts self-esteem and confidence.
- It clears the head and improves concentration.
- It lowers the risk of heart disease and stroke. Exercise not only strengthens the heart muscle, it reduces some of the risk factors associated with heart

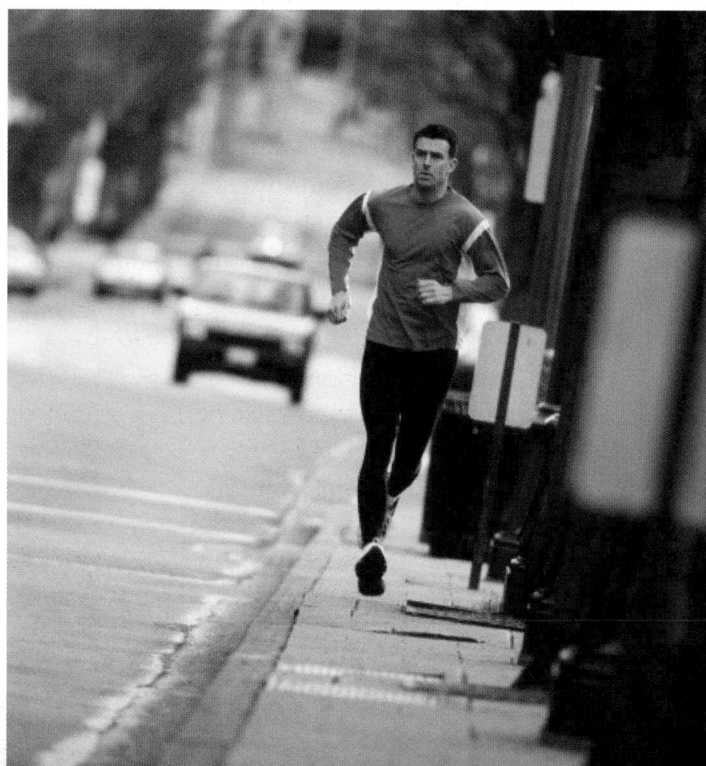

The psychological benefits of regular physical Activity

disease and stroke, such as high blood pressure and cholesterol, as well as the problems with being overweight and obesity. Exercise lowers blood pressure and has a favourable effect on blood lipid profiles, improving blood flow.

Key Terms

Blood lipid profiles These reflect an individual's risk of coronary heart disease and include measures of total cholesterol, HDL cholesterol (often referred to as 'good' cholesterol), LDL cholesterol (often referred to as 'bad' cholesterol) and triglycerides.

Osteoporosis A condition involving a decrease in bone mass, making bones more fragile.

- It raises high-density lipoprotein (HDL) levels, the so-called 'good' cholesterol, and lowers the low-density lipoprotein (LDL) levels, the 'bad' cholesterol.
- It lowers body weight and body fat, assisting in the maintenance of optimal body weight and composition. A programme of regular exercise combined with a healthy diet is the best way to lose excess weight. Maintaining a regular programme of exercise provides the best opportunity for maintaining weight loss. Physical activity and exercise facilitates the development and maintenance of muscle mass, thereby improving the body's ability to burn calories.
- It lowers the risk of Type 2 diabetes and increases the uptake of glucose in those who are already sufferers, primarily by reducing body fatness.
- It lowers the risk of certain types of cancer, such as cancer of the breast and colon.
- It lowers the risk of osteoporosis as regular exercise promotes bone density by the pulling and tugging on the bones by muscles during exercise, which stimulates the bone-making cells.
- It alleviates the symptoms of arthritic pain by keeping joints flexible and maintaining the strength of muscles surrounding joints.
- It combats ageing by maintaining the effectiveness of body systems, such as the respiratory, circulatory and musculoskeletal systems. As we age, several structural and functional changes occur which result in a decline in optimum physical capacity. Factors such as breathing capacity, heart function and muscular strength are greatly influenced by fitness level, while other age-related changes (such as changes in skin, vision and hearing) occur irrespective of fitness level.
- It improves digestion as exercise and activity support the proper functioning of the gut and reduce the risk of indigestion and constipation.

The World Health Organization has reported that physical inactivity is one of the ten leading causes of death in the developed world.

Remember!

Walking and cycling provide great opportunities for increasing physical activity in the sedentary population and present low risks in terms of injury.

Theory into practice

Working in small groups, undertake a short survey within your college to establish the level of physical activity and exercise participation of staff and students.

You should:

- consider how you are going to undertake your survey and what information you want to obtain
- assess for knowledge of current physical activity and exercise guidelines aimed at promoting health and well-being
- consider how you are going to collect, analyse and present your data
- present your findings in an appropriate media (e.g. poster, flyer, article on college Intranet).

Taking it further

'While low levels of physical activity can afford you some health benefits, moderate to high levels are required to deliver major benefits to your health and well-being.' Undertake your own research of scientific journals and key authoritative sources on physical activity participation, such as the American College of Sport Medicine (ACSM) and the British Association for Sport and Exercise Sciences (BASES) to investigate the scientific bases for this statement.

Remember!

The diseases that can be prevented or treated by physical activity and exercise participation can be thought of as chronic or persistent. For physical activity or exercise to have optimal benefits in their management and treatment, it needs to be current and ongoing.

Web links

Visit the Department of Health website at www.dh.gov.uk to view the chief medical officer's report called 'At least five a week: evidence on the impact of physical activity and its relationship to health'. This report sets out the latest research evidence on the benefits of exercise and physical activity for health. You can find the publication by entering the search terms 'At least five a week' into the 'Search this site' box.

Remember!

Current recommendations for physical activity for health gain recognise the importance of accumulating physical activity through a number of shorter bouts of activity.

Avoiding excessive alcohol

Alcohol is the product of the fermentation of carbohydrates by yeasts. It is a concentrated source of energy providing 7 calories per gram. However, this energy is unavailable to working muscles during exercise. Any energy derived from alcohol in excess to energy requirements will be stored as fat.

Alcohol is a drug that affects every organ in your body. It is a central nervous system depressant that is readily absorbed from your stomach and small intestine into your bloodstream. Your liver is responsible for metabolising alcohol.

The intensity of the effect of alcohol on your body is directly related to the volume consumed. Binge drinking (excessive alcohol consumption) is becoming a major public health concern.

Recommendations and guidelines

Alcohol consumption of any type in moderation is thought to be beneficial, particularly in reducing the risks of heart disease. However, excessive intakes can cause health problems such as cirrhosis of the liver, certain forms of cancer and psychological health problems.

Current safe limits for alcohol consumption are up to 3–4 units per day for men and up to 2–3 units per day for women.

It is also advised to spread alcohol intake throughout the week to avoid binges and to include two or three alcohol-free days each week.

Key Term

Cirrhosis Scarring of the liver tissue, which blocks the flow of blood.

Remember!

Binge drinking is a serious risk to health and well-being.

Risks associated with excessive drinking

Excessive alcohol consumption has been linked to a range of illnesses and disease including malnutrition, cancer and cirrhosis of the liver. Excessive consumption can also have a detrimental impact on the social and psychological health of an individual, such as depression and mood swings.

Key Term

Hypertension High blood pressure, which is when systolic blood pressure is above 140mm Hg and diastolic pressure is above 90mm Hg.

Malnutrition

Malnutrition is often associated with chronic alcohol use linked to gastrointestinal irritation, which over time can dull the appetite and food intake. This leads to lowered energy and nutrient intakes and absorption.

Cancer

Excessive alcohol consumption can lead to the development of cancers of the digestive system such as the mouth, oesophagus, stomach and liver.

Stroke

A stoke occurs when brain tissue dies as a result of a sudden and severe disruption of blood flow to the brain. Heavy alcohol use has been associated with increased risk of stroke.

Cirrhosis

Chronic abuse of alcohol over a prolonged period can lead to cirrhosis of the liver, which may result in liver failure and death.

Hypertension

The relationship between alcohol use and blood pressure is important as hypertension is a key risk factor in the risk of coronary heart disease and stroke.

Depression

There is evidence to suggest that excessive alcohol consumption has a role to play in causing depression. Alcohol dependence and depression may occur together. Depression is a common feature reported in those being treated for alcohol dependence.

Mood swings

The effects of alcohol can contribute to the increased likelihood of mood swings and aggressive behaviour. The brain is affected by reducing the anxiety associated with the consequences of individual behaviour. Thinking and problem-solving abilities in conflict situations are also affected, which can result in an excessively emotional response.

Remember!

One unit of alcohol is equivalent to 8g of alcohol, typically a small glass of wine, half a pint of beer, lager or cider or a single pub measure of spirits.

Taking it further

Using the Internet and evidence from scientific journals, undertake your own research into the benefits and risks to health and well-being from alcohol consumption.

Theory into practice

Working in small groups, undertake a short survey within your college that aims to establish the level of alcohol consumption by students.

You should:

- consider how you are going to undertake your survey and what information you want to obtain
- assess for knowledge of current alcohol consumption guidelines aimed at promoting health and well-being
- consider how you are going to collect, analyse and present your data
- present your findings in an appropriate media (e.g. poster, flyer, article on college Intranet).

Not smoking

According to the World Health Organization, smoking is responsible for more than five million deaths each year and is related to around 25 different diseases. Tobacco smoke contains more than 4,000 chemical constituents. Nicotine and tar are particularly damaging to health. Nicotine is a very powerful drug that causes addiction. It stimulates the central nervous system and increases heart rate and blood pressure. Tar is a complex mixture of chemicals, many of which can cause cancer. It is largely deposited in the respiratory tract and gradually absorbed.

Smokers in their 30s and 40s are five times more likely than non-smokers to have a heart attack. In the UK, more than 20,000 people die from lung cancer every year.

Health risks

Some of the health risks associated with smoking include coronary heart disease and stroke, and lung problems such as cancer, bronchitis and emphysema. The risk of disease increases with the volume of smoking and number of years smoked, but also how deeply the smoke is inhaled.

Coronary heart disease

Coronary heart disease (CHD) is a generic term to describe the conditions caused by an interrupted or reduced flow of blood through the coronary arteries to the heart muscle. Many studies have provided evidence for the role of smoking in the cause of CHD. Smokers appear to have a higher risk of developing atherosclerosis (the build up of fatty deposits in the arteries), which is a primary contributor to CHD. Smoking presents an increased risk by itself, but when coupled with other risk factors such as high blood pressure, high cholesterol and physical inactivity it increases the likelihood of the blood to clot resulting in a heart attack.

Overall, smokers have a higher risk of heart attack than non-smokers (a two- to three-fold increase in risk), while smokers under the age of 40 are five times more likely to suffer a heart attack than non-smokers. Exposure to other people's smoke (passive smoking) can increase the risk of CHD in the non-smoker, which is why passive smoking is becoming an increasing public health concern.

Remember!

Smoking, high blood pressure, high cholesterol, physical inactivity and obesity are all major risk factors for coronary heart disease, all of which can be modified or controlled by adopting healthy lifestyle behaviours.

Cancer

Lung cancer is the most common form of cancer and the type most often associated with smoking. In terms of risk of developing lung cancer, the age at which smoking commences appears to be significant. Results of a study of ex-smokers showed that those who started smoking before the age of 15 years had twice as many cell mutations (an instrumental factor in the development and initiation of cancer) than those who started after 20 years of age.

The impact of smoking on cancer risk is not limited to its effect on the lungs. Smoking has also been implicated in cancers of the mouth, oesophagus, bladder, breast, cervix, colon, liver and kidneys.

Taking it further

Undertake your own research to investigate the prevalence and incidence of cancer and its different forms in the UK population.

Lung infections

Smokers are likely to suffer more respiratory tract infections than non-smokers. They are more prone to suffer from colds and flu, and take longer to recover. Pneumonia is a serious lung infection and although the condition is caused by a bacterial or viral organism, it is more common and much more likely to be fatal among smokers than non-smokers.

Bronchitis

Bronchitis is a condition of the inflammation of the lining of the bronchial tubes of the respiratory system. It can be an acute or chronic condition. The most common symptom of bronchitis is a cough. Acute bronchitis is most often caused by a viral or bacterial infection, while chronic bronchitis is most often seen in smokers. Smoking causes damage to the cilia that line the airways. This means that over time they become less efficient at clearing debris and irritants, making the lungs more susceptible to infection.

Key Terms

Cilia Hair-like projections that line the upper respiratory tract and filter out dust and other particles that enter the respiratory tract in the air breathed.

Gaseous exchange Loading oxygen and unloading carbon dioxide at the lungs.

Emphysema

Emphysema is a chronic disease of the lungs, meaning that once a sufferer is diagnosed, the condition is unlikely to get better. Over time, the alveoli (air sacs) of the lungs are destroyed, reducing the surface area of the lungs available for gaseous exchange. The alveoli also lose their elasticity. Smoking is the most common cause of emphysema. Sufferers present with shortness of breath, particularly on exertion, but as the disease progresses this may be evident at rest. Exercise tolerance is significantly reduced. Sufferers also experience frequent coughing and the production of thick mucus.

Avoiding excessive stress

Stress is a physiological and mental response to triggers in our environment and can impact on our physical and mental health and well-being. Factors that produce stress are known as 'stressors'. Stressors can take different forms. Potential stressors include major life events such as marriage, divorce and moving house, injury or trauma, and environmental situations such as a demanding work environment. Whatever the stressor, the physical and mental responses usually include feelings of anxiety and tension.

Health risks of excessive stress levels

Chronic stress exposes your body to persistently elevated levels of stress hormones such as adrenaline and cortisol. The effects of chronic stress may manifest themselves in different ways, such as lowered resistance to disease, increased risk of heart disease, hormonal imbalances, back or joint pain, and emotional and eating disorders.

Hypertension

Scientists remain unsure about the possible links between stress and hypertension (high blood pressure). It is thought that long-term stress can contribute to hypertension through repeated blood pressure elevation. In the case of short-lived stress, we know that stress causes blood pressure to rise for a while, but once the stress is relieved blood pressure returns to normal.

Angina

Angina is a pain or constricting feeling in the centre of the chest that can radiate down one or both arms, but usually the left. This pain or tightness results from ischemia – a lack of oxygenated blood reaching the heart. It is an indicator of coronary heart disease caused by the build up of fatty deposits in the coronary arteries that supply blood to the heart muscle, which results in their narrowing. When stress causes an increase in blood flow to the heart, angina can occur.

Stroke

Stress can cause blood pressure to rise. Evidence suggests that people whose blood pressure rises with exposure to stress have a greater risk of stroke.

Heart attack

Stress is thought to increase the risk of coronary heart disease (CHD), although as yet the direct links are unclear. However, it appears likely that stress may contribute to the development of other major risk factors for CHD such as smoking, inactivity, obesity and high blood pressure.

Ulcers

Most ulcers (75 per cent) are caused by bacterial infection. However, there is support for the theory that stress is a possible cause. Stress may act by the stimulation of gastric acid production or by promoting behaviour that causes a risk to health.

Depression

Mental health problems are increasing in prevalence, with anxiety and depression forming the most common causes of mental ill health in the UK. Individuals may develop depression after stressful life events such as the death of a partner or the loss of a job. Whether a stressful event alone can cause a person to become depressed is not fully known. In fact, some people can become depressed when there appears to be little or no stress in their lives, while negative beliefs about the ability to manage stressful situations might make some people more prone to developing depression.

Colitis

Colitis refers to inflammation of the large intestine. Stress-related colitis is known as irritable bowel syndrome (IBS), a condition characterised by cramping, abdominal pain, bloating, constipation and diarrhoea. Stress can cause colon spasms in IBS suffers, but this process is not fully understood.

Remember!

People who suffer from high levels of stress may not engage in health-promoting lifestyle activities such as eating healthily, taking regular physical activity or getting enough sleep.

Taking it further

Active individuals report fewer symptoms of anxiety or emotional distress. Undertake your own research into the role of exercise in the management of stress.

Healthy diet

The word 'diet' refers to your typical pattern of food consumption, while the term 'balanced diet' describes a diet that provides the correct amount of all the nutrients required by your body without excess or deficiency.

A healthy diet should fulfil the following objectives. It should:

- provide adequate energy and nutrients to maintain your normal physiological functioning
- permit the growth and replacement of your body tissues
- offer you protection against the risk of disease.

It is possible that on a day-to-day basis when planning meals these objectives are overlooked.

Benefits of a healthy diet

Scientific research continues to provide evidence of direct links between good eating habits and disease prevention. Benefits of a healthy diet include increased energy and vitality, improved immune system function, control of weight gain and maintenance, and reduced risk of chronic disease.

Healthy eating involves choosing the right foods in the right balance to provide all the essential nutrients and energy required by your body to maintain it in optimal health. The principles of healthy eating aim to reduce your risk of chronic disease (such as heart disease, obesity, diabetes and cancer) and help you to maintain a healthy immune system. These principles will also benefit performance in sport and exercise.

Effects of poor nutrition

Deficiencies, excesses and imbalances in dietary intakes all have the potential to produce negative impacts on health, which can lead to a range of dietary related disorders. Disorders of deficiency include scurvy (lack of vitamin C), osteoporosis (lack of calcium) and anaemia (lack of iron), while disorders of excess include obesity (excess calories) and coronary heart disease (excess fat).

Imbalances of dietary intake may occur during periods of high nutritional demand such as growth or pregnancy, or when physical or psychological difficulties impact on meeting adequate nutritional intake such as during old age.

Recommendations and guidelines

Numerical targets for dietary intakes of the UK population were first established in the 1980s. These were reviewed in the 1990s in the Committee on Medical Aspects of Food Policy (COMA) report on 'Dietary reference values for UK subjects'. Healthy eating principles aim to assist the population in meeting these dietary targets. The current dietary targets for the UK population are given below.

Nutrient	Recommendation
Total fat	< 35% of total energy
Saturated fat	No more than 11% of total energy
Protein	< 15% of total energy
Carbohydrate	50% of total energy
Fibre (non-starch polysaccharide)	18g per day
Salt	6g per day

Dietary targets for the UK population

Remember!

A simple guide to healthy eating:

- eat the correct amount to maintain a healthy body weight
- cut back on your fat intake, particularly from saturated sources
- eat plenty of foods with a high starch and fibre content
- don't eat sugary foods too often
- use salt sparingly and reduce your reliance on convenience foods
- ensure adequate intakes of vitamins and minerals by eating a wide variety of foods
- if you drink alcohol, keep within sensible limits
- enjoy your food and don't become obsessed with your diet or dieting.

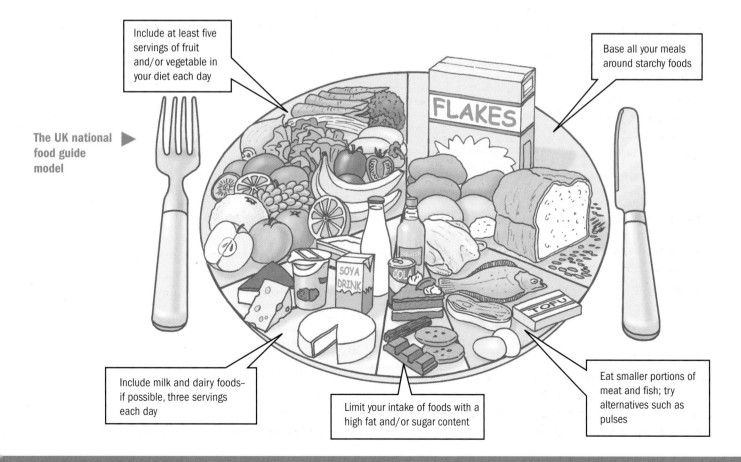

Include at least five servings of fruit and/or vegetable in your diet each day

Base all your meals around starchy foods

FLAKES

SOYA DRINK

COLA

TOFU

Include milk and dairy foods– if possible, three servings each day

Limit your intake of foods with a high fat and/or sugar content

Eat smaller portions of meat and fish; try alternatives such as pulses

The UK national food guide model

Balance of good health

The balance of good health model (see page 269) is the UK's national food guide. It was devised by the Health Education Authority as a simplified means of helping you to understand and implement healthy eating. The model identifies the types and proportions of food groups you require to achieve a healthy, balanced and varied diet.

The model shows a tilted plate with divisions of varying sizes representing each of the five main food groups. Those with a larger slice of the plate should feature in higher proportions in your diet, whereas those with the smallest slice should be consumed in smaller proportions or used only as occasional foods, especially in the case of those with a high fat and/or sugar content.

Case study

What changes would you recommend?

Sasha is a 27-year-old housewife with two small children; one aged 3 years and the other 10 months. She has not taken part in any regular exercise since discovering she was pregnant with her second child. She is approximately one stone overweight and a typical day's diet is as follows.

Breakfast	• Cornflakes with full cream milk and sugar • Two slices of toast with butter • Coffee with milk and two sugars
Mid-morning	• Coffee with milk and two sugars • Chocolate biscuit
Lunch	• Cheese, ham or tuna salad sandwich on two slices of white bread with butter and mayonnaise • Yoghurt and orange squash
Mid-afternoon	• Tea with milk and two sugars • Piece of cake or chocolate biscuit
Evening	• Meat, fish or chicken with mashed potatoes and vegetables, fish and chips or pizza • Ice cream or cheese and biscuits
Supper	• Tea with milk and two sugars • Two chocolate biscuits
Alcohol	• Approximately 14 units a week

1. **What changes to Sasha's diet would you suggest to help her improve her diet?**
2. **Devise a suitable diet plan taking into account your suggestions. Before you start you might want to devise a suitable template for this purpose.**
3. **Explain the recommendations you have made regarding these dietary improvement strategies.**

▼ A healthy lifestyle

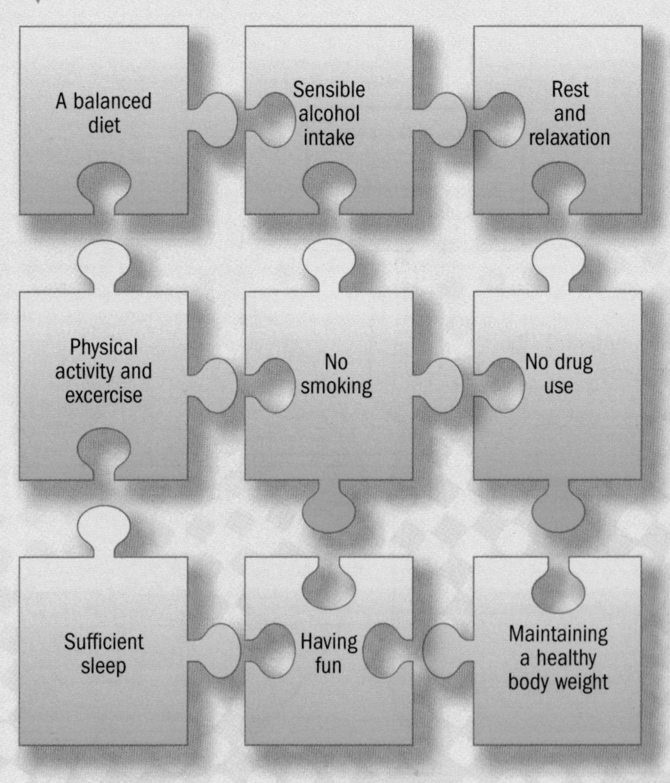

Assessment practice

Imagine your college decides to undertake a health promotion campaign where the focus is on a healthy campus.

1 Working in small groups, decide on the healthy lifestyle factors to be promoted. Research the healthy lifestyle factors in terms of recommendations and health risks associated with each lifestyle behaviour, and present your findings in an information booklet. **P1**

2 Your booklet should explain lifestyle factors that have an effect on health. **M1**

grading tips

Grading Tip 

Describe the following lifestyle factors, which have an impact on health: physical activity, alcohol consumption, smoking, stress and diet.

You should consider the benefits of physical activity and make recommendations for alcohol consumption, together with describing the health risks associated with excessive drinking, smoking, high stress levels and an unhealthy diet.

Grading Tip 

You must explain the effects of the identified lifestyle factors on health. Physical activity and alcohol consumption, together with the health risks of excessive drinking, smoking, high levels of stress and an unhealthy diet, should all be covered.

7.2 Be able to assess the lifestyle of a selected individual

In this unit you will provide advice on lifestyle improvements and plan a health-related physical activity programme, but before you can do this it is essential to be able to assess the lifestyle of the client. To do this, you will need to undertake a consultation with the client and assess their lifestyle.

Remember!

Lifestyle relates to a particular way in which an individual lives their life. In this unit we will focus on health-related behaviours such as activity, smoking, stress, diet and alcohol consumption.

Lifestyle questionnaire

It is important to assess health status prior to planning a health-related physical activity programme. An objective evaluation of current exercise, health and lifestyle status will provide information on the participant's strengths and weaknesses providing the basis for the establishment of realistic goals and the avoidance of injury and illness. Testing initial fitness levels can also provide a useful benchmark against which progress can be measured. Periodic testing provides motivating feedback as the physical activity or exercise programme progresses.

Levels of physical activity

Physical fitness assessment may form part of the overall screening process. However, it is essential that health and lifestyle screening takes place prior to this assessment, preferably by a medical or fitness practitioner. This is usually carried out in the form of an interview or questionnaire. Comprehensive lifestyle and pre-exercise screening will help to identify medical conditions that may prevent the participant from exercising safely. It also highlights the participant's objectives and ensures that the exercise and lifestyle prescription fulfils their needs.

Pre-exercise health screening can take many different forms and can be self- or practitioner-administered. The choice of method depends on a number of factors such as the age and health status, previous training history and resources.

Web links

An example of a physical activity readiness questionnaire (PAR-Q) is available from the Canadian Society for Exercise Physiology at www.csep.ca. This questionnaire is designed for use by individuals between the ages of 15 and 69. It aims to identify the small number of individuals for whom physical activity might be inappropriate or people who would require medical advice before embarking on a programme.

Remember!

- If in any doubt about an individual's suitability or readiness to exercise, make sure they consult their doctor.
- It is important that any information obtained from health and lifestyle screening is stored in a secure place for reasons of confidentiality, and that the information is accessed only by people who are authorised to do so.

The key features of a good lifestyle screening protocol are that it:

- takes account of participant's past and current medical history
- takes account of family medical history
- records blood pressure
- measures body composition
- measures current fitness status and exercise history
- records diet and alcohol history
- records smoking history
- investigates stress and sleep patterns.

Alcohol consumption

Questionnaires aimed at assessing alcohol consumption should address volume (unit) and frequency (days) of consumption.

Smoking

Questionnaires aimed at assessing smoking habits should consider the type of smoking (cigarettes, cigars, pipes), the duration of smoking (number of years) and volume (number per day).

Stress levels

Questionnaires aimed at assessing stress levels might consider major life events and recent changes in personal situation (such as marriage, divorce, bereavement and job loss). They could also look at issues related to recent health status, eating habits and sleeping patterns.

Diet

There are five basic methods for assessing dietary intake. Two of these methods use records of food consumption made at the actual time of eating – one with the actual weight recorded by the client and the other by using estimations of weights of food consumed using standard household measures.

The other three methods attempt to assess diet and food consumption in the recent past by asking about food intake the previous day (24-hour recall), over the past few weeks (diet history) or in the recent or distant past (questionnaires). These are usually devised for completion by the client without supervision (food frequency questionnaire).

One-to-one consultation

You are most likely to gather information to assess the lifestyle of a selected individual through a one-to-one consultation. Key factors in a successful consultation include effective communication skills and client confidentiality.

Think it over

What objective measures of fitness would you include in a pre-exercise fitness assessment?

Theory into practice

Complete the following lifestyle assessment questionnaire. The purpose of this questionnaire is to raise your awareness of healthy and unhealthy lifestyle choices you make before you move on to working with a selected individual.

Please answer True or False to the following questions.

Lifestyle assessment questionnaire

1 ***Diet***

I usually try to eat three balanced meals each day **True/False**
I usually eat at least five servings of fruit/vegetables each day **True/False**
I eat the right amount to be a healthy body weight **True/False**
I only consume alcohol within the recommended guidelines **True/False**

2 ***Physical activity and exercise***

I undertake at least 30 minutes of moderate-intensity physical activity at least five times per week **True/False**

3 ***Stress***

I get plenty of rest **True/False**
I rarely feel tense or anxious **True/False**

4 ***Sleep***

I usually get at least eight hours' sleep each night **True/False**

5 ***Smoking***

I never smoke **True/False**

6 ***Drugs***

I never take drugs **True/False**

How to calculate your score

Allow yourself one point for each true answer:
9–10: very healthy lifestyle
7–8: generally healthy lifestyle
5–6: average lifestyle
0–4: unhealthy lifestyle, with many improvements needed

This exercise should have helped you highlight which aspects of your lifestyle require changes to improve your health. If you have many aspects to change, prioritise them and start with the changes you know you can easily make first.

Consultation

Communication

Effective communication is crucial in the consultation process. Communication is about giving and receiving information. Your questioning, listening and non-verbal communication skills will be important to ensure you set the correct tone for the consultation. Whether the subject feels at ease and whether your information is received in the way you intend it to be, will depend on the effectiveness of your communication skills.

Remember!

Non-verbal communication, such as facial expressions, hand gestures and general body language, sends out messages without you even speaking.

▲ **The consultation process is an important part of assessing the lifestyle of a particular individual**

The key factors to ensure effective communication in the consultation process include:

- maintaining eye contact with your subject
- making them feel at ease by welcoming them, introducing yourself and explaining the consultation process
- maintaining a professional approach and avoiding being over-familiar with them
- asking permission if you intend to keep notes of your consultation
- maintaining an open and friendly posture at all times.

Activity

1. In pairs, practise your consultation technique.
2. Once you are happy with your technique, ask another student or your tutor to observe you and provide constructive feedback on your verbal and non-verbal communication skills.
3. Be sure to ask the client to provide feedback on your consultation skills.

Client confidentiality

Information about a client belongs to the client. Client confidentiality ensures that you should not release information about your clients to a third party without their informed consent.

Assessment practice

Imagine your college has invested in a new health and fitness suite with the primary emphasis on improving the health and well-being of staff and students. Your class has been asked to design a lifestyle screening questionnaire for use in this facility.

1. Design a lifestyle questionnaire to describe the strengths and areas for improvement of the lifestyle of a selected individual. **P2**
2. To assess the usability of the questionnaire, use it on a client and explain the strengths and areas for improvement of their lifestyle. **M2**
3. Evaluate the lifestyle of the selected individual and prioritise areas for change. **D1**
4. Write up your findings in a report.

grading tips

Grading Tip 

You need to collect information on the lifestyle of an individual using a suitable questionnaire and one-to-one consultation.

Grading Tip 

Make sure you explain the strengths and areas for improvement of the selected individual's lifestyle and explain your recommended lifestyle improvements strategies.

Grading Tip 

You need to evaluate the lifestyle of the selected individual and prioritise areas for change. In doing this, you may need to make some value judgements about the strengths and areas for improvement.

7.3 Be able to provide advice on lifestyle improvement

In this section you will consider strategies for lifestyle improvement in respect of physical activity, alcohol consumption, smoking and stress reduction.

Strategies

Poor health is a serious drain on national resources and increases the amount required to be spent on health care by the government.

We may encounter many difficulties in attaining wellness. Our age, ethnicity and socio-economic status may present challenges to achieving wellness.

Taking it further

Using the Internet or your local health promotion office, investigate the range of local and national initiatives aimed at improving the nation's health.

Physical activity

Despite the strong case presented for keeping active, many individuals find it difficult to incorporate physical activity or structured exercise into their daily lives.

For lots of people, the mere notion of physical activity or exercise conjures up unpleasant thoughts or images of boring exercise classes or rough competitive sports, where the risk of injury would be a real turn-off.

Those who have never exercised before or are in poor shape should not expect to see immediate results. Achieving physical fitness requires time and consistency. There may be many barriers to adopting a regular exercise programme.

■ Ways to increase physical activity levels

Walking

Walking is our main form of locomotion. Scientific evidence supports the benefits of regular walking for health and well-being, with walking shown to have positive effects both physically and psychologically. Walking is an easy and economical way to become and stay active. It can be participated in by all age groups and is a good social activity. Classed as an aerobic activity if undertaken regularly, it has positive effects on cardiorespiratory fitness.

Key Term

Pedometer Also known as a step counter, this is a portable electronic device usually worn all day on the belt, which counts each step as it is taken.

To achieve the health benefits of walking, the target is 10,000 steps a day (about five miles). The average sedentary individual achieves much lower counts than this (2,000–3,000 steps per day). Pedometers have become useful at motivating people to walk and measuring their progress. A good target to aim for is to increase average daily steps each week by 500 per day until the 10,000 target is achieved.

Taking it further

Undertake your own research into walking initiatives in your local area.

Stair climbing

Encouraging the use of stairways to promote physical activity in the workplace and other settings may have significant health gains to offer.

Evidence suggests that moderate-intensity lifestyle activities (such as taking the stairs instead of the lift or escalator) may be more successfully promoted than vigorous exercise programmes.

Stair climbing can be accumulated throughout the course of a day, and with an energy cost of approximately 8–10kcals per minute it can help with weight control. It also has benefits in terms of leg power, bone strength and cardiovascular fitness.

Cycling

Cycling can be an effective and enjoyable aerobic exercise. Daily cycling has been shown to be sufficient to significant health benefits. People of most fitness levels can participate in cycling, although anyone with heart disease or other pre-existing conditions should consult their doctor before staring a cycling programme. Cycling offers a healthy leisure activity and an alternative mode of transport.

Daily cycling has been shown to lead to significant health benefits

Theory into practice

Working in small groups, undertake a survey on walking, stair climbing and cycling participation among staff and students at your college.

You should report your findings using appropriate media (e.g. posters leaflets, college Intranet) and aim to promote increased participation in these lifestyle activities.

Activity

1 In pairs, write a list of all the reasons that you can think of that could stop you from exercising.

2 Check out your ideas with those identified in the spider diagram on page 277.

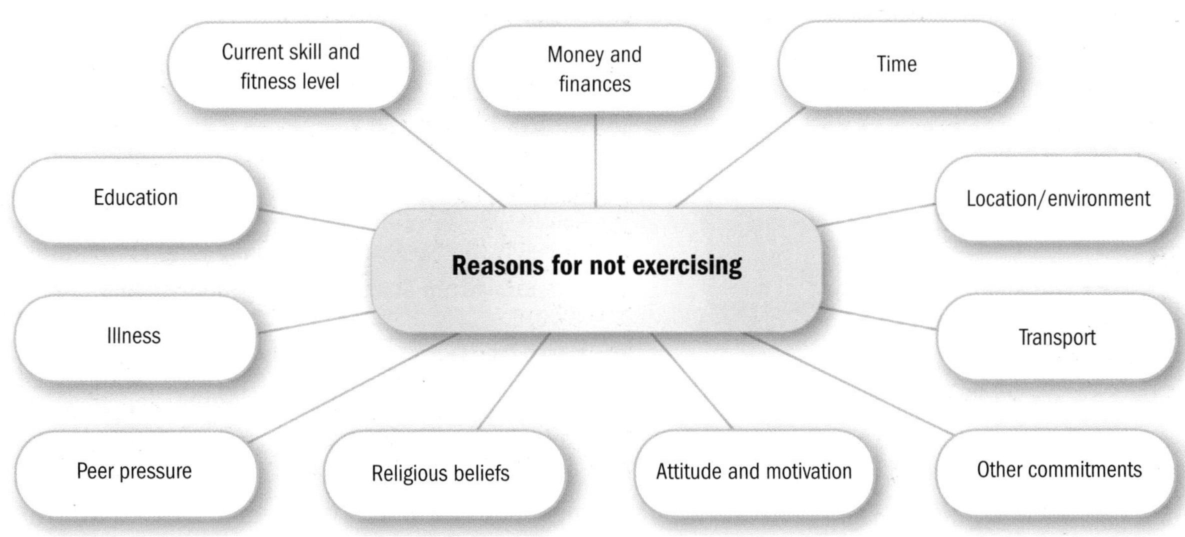

Potential barriers to physical activity participation

Case study

Barriers to physical activity participation

Pamela is 35 years old. She is 1.63 metres tall and weighs 120kg. Pamela was moderately overweight as a child. Her weight has steadily increased over the last ten years, with her lowest adult weight being 74.0kg. Over the years, she has been concerned about the weight around her thighs but recent weight gain appears to be on the upper body, particularly around her waist.

She is an accounts manager who has worked in sales for 15 years, working her way up to her current position. She is considering working freelance due to the high levels of stress associated with her current position.

She lives with her partner, who is also overweight. She has no children, and enjoys eating out, fine wines and foreign holidays. Pamela suffers from low back pain, which impacts on her ability to be physically active. She has a family history of heart disease and stroke. Her father died at a young age from a sudden heart attack.

At a recent fitness assessment at a private health and fitness club, Pamela's resting heart rate was recorded as 105–110 beats per minute. She joined the club about a month ago but has found little time or motivation to attend since. The club has extensive and excellent facilities. Pamela is concerned about her current appearance and does not feel confident in the exercise environment.

In the past she has enjoyed going for an occasional swim at the ladies-only sessions at the local swimming baths.

1. **How would you summarise Pamela's lifestyle and exercise habits?**
2. **What potential barriers do you think there are to Pamela engaging in a regular programme of physical activity and exercise?**
3. **How might she overcome some of these barriers?**
4. **What physical activity and exercise recommendations would you make?**
5. **Are there any safety aspects that require consideration in this case?**

Remember!

The risks associated with participation in a regular programme of physical activity or exercise are usually less than the risks associated with living a sedentary lifestyle. However, the potential benefits of exercise must outweigh the potential risks to the participant.

Alcohol

We all have the option of drinking or abstaining (either for religious or health reasons) from alcohol, and it is down to individual choice for deciding the occasions on which to drink and the amounts to be consumed. For some individuals, alcohol use becomes a problem to the point when it is detrimental to their overall health and well-being. Where alcohol consumption becomes so excessive and frequent that it has a severe and negative impact on the health of an individual, this would be called alcoholism. Alcoholics exhibit intense cravings for alcohol. They become physically dependent on it and are unable to control their use. If deprived, they will suffer withdrawal symptoms including hallucinations and uncontrolled shaking.

Seek alternatives

Problem drinking and alcoholism are serious, but recovery is possible if the person is strongly motivated to stop drinking. Alternatives sought might include counselling and therapy, self-help groups (either face-to-face or online) or alternative treatments and therapies.

Counselling and therapy

Problem drinkers can undertake individual or group counselling provided by specially trained therapists, which might involve other family members. Exploring and developing awareness of triggers for alcohol consumption and the breaking of habitual behaviours are likely areas of focus for counselling and therapy. Relapse is often high for the alcohol abuser, and preventing relapse may be a key feature of the counselling and therapy process.

Detoxification

Treatment for alcohol abuse often begins with detoxification and withdrawal from alcohol. This is particularly necessary when alcohol consumption has continued for long periods of time. It can be an uncomfortable process and symptoms may take the form of tremors, increased perspiration, insomnia, confusion and hallucinations. In extreme cases it can be fatal, which is why detoxification is usually undertaken under supervision within an alcohol-treatment facility.

Self-help groups

There are a number of treatment options available for the problem drinker or alcoholic, but success depends on recognition of the problem by the sufferer. Self-help groups such as Alcoholics Anonymous (AA) have helped many sufferers tackle their problem drinking through a step-by-step programme of recovery.

Alternative treatment and therapies

Some alcohol users may seek alternative treatments and therapies, such as acupuncture and hypnosis. These treatments are thought to lessen the symptoms of withdrawal, but there are mixed views within the medical field concerning there value.

Taking it further

Undertake your own research to investigate other options available to support those who believe they have a problem with excessive or frequent alcohol consumption.

Smoking

Smoking is a serious risk to health that increases the risk of lung and heart disease. As with most behaviour modification goals, in order to stop smoking the smoker has to have the desire to stop. Once this is realised, there are a number of approaches that can be taken to support the attainment of the goal.

Acupuncture

Acupuncture is a traditional Chinese therapy. It is a technique where very fine needles of varying lengths are inserted through the skin. Acupuncture may assist with smoking cessation by increasing the body's production of mood-enhancing endorphins that reduce or alleviate withdrawal symptoms.

NHS smoking helpline

The NHS smoking helpline was launched in 2000 as part of a government initiative to encourage 1.5 million people in the UK to give up smoking by the year 2010. The helpline offers information, advice and support to those that wish to give up smoking. The number is 0800 169 0169.

NHS stop-smoking services

The range of services promoted include group and one-to-one counselling, and information on nicotine replacement therapy.

Nicotine replacement therapy

Nicotine replacement therapy refers to a range of products (gums, patches, lozenges and sprays) that can be used to help the smoker during giving up. They are available on prescription and are suitable for most smokers, although pregnant women or people taking regular medication should consult their doctor before using. Unlike cigarettes, they do not contain the harmful cancer-causing toxic chemicals.

Taking it further

Investigate the range of options available to support people who want to give up smoking.

Stress management techniques

To control stress there are two general approaches that can be taken:

- trying to reduce the amount of overall stress
- developing coping or stress management techniques.

To reduce overall stress requires the identification of the factors that promote stress, usually known as stressors, and if possible eliminating or reducing these factors. For example, a frequent cause of stress for many individuals is over-committing themselves at work or in their social life. Careful time management and prioritisation of your workload and commitments may help to manage stress better.

It is not possible to eliminate all the stresses we face in daily life, so using techniques that can reduce levels of stress will have a positive impact on your health and well-being. Exercise can be viewed as a positive stress for the body. The choice of pleasant exercise surroundings can help to cancel out the negative stresses that accumulate in daily life. Taking part in an activity that is social can help here too, or participating in exercise undertaken to music.

Assertiveness

Assertiveness is the ability to express your feelings and rights while respecting those of others. Although assertiveness may come naturally to some, it is a skill that can be learned. Once mastered, assertiveness can help you to deal with conflict situations that may be a cause of stress in daily life. Assertive behaviour should not be confused with aggressive behaviour.

Goal setting

Properly set goals can be motivating and rewarding. In respect of stress management, achieving goals can build self-confidence and reduce stress.

Time management

Time management can be considered to go hand in hand with stress management and is a critical element of effective stress management. Time management is about achieving your tasks in good time by using techniques such as goal setting, task planning and minimising time spent on unproductive activities.

Physical activity

Physical activity can have a positive effect on anxiety, depression, self-esteem and mood. It can be a stress reliever by producing an outlet for frustration, releasing endorphins – the 'feel-good' hormones that lift mood – and providing a distraction from the stressor.

Regular exercise, such as walking, cycling, swimming and dancing, provides an outlet to drain off ongoing stress and keep it under control.

Positive self-talk

Effective stress management requires a positive perspective, particularly as perceived pressures increase.

Self-talk is the inner conversation you have with yourself. It influences most of your emotional life and reflects how you respond to your thoughts, feelings and actions. It can be negative or positive.

Positive self-talk involves taking an optimistic view of life and situation. Positive thinking will help you to be better able to cope with stress.

In our daily lives we face constant challenges, difficulties and deadlines, so being able to take a positive view of these and have constructive ways of dealing with them will help to reduce and manage stress.

Relaxation and breathing

Relaxation techniques and breathing exercises can also be beneficial in controlling stress.

There are many types of relaxation techniques but most focus on contracting and relaxing muscles to ease tension.

Focusing on breathing exercises is also another simple way of trying to control or reduce stress and usually involve controlled inhalation and exhalation. They are best undertaken in quiet and comfortable surroundings.

Healthy eating should be something that is enjoyed by all and not simply endured. In order to be able to safely and effectively plan and implement lifestyle improvement strategies around healthy eating programmes, it is necessary to critically evaluate your own eating habits and what influences them.

Taking it further

Once you have kept your diet record, swap it with a partner. Compare it to the balance of good health guidelines (see page 269) and write a short evaluation to provide feedback to your partner on the strengths and areas for improvement in their diet.

Theory into practice

To assess your own eating habits, keep a record of all food and drink you consume for at least a three-day period, which should include one weekend day. (For a more detailed evaluation, record your intake for a full week.)

Write down *everything* you eat and drink. You must be as accurate and honest as possible, and be sure not to modify your usual intake at this stage otherwise you will not be evaluating your typical diet. You will need to carry your record around with you at all times and record food and drink as it is consumed to avoid forgetting any items. Your record should describe the following.

- The type of food and drink consumed and how much. Either estimate the portion size using standard household measures (such as slices of bread, pints of fluid, tablespoons of vegetables), or give the weight.
- The time the food and drink was consumed and where you were when you ate it. These points are useful when assessing external factors that affect your dietary intake.
- Your cooking methods and type of food preparation.
- Any activity or exercise you took part in, including an indication of its duration and intensity, i.e. light, moderate or hard.

Timing of food intake

Timing of meals is one of the main components of a person's food habits. Food habits develop over time and are largely resistant to change. Their acquisition is mainly subconscious as they are acquired at a young age from your parents.

In areas of the world where food is readily available 24 hours a day, intake can occur at any time. However, most of us do not eat continually but stick to reasonably defined mealtimes with snacks in between. In Western culture this had lead to a three-meals-per-day approach supplemented by snacking. As lifestyles become more busy and flexible, more snacking may occur, but overall nutritional density of the diet remains important. Investigating the time that food and drink are consumed and where you were at the time, are often useful factors to consider when assessing external factors that affect dietary intake.

Taking it further

Investigate the likely effects of shift-working on food intake and the ability to obtain a balanced diet.

Eating more or less of certain foods

The government has set targets or dietary intake goals aimed at improving the nation's health and reducing the risk of chronic disease (see page 268). Your diet should be balanced across the five main food groups to ensure that you achieve adequate energy and nutrients without excesses or deficiencies. As a population, we are advised to eat more wholegrain starchy carbohydrate food and fruits and vegetables, and to eat fewer fatty and sugary foods. This is expressed in the percentage contribution of food groups within the balance of good health model (see page 269).

Food preparation

Most foods you eat require some form of preparation before consumption. Food preparation depends largely on cooking skills, facilities and the time available to prepare the food. Awareness of an individual's cooking skills and facilities is important when suggesting strategies for improving dietary intake in order for realistic and achievable goals to be set. Food handling and safety are also important aspects of food preparation in ensuring health and well-being.

Taking it further

Visit your GP surgery or local health promotion unit to collect information and leaflets on the treatment and management of lifestyle issues such as smoking, physical activity, diet, and drug and alcohol use.

▼ Main components of food habits

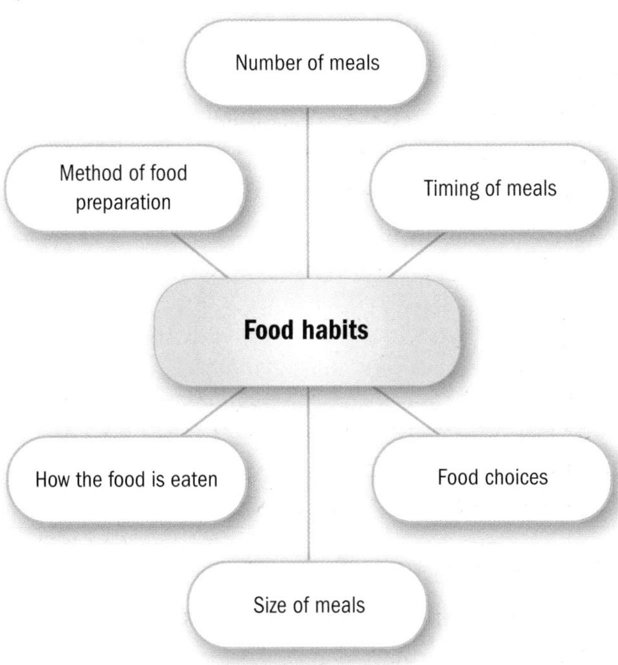

Activity

Your food record should allow you to further examine your normal eating patterns. As well as the types and amounts of food consumed, it may give you an idea about how your lifestyle dictates what, when, where and why you eat.

1 Take another look at your diary with a friend and consider the following questions.
   a In relation to healthy eating principles, is your diet better than you first thought or is there room for some improvement? What healthy eating goals might you not be achieving and why?
   b Are your meal times structured and regular? Maybe you eat differently at weekends? Does where and what time you eat dictate your food choice and selection?
   c Do you rely heavily on convenience foods and takeaways? If so, what influences this?
   d What constraints do you foresee that may prevent you from making any of the necessary changes you have identified as a result of your evaluation? Do you think you will be able to overcome them?

e Suggest strategies for improvement where necessary.

2 Summarise the changes you want to make. Make sure they are realistic. Try to implement these changes over the coming weeks. Tackle them one at a time – they don't all need to happen overnight.

3 You may have discovered that to improve your diet you need to consider the types and quantities of food you consume, or maybe you need to alter your cooking methods or timings of meal and snack consumption. In order to monitor the effectiveness of your dietary changes, repeat this exercise in a month's time to see if you have successfully managed to implement the changes you and your partner identified to eat a healthier diet.

Behaviour change

Behaviour modification has its basis in psychological principles of learning theory and is used to change or modify a person's behaviour. Behaviour modification techniques can be used to eliminate unhealthy lifestyle behaviours.

Various models have been proposed to support behaviour change processes. One of the most common approaches for promoting lifestyle behaviour modification is the stages of change (or transtheoretical) model (as below).

Stages of change

There are five stages in this model.

- Precontemplation: at this stage you are not thinking about changing behaviour in the near future. Most people at this stage fail to notice or have any concerns for a particular behaviour, such as overeating or lack of physical activity.
- Contemplation: this is when you become aware that a change may be desirable. For example, you have decided that you cannot fit into your clothes, and you need to lose some weight by cutting down on your food intake and increasing your physical activity levels.
- Preparation: you begin to set yourself targets and goals to improve behaviour.
- Active: at this stage you start to implement your plan of behaviour change. Obstacles should be expected and strategies for overcoming them may need to be considered.
- Maintenance: you should be able to acknowledge that setbacks will come along from time to time, but you are able to remind yourself of your goals and positive benefits of the change.

Understanding these stages and being able to evaluate where in the cycle of change an individual is in relation to changing health behaviour, is thought to be a predictor of successful outcome.

Here are some simple steps to behaviour modification:

- identify the problem (or problems) and understand the need to change
- understand the influences on the problem
- establish short-, medium- and long-term goals for tackling the problem and record them
- develop a strategy to facilitate change and understand the resources or skills required for success
- implement the strategy, and record and monitor progress
- evaluate progress and consider your strategies to maintain your change in behaviour if successfully achieved.

Remember!

The stages of change model attempts to modify an individual's behaviour using various processes of change that are matched to their stage of change.

Case study Assessing lifestyle

Carl is a 43-year-old male maintenance worker who was screened at his company's occupational health centre and found to have a high percentage of body fat. The occupational health nurse has told him he needs to lose some weight and begin a programme of physical activity. He was a 40-a-day smoker up until three years ago when he quit on his 40th birthday, but since giving up smoking he has gained weight progressively.

He admits to a sedentary lifestyle away from work, preferring to watch sport from the comfort of his armchair rather than participate in it. He was a competitive athlete in his early youth, winning medals for distance running, but cannot seem to get motivated to do any exercise at present. He has thought about joining his local health club, but is sensitive about his current size and poor level of fitness.

1 **What initial assessment do you make of Carl's current lifestyle and motivation to change?**

2 **What benefits would a regular programme of physical activity or exercise bring for Carl?**

3 **How long would you expect it to take before Carl would notice any benefits to participation in a regular programme of physical activity or exercise?**

4 **What do you think would be the most appropriate types of exercise to include in a regular programme of physical activity or exercise at this stage?**

▲ Carl can benefit from lifestyle improvement strategies

5 **What strategies could you use to overcome Carl's current barriers to participation in a regular programme of physical activity or exercise and get him motivated to start?**

■ Common barriers

Different barriers may present themselves in tackling the health behaviours identified in this unit. However, some common barriers may apply across all, including:

- lack of knowledge about the benefits of the behaviour change
- lack of self-confidence in making the behaviour change
- setting unrealistic goals for behaviour change
- lack of commitment or motivation to make the change
- lack of control over your environment to make the change
- lack of support from others to make the change
- falling at the first hurdle.

Think it over

Think about the common barriers identified on page 283 and think back to when you have attempted to make a behaviour change that failed.

What were your barriers to success?

Cognitive and behavioural strategies

Cognitive and behavioural strategies are a range of approaches to behaviour change based on psychological models of human behaviour.

They include a broad range of approaches along a continuum from structured individual psychotherapy at one end to self-help at the other.

In cognitive behavioural therapy (CBT), a skills-based approach, the client and therapist work together to form a therapeutic alliance (a safe and trusting relationship) to identify and attempt to understand the client's problem behaviour.

A key element of this approach is to help the client to understand the relationship between thoughts, feelings and behaviour. Once this is explored, the client and therapist try to establish a shared understanding of the problem.

This leads to the formulation of personalised, time-bound therapy goals and strategies for tackling the problem that are monitored and evaluated over time. During this process, the client learns to develop psychological or practical skills for problem solving or management.

The overall aim of cognitive and behavioural approaches is for the client to attribute improvements in their problems to their own efforts, not those of the therapist.

The possible approaches for helping people change unhealthy lifestyle behaviours include:

- advice such as leaflets
- individual counselling and support
- group counselling and support
- campaigns and displays
- community-based activities.

Assessment practice

Select an individual that would benefit from lifestyle improvement (such as a friend or relative who wishes to lose weight), to follow a more healthy diet, to give up smoking, to reduce alcohol intake or to increase physical activity.

1 Give the individual appropriate lifestyle improvement strategies. **P3**

2 Explain the recommendations you have made regarding lifestyle improvement strategies. 

3 Analyse the range of lifestyle improvement strategies that are appropriate for your selected individual and how you can monitor and evaluate their effectiveness. **D2**

grading tips

Grading Tip P3

You need to provide lifestyle improvement strategies for the selected individual, including advice where appropriate on stress management, smoking cessation, alcohol reduction and diet.

Grading Tip M3

Explain the lifestyle improvement strategies in terms of their suitability for the selected individual.

Grading Tip D2

Analyse a range of lifestyle improvements strategies for the selected individual. This requires you to investigate the strengths and weaknesses of different strategies, and how you can monitor and evaluate their effectiveness.

7.4 Be able to plan a health-related physical activity programme for a selected individual

There are many different kinds of health-related fitness (often referred to as exercise-related fitness), which enable your body to function with maximum physical efficiency to cope with the demands placed on your body by daily life.

Health-related fitness has several components and you require a minimum level of fitness in each of these components to cope with everyday living. Athletes require higher levels of fitness in these components, and different sporting activities require the development of different aspects of health-related fitness.

Collect information

Before being able to plan a health-related physical activity programme for a selected individual, it is necessary to collect relevant information to assist you in the planning process. This should cover the individual's personal goals, and take account of their lifestyle, medical and physical activity history, as well as consider their attitude towards physical activity and exercise and their motivation to adhere to your plan.

A health-status questionnaire similar to the one on page 286 could be used as a starting point in your information gathering.

▼ The components of fitness

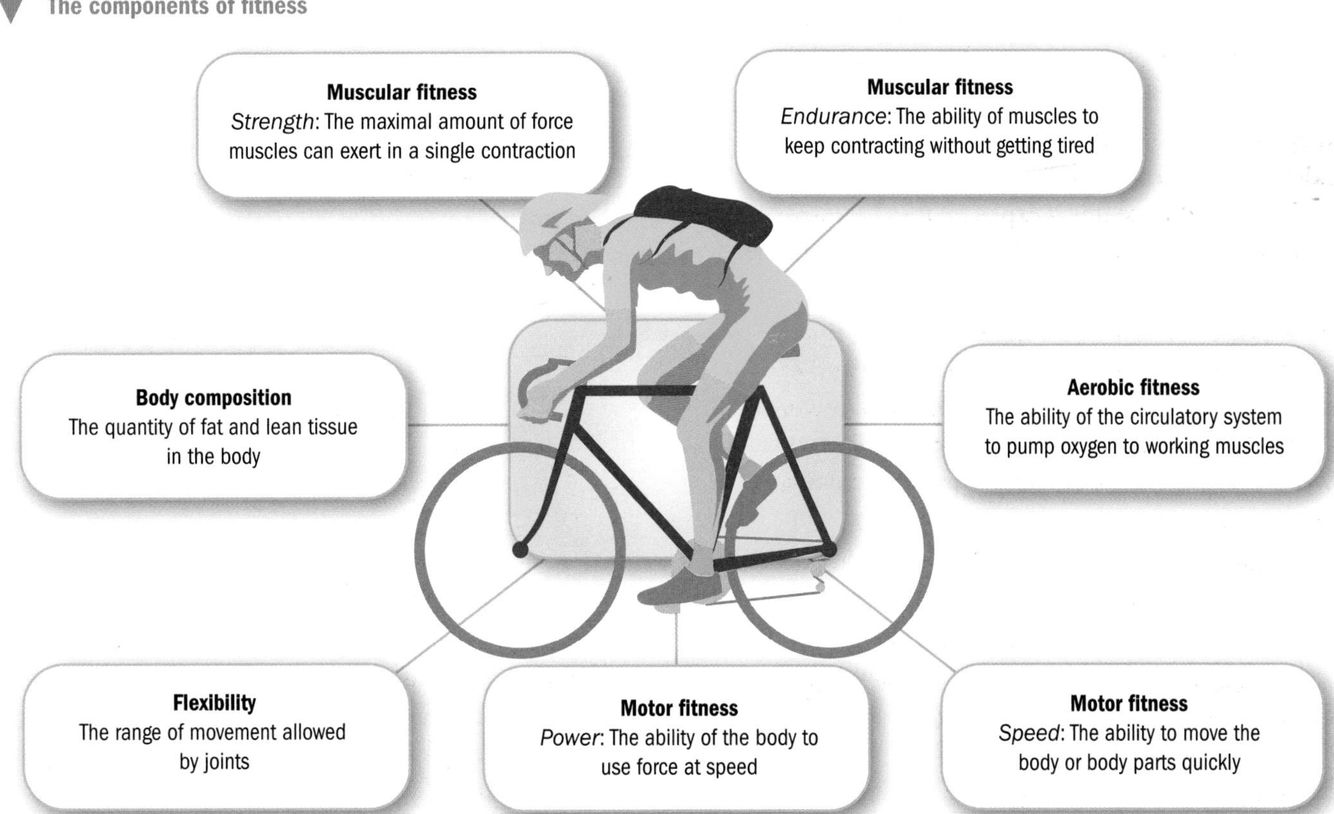

Muscular fitness
Strength: The maximal amount of force muscles can exert in a single contraction
Muscular fitness
Endurance: The ability of muscles to keep contracting without getting tired
Body composition
The quantity of fat and lean tissue in the body
Aerobic fitness
The ability of the circulatory system to pump oxygen to working muscles
Flexibility
The range of movement allowed by joints
Motor fitness
Power: The ability of the body to use force at speed
Motor fitness
Speed: The ability to move the body or body parts quickly

Name: .... Date: ....

The following questions are designed to find out whether you can participate in the practical exercise and physical activities outlined below. If you answer Yes to any of the questions in this questionnaire, you should have a thorough medical examination prior to participating in the practical tasks.

1 Have you ever had a heart condition or experienced chest pains or a sensation in your chest associated with exercise? Yes/No

2 Do you have a family history of heart disease below the age of 55? Yes/No

3 Have you ever suffered from high or low blood pressure? Yes/No

4 Are you taking any prescribed medication? Yes/No

5 Do you suffer from any respiratory problems such as asthma or shortness of breath with minimal exertion? Yes/No

6 Have you ever had any condition or injury affecting your joints or back that could be aggravated by exercise? Yes/No

7 Do you suffer from diabetes or epilepsy? Yes/No

8 Has your GP ever advised you not to participate in exercise? Yes/No

When undertaking exercise and physical activities, start at a slow pace and listen to your body. If you experience any signs of discomfort or stress, end the activity immediately and seek medical advice as soon as possible.

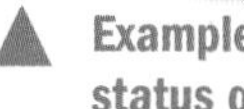

Example of a health status questionnaire

Periodic objective evaluation of your fitness is important to maintain interest and motivation to sustain physical activity or exercise programmes. Monitoring fitness goals and outcomes can provide useful information in the design and progression of physical activity and exercise programmes. Methods of monitoring can be sophisticated and complex, such as the direct measurement of VO_2 maximum, or simple measures of body weight and composition.

Key Term

VO_2 maximum The highest rate at which oxygen can be taken up and utilised during exercise by a person. See Unit 2.

Personal goals

A person's motivation to start a physical activity or exercise programme can be influenced by a range of goals: from improving all or specific elements of health-related fitness, to weight loss and maintenance, to getting fit for a certain occasion or challenge. Knowing what these are as you embark on planning will allow you to tailor your programme and provide a focus for continuing with it should motivation dip along the way.

Lifestyle

Key features of lifestyle screening have been covered on pages 271–274, but the most important elements in a lifestyle history should relate to:

- type of occupation and family commitments
- smoking and alcohol use
- perception of stress
- perceived challenges or barriers to success in achieving personal goals.

Medical history

The most important elements of a medical history should relate to:

- any current existing medical conditions
- any previous medical history
- any family history of chronic disease
- previous medical examination results, if available
- medications or drug use.

Physical activity history

The most important elements of a physical activity history should relate to:

- exercise and activity history (frequency, intensity, time and type – FITT) (see page 289)
- exercise and activity preferences.

Attitudes and motivation

Monitoring progress in attaining and maintaining physical fitness is a vital factor in providing the motivation to continue and the development of exercise adherence to lifetime fitness.

Progress can be monitored by keeping training logs or diaries that record the distance walked or run, or the amount of weight lifted for example.

Another means of monitoring fitness progress is by fitness testing. Fitness testing can provide strong positive feedback when fitness levels are improving, but it may be demotivating when they are not.

Some people may have a poor attitude or motivation towards exercise based on previous bad experiences, or because of poor self-esteem or confidence in the exercise environment.

Goal setting

Goals

Short-, medium- and long-term goals

Physical activity and exercise plans to promote health and well-being should encourage the development of all components of health-related fitness.

The first step in undertaking a physical activity or exercise programme is committing to doing it. To ensure that you do this, it is important to set short-, medium- and long-term goals to keep you on track. These goals should be dependent on your personal wants and needs in respect of your health and well-being. Setting realistic goals gives a target to aim for and an incentive to continue, especially if the going gets tough or your motivation starts to wane. Attaining goals improves self-esteem and motivation.

Short-term goals should aim to be achieved within the first six to eight weeks of a programme; long-term goals might take account of the first 12 months of a programme. Medium-term goals are aimed at the first three, six and nine months. Long-term goals can be modified to meet changes in needs or circumstances, or if a faster-than-expected rate of progression is achieved.

Remember!

Achieving short-term health-related fitness goals provides great motivation to continue with your programme.

SMART targets

When designing the physical activity programme, it is important that you set goals that are based on SMART targets:

- **S** – specific: they say exactly what you mean
- **M** – measurable: you can prove that you have reached them

- A – achievable: you can reach them in the next few weeks
- R – realistic: they are about action you can take
- T – time-bound: they have deadlines.

Principles of training

Being physically fit is about having enough energy, strength and skill to cope with the everyday demands of your own environment. Individual fitness levels vary greatly from low levels required to cope with daily activities, to optimal levels required by some performers at the top of their sport. Improving fitness improves the physiological functioning of your body.

The preparation and construction of an effective exercise or physical activity programme needs to be based on the manner in which the body adapts to different training regimes. Programmes can be constructed to emphasise one or many aspects of fitness – for example, strength, aerobic endurance and flexibility – but the following factors should be given careful consideration:

- overload
- specificity
- progression
- individual differences
- variation
- reversibility.

Overload

To achieve a higher level of fitness, it is necessary to stress your body's systems and place them in a state of overload – a point that reaches above and beyond that which is usually achieved. If this greater level is not achieved, adaptation will not occur. To avoid the problems associated with injury, illness and motivation it is important that the training load is progressively increased. Rest and recuperation are also important. It is important to remember that, when working with the general population to develop health-related fitness, the overload required may be very small and take some time to achieve.

Consider the novice gym user who at the start of their training programme can only perform six repetitions of a press up. After two or three weeks of training two to three times per week, they should be able to increase the number of repetitions achieved beyond this. They can then think about including sets of repetitions.

Remember!

To achieve a higher level of fitness, it is necessary to stress the body's systems and place them in a state of overload.

Specificity

Adaptations to training are highly specific to the type of activity undertaken and the intensity to which it is performed. Specificity relates both to the muscle groups involved and the energy sources used. Training for one sort of activity does not lead to fitness for all activities.

Take a squash player who sprints around the court returning every shot and keeps going long after their opponent looks exhausted and concedes defeat. If the same squash player took part in a long-distance road race, they might manage to get around the course, but are unlikely to win the event. They might even get out of breath and have to stop along the way.

Similarly, there is little transfer of training from strength training to cardiovascular efficiency. Take a marathon runner – they would not spend a great deal of time lifting heavy weights or doing short sprint intervals. The power lifter would not overemphasise distance running or low-intensity resistance training, while prolonged long-distance running is unlikely to improve endurance swimming time.

Progression

When exercise is performed over a period of weeks or months, your body adapts. The physiological changes that occur with repeated exposure to exercise improve the body's capacity and efficiency. With aerobic training such as running and cycling, the heart and lungs become more efficient and endurance capacity increases, whereas the muscles become stronger with resistance training such as weight training. Adaptations derived from training are highly specific to the type of exercise or activity undertaken.

Individual differences

Genetics plays a large part in determining how quickly and to what degree you will adapt to a specific exercise regime. Two people are unlikely to show the same rate and magnitude of adaptation in response to the same training programme. As a result, the principle of individual differences must be taken into account when designing health-related physical activity and exercise programmes.

Variation

Variation in a physical activity or exercise programme is important to progression of fitness goals as well as for motivation to continue with the programme. Variation can be achieved by manipulation of the training variables: frequency (how often you undertake the activity), duration or time (for how long), intensity (how hard) and obviously the type of activity.

Reversibility

The effects of training are reversible. This means that, if the benefits of adaptation to an exercise programme are to be maintained and improved, regular activity has to be adhered to. It is possible to 'lose it by not using it'. All components of fitness can be affected by inactivity. However, once a level of fitness has been achieved, this level can be maintained with a lower degree of effort than was initially required for its development.

Frequency, intensity, time and type (FITT) principles

FITT stands for:

- F – frequency of exercise: the number of times, usually expressed in times per week, that the exercise is undertaken
- I – intensity of exercise: the amount of stress or overload that is applied
- T – time (duration) of exercise: how long the activity is carried out
- T – type of exercise: the type of exercise performed.

Adherence to the programme should produce the desired adaptations in response to the prescribed exercise or activity programme.

When preparing an exercise programme, the correct form and level of exercise is required to promote gains in physical fitness components. Exercise prescription should be tailored to the individual. You must consider: their fitness goals (which should be realistic), the mode and form of exercise, how often it is to be undertaken, for how long and at what intensity, and that it must be maintained to be effective.

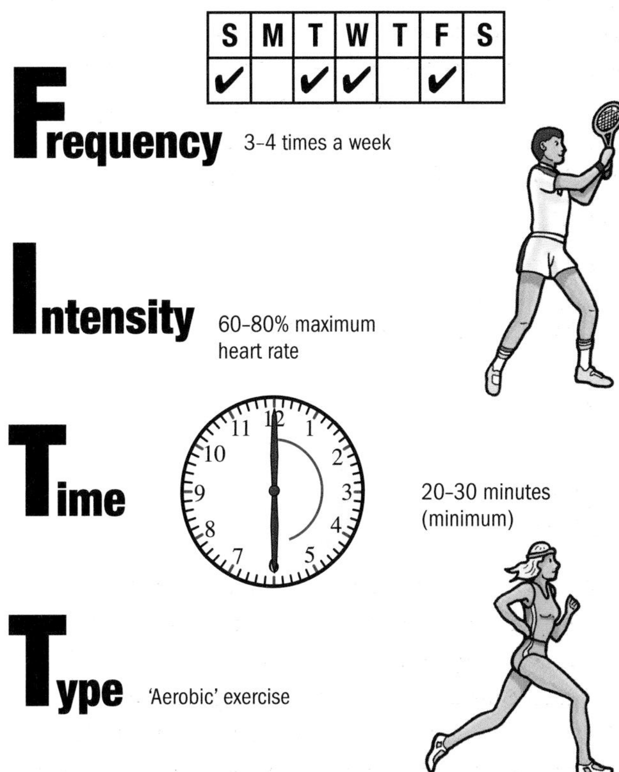

▲ The principles of exercise programming

Appropriate activities

Different types of exercise provide different health and well-being benefits. Once fitness goals have been determined, the exercise undertaken must allow for the type of benefits that are desired (such as weight control, stress management, prevention of disease, muscle definition or the maintenance of flexibility). Important factors to be taken into consideration are convenience, cost, motivation and enjoyment. If you are going to sustain a physical activity or exercise programme, you need to enjoy it.

Walking

Do not underestimate walking as a form of exercise – it is possibly the perfect aid for weight loss and improving general fitness levels. Regular walking helps you get fitter, strengthens your heart, tones your muscles and gives a general feeling of well-being and positive self-esteem.

Cycling

Getting on your bike regularly protects you against a wide range of health issues and makes you feel better. There are no real age barriers to cycling, and people of most fitness levels can do it, slowly and gently if necessary. Anyone with heart disease or other conditions affecting their activity should consult their doctor before starting any exercise programme. Those of all body shapes, and all but the most extreme body weights, can ride a bike.

A study carried out for the Department for Transport found that even a small amount of cycling can lead to significant gains in fitness. The study found that aerobic fitness was boosted by 11 per cent after just six weeks of cycling short-distances four times a week.

Hiking

Hiking, usually undertaken on trails and in rural areas, is a form of walking in order to explore and enjoy the scenery. Trails range from easy to challenging. Beginners are advised to start on the flat, while those with more experience and fitness may take on the challenge of a mountain trail. Hiking is generally free and usually involves covering longer distances over more varied and rugged terrain than walking, but this is not always the case. It also requires more specialised equipment to ensure personal safety, such as a good sturdy pair of boots, wind and waterproof clothing, a backpack to carry food and drinks, and a map and compass to help find your way.

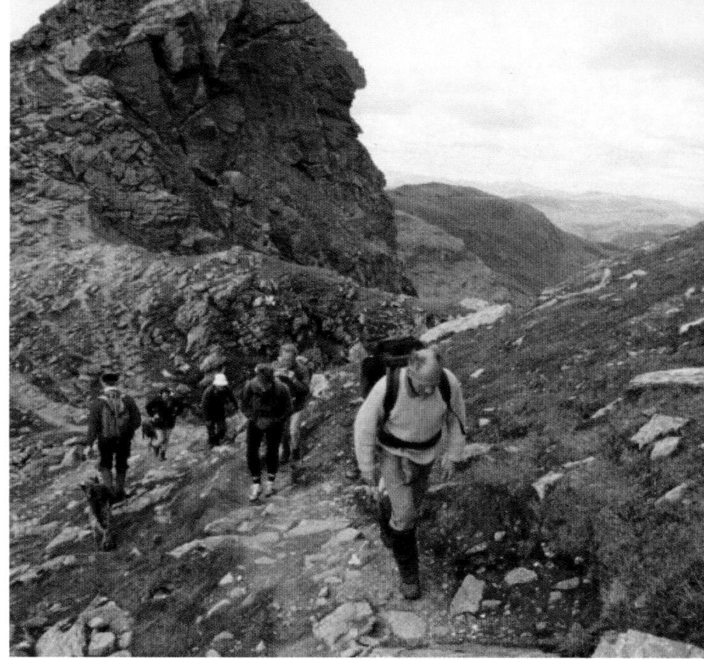

▲ Hiking is a great way to improve fitness and explore the outdoors

Hiking conditions the cardiovascular system and the major muscles of the legs. Carrying a backpack increases energy expenditure and burns more calories to assist with weight loss.

Swimming

Swimming is a great aerobic activity to improve cardiovascular fitness. Nearly all major muscle groups are recruited when you swim, offering a total body workout to improve muscle tone and strength. As swimming is non-weight bearing, it does not convey the same benefits as other forms of aerobic activities in terms of bone strength. It is appropriate for all fitness levels, particularly those who are unaccustomed to exercise, overweight, pregnant or suffering from joint problems or injury.

Exercise intensity

Exercise intensity is usually given as a percentage of maximal heart rate and provides a measure of how hard you are working.

Rating of perceived exertion (RPE)

The best way to monitor intensity during exercise is to use a combination of heart rate measures and ratings of perceived exertion (RPE). Heart rates can be taken manually or by wearing a heart rate monitor. RPE is a 10-point scale (see below) that focuses on tuning the body in to physical cues for recognising intensity of effort, such as a quickened breathing rate, breathlessness or flat-out effort. The RPE scale provides a way of quantifying subjective exercise intensity, but has been shown to correlate well with heart rate and oxygen uptake.

Intensity of effort	Rating of perceived exertion (RPE)
Nothing at all	0
Very weak	1
Weak	2
Moderate	3
Somewhat hard	4
Hard	5
Moderately hard	6
Very hard	7
Very, very hard	8
Near maximal	9
Extremely strong or maximal	10

The RPE scale

Think it over

Dr Gunnar Borg's original RPE scale was from 6–20, with 6 representing complete rest and 20 exhaustion. The reason for this rather odd numbering is reflected in the subjects he used in his original exertion studies. These were all fit individuals who had heart rates that corresponded to around 60 beats per minute at rest, and a maximum heart rate of around 200 beats per minute.

Maximum heart rate

Heart rates are dependent on age, with children having relatively higher rates than adults. When the body is in action, cardiac output can increase five to seven times in order to accelerate the delivery of blood to exercising muscles and meet their demand for increased oxygen.

During participation in sport and exercise, cardiac output is increased as a result of increases in either heart rate, stroke volume or both. Stroke volume does not increase significantly beyond the light work rates of low-intensity exercise, so the increases in cardiac output required for moderate- to high-intensity work rates are achieved by increases in heart rate. Maximum attainable cardiac output decreases with increasing age, largely as a result of a decrease in maximum heart rate. Maximum heart rate can be calculated using the formula below:

maximum heart rate = 220 – age (in years)

Key Term

Stroke volume The volume of blood that the heart pumps out with each beat.

Exercise heart rates are used to assess the strenuousness of the exercise. This information is then used in the formulation of training intensities in the exercise programme.

Remember!

cardiac output = stroke volume x heart rate
(see page 48)

Maximum heart rate reserve

Maximum heart rate reserve (or the Karvonen method, as it is also known after the Finnish physiologist who introduced the concept) provides somewhat higher values for exercise intensity compared to heart rates calculated simply as a percentage of maximum heart rate.

Wearing a heart rate monitor is a useful way of monitoring exercise intensity

The formula calculates training heart rate threshold as:

heart rate threshold = heart rate at rest + 0.60 (heart rate maximum – heart rate at rest)

For example, the heart rate training threshold for a sedentary adult female with a heart rate at rest of 85 beats per minute and a maximum heart rate of 185 beat per minute would be calculated as:

heart rate threshold = 85 + 0.60 (185 – 85)
= 85 + 0.60 × 100
= 85 + 60
= 145 beats per minute

Heart rate monitors provide immediate and potentially more accurate measures of heart rate before, during and after exercise and are less time consuming than manual measures. If they are working accurately, heart rate monitors transmit the electrical activity of the heart through an electrode harness or strap worn around the chest. This sends information about the heart's electrical activity to a watch-like receiver worn on the wrist that calculates heart rate. Wrong readings can occur, so it is a good idea to use heart rate monitors alongside RPE.

Remember!

The best way to monitor intensity during exercise is to use a combination of heart rate measures and ratings of perceived exertion (RPE).

Activity

Now that you have been introduced to a variety of training methods for different components of fitness, plan a six-week training programme suitable for yourself. Before you start, you will need to give consideration to the fitness components that you wish to develop.

Assessment practice

John is a 30-year-old business man. He is married with two young children aged 6 and 4. Recently he has become increasingly concerned about his expanding waistline. He is always tired and has noticed that he is having difficulty keeping up with his children at their weekend outing to the local park.

John works long hours, giving him little time to enjoy his membership of the local health club. He is thinking about giving up his membership as he feels he is not getting value for money. Before the pressures of his work increased, he used to enjoy playing football for the local Sunday league team.

Devise a six-week, health-related physical activity programme for John, taking into account current recommendations for physical activity. **P4**

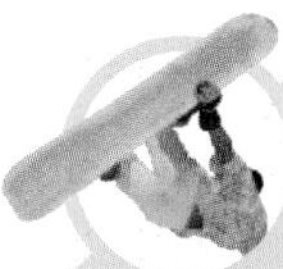

grading tips

Grading Tip **P4**

You must plan a safe and effective six-week health-related physical activity programme.

Knowledge check

1. Describe the concepts of health and wellness.
2. Identify and evaluate five major benefits of regular physical activity and exercise participation.
3. Describe the current physical activity guidelines for the prevention of chronic disease.
4. Explain why it is important to undertake a thorough health, fitness and lifestyle assessment before formulating a health-related physical activity programme for an individual.
5. Which key components would you include in the design of a lifestyle assessment questionnaire?
6. Describe the key elements of a physical activity or exercise prescription.
7. In relation to physical activity and exercise prescription, what is overload and why is it important?
8. Define stress and consider why the control of stress is important to maintaining health and well-being.
9. Describe the components of a healthy balanced diet.
10. Describe and evaluate three strategies to support someone who wishes to stop smoking.
11. Which dietary modification techniques could be implemented to assist with weight loss?
12. Describe behaviour modification and the steps that might be involved in changing unhealthful behaviours.
13. Explain SMART goal setting and the requirement to consider short-, medium- and long-term goals in implementing lifestyle improvements strategies.
14. What is RPE?
15. How would you determine maximum heart rate?

Preparation for assessment

Select an individual who would benefit from exercise, health and lifestyle improvement, particularly increased physical activity participation.

1 After a brief consultation, describe and explain the lifestyle factors that have an effect on their health. 

grading tips

Grading Tip P1

Describe the following lifestyle factors, which have an impact on health: physical activity, alcohol consumption, smoking, stress and diet.

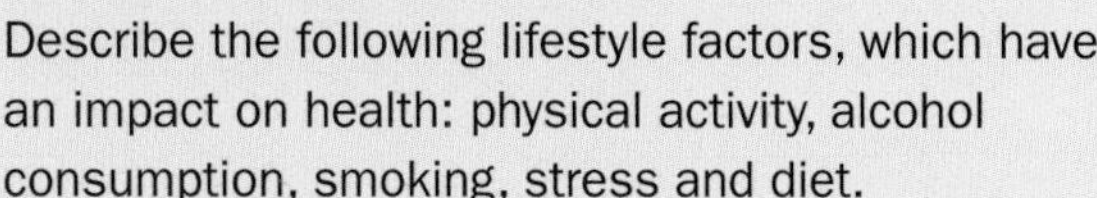

You should consider the benefits of physical activity and make recommendations for alcohol consumption, together with describing the health risks associated with excessive drinking, smoking, high stress levels and an unhealthy diet.

Grading Tip M1

You must explain the effects of the identified lifestyle factors on health. Physical activity and alcohol consumption, together with the health risks of excessive drinking, smoking, high levels of stress and an unhealthy diet, should all be covered.

2 Design a lifestyle questionnaire to assess the individual's lifestyle. You should include questions relating to physical activity, dietary intake, alcohol consumption, smoking and levels of stress. P2

3 Conduct a one-to-one lifestyle consultation with your selected individual. P2

4 Describe and explain areas of strength and areas of improvement for the individual. P2 M2

5 In negotiation with the individual, prioritise areas for change. D1

grading tips

Grading Tip 

You need to collect information on the lifestyle of an individual using a suitable questionnaire and one-to-one consultation.

Grading Tip M2

Make sure you explain the strengths and areas for improvement of the selected individual's lifestyle and explain your recommended lifestyle improvements strategies.

Grading Tip D1

You need to evaluate the lifestyle of the selected individual and prioritise areas for change. In doing this, you may need to make some value judgements about the strengths and areas for improvement.

6 Provide advice on lifestyle improvement strategies for the individual based on the identified priority areas for change. P3

7 Explain the advice and recommendations you have made regarding lifestyle improvement. M3

8 Analyse a range of lifestyle improvement strategies to identify the positive and negative factors of these strategies. D2

9 Plan a safe and effective six-week health-related physical activity programme for the individual, taking into account the principles of training, methods of monitoring intensity and suitable activities. P4

grading tips

Grading Tip 

You need to provide lifestyle improvement strategies for the selected individual, including advice where appropriate on stress management, smoking cessation, alcohol reduction and diet.

Grading Tip 

Explain the lifestyle improvement strategies in terms of their suitability for the selected individual.

Grading Tip D2

Analyse a range of lifestyle improvements strategies for the selected individual. This requires you to investigate the strengths and weaknesses of different strategies, and how you can monitor and evaluate their effectiveness.

10 Produce a portfolio of evidence containing:

- your completed lifestyle assessment questionnaire
- a summary of your one-to-one consultation
- information on the advice on lifestyle improvement provided
- the six-week health-related physical activity programme.

grading tips

Grading Tip 

You must plan a safe and effective six-week health-related physical activity programme.

Grading criteria

To achieve a pass grade the evidence must show that the learner is able to:	To achieve a merit grade the evidence must show that, in addition to the pass criteria, the learner is able to:	To achieve a distinction grade the evidence must show that, in addition to the pass and merit criteria, the learner is able to:
P1 describe lifestyle factors that have an effect on health **Assessment practice pages 271, 294**	**M1** explain the effects of identified lifestyle factors on health **Assessment practice pages 271, 294**	
P2 design and use a lifestyle questionnaire to describe the strengths and areas for improvement for the lifestyle of a selected individual **Assessment practice pages 274, 294**	**M2** explain the strengths and areas for improvement for the lifestyle of a selected individual **Assessment practice pages 274, 294**	**D1** evaluate the lifestyle of a selected individual and prioritise areas for change **Assessment practice pages 274, 294**
P3 provide lifestyle improvement strategies for a selected individual **Assessment practice pages 284, 294**	**M3** explain recommendations made regarding the lifestyle improvement strategies **Assessment practice pages 284, 294**	**D2** analyse a range of lifestyle improvement strategies **Assessment practice pages 284, 294**
P4 plan a safe and effective six-week health-related physical activity programme for a selected individual **Assessment practice pages 293, 294**		

20 Applied sport and exercise psychology

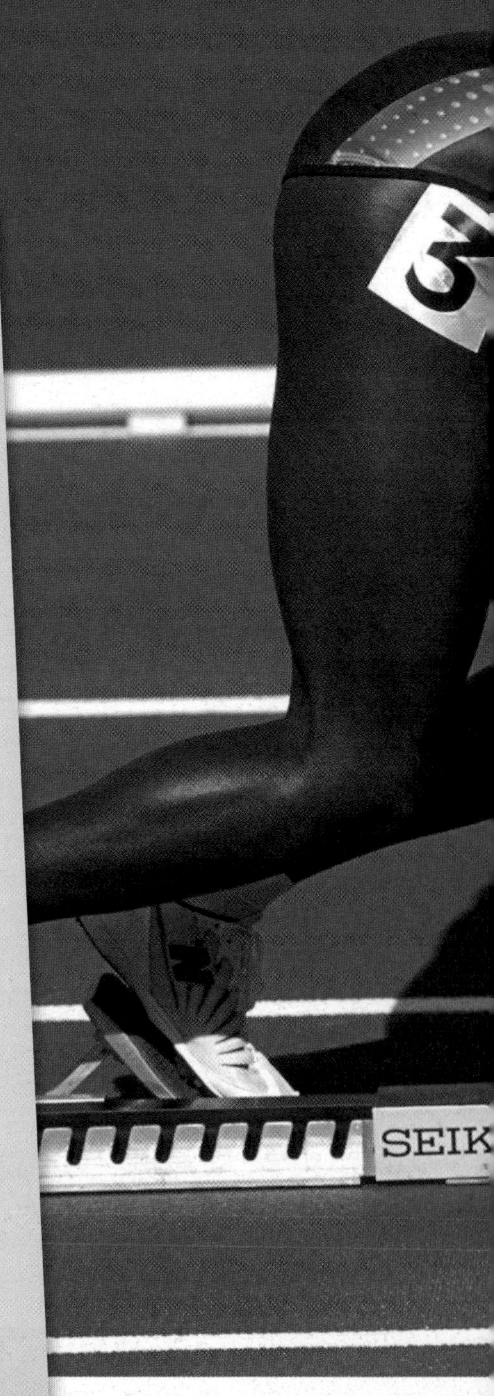

Introduction

Sport and exercise psychology is an exciting new area. It focuses on human behaviours in different environments. Applied sport and exercise psychology looks at how knowledge from the areas of sport and exercise psychology can be used within professional settings.

Sport and exercise psychologists make a living by helping people at all levels of sport and exercise. They try to help elite athletes understand elite-level performance with a view to increasing performance to international level. At the other end of the scale, they help members of the public to achieve greater levels of personal satisfaction through participation in regular physical activity, exercise or recreational level sport.

This unit will help you to develop some of the skills required to work in the field of sport and exercise psychology. It will help you get to a point where you feel confident in designing your own psychological skills training programme for a sports performer.

After completing this unit you should be able to achieve the following outcomes:

- know about the roles of sport and exercise psychologists
- understand techniques used to influence motivation in sport and exercise
- understand the use of imagery and mental rehearsal in sport and exercise
- understand techniques used to control arousal in sport and exercise
- be able to plan and review a psychological skills training programme for a selected sports performer.

Think it over

Sport and exercise psychology is becoming a more developed and established area. One of the key aspects is helping to take what is currently an intriguing area with enormous potential into the forefront of athletic development and to the pinnacle of health services. But what do think sport and exercise psychologists actually do?

20.1 Know about the roles of sport and exercise psychologists

Roles

Sport and exercise psychologists perform a number of tasks, but generally they can be classified under one of these roles:

- research
- education
- consultancy.

Research

In any science discipline, a really important part is research. The discipline needs to keep going forward by developing new ideas. This is what research is all about.

Remember!

Research in an applied setting has benefited knowledge (and practical applications of this knowledge) within sport and exercise psychology.

Think about some of these questions.

- How do imagery and mental rehearsal benefit performance in different sports?
- What are the ways and benefits of increasing motivation levels of people in sport and exercise settings?
- How can arousal levels in athletes be regulated to achieve a peak performance?

All of these questions have, at some time, been researched by sport and exercise psychologists. Once the research has been carried out, the sport or exercise psychologist shares their findings with colleagues, coaches, athletes and perhaps has their work published in journals for others to read.

Education

Some sport or exercise psychologists fill an education role. This can be in a number of different ways:

- by working in educational establishments
- by working directly with athletes and coaches
- by producing educational materials.

Many psychologists work in universities or colleges, delivering courses such as sport and exercise sciences, applied sport psychology, exercise psychology or social psychology of sport. Others work directly with athletes and coaches to educate them on the benefits of sport psychology in a practical sport setting. They work on removing some of the stigma attached to sport psychology (e.g. if you work with a psychologist, there is something wrong with your brain!). Other psychologists work with organisations such as sports coach UK and the NHS to produce educational materials on the benefits of the different disciplines within sport and exercise psychology.

Consultancy

The consultancy role of the sport or exercise psychologist involves working with individuals or teams with a view to developing psychological skills that can enhance quality of life in some way.

Some of the areas that sport psychologists work on with both athletes and teams include: performance enhancement, injury rehabilitation, lifestyle management and team building. These are generally conducted through a series of workshops and clinics where the psychologist meets the people involved.

Exercise psychologists tend to work in a slightly different way. They work mainly in the fitness industry or in the health services. They are involved with individuals in developing suitable exercise programmes, lifestyle management skills and increasing levels of exercise adherence.

Assessment practice

For each of the following scenarios, explain which role the sport or exercise psychologist would fulfil and justify your answer.

1 A 50-year-old woman who would like to start and stick to an exercise programme.

2 A university requiring a sport psychologist to come and deliver an undergraduate degree programme.

3 An ice hockey team needing help building team cohesion.

4 The British Olympic team that wants to investigate the role of imagery in preparation for the 2012 Olympic Games. P1 M1

grading tips

Grading Tip 

Make sure you give a description of the role of a sport psychologist rather than just saying which role it is they would fulfil.

Grading Tip 

Provide some examples of things the sport psychologists would do to fulfil that role and help the client.

20.2 Understand techniques used to influence motivation in sport and exercise

In sport, it is not only important to be able to motivate individuals, you must also be able to motivate groups; there are a number of ways you can do this

Techniques

Goal setting

Goal setting is one of the best ways of increasing motivation in sport and exercise. In sport and exercise psychology, we need to be specific about what a goal is and what the different types of goal are.

Think it over

What is a goal? You will probably come up with things such as 'achieving some form of standard' and 'an objective or something you want to do'.

Types of goal

There are two main types of goal:

- a subjective goal is a general statement of intent such as 'I want to have fun'
- an objective goal is a measurable statement that relates to the achievement of some form of standard normally within a designated period of time (e.g. 'I want to lose 2kg in a month').

See page 299 for more information on goal setting.

Outcome goals, process goals and performance goals are all types of objective goals.

Outcome goals

Outcome goals relate to the outcome of an event (e.g. 'I want to win'). They tend to be unpredictable because they depend on the performance of others as well as yourself. For example, you could play the best frame of snooker you have ever played, yet still lose and fail to achieve your outcome goal because your opponent plays a little bit better than you.

People who use a lot of outcome goals usually feel less in control. This is because in order to judge whether you have achieved your goal, you have to compare yourself to someone else. Outcome goals can potentially lead to feelings of incompetence – if you lose on a regular basis, losing will be a major setback and you will constantly feel like a failure. Away from competition, outcome goals can be used to increase motivation; but focusing on outcome goals just before competition can increase anxiety. They tend to be more medium to long term as they often relate to winning a game or competition.

Process goals

Process goals look at the process the athlete must go through to achieve a desired level of performance. They relate to skills and techniques they could be required to perform at a high level (e.g. when performing a jump-shot in basketball, make sure you release the ball at the peak of the jump rather than on the way up or down).

Process goals are beneficial because you can make more precise adjustments to them than you can with outcome goals. They are particularly useful to athletes during competition, although they should be used in practice settings as well. Process goals have more of a short-term focus than outcome goals.

Performance goals

Performance goals look at achieving a certain standard of performance without comparison with other

Think it over

Concentrating on improving set shots is a process goal

At the initial team meeting at the start of pre-season, three basketball coaches are setting the goals with the team. The team agrees on the goal of finishing top of its conference (outcome goal). To do this they will need to win a high percentage of both home and away games (outcome goal). Having looked at the stats from the previous season, the coaches have identified that in order to win the games, the team needs to increase its percentage of field goals hit from 60 per cent to 70 per cent (performance goal). The coaches have also watched videos of key games from the previous season and have noticed that there were some problems with some of the players' set shot and jump shot techniques. Therefore, the coaches have said that the players need to concentrate on being square to the basket when they shoot (process goal) and they need to focus on releasing the ball at the peak of the jump (process goal).

individuals. This means that, essentially, you are competing with yourself (e.g. increasing percentage of shots on target from 50 per cent to 60 per cent). When using performance goals regularly, the athlete is trying to improve their own performance with a view to increasing the sense of mastery in performance.

Performance goals are more flexible than outcome goals as they can be adjusted more easily. Athletes that use a lot of performance goals are more likely to feel in control because goal achievement is independent of the performance of others. They are also less likely to see losing a match as failure as they can still achieve goals regardless of the outcome of an event, and as a result of this they are more likely to try to achieve further goals. Performance goals are usually set on a short-term basis.

Long-term goals alone do not change behaviour or improve performance. For changes to occur, a combination of progressively harder short-term goals, linking together to achieve an overall long-term goal, must be used. A popular technique used for this is called a goal-setting staircase. The long-term goal is at the top of the staircase and your current level of performance is at the bottom. You need to decide on a series of short-term progressive goals that will allow you to achieve the overall aim.

Theory into practice

Vision India is part of the Vision Asia project that was launched to prepare Asian countries fully for the FIFA World Cup competition. Asia has a population of approximately 3.7 billion, so in theory should have the potential to win the World Cup. In India, a project is currently in progress that was launched in 2002 aimed at improving the infrastructure of its National Association and the development of women's football. The project itself focuses on everything from the restructuring of the administration of the organisation through to referee education, talent identification and development. The short-term goals of the project need to be achieved within two years, the medium-term goals within five years and the long-term goals ten years.

Why was it important for them to set these goals?

Medium-term goals, as the name suggests, are goals that fall between short-term goals and long-term goals.

Activity

For each of the following statements, say which type of goal is demonstrated: outcome, process or performance.

- Andy Murray (tennis player) wanting to win the Grand Slam by winning each of the Open tournaments.
- Lebron James (basketball player) wanting to improve his field goal success percentage.
- Liossel Jones (swimmer) wanting to make sure she maintains a long arm pull on the freestyle section of her performance.
- Wayne Rooney (footballer) wanting to improve heading accuracy by getting better at the timing of his jump.
- Fernando Alonso (Formula 1 driver) wants to win the British Grand Prix by improving his lap times by one second. To do this, he needs to improve his line through Copse Corner.

Principles of goal setting

For goal setting to be effective, it is important to set a range of outcome, process and performance goals. Goal setting should follow the SMART principle (see page 324).

Importance of goal setting

Goals benefit performance in the following ways.

- They direct the attention of the performer towards key aspects of the skill that is being performed by the individual.
- They control and mobilise the amount of effort needed and expended by the performer to achieve an expected standard.
- They increase the level of effort that is needed until the goal is achieved.
- They motivate a performer to develop new strategies, mechanisms and tactics that are needed for performance to be successful.

Remember!

Goal setting is just one of the techniques available to sport and exercise psychologists to influence motivation.

Assessment practice

Imagine you know an 'old-school' traditional basketball coach who is a little set in his ways. He doesn't believe all the things you have been telling him about goal setting. He thinks players should just know what to do and when they have to do it, otherwise they aren't good enough to play on his team.

Some of the players are becoming increasingly frustrated by not having any form of focus or target for their performances. It is your job to persuade the coach to change his views. You decide one way to do this would be to produce a coach information leaflet to explain the benefits of goal setting to the him. To make it a convincing argument, you need to think about how you are going to set out the leaflet. Make sure you include the following information.

1 A brief description of what goal setting is that tells the coach what the different types of goal are.

2 An explanation of each of the different types of goal.

3 A short summary of some of the strengths and weaknesses of each type of goal.

4 An explanation of the SMART principle.

5 An overall summary of the benefits of goal setting. **P2 M2 D1**

grading tips

Grading Tip 

Give an accepted definition of goal setting and name the different types of goal.

Grading Tip 

Explain what each of the different types of goal are.

Grading Tip 

Take goal setting in general, then each of the different types of goal in turn. Discuss strengths and weaknesses and some examples of different types of goal.

Performance profiling

Performance profiling is another technique available to sport and exercise psychologists to influence the motivation of sports performers.

Think about when you have been playing your sport and you thought you played really well, but your coach thought you played quite badly (or vice versa). This is quite common in sport, and performance profiling is one method used to try to eliminate this difference of opinion.

Performance profiling helps to increase motivation in a number of ways.

- It can give the performer a greater sense of control over what they are doing, which in turn increases their sense of achievement and mastery – two key areas in increasing intrinsic motivation.
- It is a good way of increasing communication between the coach and the athlete, making them both feel like they are more on the same wavelength.

■ Definition and applications

Performance profiling is a way of understanding how individuals rate the qualities that are important to achieve top performance in their particular field. It has a variety of uses in the field of sport and exercise (as well as other areas such as business and education), but here we will focus mainly on how it can be used to increase motivation in sports individuals.

Performance profiling is an aspect of psychology known as personal construct psychology and is based on two assumptions.

- Everyone has a way of making sense of their experiences.
- In order to understand an individual's viewpoint of their experiences, you must look at things from their perspective.

Benefits

From a practitioner's point of view, it is important that you explain to the client what the purpose of performance profiling is. You need to make sure that the practitioner and the client are clear about what is meant by each of the qualities and components identified. Performance profiling only works if the practitioner does not influence the client's choice of qualities for top performance or the meanings that are attached to them. As a technique, performance profiling is one of the most flexible, as it can be altered to meet the needs of both the client and the practitioner to form a solid basis for the design of different training programmes.

Performance profiling has a number of benefits.

- It allows the practitioner to consider things from the client's perspective.
- It encourages the practitioner to tailor their work to the needs of the client.
- It provides an opportunity for communication between the client and the practitioner, to resolve any discrepancies between the opinions or perceptions of either the practitioner or the client.
- It helps the practitioner to develop an understanding of what the client feels is important to performance.
- It enables both the practitioner and the client to have an input into the training programme design.
- It commits the client to training due to the level of investment they have put in to the programme design. The client's levels of intrinsic motivation also increase due to the greater degree of control they feel they have had over the training design.

Process

Performance profiling has five main stages.

1 Identify and define key qualities for performance: introduce the idea by asking the client what attributes they think are important for top performance. This is sometimes known as eliciting constructs, but it is often best not to use this term as it is quite a scary one! Many athletes prefer to think of this as simply assessing their performance. When using performance profiling in a sports setting, the athlete could be asked to think of an elite performer and try to write down what qualities the athlete possesses. The table below highlights some prompts that can be used with different clients.

Psychological	Physical	Attitudinal/ character
Confidence Concentration Relaxation Visualisation Emotional control Motivation	Strength Stamina Endurance Flexibility Power Speed Balance Reaction time	Weight control Discipline Determination Will to win Positive outlook

Examples of qualities

It will be useful for the client to record the qualities necessary for performance and their definitions in a table. This helps both the client and the practitioner to develop an understanding of what the terms mean. To avoid any misunderstanding, make sure the definitions used are those devised by the client. There is no limit to the number of qualities that can be identified initially, but the list should be narrowed down to 20 key qualities. When identifying and defining the various qualities, it is important that the client is made aware that there are no right or wrong answers and this process is not a test.

2 Profile the practitioner's perceptions of the client's levels and profile the client's own perceptions: this is an assessment of the current level of performance by the practitioner and the client. The practitioner and the client write the 20 key qualities in each of the blank spaces around the outside of the grid.

Each quality is given a rating from 0 to 10, where 0 means that the client/practitioner feels there is no evidence of that quality in the client, and 10 means that the client/practitioner feels that the client possesses high levels of that quality.

3 Discuss the practitioner's and the client's profiles: in this stage, you are using the results. This involves interpreting the results of the performance profiles by identifying areas of perceived strength and areas of perceived weakness. When looking at the differences between the two profiles, if the difference is small you could suggest that the practitioner and the client are on the same wavelength. However, if the difference is large this would suggest that the working relationship is not so good. If there are large differences between levels (a large difference is classed as two points or more), this should lead to a discussion between the practitioner and the client about why the different levels have been given.

Activity

Using the profiles in the diagram below, identify which qualities have a mismatch in terms of the performer's and the practitioner's opinions of performance levels.

4 Agree on goals and how they will be achieved: the practitioner and the client agree on what they would like the client to have achieved (i.e. set the

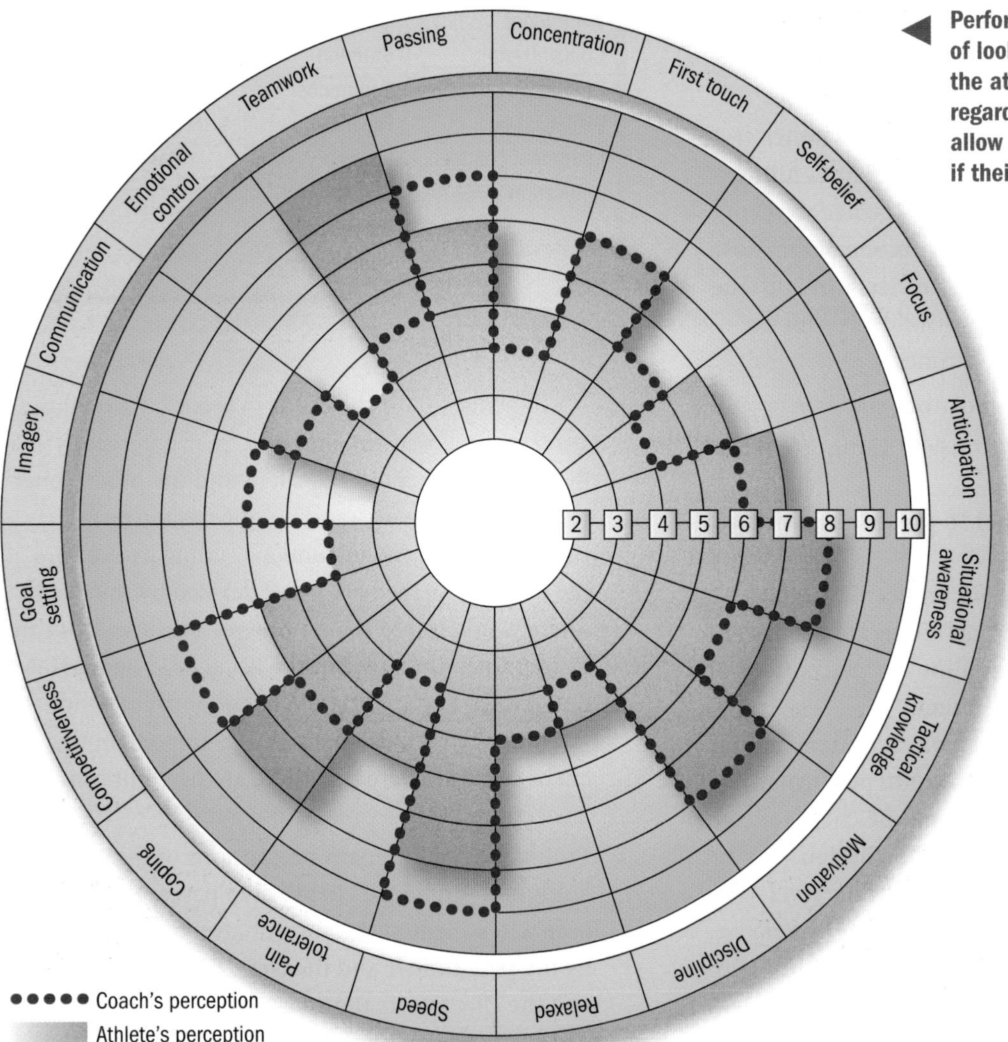

Performance profiles are a good way of looking at whether the coach and the athlete have the same opinion regarding performance levels; they allow the coach and the athlete to see if their opinions differ

benchmarks for each of the qualities). The results are used to set the goals to be achieved through the psychological skills training (PST) programme. Normally, each of these desired benchmarks will be at level 10 – any target level below this on the client's behalf would suggest that there is some form of resistance to achieving the ultimate level of performance.

5 Repeat the profiling to monitor progress: performance profiling can be repeated on a number of occasions to assess the client's progress. The aim is that the client will gradually progress further towards the outside of the scale (closer to the rating of 10). If the client does not make the desired progress, the practitioner and the client need to discuss why progress is not being made. Usually this is because the training programme did not take into account a particular quality (errors in design of programme), the client and the practitioner have different views on the importance of a quality (errors in communication and understanding) or the client has not put in the effort to achieve the improvements in performance.

Areas resistant to change

All target levels for performance should (at some point) progress to be level 10. If the client sets a target below this and does not agree to progress to this target, it would suggest that there is some form of resistance to change. This normally becomes evident when the client does not consider something as important as the practitioner. From this, some form of training programme can be produced that will help the client to achieve the desired levels of performance. The design of PST programmes will be discussed on page 320.

Decision balance sheet

A decision balance sheet (see page 306) evaluation of advantages and disadvantages of taking part in a particular behaviour. It is linked to the transtheoretical model or stages of change model (see page 282). The transtheoretical model is a model of behaviour change that says people will go through different stages in order to change behaviour.

grading tips

Grading Tip 

You need to work through all the four points in order to describe performance profiling and explaining its benefits.

Assessment practice

A local rugby team has come to you and asked you about something called performance profiling. They have asked your advice about whether or not you think performance profiling is worthwhile and whether you think they should use it with their team. You need to write back to the rugby team, explaining your views. You need to write the letter in the context of a sporting environment (so think about what terms you could use instead of client and practitioner). Include the following information in your letter.

1 An explanation of what performance profiling is.
2 An explanation of the different stages of performance profiling.
3 An explanation of how performance profiling can benefit the coach and the athlete.
4 An explanation of how performance profiling can increase the intrinsic motivation of the athlete.

Gains to self	Losses to self
Look better Feel better	Less time to spend with friends Cost
Gains to others	**Losses to others**
More attractive to partner Will be able to have a kick about with friends at the park	Partner will spend less time with me
Approval from self	**Disapproval from self**
I feel better about myself I am more self-confident	I feel a bit embarrassed exercising in front of people
Approval from others	**Disapproval from others**
Partner sees me leading a healthier lifestyle Children like it when I can be more active and play with them	My colleagues are worried that I will take too much time away from work

An example of a decision balance sheet about whether to start an exercise programme

The pros and cons of exercise behaviour and stage of change are linked. There is normally some overlap between the pros and cons at the contemplation or preparation stage (i.e. the pros become more powerful than the cons). The closer you get to the maintenance stage, the more powerful the advantages become.

A decision balance sheet is a motivational tool used to predict or determine behaviours in a number of different settings. It is particularly useful in increasing exercise behaviours and benefiting areas such as exercise adherence.

Gains and losses/approval

When completing a decision balance sheet, the athlete writes down the effects of taking part in an exercise programme under these four headings:

- gains and losses to self
- gains and losses to others
- approval or disapproval from self
- approval or disapproval from others.

Benefits

Achieving outcomes

A decision balance sheet can be used to increase awareness of the potential benefits and consequences of taking part in an exercise programme. This technique is an effective way of including clients in the decision-making processes involved with starting an exercise programme.

Directing energy

A decision balance sheet intervention may be of some use to people who are contemplating starting an exercise programme, because it directs their energy towards thinking about why the exercise programme will be beneficial. In this case, the person is more likely to begin to take part in exercise. By considering the advantages and the disadvantages, the individual is starting to take part in self-persuasion that the exercise will be beneficial for them.

Exercise adherence

Due to the nature of the decision balance sheet, the individual will feel they have a greater degree of control over the programme and will experience greater levels of self-determination. This will increase levels of intrinsic motivation (see page 302) and improve the chances that the programme will be adhered to. For many individuals, the decision to exercise is a critical aspect of their long-term commitment to exercise, so repeated administrations of the decision balance sheet may be useful in increasing exercise adherence, as the individual is repeatedly reviewing the reasons why they want to take part in exercise.

Activity

Using the decision balance sheet opposite as a guide, produce one of your own, reflecting your thoughts, feelings and emotions.

Assessment practice

For the following scenarios, select a suitable method of increasing motivation and evaluate why the one you have selected is more appropriate than the others.

Remember, it is the quality of argument that you can make that is important.

1 A mid-20s man looking at starting an exercise programme but doesn't know if it is worth it or not.
2 An alpine skier who is unsure of what he wants to achieve in his next competition.
3 A netball coach who is having problems with communicating with her players about their current level of performance. P2 M2 D1

grading tips

Grading Tip 

You need to describe and explain the benefits of three different techniques used to increase motivation. Why not select a different technique for each of these scenarios and work from there?

Grading Tip 

You need to make sure that you evaluate all three of the different techniques you select.

Taking it further

Using books and Internet search engines, find out as much as you can about two theories: the self-determination theory and the cognitive evaluation theory. Try to use the information you find to discuss why involving your clients in decision-making processes can be beneficial for motivation.

20.3 Understand the use of imagery and mental rehearsal in sport and exercise

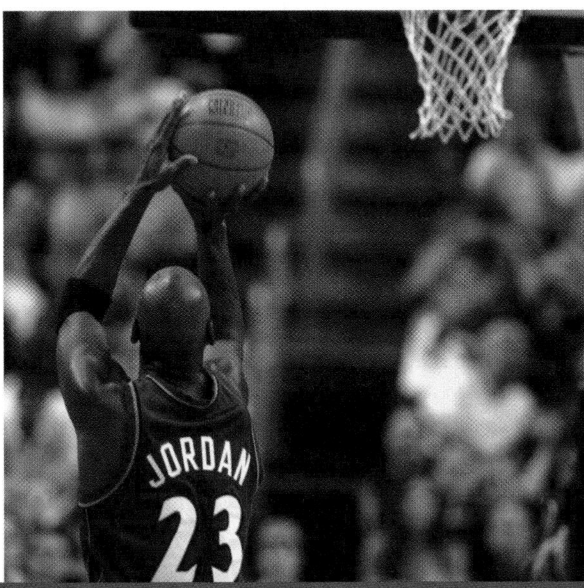

Some people can use imagery so well that they can perform some sporting actions with their eyes closed

Imagery and mental rehearsal are techniques that are frequently used in sport and exercise psychology because of the variety of applications they have in different settings.

Imagery

Think about your favourite athlete in any sport. Now think about when you have watched that sports player performing. Consider when you have thought about what that athlete has done during their performance, tried to see yourself doing that in a future competition, and then copied what they did during your performance. This is something that everyone does, and is just one example of how our mind allows us to remember different events and then attempt to recreate them. It is imagery in one of its many forms.

Definition

Imagery is a polysensorial and emotional creation or recreation of an experience that takes place in the mind. It should involve as many senses as possible, as well as trying to recreate emotions experienced through the activity you take part in. The most effective imagery uses kinaesthetic, visual, tactile, auditory and olfactory senses.

Theory into practice

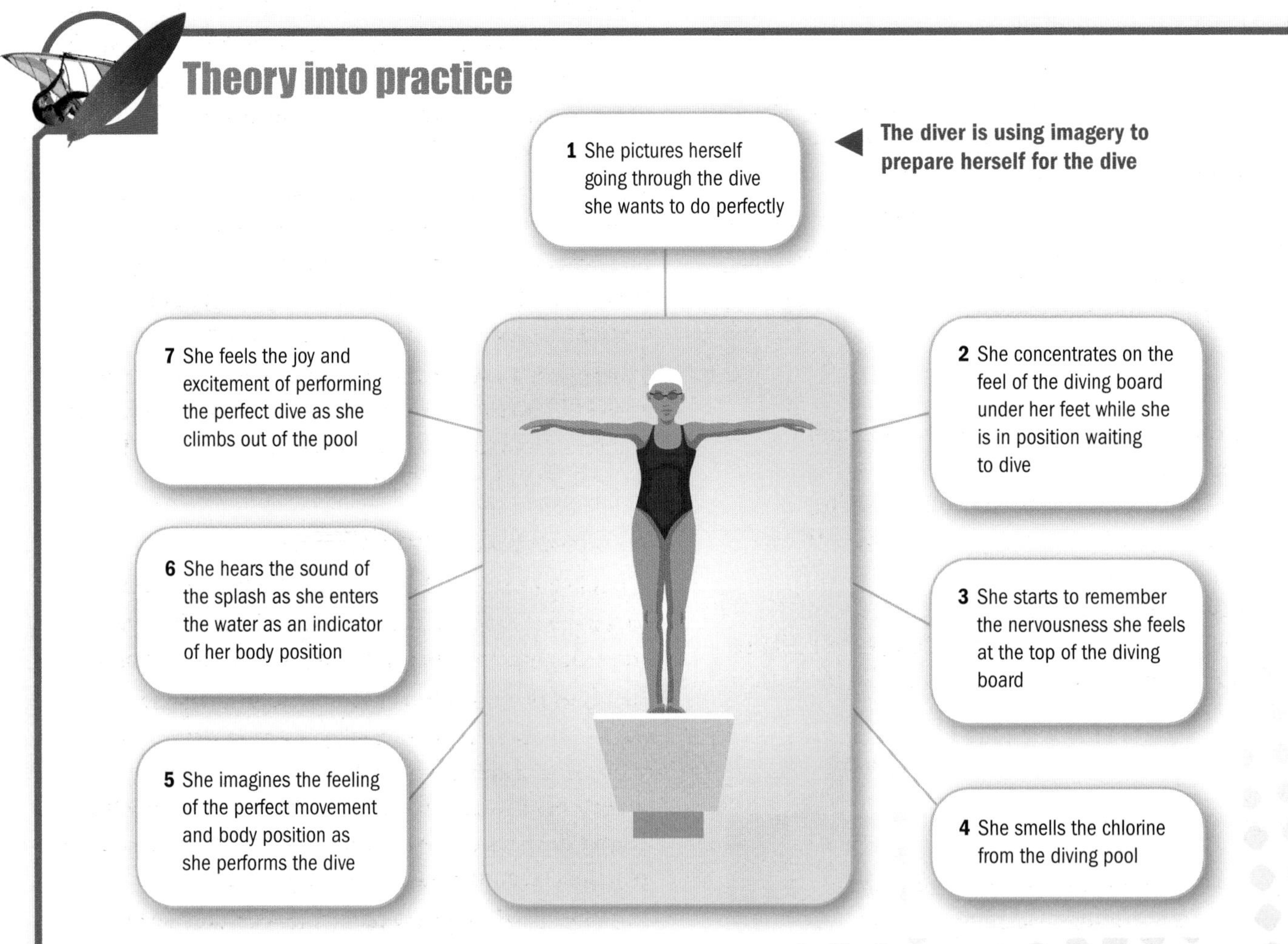
1 She pictures herself going through the dive she wants to do perfectly
2 She concentrates on the feel of the diving board under her feet while she is in position waiting to dive
3 She starts to remember the nervousness she feels at the top of the diving board
4 She smells the chlorine from the diving pool
5 She imagines the feeling of the perfect movement and body position as she performs the dive
6 She hears the sound of the splash as she enters the water as an indicator of her body position
7 She feels the joy and excitement of performing the perfect dive as she climbs out of the pool

The diver is using imagery to prepare herself for the dive

An Olympic diver is preparing to dive off of the high board. She pictures herself going through the dive she wants to do perfectly (visual external imagery). She concentrates on the feel of the diving board under her feet (tactile sense) while she is in position waiting to dive. She starts to remember the nervousness she feels at the top of the diving board (emotional recreation). She smells the chlorine from the diving pool (olfactory sense). Then she imagines the feeling of the perfect movement and body position as she performs the dive (kinaesthetic sense). She hears the sound of the splash as she enters the water as an indicator of her body position (auditory sense). Finally, she feels the joy and excitement of performing the perfect dive (emotional recreation) as she climbs out of the pool.

Draw a similar diagram for a sport of your choice (see page 309 for key terms).

Key Terms

Polysensorial Involving many of your senses in the imagery process.

Kinaesthetic You concentrate on the feel of the movement.

Visual You concentrate on the different things that you can see during the movement.

Tactile You concentrate on your sense of touch throughout the movement.

Auditory You concentrate on the different sounds that you associate with a sporting movement (e.g. hitting the sweet spot on a cricket bat).

Olfactory You concentrate on the different smells that you associate with a sporting action (e.g. the smell of freshly cut grass on the first game of the season for you football team).

There are two main types of imagery in sport and exercise: internal and external.

- **Internal imagery** is imagining yourself doing something and concentrating on how the activity feels.
- **External imagery** is imagining yourself doing something as though you are watching it on a film so that you can develop an awareness of how the activity looks.

Uses

Imagery has a number of uses in different areas of performance including relaxation, goal setting, concentration, developing confidence, controlling emotions and handling pressure, and decision making.

Relaxation

A sprinter is in the start position in the final of the women's 100m at the Olympic Games. In this example, the athlete would imagine emotions associated with relaxation and, together with other techniques such as breathing exercises, could try to control anxiety, arousal and stress levels.

Goal setting

Imagery can be used to highlight specific faults in performance, which can then be used to set goals to improve performance.

Concentration

A golfer is waiting to putt to win the Masters at Augusta. He concentrates on the feel of the putter in his hand, the distance between the ball and the hole, the changes in the ground, the feel of the movement when he goes to stroke the ball and the smell of the green. He closes out any noises from the crowd so that he can listen to the contact of the club on the ball.

A key aspect to concentration is being able to focus on relevant cues in your environment (e.g. things that directly affect your sports performance) and being able to close out factors that don't directly effect your sport performance (e.g. crowd noise and banners).

By imagining what you want to achieve and what you need to be able to do to achieve it, you can prevent your attention from focusing on irrelevant aspects and focus on relevant aspects instead.

Developing confidence

A football player has been taking penalties for his team on a regular basis but keeps missing them, which has knocked his confidence in his ability to score penalties.

The sport psychologist could work with the player, asking him to remember having a strong support foot placement, striking the ball hard and true, thinking about where exactly he wants the ball to go, seeing the ball hit the back of the net and thinking about the elation experienced at successfully scoring a goal.

The sport psychologist would do this because seeing yourself perform well in your mind is a good way of increasing a sense of mastery. It increases your belief in your ability to perform a task.

Controlling emotions and handling pressure

A cricket player is preparing to go out and bat in the Ashes Test Series. He starts to visualise situations in the past where he has been bowled out against Australia and then starts to breath deeply and change the image from being bowled out to successfully striking the ball and scoring combinations of quick singles, 4s and 6s.

One of the benefits of using imagery is that you can imagine things that have gone wrong in previous performances (such as missing penalties, being bowled out, experiencing poor officiating). Then you can imagine yourself coping with these negative influences in a number of ways and being able to perform the task successfully.

Decision making

An elite tennis player is in the dressing room before the men's singles final at Wimbledon. He is going through possible shots that his opponent could play during the games, imagining how he could respond to these shots and what the possible outcomes of the different performances could be.

He begins to think about when he has played this opponent before, some of the positions his opponent took up on the court and how he beat him previously using different types of shot.

Eventually, the player has gone through all of the possible options for a number of game situations including serves and returns.

During the game, he is in some of these situations and is able to catch his opponent off-guard by making decisions quickly.

Decision-making skills are benefited greatly by imagery because the use of imagery allows individuals to look at a number of options in different situations and the consequences of making different decisions.

The benefits of imagery in this area tend to be greater for experienced performers rather than novices, because it helps them to refine skills and make the necessary decisions quickly.

Assessment practice

You have been asked by sports coach UK to produce an information leaflet to educate athletes about imagery and the uses of imagery. You have been given the following tasks to complete the leaflet.

1 Define imagery. 

2 For a sport of your choice, provide a practical example of a polysensorial and emotional imagery routine. P3

3 List the uses of imagery. 

4 Explain each of the uses of imagery, providing sporting examples from different sports. M3

grading tips

Grading Tip 

Provide an accepted definition of imagery. Discuss the different types of imagery and describe a range of uses.

Grading Tip 

Provide practical examples of the uses of imagery and explain how they could benefit sporting performance.

Mental rehearsal

Definition

Mental rehearsal is one aspect of imagery. It is a strategy for practising something in your mind before actually performing the task. The difference between mental rehearsal and imagery is that mental rehearsal does not take into account how the skill is rehearsed or what senses and emotions are used throughout the skill. It is the cognitive rehearsal of a skill without any physical movement.

Uses

There are a number of ways in which mental rehearsal is used including skills practice and rehearsal, practising for events, competition practice, practising 'what if' scenarios, replaying performance and performance routines.

A link can also be made here between mental rehearsal and pre-performance routines, as mental rehearsal can allow the performer to rehearse how they want to complete an activity before they actually start the performance. The use of mental rehearsal of future performance ensures that athletes take time to review physical, technical and mental aspects of the activity and produce strategies that will help individuals to meet its demands.

Theory into practice

Think about how many times you have seen a player stand on the service line, close their eyes, take a deep breath, open their eyes and bounce the ball before the serve. What do you think they will have been doing when they have their eyes closed? Often, they are mentally rehearsing the skill, running through the finer points in their mind so that they are focused on the key aspects of the skill (e.g. getting the toss right, getting a full back scratch with the racquet, hitting the ball on the sweet spot and then seeing the ball hit the court where they intended).

How could you apply this approach to your sporting activities?

Skills practice and rehearsal

Although it is not as effective as physically practising a skill, mental rehearsal is more beneficial than not practising the skill at all. It actually helps to develop neuromuscular patterns associated with different movements. It is important for the performer to rehearse both good and bad movement patterns so that they can get to know the difference between the two, to develop the appropriate neuromuscular responses.

Practice for events

Using mental rehearsal in the lead up to competition, as well as in practice settings, has been shown to benefit skill practice and development.

In competition practice

Mental rehearsal gives the athlete the opportunity to practice their skills during an event without having to expend any energy or perform any movements. This is a useful way of concentrating on a particular aspect of the skill and further developing it.

Practice 'what if' scenarios

Mental rehearsal gives the performer the opportunity to practice 'what if' scenarios (e.g. what if I did it this way?) to assess whether something different would work in the same scenario.

Replay performance

'What if' are often combined with replaying performance in your mind, where you go through previous performances and detect errors in performance using the mental rehearsal.

Performance routines

Mental rehearsal forms an important part of performance routines. Think about when you have seen a tennis player getting ready to serve during a game. They stand on the service line, take a deep breath, look at the other end of the court, take another deep breath, sometimes close their eyes and then serve. This is all part of a performance routine. During this routine, the player is mentally rehearsing the serve before actually performing the movement.

Assessment practice

Imagine you are working with a baseball player who is his side's leading run scorer. He is currently injured and is worried about losing his batting technique during this injury period. You need to explain to the athlete what mental rehearsal is and how it can benefit his skill level. Make your argument convincing: he isn't really into sport psychology and doesn't understand how seeing something in your head can benefit physical performance! P3 M3

grading tips

Grading Tip P3

Describe what mental rehearsal is and how it has been shown to benefit performance.

Grading Tip M3

Produce an applied explanation of the benefits of mental rehearsal rather than one based on theory. You could use the Theory into practice information on page 311 as the basis for your explanation.

Taking it further

Try researching the following theories to see if you can produce an even more convincing answer to explain how mental rehearsal and imagery can benefit physical performance:

- psychoneuromuscular theory (Carpenter, 1894)
- symbolic learning theory (Sackett, 1934)
- bioinformational theory (Lang, 1977, 1979).

20.4 Understand techniques used to control arousal in sport and exercise

Arousal is an important aspect of sport and exercise because it can affect performance either positively or negatively, depending on how you perceive the arousal. Therefore, it is important to understand ways of regulating arousal and how this can benefit performance.

Remember!

Do not confuse the terms 'arousal regulation' and 'arousal reduction'. Reducing arousal isn't always the best thing for optimal performance – sometimes you may need to increase arousal levels.

Techniques

Arousal reduction

Key Term

Over-arousal When arousal levels for a particular individual affect performance in a negative way.

Over-arousal is often experienced by athletes for reasons such as lack of confidence or seeing competition as a threat.

The effects of over-arousal are generally the same regardless of the performer: physical and psychological discomfort that leads to reduced performance.

The role of the sport psychologist would be to help the athlete to understand the causes of over-arousal, to recognise the symptoms of over-arousal and then to help athletes to apply appropriate arousal management strategies to reduce levels to an optimal point. Common arousal reduction techniques include progressive muscular relaxation, breathing control, biofeedback, mind to muscle techniques and imagery.

■ Progressive muscular relaxation

Muscle tension is one of the most uncomfortable and devastating symptoms of an over-aroused state and can severely hinder performance due to losses in coordination (and therefore disruption to technique). It can also lead to an increased risk of injury due to vastly decreased flexibility.

Progressive muscular relaxation (PMR) is an easy-to-use technique that can help to reduce muscle tension. It is a useful technique because it increases an individual's awareness of their levels of muscle tension and, through the relaxation phase, helps the individual to distinguish between what is a state of tension and relaxation.

The technique involves tensing and relaxing groups of muscles in turn over the whole body. The process involves tensing a muscle group for five seconds, releasing the tension for five seconds, taking a deep breath and repeating. It is called progressive muscular relaxation because the athlete progresses from one muscle group to the next until all muscles have been tensed and relaxed.

■ Breathing control

When you start to experience increased pressure in sports' situations, an automatic tendency is to hold your breath a little. Unfortunately, when you do this, it increases factors that can be detrimental to performance (such as muscle tension). The best time to use breathing control is when you are in a sporting situation that allows you to take a break.

Controlled breathing is one of the easiest techniques for reducing anxiety symptoms and it has a range of physiological and psychological benefits. The physiological benefits include oxygen transport, carbon dioxide removal, reduced muscle fatigue and reduced chances of injuries such as cramp. However, the psychological benefits are also important.

One of the biggest problems with over-arousal is the reduced concentration levels that accompany it – for example, focusing on the negative aspects, such as muscle tension, increased heart rate and (in some cases) the nausea that can be symptoms of over-arousal. Using breathing control techniques can be beneficial in reducing arousal in two main ways:

- it reduces the physiological symptoms of arousal and anxiety
- it focuses the athlete's attention away from the negative aspects, because they have to concentrate on getting the breathing techniques correct.

As a result of these different aspects, the athlete will benefit through increased concentration, confidence, control and well-being. The best time to use breathing control in a competitive situation is when there is some form of break in the play, because it gives the athlete

Theory into practice

A snooker player is stood at the table, waiting to pot the black. He is currently on 140 points for the break and needs this to hit the 147 break. He leans over the table and begins to move the cue, but his neck, shoulders and triceps feel very tense. He has experienced this on a number of occasions and has worked with a sport psychology consultant on ways of reducing this tension.

As a result of this, he is able to recognise the tension and purposefully further tenses then relaxes each muscle group. This means that the tension is released and he does not lose the flexibility in his upper arms or the coordination of his movement.

Try this approach in a sporting situation for yourself. Does it help?

the chance to be slow and deliberate in their breathing technique. This helps them regain their composure.

Biofeedback

Biofeedback involves the use of different equipment to detect physiological responses to arousal. This helps the athlete to learn how to control those responses. The technique generally uses either visual or auditory feedback of different physiological responses. The common physiological responses that biofeedback is used with are heart rate, breathing, skin temperature and muscle tension. It has not always been shown to improve performance, but it is effective in helping the athlete to detect and reduce physiological symptoms of arousal and anxiety.

Theory into practice

Here are some examples of biofeedback in action.

A sprinter is worried that his heart rate always increases greatly before important events. His sport psychology consultant provides him with a heart rate monitor that beeps with every heart beat. When the beeps start to increase, the sprinter is encouraged to think calming, positive thoughts and listen to the heart rate reducing. As the sprinter can actually hear the heart rate decreasing, with practice he will be able to use the technique effectively.

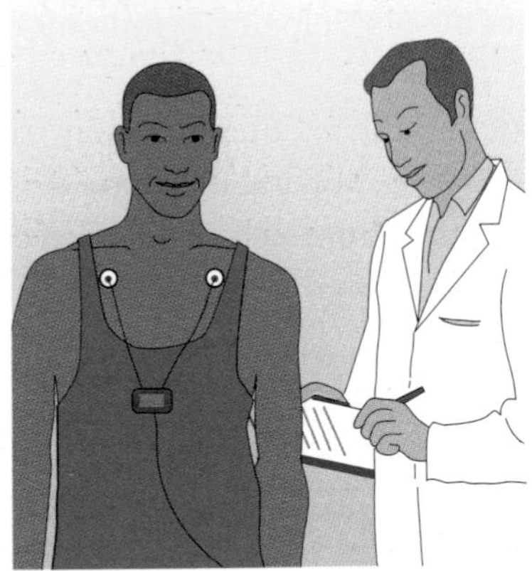

A golfer feels really stiff in her upper back, neck and shoulders every time she go to putt on the green. An electromyogram (EMG) could be used to detect where the different levels of muscle tension are and her sport psychology consultant could encourage the use of a relaxation technique such as PMR to help her to alleviate tension in different areas. The use of the EMG would help the athlete to detect and recognise the tension symptoms. The use of PMR would allow the golfer to systematically reduce tension in different areas and reduce the chances of her performance being decreased.

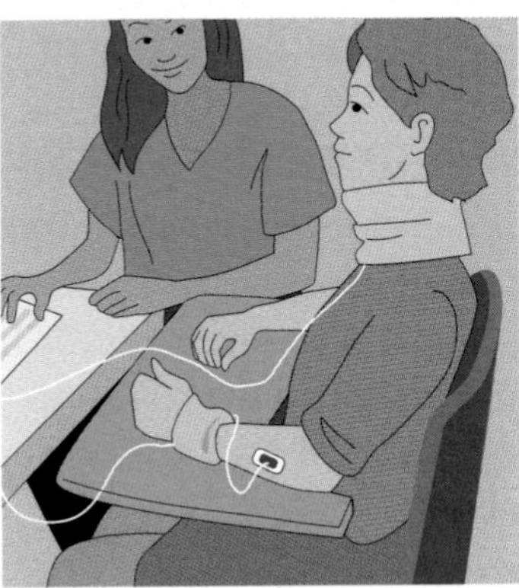

A football player is in the changing rooms before the game. The player has noticed on a number of occasions before a game that his hands feel cold. This can be explained because high arousal causes less blood flow to the fingers. His sport psychology consultant could attach a thermometer to the player's fingertips so that he can see the differences in body temperature. He could attempt to reduce arousal levels using factors such as calming thoughts. The idea is that after the arousal management technique has been used, the footballer will see the thermometer gauge increase and will be aware the arousal and anxiety symptoms are decreasing.

How could you use biofeedback in your chosen sport?

Key Term

Autogenic training A type of self-hypnosis that you do to try to develop feelings of warmth and heaviness.

Mind to muscle techniques

The aim of mind to muscle relaxation is to train the muscle to be able to recognise tension so that it can be released and a relaxed state can occur. Common examples of mind to muscle relaxation techniques include imagery, PMR and autogenic training.

Imagery

Imagery is one of the most common psychological skills techniques because it can be used to reduce arousal symptoms before, during and after competition.

The process by which imagery reduces anxiety is a relatively simple one. If the athlete can use calming, tranquil and relaxing images, this will reduce the symptoms of arousal and anxiety to a level that will not debilitate performance. For more a more detailed explanation of the uses of imagery, see page 307.

Arousal increasing

Just as over-arousal can be detrimental to performance, under-arousal can also be as damaging. It is generally based on the interaction between the situation in which the individual finds themselves and their psychological appraisal of that situation.

Under-arousal is nowhere near as common in a sporting situation as over-arousal. However, when an athlete is virtually guaranteed success, this phenomenon is quite understandable. The sport psychologist's role would be to consult with athletes and teams to develop ways of increasing arousal levels again.

Some common ways of increasing arousal levels in a sport or exercise setting include: using energising imagery, increasing breathing rate, use of music, affirmations and acting energised (sometimes known as high-energy body language).

Energising imagery

In the same way that imagery can be used to reduce arousal and anxiety, it can also be used to increase arousal. This can be achieved through the use of high-energy images of competition (e.g. a hard tackle in rugby), playing well (e.g. crossing the finish line first in a race), and high levels of effort (e.g. being able to lift a new weight in the gym). For more a more detailed explanation of the uses of imagery, see page 307.

Increasing breathing rate

Think about when you have watched the Olympics and a weightlifter has been attempting to lift the next weight up. When they try to lift the weight, they take a series of really short, sharp breaths. This is a way of increasing arousal levels – you take a series of short, sharp breaths until you feel energised. This technique is also often used in other sports such as tennis.

Use of music

Music is more widely researched in the exercise domain than in the sports domain, but it is often used in both areas to increase arousal levels. It has been shown to be effective at increasing arousal levels by eliciting both emotional and physiological responses in different individuals.

The use of music increases arousal in a number of ways. By narrowing a performer's attention, music can divert their focus away from sensations of fatigue. The benefit of this is that the performer will have an elevated mood state through avoidance of negative thoughts. Another benefit of music is that the music which people consider to be exciting can increase body temperature, heart rate and breathing rate, all of which will improve sports performance.

The Brunel music rating inventory is a questionnaire that assesses the motivational qualities of music. For a piece of music to be beneficial in increasing arousal (or influencing sport or exercise performance in any way), it must have strong rhythmic qualities that match the activity that is being completed (e.g. aerobics class, basketball warm-up). The tempo of the music must also be matched to the activity and the individual, because it should match (or reflect) the predicted heart rate. The melody and harmony of the music needs to be energising for the listener, as this leads to increased levels of effort. The music should also be something that the individual selects and likes to listen. The personality of the individual also has an effect on the degree of arousal that the selected music will cause.

In an exercise setting, it is useful for the music to be associated with physical activity, either through the lyrics, containing words or phrases such as 'pump it up!' or 'work your body!'

In both sport and exercise settings, having music that has associations with other media such as films or television programmes has been shown to increase arousal levels (an example of this can be seen through Survivor's *Eye of the Tiger*, which is part of the soundtrack to the series of *Rocky* movies).

■ Affirmations

An affirmation is a positive statement that is designed to confirm goal achievement. It is often used alongside other forms of arousal-increasing techniques such as imagery or acting energised, to increase arousal levels. When using affirmations, the following guidelines should be followed to make the affirmations effective.

- Phrase affirmations using the first-person singular, and be personal with your statements: say 'I', 'me' or your first name, so they are personal to you.
- Make affirmations as positive as possible: avoid the use of 'no', 'don't', and 'not', because if you ask yourself *not* to think about something, you are more likely to think about it.
- Phrase affirmations in the present tense: use statements like 'I am confident of achieving the best result'.
- Make affirmations short, clear and simple: statements that are too long are difficult to internalise, so shorter and simpler is better.
- Make affirmations polysensorial: in the same way as imagery needs to be polysensorial, phrases should be used that make you think about how something feels, sounds, etc. In order to make affirmations polysensorial (see page 308), you should try saying them out loud, perhaps standing in front of a mirror so that you can see yourself saying them at the same time as being able to hear yourself saying them.
- Make affirmations emotional: use phrases that make you feel happy, empowered and self-assured, such as 'It makes me happy when I know I've competed hard.'

When you use affirmations, it is important to review them on a regular basis. Good practice would be to change affirmations when you change the goals you set. It is important to do this so that further progress can be made.

■ Acting energised

How many times have you seen an American football player butt helmets with a team mate? What about when a tennis player wins a key point in tennis and screams at the crowd? Or the basketball players who touch fists with each other when they win free throws, hit hard dunks or sink threes during a game?

These are examples of a technique known as acting energised. These actions have different common characteristics, and generally involve the combination of quick and forceful movements, positive thinking and strong emotional releases.

Acting energised increases arousal levels in a number of ways that can benefit performance. It can heighten concentration levels, reprioritise goal achievement, increase motivation levels and make the athlete excited about competing again. In an elite sport setting, the use of this type of body language can also increase arousal levels in athletes. It increases the arousal levels of the crowd (often displayed through cheering on the team more), which further benefits the athlete.

Assessment of arousal

Key Terms

Cognitive anxiety The thought component of anxiety that most people refer to as worrying about something.

Somatic anxiety The physiological response to anxiety.

In Unit 3 we looked at how arousal and performance are related, and some of the somatic and cognitive changes that happen with this (somatic and cognitive anxiety). A sport psychology consultant needs to assess different levels of cognitive and somatic anxiety to determine the performer's current status and decide on appropriate strategies to help the athlete. Questionnaires such as the CSAI 2, SCAT and Sport Anxiety Scale are often used to do this.

Questionnaires

CSAI 2

Martens, Vealey and Burton (1990) developed a self-report questionnaire based on the multi-dimensional anxiety theory that measured levels of anxiety on three different scales: cognitive state anxiety, somatic state anxiety and self-confidence. This questionnaire is known as the CSAI 2 and looks specifically at anxiety in a competitive situation. Each of the scales (cognitive anxiety, somatic anxiety and self-confidence) range from a score of 9 to 36, with 9 indicating low levels of anxiety or confidence and 36 indicating high levels of anxiety or confidence.

Activity

The form below shows a number of statements that athletes have used to describe their feelings before competition. Using tracing paper, read each statement and then circle the appropriate number next to each statement (1 = Not at all; 4 = Very much so). You need to indicate how you feel now. There are no right or wrong answers. Do not spend too long on any one statement but choose the answer that best describes your feelings.

		Not at all		Very mch so	
1	I am concerned about this competition.	1	2	3	4
2	I feel nervous.	1	2	3	4
3	I feel at ease.	1	2	3	4
4	I have self-doubts.	1	2	3	4
5	I feel jittery.	1	2	3	4
6	I feel comfortable.	1	2	3	4
7	I am concerned I may not do as well as I should.	1	2	3	4
8	My body feels tense.	1	2	3	4
9	I feel self-confident.	1	2	3	4
10	I am concerned about losing.	1	2	3	4
11	I feel tense in my stomach	1	2	3	4
12	I feel secure.	1	2	3	4
13	I am concerned about losing.	1	2	3	4
14	My body feels relaxed.	1	2	3	4
15	I am confident I can meet the challenge.	1	2	3	4
16	I am concerned about performing poorly.	1	2	3	4
17	My heart is racing.	1	2	3	4
18	I am confident about performing well.	1	2	3	4
19	I am worried about reaching my goals.	1	2	3	4
20	I feel my stomach sinking.	1	2	3	4
21	I feel mentally relaxed.	1	2	3	4
22	I am concerned that others will be disappointed with my performance.	1	2	3	4
23	My hands are clammy.	1	2	3	4
24	I am confident because I mentally picture myself reaching my goal.	1	2	3	4
25	I am concerned I won't be able to concentrate.	1	2	3	4
26	My body feels tight.	1	2	3	4
27	I am confident of coming through under pressure.	1	2	3	4

To calculate your scores, add up all of the numbers you circled for the scores (as outlined below), to get a score for each scale. However, statement 14 is reverse scored (e.g. score 4 points if you circled 1, 3 points for answer 2, 2 points for answer 3 and 1 point for answer 4).

***Cognitive state anxiety score**: add up your scores for statements 1, 4, 7, 10, 13, 16, 19, 22 and 25.*

***Somatic state anxiety score**: add up your scores for statements 2, 5, 8, 11, 14, 17, 20, 23 and 26.*

***Self-confidence score**: add up your scores for statements 3, 6, 9, 12, 18, 21, 24 and 27.*

Key Term

Trait anxiety A behavioural tendency to feel threatened even in situations that are not really threatening, and then to respond to this with high levels of state anxiety.

SCAT

The Sport Competition Anxiety Test (SCAT) was designed by Martens in 1977 to assess levels of competitive trait anxiety. Although SCAT has been shown to be a useful measure, it is still a personality measure that should not be used without taking into account the situation that the individual is in as well. If you score high on the SCAT, this is an indicator that you are less likely to control anxiety well and you are more likely to become nervous in competitive situations. If you score low on the SCAT, you are less likely to become nervous in competitive situations and you are more likely to be able to cope with anxiety symptoms.

Activity

Using the form below, assess your levels of competitive trait anxiety. The statements are about how people feel when they compete in sports and games.

Read each statement and then (using tracing paper) circle the appropriate letter next to each statement (A = Hardly ever; B = Sometimes; C = Very often). There are no right or wrong answers.

Do not spend too long on any one statement, but choose the answer that best describes your feelings when competing in sports and games.

		Hardly ever	Some-times	Very often
1	Competing against others is socially enjoyable.	A	B	C
2	Before I compete, I feel uneasy.	A	B	C
3	Before I compete, I worry about not performing well.	A	B	C
4	I am a good sports person when I compete.	A	B	C
5	When I compete, I worry about making mistakes	A	B	C
6	Before I compete, I am calm.	A	B	C
7	Setting a goal is important when competing.	A	B	C
8	Before I compete, I get a queasy feeling in my stomach.	A	B	C
9	Just before competing, I notice that my heart beats faster than usual.	A	B	C
10	I like to compete in games that demand considerable physical energy.	A	B	C
11	Before I compete, I feel relaxed.	A	B	C
12	Before I compete, I am nervous.	A	B	C
13	Team sports are more exciting than individual sports.	A	B	C
14	I get nervous waiting to start the game.	A	B	C
15	Before I compete, I get uptight.	A	B	C

To calculate your score, add up the total number of points according to the following.

For statements 1, 4, 7, 10 and 13: *disregard your answers.*

For statements 2, 3, 5, 8, 9, 12, 14 and 15: *A = 1 point, B = 2 points, C = 3 points.*

For statements 6 and 11: *A = 3 points, B = 2 points, C = 1 point.*

Sport Anxiety Scale

Smith, Smoll and Shutz (1990) used the multi-dimensional model of anxiety to produce the Sport Anxiety Scale (SAS), which measures levels of trait anxiety. The SAS measures worry and concentration disruption (cognitive anxiety) as well as somatic anxiety to give you a total trait anxiety score.

The worry scale ranges from a low level of 7 to a high level of 28. The concentration disruption scale ranges from a low of 5 to a high of 20. The somatic anxiety scale ranges from a score of 9 to 36, with 9 being low somatic anxiety and 36 being high somatic anxiety. The overall trait anxiety levels range from a low of 21 to a high of 84.

Activity

Using the form below, assess your levels of trait anxiety. The statements are about how people feel when they compete in sports and games.

Read each statement and then (using tracing paper) circle the appropriate number next to each statement (1 = Never; 4 = Very often). There are no right or wrong answers.

Do not spend too long on any one statement, but choose the answer that best describes your feelings. Remember to share your true reactions to the sport setting – do not be ashamed if you feel nervous or worried.

		Never			Very often
1	I feel nervous.	1	2	3	4
2	I find myself thinking about unrelated thoughts.	1	2	3	4
3	I have self-doubts.	1	2	3	4
4	My body feels tense.	1	2	3	4
5	I am concerned that I may not do as well in competition as I could do.	1	2	3	4
6	My mind wanders during sport competition.	1	2	3	4
7	While performing, I do not pay attention to what's going on.	1	2	3	4
8	I feel tense in my stomach.	1	2	3	4
9	Thoughts of doing poorly interfere with my concentration during competition.	1	2	3	4
10	I am concerned about 'choking' under pressure.	1	2	3	4
11	My heart races.	1	2	3	4
12	I feel my stomach sinking.	1	2	3	4
13	I am concerned about performing badly.	1	2	3	4
14	I have lapses in concentration because of nervousness.	1	2	3	4
15	I sometimes find myself trembling before or during a competitive event.	1	2	3	4
16	I am worried about reaching my goal.	1	2	3	4
17	My body feels tight.	1	2	3	4
18	I am concerned that others will be disappointed with my performance.	1	2	3	4
19	My stomach gets upset during or before performance.	1	2	3	4
20	I am concerned I won't be able to concentrate.	1	2	3	4
21	My heart pounds before competition.	1	2	3	4

To calculate your scores, add up all of the numbers you circled for the scores as outlined below to get a score for each scale.

***Worry score**: add up your scores for statements 3, 5, 9, 10, 13, 16 and 18.*

***Concentration disruption score**: add up your scores for statements 2, 6, 7, 14 and 20.*

***Somatic trait anxiety score**: add up your scores for statements 1, 4, 8, 11, 12, 15, 17, 19 and 21.*

***Trait anxiety score**: total your scores for the three scales above.*

Assessment practice

There are problems with two different players in a rugby union team.

- The next game is against an opponent where the team has no chance of winning. Player A seems bored in the week leading up to the game and doesn't seem to be able to 'get up' for the game.
- In the same situation, player B has got himself really worked up about the game and is worried that the team is going to be made to look like fools because it has no chance of winning.

For each of the situations, complete the following tasks.

1 Say whether the player is over-aroused or under-aroused and give evidence to support your answer.

2 Select an appropriate method of arousal regulation that you think could help each player and explain the methods. **P4 M4**

3 Say why the methods of arousal regulation would benefit the athletes in those situations. **D2**

Grading Tip M4

You need to make sure that you explain each method that you select.

Grading Tip D2

You need to say why those methods are particularly useful in the situations you have selected them for.

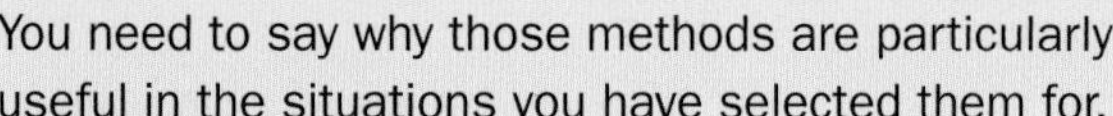

20.5 Be able to plan a psychological skills training programme for a selected sports performer

Psychological skills training (PST) is the acquisition and development of a range of psychological skills that are designed to improve performance over a period of time. PST programmes involve three main phases:

- education (teaching the athlete why PST is beneficial)
- acquisition (learning different psychological skills)
- practice (providing opportunities to use techniques in competition).

PST programmes require you to conduct baseline assessments, plan the programme, take part in the programme, conduct reassessments and review the programme.

Before deciding on the aims and objectives of the PST programme, you need to carry out an initial assessment of the psychological strengths and areas for improvement in your athlete. This can be achieved through:

- interviews – semi-structured interviews (see page 135) are often best
- questionnaires – these assess levels of different psychological factors in sport and the athlete's current psychological skills (for an example, see ACSI on the next page)
- other methods such as performance profiling (see page 302) and decision balance sheets (see page 305).

▲ **Psychological skills training is something that involves athletes, coaches and their support staff, and is something that can take place in a variety of situations**

Key Term

Psychological skills Qualities that the athlete needs to obtain through the PST programme.

A good way of assessing your client's current psychological strengths and areas for improvement is to use a combination of all three methods.

The Athletic Skills Coping Inventory (ACSI) is a questionnaire that can be used used to assess the athlete's current psychological skills. It shows the athlete's psychological skills in a number of areas, including: coping, peaking, goal setting and mental preparation, concentration, confidence, achievement motivation and coachability. The ACSI is useful for sport psychology consultants wanting to get to know the psychological skills of their athletes, but it is important to tell athletes that it will *not* be used for the purposes of team selection – would you answer it honestly if you thought your answers could get you kicked off the team?

When considering your overall PST programme, you should always place your initial assessments in the first one-to-one meeting that you have with your client. This session could take up to two or three hours (as the interviews alone can take up to about an hour to complete).

After you have completed your initial assessments with the athlete, you should complete a needs analysis. This is a written document that outlines what the athlete's main strengths and areas for improvement are; what you can offer the athlete to help them to improve; and some initial

Assessment practice

You are now going to start to understand the roles of a sport psychologist. The activities in this section are linked, so make sure you keep all your work. The information on this page will help.

In pairs, one of you will take on the role of the sport psychologist and the other is the sports athlete. Using a range of techniques, assess the psychological skills of the athlete. Remember, it is good practice to include an objective assessment (such as the ACSI), a subjective assessment (such as performance profiling) and an interview. When you have completed the task, swap roles.

  M5 

grading tips

Grading Tip 

To be able to plan your PST programme, you need to have a good range of assessments to base your plan on.

Grading Tip P6

Use the initial assessments to identify strengths and areas for improvement for the athlete. Conduct the initial assessments thoroughly as they will also form the basis of your review at the end of the PST programme (they will tell how far the athlete has come).

Grading Tip M5

Use the initial assessments conducted with the athlete to explain their strengths and areas for improvement.

Grading Tip D3

Use strengths and areas for improvement discovered from initial assessments of the athlete to justify the inclusion of psychological techniques.

suggestions of what they can do to improve. The needs analysis allows you to make your PST programme more effective, by personalising it according to your athlete. From this needs analysis, you can start to put together the aims and objectives of the PST programme in conjunction with the athlete, managers, coaches, etc. The needs analysis document should be given to the athlete in the second one-to-one meeting you have with them. Make sure the session is long enough for you to explain the needs analysis form and for the athlete to ask you any questions about it.

Needs analysis

Client's name ....

Sport psychologist's name ....

The following initial assessments were undertaken (*name the assessment methods and state what they were used for*):

1 ....

2 ....

3 ....

Results from assessment 1: ....

....

Results from assessment 2: ....

....

Results from assessment 3: ....

....

Your main strengths are ....

Your main areas for improvement are ....

You could improve your performance using the following techniques: ....

....

....

....

....

Assessment practice

Using the initial assessments you completed for the Assessment practice on page 321, produce a needs analysis for your partner. Use the information on this page to help you.

Remember to report the results of your initial assessments to highlight the athlete's strengths and areas for improvements. **P5 P6 M5 D3**

Plan

The planning stage of a PST programme comes after you have conducted your needs analysis with the athlete. The strengths and areas for improvement you have identified will help you to decide on the aims and objectives of the PST programme. During the planning stage of the PST programme, you need to consider the aims and objectives, targets, content, resources required and any other considerations relating to the athlete's personal circumstances.

Aims and objectives

The aims and objectives of the PST programme are what you and the athlete want to achieve through the programme.

Key Terms

Foundation skills The most basic and necessary psychological skills that relate to motivation to achieve success, being aware of how you feel when performing at your best and worst, and having a belief that you are competent in your sport.

Performance skills The traditional skills that a sport psychology consultant would try to teach. They are skills that, without which, high-level performance cannot be achieved.

Facilitative skills Skills that can benefit sports performance through personal development.

Content

When discussing the content of the PST programme, you need to talk about the psychological skills that need improving and the methods athletes can use to improve them.

In 1988, Vealey produced a classification of skills that should be developed through PST programmes. These are foundation skills, performance skills and facilitative skills (see page 322). Examples of each of these skills are summarised in the table below.

Foundation skills	Performance skills	Facilitative skills
Volition: an athlete being motivated to achieve success	Arousal regulation	Interpersonal skills: being able to 'get on' and communicate well with others
Self-awareness: an athlete knowing how they think and feel when playing at their best and worst	Focus and concentration	Lifestyle management: time management, being responsible for your own actions, making the right career moves
Self-esteem and self-confidence: feeling you are competent in your sport and believing you can be successful		

Examples of skills that should be developed through PST programmes

It is important that your PST programme also includes times for meetings between you and your athlete. This will allow you to monitor progress on the programme and give further education or advice on the different techniques used. It is beneficial for the athlete if you include short frequent meetings so that you can get regular feedback on progress. This is better than having long meetings less often. It is also useful if you have a mixture of both formal and informal meetings.

Key Terms

Formal meeting A structured appointment between consultant and athlete.

Informal meeting A meeting that is less structured than a formal meeting and can take the form of chats on the team bus or in the changing room.

Identification of relevant techniques

We have already discussed the techniques used to increase motivation, the roles of imagery and mental rehearsal, and techniques to control arousal levels. You need to use this information when you look at the content of your PST programme.

Vealey also suggested some methods for developing the skills required, as summarised in the table below.

Foundation methods	Psychological skills methods
Physical practice Education	Imagery Goal setting Thought control, concentration and attention Arousal regulation

Methods of developing skills

What the first column shows us is that, in order for a PST programme to be successful, the athlete must use it alongside physical practice where possible and they must understand what they can gain from participating in a PST programme. From this, the athlete will be able to learn different psychological skills. The second column shows a range of methods that can be used to help the athlete develop these psychological skills.

The techniques that you include in your PST programme will be chosen to meet the specific aims and objectives of your programme.

For example, if your athlete showed that they were under-aroused, you would need to select techniques such as music, acting energised, imagery or affirmations to benefit them.

Ideally, any skills or interventions included in the PST programme should be decided on between the coach and the athlete.

Targets

When you and the athlete have decided on the aims and objectives of the PST programme, you must work with your athlete to prioritise the aims and objectives.

As a general rule of thumb, the biggest areas for improvement (i.e. the skills that the athlete has the lowest level of skill in), or the skills that are the most important to the athlete's performance are the highest priority.

SMART targets

After you have prioritised the aims and objectives, you need to produce SMART targets (see page 287). This means your goal setting should follow the SMART principle.

- **S** – **s**pecific: goals must be clear if they are to be achieved. The more unambiguous the goal, the more likely it is to be achieved.
- **M** – **m**easurable: goals must have some form of objective standard that needs to be attained.
- **A** – **a**chievable: need to be within the range of expectations agreed by both the coach and the athlete.
- **R** – **r**ealistic: the individual's motivation will increase if the goal is difficult enough to challenge them while at the same time being realistic enough to be achieved. If goals are too easy, they will lose interest; if the goals are too hard, they could become frustrated.
- **T** – **t**ime-bound: goals need to have a timescale giving a date when it must be achieved.

Resources

The successful completion of the PST programme is dependent on the use of human, financial and physical resources.

Human

Human resources are those people you will need to help the athlete complete the PST programme, such as participants, co-researchers or research assistants and research supervisors.

Financial

Financial resources means any costs associated with completing the PST programme. Can the athlete afford these costs?

Physical

Physical resources means the actual things the athlete will need to complete the PST programme. Where will the PST programme be completed?

Other considerations

Other considerations when you are designing the PST programme include the following.

- How much time is going to be available to complete the PST programme?
- Will the athlete only have pre-season to practise the PST programme or will there be time during competitive season as well?
- Does your athlete have other responsibilities (e.g. family or work commitments, hobbies) that could affect their progress through the PST programme?

Other responsibilities and personal demands

If your athlete has other responsibilities such as children or work commitments, or other hobbies, these could have an impact on their progress through the PST programme. Therefore, it is important to incorporate these factors into each individual's PST programme on an individual basis.

Assessment practice

1 Based on the initial assessments and needs analyses you have conducted for the Assessment practices on pages 321 and 322, produce a six-week plan for a PST programme.

You need to produce a six-week plan that is broken down into six individual weeks rather than an overall six-week block. It may also be useful to produce a detailed plan for each day where you introduce a new technique (e.g. if you introduce imagery as a new skill to be learned, show which type of imagery you will be using and how you will help the athlete develop their imagery skills).

It will be beneficial for your athlete if you say why you have included different aspects into the PST programme by saying how they can improve performance. Use the following headings to check you have produced a good plan for a PST programme:

- Aims and objectives
- Content
- Relevant techniques
- Targets
- Resources
- Other considerations. 

2 When you have produced the plan for your PST programme, deliver it to your partner and ask them to take part in the PST programme you have planned for them. P5 P6 M5 D3

grading tips

Grading Tip 

To show you have effectively planned the PST programme, you need to relate your aims and objectives to the strengths and areas for improvements identified in the initial assessment.

Grading Tip 

Use the review tools discussed on pages 320 to 324, including repeats of your initial assessments, as the initial review of your PST programme.

Grading Tip 

Make sure you explain each of the six bullet points highlighted above. For example, explain each of the relevant techniques using language suitable for your athlete.

Grading Tip 

Use the strengths and areas for improvement you discovered in your initial assessments to justify the inclusion of different psychological techniques. Suggest future relevant activities for your athlete.

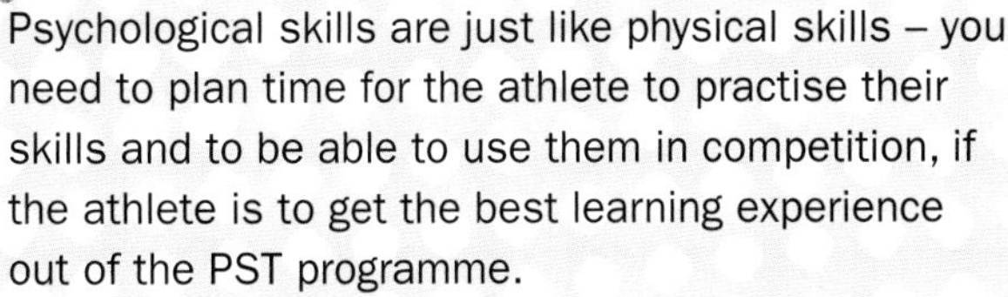

Remember!

Psychological skills are just like physical skills – you need to plan time for the athlete to practise their skills and to be able to use them in competition, if the athlete is to get the best learning experience out of the PST programme.

Time

When producing a plan for any PST programme, you need to think about how much time needs to be spent on different aspects of the programme. If you are introducing new skills to the PST programme, then 15–30-minute sessions, (in addition to physical practice sessions), three to five times a week are beneficial. Gradually, the aim is to move away from needing distinct sessions to allow the psychological skills to be integrated with normal practice, but this becomes possible only when athletes become more proficient in their new skills.

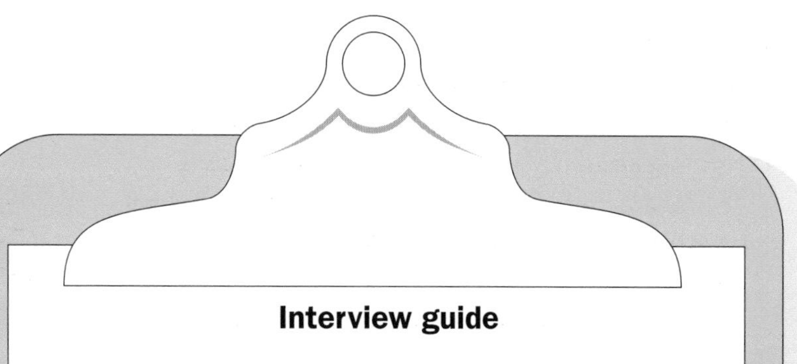

Interview guide

Sport psychology consultant evaluation session

Nature of interview (please circle): Individual Group

1 Working with the consultant

- **a** How useful did you find the individual sessions with the consultant?
- **b** How useful did you find the team sessions with the consultant?
- **c** Did you prefer the formal or informal meetings?
- **d** How approachable did you find the consultant?

2 Techniques used during the programme

- **a** Which techniques did you think worked best?
- **b** Did the programme take into account your personal circumstances?
- **c** Do you feel you were given enough time to develop the skills throughout the programme?

3 Future recommendations

- **a** Do you think that anything should be included in the programme?
- **b** Do you think anything needs to be taken out of the programme?
- **c** What do you see as the major strengths of the programme?
- **d** What do you see as the major limitations of the programme?

Review

Reviewing your PST programme is important as it provides an opportunity for:

- feedback from both the athlete and the consultant
- highlighting the strengths and limitations of the programme
- subjective and objective assessment of the programme.

Methods

Feedback

The main ways of reviewing a PST programme are interviews (group or individual), questionnaires and monitoring physical performance (including collecting objective performance data). These are all ways of getting feedback, which is key to reviewing your programme.

Interviews

Interviews provide you with a good way of getting more in-depth information from your athletes regarding the effectiveness of the PST programme. It is best if you can use semi-structured interviews as this allows you to probe into different areas that might arise during the interview. Above is a sample interview guide that could be used in either group or individual settings. It allows the consultant to get qualitative feedback from their clients.

Questionnaires

One way of getting feedback from your client is through the use of a consultant evaluation form. A consultant evaluation form is a questionnaire that the athlete fills in. It provides the consultant with both qualitative and quantitative feedback on three areas:

- characteristics of the consultant
- effectiveness of the consultant
- suggestions for improvement of future consultancy work.

The form opposite shows one way of reviewing the effectiveness of the PST programme. This form can be used by all clients the sport psychologist has come into contact with (e.g. athletes, coaches). One of the ways you can find out if there has been any change in the athlete's psychological skills since the start of the programme, is to repeat the initial assessments you conducted and compare them to pre-training levels. In the same way that repeated physical fitness tests can assess any physical changes, repeated psychological skills testing can assess any psychological changes.

Consultation evaluation form

Client's name ______________________________

Consultant's name ______________________________

1 Characteristics of the consultant

For each of the following statements, please provide a rating from 1–5, with 1 being the lowest rating and 5 being the highest.

Statement	Rating
a The consultant could provide me with information on skills training that applied directly to my sport.	
b The consultant produced a programme that was geared to my individual needs.	
c The consultant was flexible and was happy to work around me.	
d The consultant was positive.	
e The consultant made me feel comfortable.	
f I understood exactly what the consultant expected of me.	

2 Effectiveness of the consultant

Please circle the number that you feel best describes how effective you feel the consultant was in helping overall sporting performance.

a Overall individual performance										
Limited performance								***Helped performance***		
–5	–4	–3	–2	–1	0	1	2	3	4	5
b Overall team performance										
Limited performance								***Helped performance***		
–5	–4	–3	–2	–1	0	1	2	3	4	5

3 Recommendations for improvement

Please use the space below to provide any recommendations you feel will increase the quality of service provided by the consultant. Please continue on the back of this form if necessary.

Monitoring physical performance

Observing performance is useful in assessing the effectiveness of your consultancy work because it allows you to detect any changes in physical performance. It allows you to collect any objective data relating to performance.

When you observe performance, you will be able to look for:

- changes in psychological factors (such as arousal and somatic anxiety)
- changes in body language
- differences in the skill level of the athlete.

For example, you may have been working with a player who has very low levels of arousal. One of the strategies you decided to use was acting energised in a game situation. By observing performance, you will be able to see if the athlete has

Observe performance after imagery training to see whether the golfer's technique has improved

adopted any of the strategies such as high-fives, touching fists, hand clapping, etc. If you did not notice the athlete adopting these strategies, this would tell you that you would need to do some more work with the athlete in this area.

In another situation, you could have been working with a golfer through imagery training to improve their golf putting technique. Through observing performance, you could see if the skill level of the golfer has increased and suggest any future changes as required afterwards.

In terms of collecting objective performance data, imagine you have been working with an Olympic archer. One of the PST programme's aims was to help the performer relax before taking high-pressure shots during competition. Your objective to achieve this was scoring either 9, 10 or 10x with all of the performer's arrows. You recorded the results and found that he was not in this range. You noticed that when he was shooting, the performer was still shaking. In this case, you need to devise new techniques to improve performance.

Strengths, areas for improvement and identification of future needs

A key aspect of consultancy work within sport psychology is being able to critically analyse your work. This means identifying strengths of your work, areas for improvement within your work and suggestions for future PST programmes.

At the end of your review period, you should also provide your client with some indication of their strengths, areas for improvement and future needs. This will be linked in with all of your other review techniques and is often given to the client in the form of written feedback. This is also some of the information you need to include to critically analyse the PST programme you have planned and implemented with your athlete.

Assessment practice

1 At the end of the six-week PST programme that you asked your athlete to take part in, conduct a review of the overall programme with your partner.

You need to produce a summary that:

- evaluates any improvements they have made over the six-week programme
- evaluates any areas they still need to improve on
- provides suggestions for future activities they may wish to take part in, to keep the improvements they have made.

2 After you have reviewed the athlete's progress, ask them to review your role as a sport psychologist by producing a summary of your strengths and areas for improvement, and ways you could improve your role the next time you do it. P5 P6 M5 D3

grading tips

Grading Tip 

You need to select an athlete of your choice and actually plan a PST programme for them. Not only will it allow you to attain the criteria doing it this way, it will also be more enjoyable for you.

Grading Tip 

You need to use a range of techniques to review the progress of the athlete and to allow the athlete to judge your effectiveness as a sport psychologist. You need to make specific reference to how the strengths and areas for improvement for the performer have altered over the six weeks.

Grading Tip 

You need to make sure that you identify the strengths and weaknesses of the particular athlete you are working with and explain the techniques you will use throughout all of the stages of the PST programme.

Grading Tip 

You need to say how the different techniques you have selected to use throughout your PST programme will maintain and develop the strengths of the athlete, as well as saying how it will improve the athlete's weaknesses.

Knowledge check

1. Name and explain the main roles of a sport and exercise psychologist.
2. What are the main techniques used to increase motivation within sport and exercise psychology?
3. Explain the main techniques used to increase motivation within sport and exercise psychology.
4. What are the benefits of the techniques of increasing motivation within sport and exercise psychology?
5. Define imagery and explain the different types of imagery.
6. What can imagery be used to benefit?
7. What is mental rehearsal?
8. What are some of the uses of mental rehearsal?
9. What techniques can be used to reduce arousal levels?
10. For each of the techniques highlighted in Question 9, explain how to conduct the techniques and say how they can benefit performance.
11. What techniques can be used to increase arousal levels?
12. For each of the techniques highlighted in Question 11, explain how to conduct the techniques and say how they can benefit performance.
13. What must you conduct with your athlete before planning a PST programme?
14. What must you consider when planning a PST programme?
15. What techniques can you use to review a PST programme?

End of Unit assessment

Preparation for assessment

Your task is to work with a specific athlete in a sport of your choice with a view to improving their performance. All the tasks required to complete this unit should be presented as a portfolio of evidence in a ring binder, lever-arch file or some other suitable methods of presentation. You need to complete the following tasks.

1 Produce a letter that introduces you as the sport psychologist. Explain the roles that sport and exercise psychologists fulfil and then explain which of these roles you will be adopting throughout your consultancy work. It will also be useful if you explain how each of the roles you fulfil will benefit the athlete. P1 M1

grading tips

Grading Tip 

Make sure you give a description of the role of a sport psychologist rather than just saying which role it is they would fulfil.

Grading Tip 

Provide some examples of things the sport psychologists would do to fulfil that role and help the client.

2 Produce three information sheets to show the athlete the benefits of adopting different aspects of psychological skills training. Include the following information:

a Sheet 1: explain three different ways that the athlete can help themselves to increase motivation. Evaluate the effectiveness of each of the different techniques, highlighting strengths, limitations and uses of different techniques for the athlete. P2 M2 D1

grading tips

Grading Tip 

Give an accepted definition of goal setting and name the different types of goal.

Grading Tip 

Explain what each of the different types of goal are.

Grading Tip D1

Take goal setting in general, then each of the different types of goal in turn. Discuss strengths and weaknesses and some examples of different types of goal.

b Sheet 2: tell the athlete what imagery and mental rehearsal are and explain to them how these techniques can improve sports performance. Then say how the performer can develop imagery skills. Use as many practical examples as you can to illustrate your points. P3 M3

grading tips

Grading Tip 

Give definitions of imagery and mental rehearsal. Discuss the different types of imagery and describe a range of uses.

Grading Tip M3

Provide practical examples of the uses of imagery and explain how they could benefit sporting performance.

c Sheet 3: explain three different ways that the athlete can help themselves to regulate their arousal levels. Evaluate the effectiveness of each technique, highlighting strengths, limitations and uses of different techniques for the athlete. Use as many practical sport-based examples as you can to illustrate your points. P4 M4 D2

grading tips

Grading Tip 

You need to explain each method you select.

Grading Tip 

You need to say why those methods are particularly useful in the situations you have selected.

3 You are now at a stage where you will have educated your athlete on the benefits of different aspects of sport and exercise psychology. You now need to produce a plan for your PST programme.

a Conduct a needs analysis with your selected sports athlete. Remember to use a range of analysis techniques, e.g. CSAI 2, ACSI, performance profiling. Produce client notes for your benefit that summarise the needs analysis.

b Produce a letter of feedback to your sports performer that outlines the needs analysis and your planned PST programme to them. Include the results of all of the assessment techniques you used, the athlete's strengths and areas for improvement, an explanation of the PST programme and an evaluation of how the techniques you have selected will benefit them. You will want to round off your letter suggesting that the athlete now takes part in the programme you have suggested for a period of six weeks. P5

grading tips

Grading Tip 

To be able to plan your PST programme, you need to have a good range of assessments to base your plan on.

4 After the six-week period, meet your client again and review the programme. The minimum your review should involve is a repeat of your needs analysis, but ideally you should be looking to incorporate other techniques into your review so that the performer has the opportunity to give feedback on your role as a consultant, as well as you reviewing their progress as an athlete. P6 M5 D3

grading tips

Grading Tip 

Use the initial assessments to identify strengths and areas for improvement for your athlete. Conduct the initial assessments thoroughly as they will also form the basis of your review at the end of the PST programme – they will tell how far the athlete has come.

Grading Tip 

Use the initial assessments you have conducted with your athlete to explain their strengths and areas for improvement.

Grading Tip 

Use the strengths and areas for improvement you discovered from your initial assessments to justify the inclusion of different psychological techniques.

Grading criteria		
To achieve a pass grade the evidence must show that the learner is able to:	**To achieve a merit grade the evidence must show that, in addition to the pass criteria, the learner is able to:**	**To achieve a distinction grade the evidence must show that, in addition to the pass and merit criteria, the learner is able to:**
P1 describe the role of the sport and exercise psychologist **Assessment practice pages 299, 330**	**M1** explain the role of the sport and exercise psychologist **Assessment practice pages 299, 330**	
P2 describe three different techniques used to increase motivation and describe their benefits **Assessment practice pages 302, 305, 307, 330**	**M2** explain three different techniques used to increase motivation and describe their benefits **Assessment practice pages 302, 305, 307, 330**	**D1** evaluate three different techniques used to increase motivation and describe their benefits **Assessment practice pages 302, 307, 330**
P3 describe imagery and mental rehearsal and their use in sport and exercise **Assessment practice pages 310, 312, 330**	**M3** explain the use of imagery and mental rehearsal in sport and exercise **Assessment practice pages 310, 312, 330**	
P4 describe methods that can be used to control arousal levels **Assessment practice pages 320, 331**	**M4** explain methods that can be used to control arousal levels **Assessment practice pages 320, 331**	**D2** evaluate methods that can be used to control arousal levels **Assessment practice pages 320, 331**
P5 plan a six-week psychological skills training programme for a selected sports performer **Assessment practice pages 321, 322, 325, 328, 331**		
P6 review the six-week psychological skills training programme for a selected sports performer, identifying strengths and areas for improvement **Assessment practice pages 321, 322, 325, 328, 331**	**M5** explain the six-week psychological skills training programme for a selected sports performer, and identified strengths and areas for improvement **Assessment practice pages 321, 322, 325, 328, 331**	**D3** justify the six-week psychological skills training programme for a selected sports performer, and identifying strengths and areas for improvement **Assessment practice pages 321, 322, 325, 328, 331**

Applied sport and exercise physiology

Introduction

Have you ever wondered why footballers do not overheat when running around a football pitch for 90 minutes? Why it is that some athletes train at altitude? Do you consider this to be more 'performance enhancing' than taking anabolic steroids?

This unit investigates these kinds of issues: how temperature, altitude and age affect performance and what is the implication of race when considering performance. Are girls naturally better gymnasts than boys? Will athletes of West African origin have a natural advantage over athletes of Asian origin when it comes to the 100-metre Olympic final in London in 2012?

As a sport and exercise scientist, your understanding of these issues will allow you to answer a number of complex and often controversial questions that the world of professional sport faces today, such as are males better at sport than females and are Africans better runners than Europeans?

After completing this unit you should be able to achieve the following outcomes:

- understanding how temperature and altitude affect exercise and sporting performance
- know about the physical differences between people of different gender and race and their affect on exercise and sporting performance
- understand the impact that the physiological effects of ageing have on exercise and sporting performance
- understand the effects and implications of using ergogenic aids for exercise and sports performance.

Think it over

The average daily temperature during the Athens Olympics during August 2004 was estimated beforehand to be approximately 28°C. However, it was not uncommon to see temperatures reaching 35 to 38°C for days on end. The heat was often relentless and even at night the temperatures remained high.

Contrast these temperatures with those of London, where the average daily temperature is 22°C – there is a potential difference of 16°C. How do you think British athletes coped with these temperatures and what precautions do you think they had to take?

21.1 Understanding how temperature and altitude affect exercise and sporting performance

As sport becomes more and more commercial, the expectation of global competition increases.

An elite athlete can now expect to compete around the world, from London in Britain to Wellington in New Zealand.

This global competition means elite athletes need to cope with a diversity of conditions. Temperature and altitude can vary considerably depending on where you are. For example, tennis players can find themselves in Dubai, where the temperature can be 40°C, and the following week in Stockholm, where the temperature can be below freezing.

Temperature

Key Terms

Hyperthermia A condition involving raised body temperature.

Hypothermia A condition were low body temperature results from exposure to cold.

Dehydration A condition of excessive water loss.

A major challenge for any athlete is maintaining a suitable body temperature, so that their body can perform and function effectively while training or competing.

Depending on the environmental conditions, the athlete must try to avoid overheating (hyperthermia). On the other hand, the athlete might try and avoid losing body temperature (hypothermia).

The table indicates body temperature and likely effects on the body. Note that the figures do not refer to the environmental temperature, but to the athlete's body temperature.

Body temperature (°C)	Effects
26	Death
28	Severe heart rhythm disturbances; breathing may stop
31	Comatose; shallow breathing; serious heart rhythm problems
32	Hallucinations; delirium; progressive comatose; no shivering
33	Confusion; sleepiness; loss of shivering; slow heart beat; shallow breathing
34	Severe shivering; loss of movement in fingers; some behavioural changes
35	Hypothermia; intense shivering; numbness and bluish tint to skin
36	Mild to moderate shivering
37	Normal body temperature
38	Sweating; feeling uncomfortable
39	Severe sweating; flushed and very red; fast heart rate; exhaustion
40	Fainting; dehydration; weakness; vomiting; profuse sweating
41	Fainting; vomiting; severe headache; dizziness; palpitations; breathlessness
42	Convulsions; vomiting; delirium; comatose
43	Brain damage; convulsions; shock; cardiorespiratory collapse
44	Death

The effects of temperature on the body

Responses of body to high temperature

The body's thermoregulatory system reacts enables an athlete to cope with a variety of temperature changes.

During exercise, the body's metabolic rate can increase some 20-fold and this increased in energy consumption can raise the body temperature significantly.

Sweating

Perhaps the most well-known bodily response to high temperature is sweating. The process of sweating involves the secretion of sweat on to the surface of the skin.

Sweating provides an effective cooling process as the sweat on the surface of the skin evaporates. However, it provides little or no cooling if it just drips off the body.

Remember!

Sweating is not simply a response to an increase in physical activity or temperature, it also increases during periods of mental and emotional arousal.

Function of the hypothalamus

The hypothalamus has a number of roles within the human body, but perhaps its most important is that of the body's thermostat. The hypothalamus contains the central point within the body for temperature regulation.

A group of specialised neurones at the base of the brain help to regulate body temperature within a narrow band around 37°C.

The hypothalamus itself receives a more generous blood supply than any other brain structure. It is mainly through this increased blood supply that it is in an ideal position to watch over or administer body temperature.

The hypothalamus carries out this role to allow normal bodily function and to protect the body's core temperature by initiating responses when that temperature changes due to heat gain or heat loss.

Key Terms

Hypothalamus The region of the brain responsible for integration of many behavioural patterns, especially those concerned with the regulation of the body's internal environment.

Core temperature The temperature of the inner body, particularly the internal organs.

These heat regulation mechanisms are activated in the following ways:

- thermal receptors located in the skin provide the information to the hypothalamus
- temperature changes in the blood contact the hypothalamus directly, thus stimulating temperature control.

Methods of heat loss

Key Terms

Conduction The transfer of heat from one object to another through direct surface contact.

Evaporation The conversion of liquid into vapour (e.g. sweat into vapour).

Radiation The emission or transfer of radiant energy as heat waves or particles.

Respiration The emission of waste gases and water vapour via the respiratory system.

Athletes dissipate heat by a number of methods. Each method has a different level of efficiency depending on certain characteristics of the athlete such as age, race, gender and training.

- Conduction: this involves warming the air molecules surrounding the body or warming any cooler surfaces that are in contact with the skin. Conduction involves the transfer of heat through a liquid, solid or gas by direct contact. The rate of heat loss depends on the temperature difference between the skin and the surroundings, and, of course, the thermal characteristics of those surroundings. For example, if air is moving around the body, warm air (generated by the body's heat) is moved away and replaced by cooler air. The quicker the air moves around the body, the greater the quantity of heat conducted from the body.

- Evaporation: this the body's major defence against overheating. Water vaporatisation lost via the breathing process or sweating through the skin continually transfers heat from the body to the environment. In response to overheating, the body's sweat glands secrete large quantities of saline solution (NaCl dissolved in water), which manifests itself as sweat. The cooling process occurs when sweat reaches the surface of the skin and then evaporates. As in conduction, air plays a major role in the removal of heat. As the air surrounding the body becomes saturated with the evaporated fluid, new air arrives to accept further evaporated sweat. If, however, the air close to the body becomes saturated with sweat or moisture, evaporation as a method of heat loss is impaired. This situation becomes more heightened in humid conditions in which the air is already saturated with moisture, and the sweat generated by the body will not evaporate.

When considering the likely environments an athlete might compete or exercise in, the following outcomes should be considered when evaporation is used as a cooling method.

- In hot and dry environments, the limiting factor for evaporation as a method of heat loss is the rate of sweat production. Ensuring the athlete is hydrated properly is vital in these conditions.
- In hot and humid environments, the limiting factor for evaporation as a method of heat loss is the capacity of the environment to receive moisture. In an environment of high humidity, this is likely to be slight (as the air is already saturated with moisture). Therefore, athletes have to be careful they do not overheat when exercising or competing in hot and humid conditions.
- Radiation: this is the transfer of heat through from one object to another without contact. When an athlete loses heat through conduction, it involves the transfer of heat through a liquid, solid or gas by direct contact, generally from the skin to either the environment or clothing. However, during radiation heat loss, the athlete radiates heat towards cooler objects. The closer the two temperatures (athletes and object), the less heat the athlete will lose. At rest, radiation is the main method of dissipating body heat. The naked body loses approximately 60 per cent of its heat by radiation.
- Respiration: breathing mechanisms and the expulsion of waste air from the lungs allows for a small amount of heat loss via an athlete's exhaled breath.

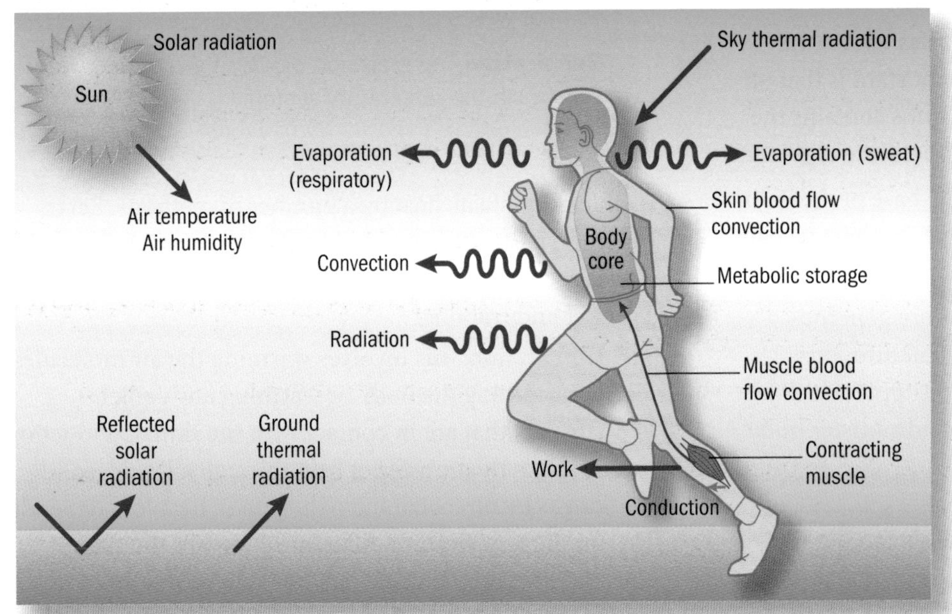

In order for an athlete to perform efficiently, excess body heat must be dissipated to the environment to regulate core temperature; this is done by conduction, evaporation, radiation and respiration

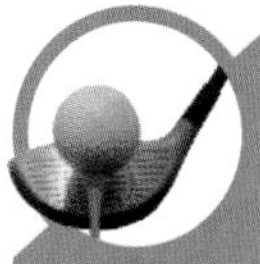

Think it over

What do you think are the major sources of heat loss for the following sports: conduction, evaporation, radiation or respiration?

- swimming 200m freestyle
- marathon running
- bodybuilding competition (static posing)
- equestrianism (cross country).

Responses of body to low temperature

Hypothermia is a condition where low body temperature results from exposure to cold. This exposure causes the body's core temperature to drop. Breathing, blood pressure and heart rate decrease and drowsiness sets in. If uncorrected, hypothermia can be fatal as body temperature approaches 28°C (see page 336).

Hypothermia develops if the rate of heat loss from an athlete's body exceeds the rate at which the body is producing heat. There are three types of hypothermia:

- immersion: severe cold stress due to the bodily immersion in cold water
- exhaustion: less severe cold stress due to low temperatures involving wet and windy conditions
- urban: cold is relatively mild but prolonged (generally associated with the elderly or infirm but rarely encountered in a sports capacity).

There are three stages of hypothermia, as seen below.

When an athlete is exposed to a cold environment, the heat-promoting centre of the hypothalamus is triggered and a number of involuntary responses (e.g. shivering and vascular adjustments) are triggered to increase the body's core temperature. This means that, hopefully, none of the effects in the table materialise. In addition to these involuntary adjustments, athletes can take a number of actions to prevent their body core overcooling, including:

- wearing appropriate clothing for the conditions (e.g. sweatshirt, hat, gloves)
- drinking hot fluids
- increasing physical activity to generate more heat.

If these responses fail to keep body temperature at the required level for normal body functions to take place (i.e. the body's internal mechanisms may be unable to replenish the heat being lost to the surrounding environment), then hypothermia is likely to follow.

Shivering

Shivering is a series of involuntary contractions of muscle tissue in response to a cold environment. It is designed to increase body temperature. Shivering is effective because the rapid muscle activity produces heat.

Vascular adjustments

Blood vessels in the skin constrict, resulting in blood being restricted to the deep body organs and largely bypassing the skin. Because the skin is separated from the internal organs by a layer of fatty tissue, heat loss from the core body areas is reduced, and skin temperature drops to that nearer the external environment. This is why when this happens our skin feels very cold to the touch.

Stage	Body temperature	Effects
1	Drop of 1°C–2°C below normal	Mild to strong shivering occurs; blood vessels in the outer extremities contract, lessening heat to the outside environment; unable to perform complicated tasks with hands
2	Drop of 2°C–4°C below normal	Shivering becomes more violent; muscle coordination becomes apparent; movements are slow and mild confusion is shown; extremities become pale
3	Drop of more than 4°C below normal	Shivering stops; cellular metabolic process shuts down and skin becomes blue; major organs fail as pulse and respiration rates decrease; slowly heading towards brain death

The stages of hypothermia

Restricting blood flow to the skin and surface areas is not a problem for short periods. However, if this is extended over a long period of time, skin cells deprived of oxygen and nutrients from the blood begin to die. This condition is known as frostbite and can be very serious indeed.

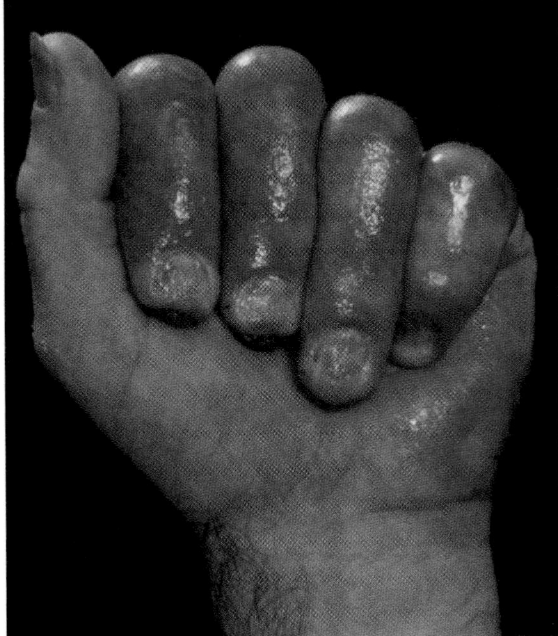

The restriction of blood flow to the skin in cold conditions for a long period of time can result in frostbite; this condition usually requires amputation of the affected areas

Effects of high temperature

Hyperthermia

Overexposure to hot and humid conditions can result in the normal heat-loss processes becoming ineffective. At this point, hyperthermia is likely to follow, which results in the hypothalamus itself being compromised. A core temperature greater than 40°C increases metabolic rate, which increases heat production. The skin then becomes hot and dry as the temperature continues to rise to an extent that organ damage becomes a possibility. This condition is known as heatstroke and can be fatal if corrective measures are not implemented immediately. This usually involves cooling the body in water and administering fluids.

Key Term

Hyperventilation Excessive ventilation of the lungs caused by increased depth and frequency of breathing.

Heatstroke develops when the body is unable to get rid of the excess heat being produced as a consequence of both the environment and exercise within that environment. Early symptoms of heatstroke include excessive sweating, headache, nausea, dizziness and hyperventilation. Without correct treatment, an athlete with full-blown heatstroke is in danger of developing irreversible brain damage, kidney damage, liver damage and, ultimately, death.

Dehydration

Dehydration is a condition of excessive water loss. When water output exceeds intake over a period of time and the body is negative in its fluid balance, dehydration results. A serious consequence of dehydration results in a lowering of blood plasma levels (blood plasma is 90 per cent water), which leads to an inadequate blood volume to maintain normal cardiovascular function. This condition is known as hypovolemic shock.

In high temperature environments, approximately 60 per cent of an athlete's cardiac output can pass through the skin for cooling and sweat production. Loss of fluid

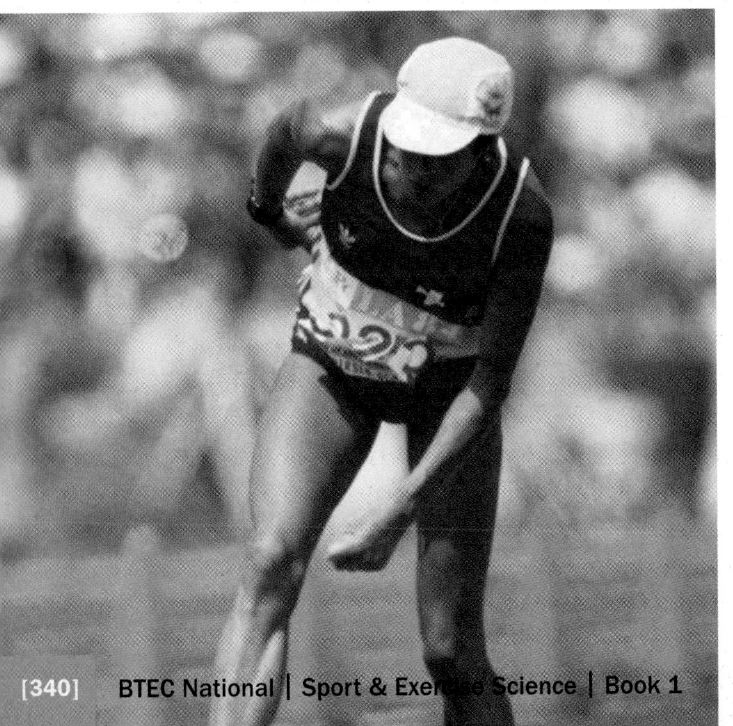

Heatstroke can be a serious condition to an athlete and must be treated readily

Key Terms

Hypovolemic shock A severe form of dehydration that results in inadequate blood volume following a reduction in blood plasma levels.

Cardiac output The volume of blood pumped by the heart in one minute.

Electrolyte Soluble salts and minerals in aqueous solution that helps maintain many body functions.

as seemingly little as 1 per cent of total body weight by sweating will lead to a decline in performance.

Dehydration is best avoided by drinking plenty of water. Drinking water beyond that of the body's needs is not a risk as the kidneys remove any excess water as urine. However, when large amounts of water are being lost through perspiration, maintaining electrolyte balance becomes an issue for the athlete, which may result in salt depletion. This is caused by sweating and can cause a range of further symptoms beyond that of simple dehydration. These include tiredness, irritability, fainting, cramps and an overall loss of performance.

Effects of low temperature

Hypothermia

Hypothermia is a low body temperature resulting from uncontrolled exposure to the cold. The effects of hypothermia are far reaching: it affects vital functions such as breathing rate, blood pressure and heart rate, while decreasing cellular function. Drowsiness is a common symptom of hypothermia, followed by a feeling of comfort felt by the victim, regardless of how cold they actually are. Shivering generally ceases when the body has used up its heat-generating abilities and occurs when the core temperature is drops below approximately 32°C. If left uncorrected and the body temperature lowers to the region of 24°C, death by cardiac arrest is likely.

Altitude

Altitude is the measurement of elevation, especially above sea level or the Earth's surface. Altitude has a number of influential factors on sports performance. However, these factors are rarely encountered by many athletes as most of the world's population live at an altitude at or relatively close to sea level.

Key Term

Hypoxia A condition in which there is not enough oxygen available for the body's tissues.

Atmospheric pressure decreases as altitude increases. This has significant implications for athletes because a fall in pressure can lead to a shortage of oxygen (hypoxia).

When altitude is encountered by athletes it is usually in competition, as happened at the 1968 Olympic Games in Mexico City. Here, athletes from around the globe experienced (many for the first time) factors such as thinner air (i.e. lower oxygen concentration). The high altitude of Mexico City (2,240 metres above sea level) compared with London (sea level) made it especially difficult for endurance athletes to adapt to the low-oxygen concentrations.

Responses of body to high altitude

Hyperventilation

Hyperventilation involves the increased ventilation of the lungs caused by an increase and frequency of breathing due to impaired gaseous exchange in the lungs.

In the UK, the majority of the population live between sea level and an altitude of approximately 500 metres. The differences in barometric pressure within this range are not enough to cause any problems when spending time in higher-altitude areas. When breathing normally, the breaths are varied to maintain normal carbon dioxide levels and supply appropriate levels of oxygen to the body's tissues. This is done automatically by measuring the carbon dioxide level in the blood.

At altitude, the air is oxygen-deficient, so the resultant low carbon dioxide levels cause the brain's blood vessels to contract. This results in reduced blood flow to the brain accompanied by spells of dizziness or light-headedness.

This is when athletes realise they are experiencing hyperventilation as a consequence of training or competing at altitude without preparation.

When an athlete leaves sea level and goes to a mountainous region, where air density and pressure are much lower, the body responds to this environment in a variety of ways. Initially the body responds with headaches, dizziness and nausea due to the respiratory adjustments. This step is known as acclimatisation. In time, the athlete will adjust to the new environmental surroundings accordingly.

Key Terms

Gaseous exchange Loading oxygen and unloading carbon dioxide at the lungs.

Acclimatisation The gradual adjustment of the body to new climatic or other environmental conditions, such as the adjustment to low levels of oxygen at high altitudes.

Tachycardia

Tachycardia is a resting heart rate that is higher than normal (more than 100 beats per minute).

An abnormally fast heart rate can result as a consequence of low body temperature. There are, however, other causes of tachycardia such as stress, heart disease and specific drugs.

Effects of high altitude

Reduction in partial pressure of oxygen

Decreases in arterial oxygen pressure cause the central chemoreceptors to become much more responsive to an increase in carbon dioxide.

This stimulates the peripheral chemoreceptors, which leads to an increase in ventilation as the brain attempts to restore gaseous exchange to a previously normal level.

Key Terms

Central chemoreceptors Neurones in the brain which regulate respiratory activity.

Peripheral chemoreceptors Specialised cells found in the carotid and aortic bodies (clusters of chemoreceptors), whose role is to regulate respiratory activity.

Haemoglobin Oxygen transporting component of red blood cells.

Given that there is less oxygen available at high altitude, this always results in lower than normal haemoglobin saturation levels in an athlete's blood.

At 5,000 metres above sea level, for example, the oxygen saturation in arterial blood is approximately 70 per cent (compared to 98 per cent at sea level). Therefore, at 5,000 metres there is less oxygen available in the blood to assist cellular respiration and bodily function. If an athlete has not acclimatised to these conditions, the lack of oxygen readily available from arterial blood may serious impair physical activity.

Reduced maximum oxygen uptake (VO_2 maximum)

When competing at altitude, the body has to compensate for a lack of oxygen. There is, for example, an estimated drop in VO_2 maximum of 2 per cent for every 300 metres above 1,500 metres above sea level. This drop in VO_2 maximum means an athlete's oxygen uptake decreases, which can (and often will, without acclimatisation) adversely affect athletic performance, particularly during endurance-based events.

Adaptation to altitude

Although body tissues receive adequate oxygen at normal conditions at altitude, problems arise when athletes are required to undertake strenuous activity and the demands of the cardiovascular and respiratory systems are increased.

Unless the athlete has undergone a period of acclimatisation, such activity, when combined with the conditions of altitude, may lead to the body's tissues becoming hypoxic (see page 341). There are essentially three major changes that occur following acclimatisation.

- Increased haemoglobin concentration: during acclimatisation, there is an increase in red blood cell count and, consequently, an increase in haemoglobin concentration. The increase in red blood cell count is brought about due to an increase in the manufacture of red blood cells in the bone marrow as a response made by the body to the altitude.
- Increased breathing rate: to compensate for the decrease in the partial pressure of oxygen in the lungs, the breathing rate of an athlete increase.
- Cellular changes: altitude causes an increase in the myoglobin content within cells, together with an increase in the number of mitochondria.

Assessment practice

A professional cricket team is going on pre-season training to Pretoria in South Africa during February and March. The team manager and the fitness coach are a little concerned about the effects of both temperature and altitude on the players, and have asked a sports scientist to prepare a short PowerPoint presentation called 'The effects of temperature and altitude' to show the players prior to departure.

To emphasise the effects of temperature, in particular the different factors involving hot and cold weather, her presentation further compares the differences in temperature between Pretoria and Wellington, New Zealand, where the team toured in April last year. She was sure the players would remember just how cold it was while playing in Wellington.

Prepare a PowerPoint presentation that she might use. Detail the effects of temperature on the body and the body's responses to altitude. She will need to inform the players about methods of heat loss, the effects of high temperature, the responses and adaptations to training at altitude and, in particular, she will need to list the potential dangers facing cricketers should they be training or playing in a practice match.

You will have to research the average temperature in Wellington, New Zealand in April, Pretoria during February and March and the area's height above sea level to determine the altitude. **P1** **P2**

grading tips

Grading Tip 

You must be able to show a basic understanding when describing the responses of the body to temperature, and their effects on exercise and sports performance. Indicate why body temperature is such an important factor in human physiology, how sports can in some cases put tremendous stress on body temperature and how the body deals with this. Mention the impact of environmental surroundings too.

Grading Tip 

High-altitude competition and training is an important aspect of applied sport and exercise physiology, so you must be able to describe the responses and effects on athletes. Ensure you explain what happens to the body with particular reference to an athlete's breathing and oxygen count.

21.2 Know about the physical differences between people of different gender and race and their affect on exercise and sporting performance

Gender refers to attributes that are categorised as male and female. Race, on the other hand, refers to a group of people who share common ancestry. To understand the physical differences between gender and race requires an examination of the anatomical and scientific evidence, as well as the sociological trends of the modern world.

Gender

Females have some essential differences from males with regard to sports performance, and this, to some extent, explains the differences between the sexes in terms of levels of physical ability. Sociological thinking tends towards an increasing tendency for equality, with females taking on more traditional male roles, and the differences between the sexes are closing.

Physical differences

Females tend to be about 10 per cent smaller than males in most physical variables such as heart size, blood volume and haemoglobin concentration. However, females also carry approximately twice the body fat of males. The net result is a total aerobic capacity of 40 per cent less than males. That said, females are capable of significant improvements in muscle gains when training, and the relative muscle strength is equivalent in both sexes.

■ Body size

The female skeleton is, on average, smaller and lighter than a male skeleton. Female skeletons have shorter appendicular components (see page 4), which results in a smaller height and weight when compared to males. These skeletal differences have many implications, not all of them disadvantageous. For example, smaller, lighter and shorter bones are helpful in events such as gymnastics when performances demand balance, flexibility and agility. By contrast, male gymnastics events make primary use of strength and explosive speed (e.g. rings and pommel horse).

■ Body composition

Females tend to have a greater percentage of body fat than males, with females averaging 25 per cent and males 12.5 per cent. Although this is an advantage in sports events such as long-distance swimming (as a result of increased buoyancy and heat insulation), increased body fat is a distinct disadvantage in weight-bearing endurance events on land (e.g. marathon running).

A raised level of body fat increases the amount of work necessary to support and propel the body effectively and efficiently. It decreases VO_2 maximum when it is measured per kilogram of body mass and decreases the efficiency of heat loss over the skin by conduction, convention and radiation. There is little evidence to suggest that females are more efficient when it comes to the utilisation of fats during endurance events.

However, trained females can be exceptionally lean and their body fat percentage can be well below that for untrained males. Therefore, females can reduce their body fat content well below what is considered normal for their gender. Loss of body fat results in a change in somatotype (see page 81).

■ Muscle mass

Key Terms

Oestrogen Female sex hormone.

Testosterone Male sex hormone.

There is no difference between male and female muscle mass. Skeletal muscle is composed of the same components and those muscles respond and perform in exactly the same way.

The major reason females do not develop skeletal muscles of a similar size to males is due to the presence of higher oestrogen levels in most females. Oestrogen deters skeletal muscle from becoming large and bulky.

Males, on the other hand, have large levels of testosterone, which allows them to build skeletal muscle mass more easily and in greater quantities.

This difference in physical size and hormone levels is a significant factor because as a result females have muscles with smaller cross-sections than males.

Muscle mass is closely related to muscular strength and muscle mass for females is approximately 20 per cent less than for males. When comparing the muscular strength of males and females, males are naturally stronger than females in all muscle groups.

Given the smaller muscle mass of females, there is less phosphagen available for maximal muscle contractions. Therefore, the peak power on average is approximately 20 per cent less for females.

Males tend to exhibit 50 per cent more upper-body strength than females. Overall, the typical female's total body strength represents about two-thirds of a typical male's.

Think it over

Serena Williams has won nearly 30 women's tennis titles during her career. Do you think she could adequately compete against male professional tennis players?

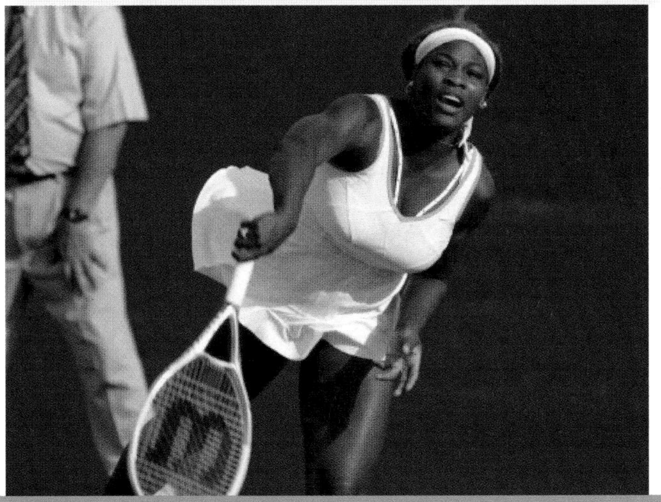

Serena Williams, tennis player

Testosterone levels

Testosterone is the male sex hormone and is ultimately responsible for the greater concentration of muscle mass in males. This comes about through increased muscle hypertrophy, which ultimately leads to an increase in muscular strength.

Females, on the other hand, have far less testosterone in their systems and much more oestrogen. Oestrogen is the hormone responsible for female sexual characteristics and is thought to be linked with the greater concentration of body fat in the female body. This higher concentration of body fat generates a longer-term energy store that can prove beneficial during training.

Haemoglobin levels

Males have slightly higher concentrations of haemoglobin in their blood than females. In theory, therefore, males have an increased capacity for oxygen delivery to the working muscles.

Think it over

Given that extended periods of exercise are supplied with energy by the aerobic method – do males have a physiological advantage over women in aerobic events? Might this explain why the men's world record for the marathon is quicker than the women's, or is it more to do with men having larger skeletal muscles?

VO_2 maximum

Aerobic and anaerobic training results in physical adaptations whereby the differences between trained male and female athletes is significantly less than those between untrained males and females.

Untrained females have much lower VO_2 maximum values (generally between 20 per cent and 30 per cent lower) than untrained males.

Endurance-trained females have VO_2 maximum values closer to those of endurance-trained males. Females are proven to excel in endurance events and currently hold many world records in long-distance swimming.

Part of this success may be down to the additional buoyancy afforded by the additional body fat found in females. However, at present, the physiology of this performance is not yet fully understood – it may be linked to improved fat metabolism and a greater tolerance of temperature variations. However, what we do understand is that VO_2 maximum can be improved by as much as 20 per cent with the right training.

Thermoregulation

The greatest difference in thermoregulation between males and females is sweating. Females generally sweat less than males because they start to sweat at higher skin and core temperatures. Despite a lower sweat output, females show heat tolerance similar to that of men and this is largely due to fact that females rely more on circulatory mechanisms for heat dissipation, whereas males make greater use of convection and evaporation. The reliance on a lower sweat output allows females greater protection from dehydration during exercise at higher temperatures.

Their relatively large surface area to mass ratio means females have a greater surface area exposed to the environment. Therefore, under similar heat conditions, women will tend to cool quicker than males through their smaller body mass across a relatively large surface area. Males, on the other hand, have a smaller surface area to mass ratio given their greater concentration of skeletal muscle tissue.

Heart size

Women have smaller hearts than men because their body tends to be smaller. Genetics dictate that heart size is often relative to body size. Because men have larger muscle mass and larger internal organs (such as liver and lungs), their hearts require a larger stroke volume to accommodate the various functions.

Flexibility

Flexibility is an important component of fitness that has many contributory factors. It is affected by the composition of a given joint, the length and position of tendons and ligaments, and the elasticity of both the muscle tissue and the skin. Females tend to be more flexible than males.

Training differences

Most studies have come to the conclusion that there are few differences between the training responses of males and females undertaking similar activities. However, given the physiological differences between males and females, there are other factors which may influence training that merit further discussion.

Key Term

Amenorrhea The absence of blood flow during the menstrual cycle.

Men risk greater trauma in sporting contests through their genitalia, and the reproductive physiology of female athletes can be susceptible to the stress of competition and training. Exercise can affect menstruation, particularly among females involved in high-intensity training and competition sports (such as long-distance running, gymnastics and swimming).

For example, female athletes can develop amenorrhea (an abnormal cessation of menstruation) during training and competition. Excessive weight loss through a reduction in body fat is believed to be one of the major causes of amenorrhea among female athletes.

Menstruation can also lead to iron deficiency in certain cases. Under these conditions, there may not be the full oxygen-binding capacity within the haemoglobin levels in a given volume of blood. This may have a detrimental effect on aerobic performance, so training adaptations or iron supplementation may be required.

Effects

Recovery periods

Recovery periods are largely dependent on an individual's level of fitness, regardless of gender.

However, females have a tendency to have a slightly lower haemoglobin count than males, which may lessen female recovery rates as glycogen levels are topped up (skeletal muscle, liver, kidneys and brain) and any muscle tissue damage is repaired after exercise.

Anaerobic capacity

Short-term high intensity exercises that involve anaerobic power often show a significant difference between the capabilities of both male and female athletes.

On the whole, male athletes have a far greater capacity for anaerobic power. This is due to a number of factors including increased body composition, muscular strength, neuro-muscular factors and, of course, all these are fed by a ready supply of ATP.

Aerobic capacity

Aerobic capacity is particularly important to endurance athletes and an increased aerobic capacity will eventually lead to an increase in VO_2 maximum.

Females have lower natural haemoglobin counts, which means the oxygen-carrying capabilities of their blood are less than those of males. However, trained females are successful in certain endurance-based events. The fact that females carry more fat tissue than males means, for trained athletes, that there is an additional fuel supply on hand in greater quantities than in males. This will ultimately be of benefit in endurance-based events.

Assessment practice

The professional cricket team is so impressed with the sports scientist's presentation on 'The effects of temperature and altitude' that she has been asked to stay on in South Africa. She will help to train both the male and female under-18 academy teams, which are due to arrive soon.

The team has asked for her input regarding the training schedule for their academy teams. Due to a limit on both time and facilities, males and females are to train together. Although they will practise batting and bowling separately, all fielding, fitness, strength and conditioning training will be carried out together.

The fitness coach is worried and has asked for her help in planning a training programme that takes into account the physiological differences between genders and the subsequent effects on exercise, but allows both teams to work together. The training schedule must include the following:

- warm-up (including flexibility training): 30-minute session
- cardiovascular workout: 30-minute session
- strength training: 30-minute session
- fielding session: 30-minute session.

Prepare a training session she might use in poster format and list what exercise both teams will do in each 30-minute session. Your poster should detail what is required in terms of flexibility, cardiovascular fitness, strength and fielding skills for cricket, and how the physiological differences between males and females can be accommodated within this training programme. **P3 M1 D1**

grading tips

Grading Tip 

You must be able to show a basic understanding when describing the physiological differences between male and female athletes and their effects on exercise and sports performance. Indicate in which (if any) of the physiological differences between males and females will affect performance in cricket and how might you train males and females together to overcome these differences.

Grading Tip M1

The merit criteria demands a bit more from you in terms of the quality of what you produce as evidence and in terms of complexity, so pay attention to detail in your responses. Explaining the physiological differences between male and female athletes requires that you can describe and explain in detail and how why these differences occur.

Grading Tip D1

You need to be able to analyse the range of physiological differences between men and women and justify the effects of each.

Race

Athletes come from a number of different racial types. These racial types are based on convention with relation to ethnicity, geography, skin colour and body form. Examples are West African, East African, Caucasian and Asian. Why not look at blood groups, muscle fibre types or any other genetic traits? Genetically, each would be as valid a criterion. The reason we do not, however, is largely sociological. The distribution of one physical or genetic characteristic is not necessarily the same as that of another, such as blood group or muscle fibre type.

Some racial types are known to perform extremely well in certain sports. So we need to consider just how accurate or how closely aligned these social conventions and genetics actually are, and their impact on applied sport and exercise physiology.

West African origin

West Africa comprises the western-most region of the Africa, occupying approximately one-fifth of the continent. It is currently composed of a number of states including Nigeria, Gambia, Ghana, Senegal and Côte d'Ivoire to name but a few.

West Africa has a complex history, but an important aspect of that history, in the context of future sport, was the colonial period during the eighteenth and nineteenth centuries in which France and Britain controlled nearly the entire region. As a consequence of this period and the resultant slave trade, many indigenous West Africans were transported to what we now know as the Caribbean and the North American continent – which

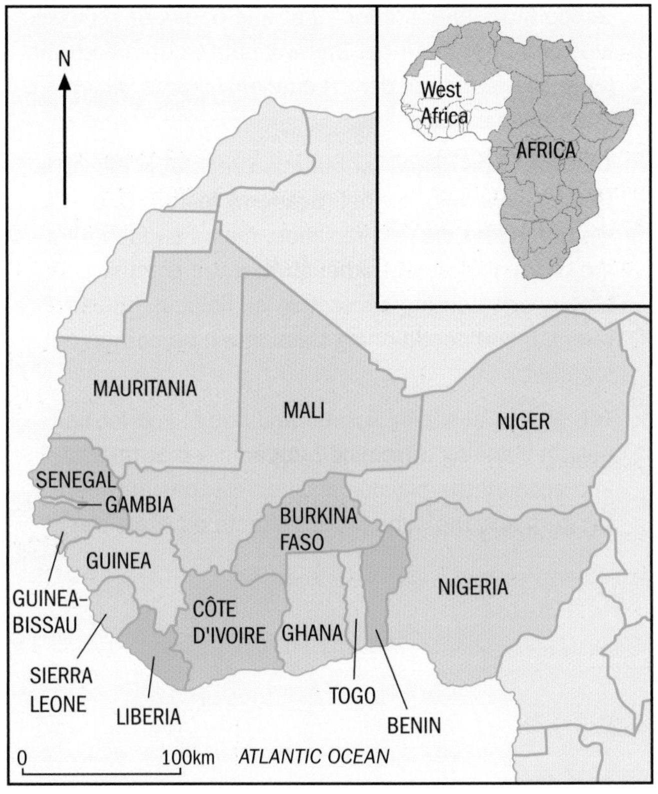

West Africa encompasses a huge area on the Atlantic Coast of the African continent, including countries now producing talented athletes in a variety of sports (such as Nigeria and Côte d'Ivoire)

were themselves former colonial territories – to work on agricultural plantations. Many African-Americans today are descendants of these people.

The Chelsea striker Didier Drogba is of West African origin. He was born in Abidjan in the Ivory Coast, but moved to France with his family at the age of five.

East African origin

East Africa comprises the eastern-most region of Africa and includes nations such as Kenya, Tanzania, Uganda and Ethiopia. The unique geography and apparent suitability for farming made East Africa an appealing target for European colonisation in the nineteenth century.

Former world 800-metre champion, Wilson Kipketer, is of East African origin. He was born in Kenya in 1972, but later applied for Danish nationality after studying there for many years.

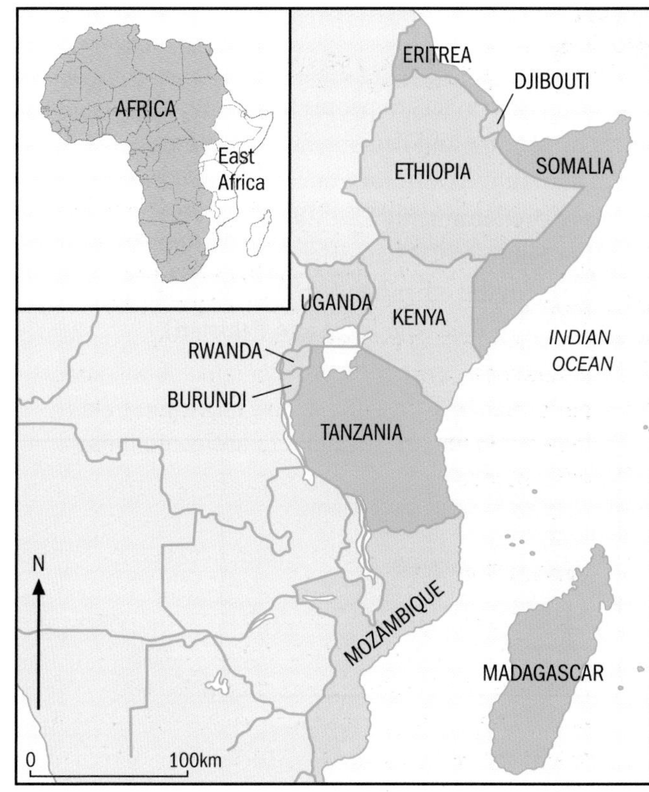

▲ East Africa includes countries such as Ethiopia, Kenya and Tanzania; these countries have large areas at high altitude where many of the world's top endurance athletes originate

Caucasian

The term 'Caucasian' is often used to refer to people whose ancestry can be traced back to Europe, the Middle East and some regions of Asia. The physical characteristics of Caucasian athletes tend to be very light to brown skin pigmentations and a variety of physical forms.

Former seven-time Formula 1 world champion Michael Schumacher is of Caucasian origin. He was born in Germany in 1969 and went on to become the most successful Formula 1 driver to date.

▼ The Caucasian race is the majority in North America and Europe, Australia and New Zealand

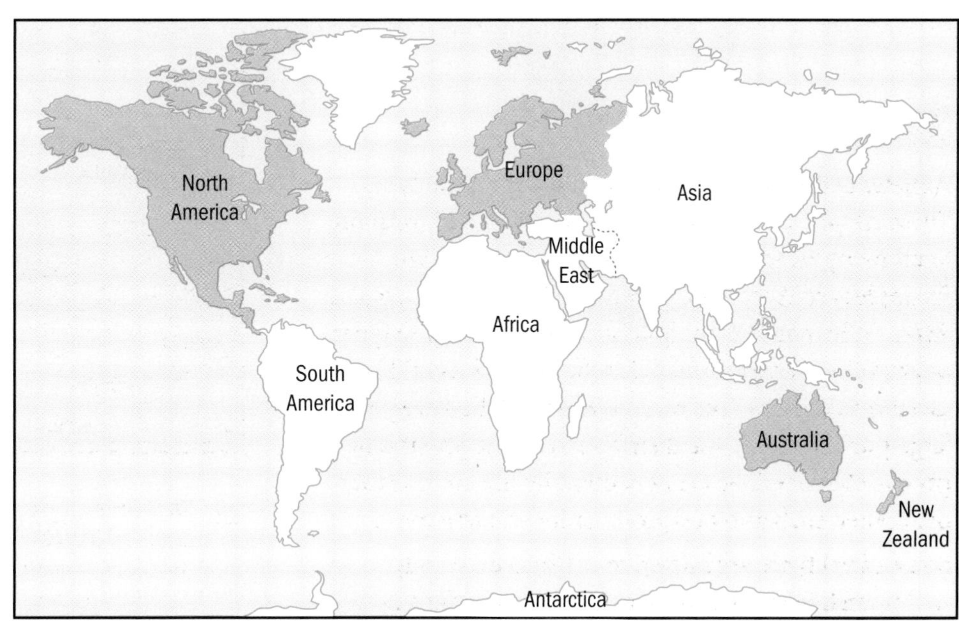

Asian

The term 'Asian' refers to people from Asia. The meaning varies by country and person, much like the term Caucasian. In the USA, for example, Asian refers to people of predominantly East Asian (e.g. China and Japan) or South-east Asian origin (e.g. Thailand and Vietnam). On the other hand, in the UK Asian generally refers to South Asia (e.g. India and Pakistan).

Former women's Olympic 100-metre breaststroke gold medallist Luo Xuejuan was born in Hangzhou, China, in 1984 and set a new Olympic record during her 2004 Olympic triumph. She has since retired from competition following heart surgery.

Asia covers a vast area from the Indian sub-continent to the Far East and South-east Asia; Asians remain the majority race in these areas

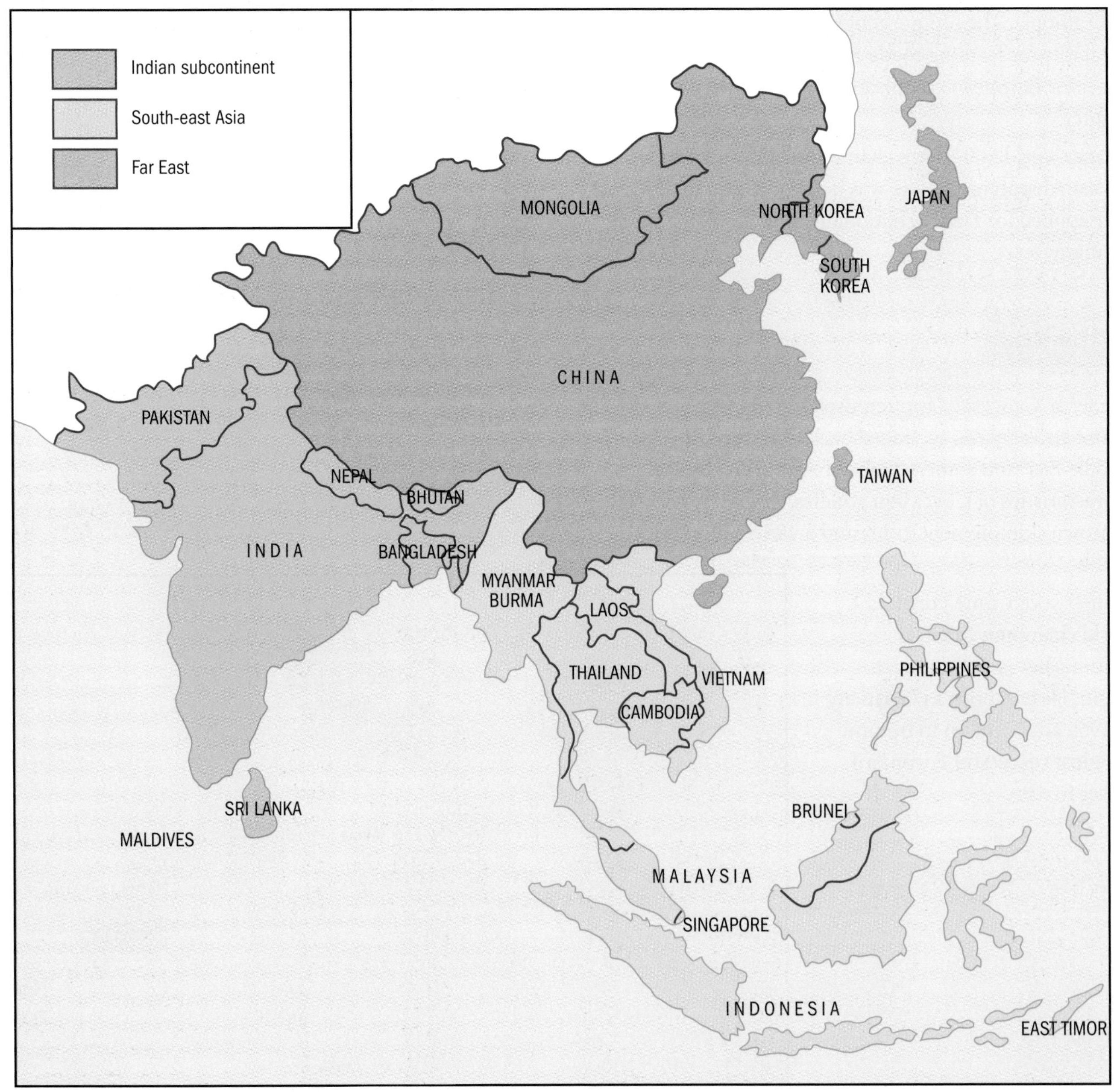

Physical differences

The human race is thought to have evolved in Africa and eventually spread out over the continents. Over time, these populations became geographically separated from one another and evolved to differ in physical appearance. It is not surprising therefore that West African, East African, Caucasian and Asian races all display many physical differences as a consequence to suit the environment they have lived in.

As a general rule, West-African athletes tend to be black-skinned and well-muscled, whereas East African athletes, although also black-skinned, have a narrower skeletal frame and a leaner muscle structure.

Caucasian athletes tend to have a light skin colour, a lighter hair colour and a fairly muscular frame. Asian athletes, on the other hand, tend to have black hair, darker skin (but not black) and a smaller physical frame than Caucasians.

Why all these racial differences occur is probably as a consequence of the processes of mutation, natural selection and genetic drift, and of course, geographical separation.

Muscle fibre types

East African athletes win approximately 50 per cent of endurance races in the world of elite athletics. Research has proven that the majority of East Africans living at altitude are born with a high number of slow-twitch muscle fibres. In all, 70–75 per cent of their muscle fibres are slow-twitch. The interesting point from a physiological viewpoint is that many of these athletes trace their ancestry to the 2,000–3,000-metre altitude highlands of the East African Great Rift Valley. Therefore, evolution has granted East African athletes a distinct physiological advantage when it comes to competing in endurance events as, their cardiovascular systems are able to function efficiently using air that has a lower oxygen pressure.

Many West Africans, on the other hand, trace their ancestry to low-lying areas towards the Atlantic coastal regions. Consequently, they have far fewer slow-twitch muscle fibres but a higher concentration of fast-twitch muscle fibres, which are ideal for explosive events such as sprinting.

Body composition

Key Terms

Endomorph Somatotype characterised by a rounded body shape and a predominance of fat, especially in the abdominal and lower body region.

Mesomorph Somatotype characterised by a stocky appearance, of medium height with well-developed skeletal muscles.

Ectomorph Somatotype characterised by a tall, thin and linear body construction.

(a) Endomorph

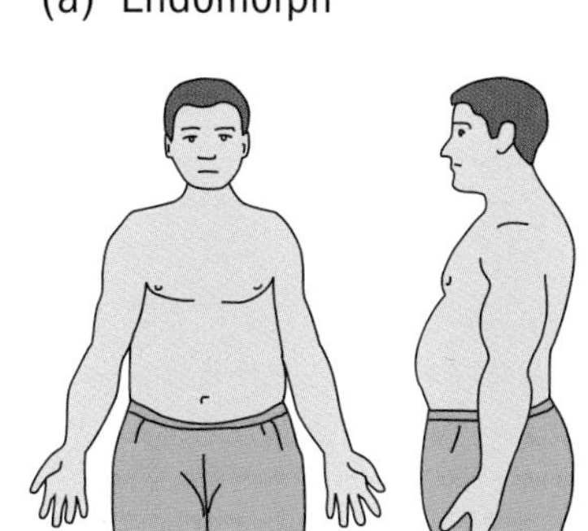

(b) Mesomorph

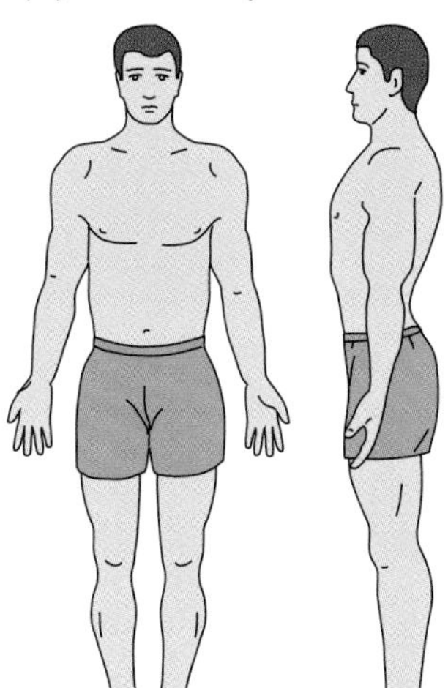

(c) Ectomorph

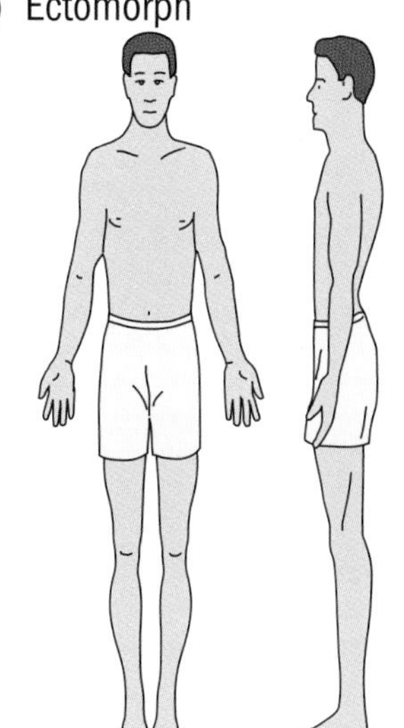

The three somatotypes: (a) endomorph, (b) mesomorph, and (c) ectomorph are basic classifications of human body types according to the prominence of different tissue types: digestive, muscular and nervous

Given his East African ancestry, Wilson Kipketer's body composition is largely ectomorphic – this gives him a physiological advantage when it comes to endurance events

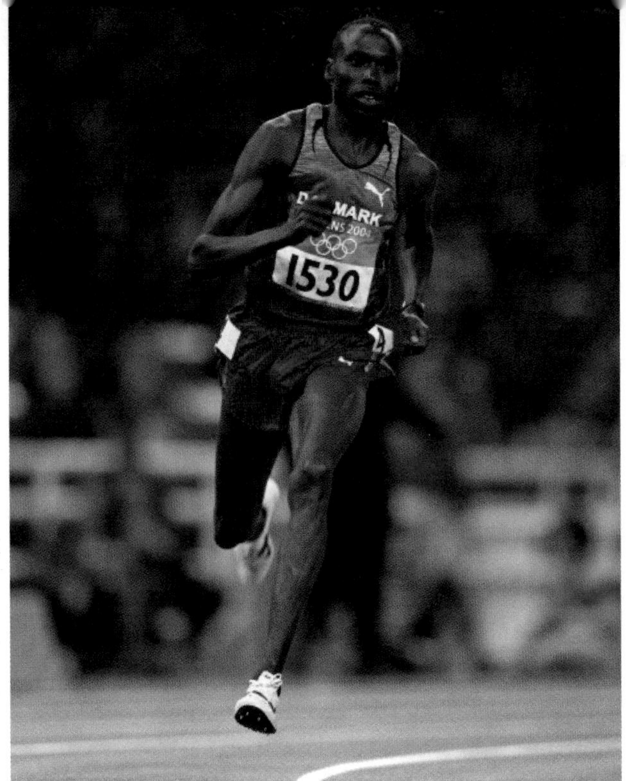

Body composition is often discussed in terms of somatotypes (see page 81). These describe the characteristic shape and physical appearance of an individual athlete, disregarding size.

The most common form of somatotyping used involves three types: endomorph, mesomorph and ectomorph. Typically, individuals are rated on a scale of 1 to 7 for each type, where 1 is a minimal rating and 7 is a maximal rating. The sequence of numbers this gives refers to components in the following order: endomorph, mesomorph and ectomorph. For example, looking at the photo of Wilson Kipketer, his somatotype rating would be approximately 2-4-5.

East African athletes tend to be ectomorphs, short in stature with long slender limbs. This makes them perfect for endurance events such as distance running. West Africans, on the other hand, tend to be mesomorphs, reasonably tall in stature with well-muscled limbs and torso, making them perfect for explosive events such as sprinting. Caucasians tend to fall in between ectomorph and mesomorph. They have upper-body strength, making them suitable for events such as weightlifting and field events. Asians tend to be similar to Caucasians in terms of body composition, only smaller. Their more ectomorphic build allows them to excel in events where flexibility is key, such as springboard diving and gymnastics.

Activity

1 In groups, identify the somatotype rating for members in your class using a copy of the table below. Remember that 1 is a minimal rating while 7 is a maximal rating.

Name	Endomorph rating (1–7)	Mesomorph rating (1–7)	Ectomorph rating (1–7)	Chosen sport

2 Do their chosen sports match their body types?

Lung capacity and haemoglobin levels

Athletes of West African ancestry tend to have small and efficient lungs in comparison with East Africans. Kenyan success in endurance running probably has something to do with the fact that many Kenyan runners come from a high-altitude region. However, Kenyans from low altitudes tend not to do well in the classic long-distance events, so it is not necessarily about being Kenyan or originating from East African that contributes to success in endurance events. It seems to be more about living or having genetic ancestry in high altitude areas. For example, South Korea is increasingly becoming a force in endurance running. In the past athletes of Asian origin were not considered to be a threat to the East African dominance. However, much of South Korea is mountainous terrain at high altitude, so this is no longer the case.

Further proof of this is the emergence of Ecuadorian athletes as an endurance-running force. Ecuador is a high altitude country in South America. Given the propensity of athletes from altitude to assimilate oxygen in regions of low oxygen pressure, these athletes tend to have increased levels of haemoglobin. This is not the case for West African athletes and most Caucasian athletes, although Asian athletes from mountainous regions of China, Japan and Korea do so. Testament to this is their increasing success in endurance-based events.

Body type

Body types (somatotypes) are of course only generalised. However, a general thought is that West Africans tend to be squat and muscular (i.e. the classic mesomorph) whereas East Africans tend to be tall and slender (i.e. the classic ectomorph). Caucasians, on the other hand, tend to be a mixture (depending on where the particular Caucasian is descended from).

Remember!

Caucasian is a general racial description whereas West and East African are geographical indicators. Asians tend to be smaller than Caucasians.

Effects

Heat tolerance and cold tolerance

Heat retention is facilitated by having a short and muscular frame. This is the case in many northern European and north Asian regions, where the climate is predominantly cool. If you evolved in East Africa, where the environment is hot, then heat loss is facilitated by being long and lean or ectomorphic (see page 351).

Sprinting ability

All the sprinters who featured in the 100m final at the Athens Olympics in 2004 can trace their ancestry to West Africa. Yet despite their wealth of distance runners, the current Kenyan 100m record stands at 10.28 seconds, which ranks virtually nowhere.

Think it over

If a Kenyan is genetically pre-disposed to run 5,000m, why bother training to run 100m?

Most of the world record holders in the 100m event are of West African origin. The interesting point is that they also tend to be West African-Americans whose race has been mixed over the generations, either with Caucasians or American Indians. Therefore, it is not easy to categorically say whether being of West African descent is a factor in being able to sprint, or whether it is the inevitable mixed race of West African with either Caucasian or American Indian (or both) that has helped them become so fast.

Where is the evidence for this? If you examine the sprinters who achieved success, they all trained in the USA, Canada, the UK or the Caribbean. However, if you look at the West African countries where these successful sprinters' ancestors hail from, none of these countries (Nigeria, Ivory Coast, Ghana, etc.) have ever produced any world records or Olympic titles.

Explanations such as wealth and resources cannot be used as a reason for this lack of success, particularly as less wealthy countries such as Kenya and Ethiopia regularly produce world records and Olympic titles at distance events. Furthermore, Alan Wells, a Caucasian, won the 100m Olympic title as recently as 1980.

Prominent Asian countries such as China and Japan also produce many talented sprinters, so the fact that most of

▼ All eight finalists at the 100m at Athens can trace their racial ancestry to West Africa – is this a genetic coincidence or a social expectation?

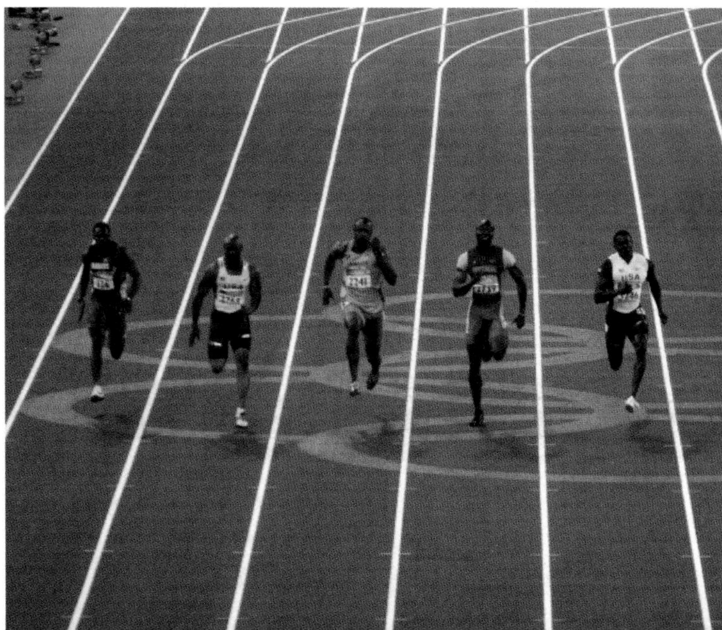

the world record holders in the 100m event are of West African origin may not be the case in future. Are our scientific assumptions based on race false? Only time will tell.

High-altitude tolerance

People who are indigenous to areas of high altitude, such as East Africa or countries like Bolivia, possess greater concentrations of haemoglobin in their blood. This allows these individuals to deliver a larger amount of oxygen to tissue under low oxygen pressure (at altitude). Consequently, it is believed these athletes have a greater aerobic capacity and, therefore, excel at endurance events.

Assessment practice

Following the success of the cricket tour to South Africa, the team has made excellent community links with local cricket clubs in Pretoria and Johannesburg. These clubs have asked if a number of their players might travel back to the UK to train here. The professional cricket team agreed and some 20 local players, mostly from surrounding township areas, are flying back with you to the UK.

The team manager has asked the sports scientist to give a brief speech to the coaching staff back in England as to the likely physiological differences between Caucasian and South or East African cricketers, and in particular the effects these differences are likely to have on performance.

Write a speech she might give. It should make reference to the following and how they might affect batting and bowling cricket performance:

- muscle fibre types
- body composition
- lung capacity
- body type
- environmental tolerance.

grading tips

Grading Tip 

You must be able to show a basic understanding when describing the physiological differences between athletes of different races and their effects on exercise and sports performance. Indicate which (if any) of the physiological differences between races will affect performance in cricket.

Grading Tip M2

The merit criteria demands a bit more from you in terms of the quality of what you produce as evidence and in terms of complexity, so pay attention to detail in your responses. Explaining the physiological differences between races requires that you can describe and explain in detail why and how these differences occur.

Grading Tip 

To be graded at distinction level means you can show an in-depth understanding, use appropriate terminology well and have a really thorough approach. Above all, you must analyse, which means showing you can break up the components of the question and respond to them with critical insight. In other words, you have the ability to see important points to do with racial differences that others might overlook, as well as identifying faults and making realistic suggestions as to how something could have been done better.

21.3 Understand the impact that the physiological effects of ageing have on exercise and sporting performance

Ageing is associated with an overall degenerative process that includes a reduction in muscular strength, weakening of the skeletal structure and longer reaction times. This process has an effect on exercise and physical performance at some point, although when this process begins and how rapidly it takes hold depends on the fitness levels of the individual concerned.

Key Terms

Atrophy Loss of mass or wasting away.

Osteoporosis Brittle bone disease caused by a decrease in bone mineral content.

Collagen fibres The most abundant of fibres found in the matrix of connective tissue.

Physiological effects of ageing

There is little doubt that the physiology and performance abilities of older people are markedly different from those of younger athletes. What is less clear, however, is whether or not these differences are due to natural biological processes, sociological constraints (such as diet) or the opportunity to exercise regularly.

During childhood, girls and boys follow similar growth patterns, resulting in similar amounts of muscle tissue, bone mass and body composition. From about seven to nine years of age, balance, coordination and agility begin to improve as the child's central nervous system develops.

Once a child reaches adolescence, sexual hormones (testosterone and oestrogen) regulate growth and development. Up until this point and regardless of gender, children have small hearts and vascular systems that result in a high resting heart rate, a small stroke volume, low haemoglobin levels and a low aerobic capacity. Children tend to have a high metabolic rate due to their larger surface area to mass ratio, resulting in greater heat loss compared with adults.

Children's flexibility decreases as they approach adolescence, as growth spurts result in increased muscle mass and bone size.

Once adolescents reach maturity, ageing affects individuals through changes in cell structure and organ function. From a physical peak of about 25 years old, there is a progressive and often marked deterioration in physical capabilities. This reduction in physical capabilities is usually as a consequence of a decrease in the efficiency of the body's major systems and how it adapts to exercise. The ageing process includes restricted joint flexibility and increases in body fat, muscle atrophy and osteoporosis.

Probably the most influential factor of ageing on the body is the formation of additional collagen fibres throughout major organs and skeletal muscles.

Maximum heart rate

Maximum heart rate decreases at an average rate of 1 or 2 beats per year. Furthermore, extra collagen fibres form between the muscles fibres of the heart. This has the effect of reducing the heart's elasticity and stroke volume. A rough approximation of the change in maximal heart rate with age is expressed by the following formula:

maximum heart rate = 220 – age (in years)

Therefore, the older a person gets, the lower their maximum heart rate will be. This lower heart rate means that maximum cardiac output is also reduced. Contributing to this reduced blood flow is the reduction in the heart's stroke rate (as discussed above).

Whether or not these changes (which readily occur) are as a direct result of the ageing process or as a

Key Terms

Peripheral resistance Resistance to blood flow offered by arterioles.

Systolic pressure Pressure when the heart contracts.

Arteriosclerosis Hardening of the artery walls.

consequence of modern living and sedentary lifestyles is a topic of considerable debate. That debate currently points to both theories.

Age also affects an athlete's blood pressure. A normal blood pressure reading for a healthy adult is 120/80mm Hg (see page 149). However, arterioles are known to lose their elasticity with age and this raises peripheral resistance (collective resistance of the thousands of arterioles in the body). Therefore, the pressure generated by cardiac output remains high. This can lead to high systolic levels of blood pressure as the heart has to apply extra force to propel the blood around stiffened arterioles. Regular exercise can lower these effects, probably as a result of a decrease in peripheral resistance as the circulation becomes more efficient in response to regular exercise.

Age-related stiffening of the arterioles can lead to a condition known as arteriosclerosis, which reduces the blood supply to vital organs and almost certainly reduces an individual's exercise capabilities. Symptoms of arteriosclerosis include an elevated heart rate and increased systolic blood pressure.

Lung volumes

Extra collagen fibres form in the lungs decreases elasticity, which reduces lung volumes. Therefore, the respiratory system's ability to carry out gaseous exchange, especially under heavy exercise workloads, is reduced.

Flexibility

As an athlete ages, the cross-linkages between the collagen fibres increase. This results in a stiffening throughout the body's skeletal muscles and tendons. This stiffening is as a result of the muscle sheaths becoming thicker and stiffer.

Key Term

Sarcopenia Loss of muscle mass.

By the time we reach 30, a loss of muscle mass known as sarcopenia occurs, as muscle proteins start to degrade more rapidly than they can be replaced. Because skeletal muscle forms much of an athlete's body mass, lean body weight and muscle strength decline in tandem with the sarcopenia.

Thermoregulation

The ability to cope with moderate temperature change as you get older does not deteriorate markedly with age. In fact, some research has indicated that the onset of age sometimes assists with acclimatisation involving heat toleration. However, age is a limiting factor during vigorous exercise in heat due to an apparent delay in sweating.

Impacts

Training

Key Term

Osteoarthritis The degeneration of articular (hyaline) cartilage, which may also affect the bones of the joint, causing pain and stiffness.

Regular exercise helps reverse sarcopenia. Those who previously did not undertake much exercise when younger often witness an increase in muscle mass and muscular strength when they begin training seriously during middle age.

Remember!

Exercise is a potent stimulator of bone deposition, which increases both bone mass and density. This delays the onset of diseases such as osteoarthritis and osteoporosis.

Recovery periods

Generally speaking, the impact of ageing on recovery periods is determined largely by the physical condition of the athlete. The ageing process affects a number of key physiological processes.

- There is a reduction in the ability to synthesise protein results in a loss of lean muscle mass. This loss reduces the basal metabolic rate (BMR). Therefore, although there is no increase in food intake, body fat levels are likely to rise. When combined, both these factors mean that smaller muscles have less capacity to store glycogen and will have to work with more intensity to exercise a body containing increased fat levels. The results of this are that glycogen levels are likely to be depleted more readily so the recovery process, as the muscles refuel, is likely to take longer.
- A loss of nerve cells in the brain affects all aspects of body movement, so the ageing process is likely to result in a decrease in the control of complex motor units. This, in turn, places more burden on the reduced skeletal muscle mass and further depletes their energy sources due to their increased inefficiency. Again, glycogen levels are likely to be depleted more readily so the recovery process, as the muscle refuel, is likely to be longer.

Key Terms

Basal metabolic rate (BMR) Energy demand of the body at rest.

Motor units Muscle fibres supplied (innervated) by a single motor neurone which either directly or indirectly controls the muscle movement.

The process of ageing and its effects of exercise, particularly recovery, is a controversial area of study and one that requires more research. However, based on the facts, there is evidence to suggest that the ageing process does result in a decline in the body's mechanism to cope with exercise and recovery. On the other hand, steady-state exercise of the correct type can at least partially overcome these affects.

Aerobic and anaerobic capacity

The onset of age has a significant impact on an athlete's aerobic capacity. As you get older, your maximum heart rate decreases. As the stroke volume lessens, an increase in resting heart rate is necessary to satisfy the needs of the cardiovascular system. This is further hampered by the probable hardening of the arteries, which increases the resting systolic blood pressure. When taking these factors into account, recovery after exercise is bound to take longer.

The onset of age also impairs the ability of the body to utilise oxygen. VO_2 maximum reaches its peak for an athlete between the ages of 18 and 25 years. After age 25, the VO_2 maximum declines steadily so that by the age of 55, an individual's VO_2 maximum will have declined by approximately 25 per cent.

However, as research into this area progresses, it is becoming apparent that those undertaking physical activity – whether recreationally or at an elite level – are more likely to maintain a healthy VO_2 maximum than those individuals who do not. There is, therefore, an increasing argument in favour of the long-term effects of physical exercise and less of an emphasis on the ageing process. Nevertheless, the ageing process still has a significant impact on the abilities of an individual.

Anaerobic capacity does not escape the ageing process either. The decline in anaerobic abilities includes muscle and strength atrophy and a shift towards a greater concentration of slow-twitch fibres. A thinning of the myelinated sheaths around muscle tissue also lengthens reaction times.

Overheating

Overheating is likely to occur in hot conditions if the athlete is dehydrated. However, there is no definitive link between age and an increased risk of dehydration leading to hyperthermia, so the likelihood of an older athlete overheating before a younger athlete, whatever the circumstances, is minimal.

Overheating (hyperthermia) is an advanced stage of heat or sun stroke during which the body absorbs more heat than it can dissipate. It usually occurs as a result of over-exposure to excessive heat, especially in competition. The heat-controlling mechanisms of the body eventually become overwhelmed and unable to deal with the heat appropriately. As a consequence, the body temperature elevates to dangerous level.

Assessment practice

Following the sports scientist's successful input onto her recent South African tour, the professional cricket club has raised its profile within the UK and now has enough interest to field a veteran team of players aged over 40 to play in a national league.

The head coach has asked her to assist the veterans' team manager (recently promoted from the under-18s team) by compiling a short guide that describes the physiological effects of ageing on sports performance. Her report should be fairly brief as the team manager has asked for something he can hand out to his players. He suggests a double-sided piece of A4, with the text in bullet-point format, which can be laminated. Produce a report which she might compile herself. **P5 M3 D2**

Produce a report which she might compile herself.

grading tips

Grading Tip 

You must be able to describe the impact of the physiological effects of ageing on exercise and sports performance. Indicate which (if any) of the physiological effects may prove to be a cause for concern when playing cricket.

Grading Tip M3

The merit criteria demands a bit more from you in terms of the quality of what you produce as evidence and in terms of complexity, so pay attention to detail in your responses. Explain the impact of the physiological effects of ageing on cricketing performance, but bear in mind that a certain amount of tact may be required in your report, given those reading it may well be affected by some of those impacts themselves.

Grading Tip D2

To be graded at distinction level means you can show an in-depth understanding, use appropriate terminology well and have a really thorough approach. Above all, you must analyse, which means showing you can break up the components of the question and respond to them with critical insight. In other words, you have the ability to see important points to do with ageing that others might overlook, as well as identifying faults and making realistic suggestions as to how to accommodate the affects of ageing.

21.4 Understand the effects and implications of using ergogenic aids for exercise and sports performance

Key Term

Ergogenic aids Supplements or substances that enhance or improve athletic performance.

Ergogenic aids are any method or factor which enhances exercise and sports performance. They are often thought of as performance-enhancing drugs, but they also include everyday items such as vitamins and minerals, and psychological techniques such as mental rehearsal or playing music.

Ergogenic aids

Athletes and coaches are continually searching for ways to gain a competitive advantage to improve athletic performance. It is therefore unsurprising that ergogenic aids are marketed and sold to athletes of all levels. The sheer range of ergogenic aids available today is vast. Some are commercially available and perfectly legal, others are available on prescription only, while others are illegal and their use and possession may result in criminal investigation. In response to the legal issue and the moral arguments surrounding cheating or doping, the International Olympic Committee (IOC) has formulated the list in the table opposite, which divides banned or illegal drugs into categories.

Many athletes today are vulnerable to the advertising claims that supplements enhance performance. Therefore, it is wise to examine the evidence of some of the most popular supplements and ergogenic aids currently available.

Vitamin and mineral supplementation is a common practice among athletes and the general population. There is little evidence to suggest that this enhances the performance of an athlete consuming a regular and balanced diet. However, athletes who participate in sports with strict weight categories are prone to dieting, weight loss and nutritional deficiency. This is particularly true for females who need to take into account both iron and calcium intakes to counteract anaemia and osteoporosis. Therefore, vitamin and mineral supplementation is important to ensure a balanced diet rather than an improvement in performance.

Banned or illegal drugs

Drug type	Examples
Anabolic agents	Anabolic steroids (see page 360)
Peptide hormones	Human growth hormone, EPO and insulin (see pages 360–362)
Diuretics	Caffeine (see page 361) and slimming agents
Masking agents	Blood doping (see page 361)
Drugs subject to restriction	Beta blockers (see page 363)
Stimulants	Amphetamines (see page 363)
Narcotics	Codeine and morphine
Anti-oestrogen agents	Tamoxifen

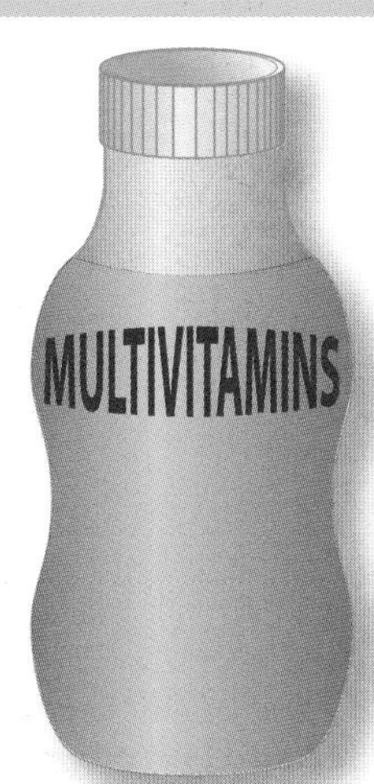

The benefits of vitamin and mineral supplementation depend on the nutritional value of an athlete's diet and their levels of physical activity

In addition to protein-containing foods, many strength athletes supplement their diets with amino acids, especially those believed to be associated with the release of growth hormone such as arginine. Amino acids are the building blocks of proteins and muscle tissue. Strength athletes supplement their diets in the belief that amino acids will supplement any shortfall in their protein intake and continue to develop or sustain muscle tissue. Amino acids are perfectly legal although most sports nutritionists maintain that an athlete consuming a well-balanced diet should never to take amino acid supplements. Over-consumption may lead to health risks, particularly as amino acids are toxic when taken in excess.

Anabolic steroids

Key Term

Anabolic Changes include the growth and development of body tissue, most notably muscle tissue.

Today's world of highly paid athletes is a short-lived one. Society loves a winner and the rewards available to them are huge, both socially and financially. It is perhaps unsurprising that many athletes resort to performance-enhancing products if it means that extra chance of success, regardless of whether or not they are legal.

The effects of anabolic steroids are designed to mimic the effects of testosterone (the male sex hormone). Testosterone is produced in both the male testes and the female ovaries, although it is present in much higher concentrations in men than women. The anabolic properties of steroids include the growth and development of many body tissues, perhaps most obvious being muscle tissue.

Use of anabolic steroids may lead to temporary infertility in males, the suppression of sex hormones and an impairment of sperm production.

Common examples of anabolic steroids include:

- nandrolone decanoate
- testosterone
- stanozolol
- methandrostenolone.

During the 1988 Olympics in Seoul, Ben Johnson was crowned 100m champion, smashing the world record as he powered to victory in a time of 9.79 seconds. Shortly afterwards he gave a urine sample that proved positive for stanozolol, an anabolic steroid. He was later stripped of his medal, the title and his time was erased from the record books.

Ben Johnson produced his now infamous 1988 Olympic 100-metre final run fuelled by anabolic steroids and was subsequently disqualified; might other sprinters do the same if they thought they could get away with it?

Severe penalties are imposed by the IOC and many other sports bodies if anabolic steroids are detected. The penalties of a positive drugs test may have serious repercussions for both the athlete concerned and the public image of the sport. In the past, anabolic steroids have been frequently associated with strength-related sports such as weightlifting. However, the current extent of anabolic steroid use extends to sports such as swimming, cycling and sprinting.

The actual level of use of anabolic steroids is hard to pin down given the legal implications of both their possession and use (depending on which country you live in). However, according to a report called 'Commission of Inquiry into the Use of Drugs and Banned Practices Intended to Increase Athletic Performance' in 1990, at least 40 per cent of the US women's team in Seoul in the 1988 Olympics had probably used steroids at some time in their preparation.

Growth hormone

Human growth hormone, also known as somatropin, is a hormone secreted by the pituitary gland. Growth hormone affects the growth of almost every organ and every type of tissue found in the human body. It has been proven to cause an increase in protein synthesis, producing an anabolic effect. Growth hormone also has a further use in a sports context. It stimulates the synthesis of fat as a source of energy, thus sparing muscle glycogen.

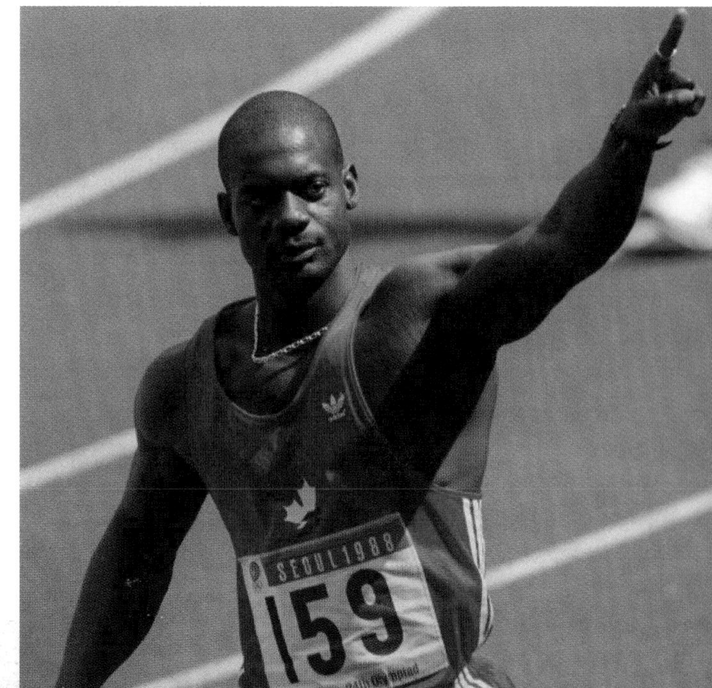

Athletes using growth hormone as a performance-enhancing drug do so to increase their size and strength. However, side effects have included skeletal changes, enlargement of internal organs, the development of diabetes and a thickening and coarsening of the skin.

Traditionally, human growth hormone was extracted from the pituitary glands of bodies donated to science after death. However, a number of cases of Creutzfeldt-Jakob disease (CJD) developed following treatment using human growth hormone extracted by this method. Consequently, most human growth hormone available today (on prescription or illegally) is genetically engineered.

Human growth hormone is often taken by athletes also using anabolic steroids and is banned by the IOC.

Creatine

Key Term

Creatine phosphate An energy-rich compound used in the production of ATP from ADP in muscle cells.

In sports such as sprinting, the rate of ATP resynthesis is more important than the capacity for energy production. The rapid resynthesis of ATP occurs as a result of the degradation of creatine phosphate. Creatine supplementation is perfectly legal. It is believed to increase the resynthesis of creatine phosphate, resulting in an increased capacity to perform explosive or strength-related exercises more efficiently. The source of most natural creatine is from foods such as meat and fish. However, creatine monohydrate is the supplement used and 1g is the equivalent to the creatine content in 1kg of fresh meat.

Insulin

Insulin is a hormone that stimulates the liver, muscles and fat cells to remove glucose from the blood for use or storage. Insulin production falls during strenuous exercise. However, in trained athletes, it does not fall as much during exercise as in untrained athletes. This allows more energy to be derived from free fatty acids. Consequently, injecting insulin prior to exercise can enhance endurance-based competition and is therefore banned by the IOC.

Caffeine

Caffeine is one of the most common and frequently used stimulants currently available. It is found at various levels of potency in tea, coffee and many soft drinks. Caffeine is also a common addition to cold and flu remedies.

Despite being freely available and not in any way illegal, caffeine is a potent and potentially addictive drug and is banned in large quantities by the IOC. Its use has been linked to a number of adverse effects including tremors, anxiety headaches and cramps. The performance-enhancing effects include an increase in heart rate, stroke volume, cardiac output and blood pressure, an increase in alertness and a decrease in the perception of fatigue. Caffeine is also proven to increase the contractile nature of skeletal muscle and metabolic rate. Other research has suggested that caffeine may enhance the utilisation of fats, thus sparing glycogen stores. This overall effect could increase the performance of endurance athletes.

Blood doping

An increasingly popular form of ergogenic aid is blood doping. This involves injecting red blood cells to enhance the blood's aerobic system.

The method is actually quite simple and involves the athlete donating blood (1–2 litres depending on body size) prior to training or competition. This blood is then frozen and kept in storage. In response to this loss of blood, the body replaces those red blood cells by way of natural reaction. However, immediately prior to training or competition, the athlete receives the stored blood by venous injection, thus raising the total red blood cell count in his or her body.

The disadvantages of blood doping are extensive. Despite the possible risk of infection, blood clotting is a heightened risk, especially if the athlete becomes dehydrated during the event.

British cyclist David Millar was convicted of doping offences (including EPO) a few months before the start of the 2004 Tour de France and served a two-year-ban

This injection (or doping) raises the red blood cell count well above normal and temporarily increases the oxygen-carrying capacity of the blood. This is highly advantageous for endurance-based events. Blood doping is a process that is banned by the IOC, although artificial blood boosting is difficult to detect.

rhEPO

Also known as erythropoietin, EPO is the hormone responsible for red blood cell production and produced in the kidneys. Although EPO has benefited many anaemia suffers, it has also been used as a blood doping agent to give healthy athletes a competitive advantage. EPO works by increasing the oxygen-carrying capacities of blood, which improves the aerobic respiratory capacity of skeletal muscles. EPO has been popular with professional cyclists and long-distance runners, but it its use is forbidden by the IOC.

rhEPO (recombinant human erythropoietin) has been used by athletes to artificially raise the blood cell count and therefore increase their oxygen-carrying capacity. While giving athletes a distinct advantage, rhEPO can be dangerous as it increases the viscosity of the blood and blood pressure. Both these symptoms can lead to heart failure or stroke. Consequently, rhEPO is on the IOC's banned substance list.

Altitude training

Altitude training is a practice used by some endurance athletes to gain a future competitive edge.

Altitude training works by the body adapting to the lack of oxygen available at over 2,000 metres by increasing the concentration of red blood cells and haemoglobin levels in the blood.

When these athletes then return to sea level to compete, they maintain the higher concentration of red blood cells for approximately two weeks. This concentration of red blood cells allows more oxygen to be supplied to the muscles, allowing for improved performance.

Glycogen loading

Glycogen loading (also known as carbohydrate loading) is a method used by endurance athletes to maximise the storage of glycogen in skeletal muscles.

Glycogen loading involves increased carbohydrate intake (in the form of pasta, rice and cereals) and decreased training for approximately three days prior to competition. Glycogen loading is based on a regular, controlled diet and is perfectly legal.

Key Terms

Hypertension High blood pressure, which is when systolic blood pressure is above 140mm Hg and diastolic pressure is above 90mm Hg.

Cardiac arrhythmia Irregular heart beat.

Migraine A severe headache.

Adrenaline A hormone that elevates heart and respiration rates.

Noradrenaline A hormone that is often referred to as a 'fight or flight' chemical. It is responsible for the body's reaction to stressful situations.

Beta blockers

Beta blockers are used to treat a wide range of medical conditions such as hypertension, cardiac arrhythmias and migraines.

Beta blockers work by preventing adrenaline and noradrenaline from exerting their effects on the body. This has the affect of reducing anxiety and muscle tremor.

Beta blockers can enhance performance in certain sports such as archery, shooting and diving, so they are on the IOC's list of banned substances. However, beta blockers are unlikely to enhance endurance events, which require prolonged periods of high cardiac output. In these cases, beta blockers would severely decrease performance capacity.

Common examples of beta blockers include:

- acebutolol
- atenolol
- nadolol
- propranolol.

Marijuana

The effects of marijuana include decreased motivation for physical activity, decreased motor coordination and changes in perception. Persistent use of marijuana is incompatible with serious sport participation because it tends to demotivate athletes, taking away their will to win. Marijuana is not on the IOC's list of banned substances but it is prohibited by the governing bodies of some sports and is illegal in the UK.

Amphetamines

Amphetamines are a class of synthetic stimulant drugs invented to suppress appetite. Amphetamines are powerful stimulants of the central nervous system, producing feelings of euphoria, alertness, mental clarity and increased energy. The implications for most sports are obvious, and the effects on an athlete would prove far-reaching for events ranging from football to track and field.

The disadvantages of amphetamines are an increased heart rate and blood pressure, together with nausea and fatigue once the effects have worn off. Amphetamines are on the IOC's banned list and their possession is illegal in the UK.

The Tour de France of 1967 witnessed the death of British cyclist Tommy Simpson. A post-mortem examination found that Simpson had taken amphetamines and alcohol.

Cocaine

Cocaine has significant effects on mood. These affect levels of friendliness, arousal, elation and positive mood states. Cocaine also has a significant effect on the brain, which includes increased activity at the neural synapses. Consequently, if cocaine is used repeatedly, the effects on behaviour can become exaggerated. Cocaine is a Class A drug in the UK, so possession is illegal. In addition, it is classed as stimulant and is therefore on the IOC's banned list.

Advantages

Decreased heart rate

A decrease in heart rate is likely to be beneficial to sports requiring fine motor skills and prolonged levels of concentration. Beta blockers work by preventing adrenaline and noradrenaline from exerting their effects on the body and the heart in particular. However, events requiring prolonged periods of cardiac output are likely to be severely hindered by taking beta blockers.

Decreased recovery time

A decreased recovery time is beneficial to any athlete as it means he or she can either compete or train much sooner than predicted. Glycogen loading will replace that used during training, but whether or not this can significantly decrease recovery time is debatable.

However, certain anabolic steroids (such as nandrolone decanoate) are known to invigorate exercised muscle so that they feel less sore or fatigued after exercise. Other ergogenic aids such as rhEPO have the ability to increase an athlete's blood cell count. This means oxygen and nutrients are able to reach the fatigued muscles and cells far quicker post-exercise.

Increased mobilisation of fatty acids

Substances such as caffeine, insulin and human growth hormone are believed to increase the mobilisation of fatty acids. This allows for a more plentiful supply of energy from the fatty acids, placing less dependence on glycogen, both of which can enhance endurance-based activities.

Disadvantages

Heart palpitations

Substances such as amphetamines and cocaine can induce heart palpitations – a rapid series of heartbeats (tachycardia) that are generally accompanied by other symptoms including sweating, faintness, dizziness or even chest pains. Palpitations are likely to be detrimental to any form of exercise and the likely benefits of taking ergogenic aids such as caffeine or cocaine (not least because the latter is illegal) are likely to be outweighed by the symptoms of heart palpitations.

Reduced fertility

Anabolic steroids in most forms are proven to reduce fertility in certain circumstances. The use of anabolic steroids may lead to the temporary infertility in males, the suppression of sex hormones and an impairment of sperm production.

Assessment practice

The fitness coach of your local cricket team is concerned about the recent press reports of professional cricketers testing positive for banned performance-enhancing substances. He has asked your opinion on how to approach the team to let them know the dangers of such substances.

He asks you to prepare a short presentation, educating the players on the variety of ergogenic aids available. The presentation should explain which aids the cricketers should never consider taking and which may be beneficial. You agree to prepare a brief PowerPoint presentation on the following.

1 Banned ergogenic aids:
   - anabolic steroids
   - rhEPO
   - amphetamines.
2 Approved ergogenic aids:
   - creatine
   - altitude training
   - glycogen loading.

grading tips

Grading Tip 

You must be able to show a basic understanding when describing the effects and implications of the six ergogenic aids. Say what the effects on performance of these individual ergogenic aids are on cricket performance and describe the likely side-effects.

Grading Tip 

The merit criteria demands a bit more from you in terms of the quality of what you produce as evidence and in terms of complexity, so pay attention to detail in your responses. Explaining the effects and implications of the six ergogenic aids and their implications on cricket performance means that you can describe and explain in detail why and how these differences occur.

Grading Tip 

To be graded at distinction level means you can show an in-depth understanding, use appropriate terminology well and have a really thorough approach. Above all, you must analyse, which means showing you can break up the components of the question and respond to them with critical insight. In other words, you have the ability to see important points to do with ergogenic aids that others might overlook, such as why people are prepared to risk being caught or even damage themselves in the pursuit of improved performance.

Knowledge check

1. What is normal human body temperature?
2. What effects does altitude have on blood?
3. List three physiological differences between males and females that might affect sports participation.
4. List the racial background or ancestry of the last three Olympic gold medalists (both male and female) for the following events: 100m; 1500m; marathon; archery.
5. Explain why an increase in collagen fibres due to ageing might affect sports performance.
6. Explain why an athlete from the highlands of Kenya is likely to beat an athlete from the lowlands of Nigeria in a long-distance running event.
7. At what points of the temperature scale in degrees Celius (both hot and cold) would you expect athletes not to be able to perform their sports effectively?
8. Make the case why females make better long-distance swimmers than males.
9. List six different types of anabolic steroids (medical or commercial names) and explain why they are banned by the IOC.
10. List the possible side effects of taking:
    - a large amounts of caffeine
    - b amphetamines.

Preparation for assessment

Following her success with the professional cricket team, the sports scientist's knowledge and ability as a sport and exercise physiologist have come to the attention of the cricketing governing body. It was so impressed with her input during the tour to South Africa and her ability to pass on complex knowledge to the coaching staff and management team that it has asked her to produce a CD-ROM for all qualified cricket coaches.

Design a CD-ROM she might use to educate all the cricket coaches on the basic principles of applied sport and exercise physiology. It should contain four sections.

1 How temperature and altitude affect exercise and sporting performance. **P1 P2**

2 The physical differences between people of different gender and race and their affect on exercise and sporting performance. **P3 P4 M1 M2 D1**

3 The impact that the physiological effects of ageing have on exercise and sporting performance. **P5 M3 D2**

4 The effects and implications of using six different ergogenic aids for exercise and sports performance. **P6 M4 D3**

The cricketing governing body has asked that your CD-ROM takes the form of a PowerPoint presentation rather than a written report. It is designed as an educational tool to complement a coach's education and development. If it proves a success, it could well be marketed to other sports. The presentation should be brief and consist of no more than 20 slides (a maximum of five slides per section).

If possible, your slides should make use of pictures to further illustrate the points being made. The actual reading time of the CD-ROM presentation should be no more than 30 minutes, and is designed to be viewed primarily when coaches are travelling or at training camps with minimal facilities such as laptops.

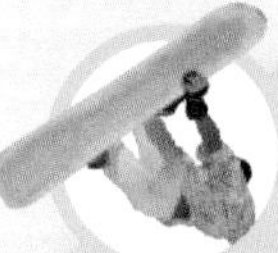

Grading Tip **P1 P2**

Ensure your CD-ROM describes how the body responds to high and low temperatures and how these changes affect aerobic and anaerobic sporting performance. You also need to describe how the body responds to high altitude and how competing at altitude affects aerobic and anaerobic performance.

Grading Tip **P3 P4 M1 M2 D1**

Your CD-ROM should describe, explain and analyse the range of physiological differences between genders and races. You need to discuss how these physiological differences can affect aerobic and anaerobic sporting performance.

Grading Tip **P5 M3 D2**

Describe, explain and analyse the physiological effects of ageing. Try to explore a range of ages including pre-adolescence, adolescence, adults and the over 50s.

Grading criteria

To achieve a pass grade the evidence must show that the learner is able to:	To achieve a merit grade the evidence must show that, in addition to the pass criteria, the learner is able to:	To achieve a distinction grade the evidence must show that, in addition to the pass and merit criteria, the learner is able to:
P1 describe the responses of the body to temperature, and their effects on performance **Assessment practice pages 343, 366**		
P2 describe the responses of the body to high altitude, and their effects on performance **Assessment practice pages 343, 366**		
P3 describe the physiological differences between athletes of different genders, and their effects on performance **Assessment practice pages 347, 366**	**M1** explain the effects of the physiological differences between athletes of different genders on performance **Assessment practice pages 347, 366**	**D1** analyse the effects of the physiological differences between athletes of different genders and races on performance **Assessment practice pages 347, 354, 366**
P4 describe the physiological differences between athletes of different races, and their effects on performance **Assessment practice pages 354, 366**	**M2** explain the effects of the physiological differences between athletes of different races on performance **Assessment practice pages 354, 366**	
P5 describe the physiological effects of ageing on performance **Assessment practice pages 358, 366**	**M3** explain the physiological effects of ageing performance **Assessment practice pages 358, 366**	**D2** analyse the physiological effects of ageing on performance **Assessment practice pages 358, 366**
P6 understand the effects and implications of six ergogen aids, their effects on performance, and their side effects **Assessment practice pages 364, 366**	**M4** describe and explain in detail why and how these differences occur **Assessment practice pages 364, 366**	**D3** analyse why and how these differences occur **Assessment practice pages 364, 366**

22 Exercise for specific groups

Introduction

There has been an increase over the last decade of health awareness in the UK and the government has recommended that all segments of the population increase their awareness of the benefits of exercise and their physical well-being.

There are many specific groups in our society who have special needs when exercising. In this unit you will learn about these groups, and the special organisations who provide exercise for them. You will research and explore the provision of exercise for these specific groups, including prenatal, post-natal, older adults, disabled people, children and young people, and also clients referred for exercise by health professionals.

As you know, exercise has many benefits, but the type of exercise you may do can differ greatly from the exercise activities undertaken by an older adult. This unit will explain the benefits of exercise for a wide variety of people and help you to plan and deliver a practical session for a specific group.

After completing this unit you should be able to achieve the following outcomes:

- know about the provision of exercise for specific groups
- understand the benefits of exercise for different specific groups
- know about exercise referral schemes
- be able to plan and deliver an exercise session for a specific group.

Think it over

You are working in a leisure centre and a client suffering from arthritis/osteoporosis has been referred for treatment. You have been asked to plan and deliver an exercise programme that the client can follow safely and effectively.

- What do you need to consider?
- What exercise programme would benefit this client?
- How will you monitor the client's progress?
- What long-term plans would you recommend to the client?

22.1 Know about the provision of exercise for specific groups

Groups can be divided into different categories depending on the age, condition and physical ability of the people within the group.

You are now going to learn about some of these groups and who will make the provision of exercise.

Specific groups

Disabled people

A person may be disabled because they have an injury, illness or impairment, or they may find something in society that stops them from taking part in a sports-related activity. Some people may have an impairment that, for example, means they require a wheelchair: but this person may still be able to exercise effectively and independently. However, there may be obstacles in their environment, such as steps leading into a sports area, which stops them or makes it more difficult to access sports-related activities.

You may have heard of the following terms:

- wheelchair bound – someone who needs to use a wheelchair to become mobile
- visually impaired – someone who is blind or partially sighted
- hearing impaired – someone who is deaf or has limited hearing
- physically impaired – someone who has a physical disability
- learning impairment – someone with a learning disability.

People with disabilities have a wide variety of exercise needs depending on the individual. Having knowledge of their needs will require you to have specialist knowledge. You will gain this from learning and by listening and being sensitive to the needs of the individual.

Activity

Make a list of the type of clients who may be classed as disabled. This will help you to understand the type of person for whom you may have to plan an exercise programme.

Prenatal

The prenatal group is for pregnant women. The prenatal period is from conception to birth. Exercise during pregnancy helps women to stay healthy and keep their weight gain within a safe range. However, there are certain restrictions on what kind of exercise they should do to keep them and their baby safe. Their pregnancy can be divided into three parts:

- first trimester (3 months pregnancy)
- second trimester (4–6 months pregnancy)
- the third trimester (7–9 months pregnancy).

All pregnancies are different; some women are very healthy and others have problems. Women who were very active before pregnancy can often continue their exercise programme, but will need to make changes to the intensity level and duration. Those who did not exercise regularly before will want to start slowly. Women will be advised by their doctors, and those who have a medical condition affecting their pregnancy (for example, miscarriage or premature labour) must be very careful about which activities they choose.

Activity

In groups, research the three terms listed below. These will be important when planning exercise activities and programmes for a prenatal group:

- hypertension
- premature labour
- miscarriage.

Post-natal

In a post-natal group, women have just had their babies. They will have extra demands on them. Many women will be breastfeeding and waking up in the middle of the night to look after their babies. Some women have trouble bringing their abdomen back to its original tone and size after having a baby. Certain exercises can help their abdomen return to its original size, but it is important to remember that their bodies have changed through having a baby.

For example, you would not expect a woman who has had a Caesarean section to exercise at the same level as someone who has had a natural birth. A Caesarean is a major operation and, therefore, in the early days after the birth the woman will only be allowed breathing exercises and gentle leg movements. A study in the USA found that women are full of good intentions about getting into shape after birth. However, results showed that they become more sedentary, with leisure time activities dropping by 14 per cent. Post-natal exercises can usually be started after the six week check-up (with permission from the health practitioner).

Think it over

Discuss why these two terms are commonly used for women who have recently given birth:

- baby blues
- urinary incontinence.

Older adults

Who do you think this group might include? Older people used to be defined as those who had reached retirement age or older. However, working patterns have changed and half of all working men in the UK are no longer in paid employment by the age of 61. Half of all working women have retired by the age of 51. If you think about older adults as being people of 50 years or over, then you can consider all those who have retired or no longer work.

It is also important to know that individuals do not grow old in the same way and, therefore, this group can have a wide variety of exercise needs. What you have inherited from your parents will play a part in how fit you are as you grow old. The list below gives you an idea of how many factors can affect the ageing process:

- gender
- nutrition
- disease
- smoking
- stress
- trauma
- inactivity
- living conditions.

The main providers for this specific group would be found at classes run by the local authority at leisure centres, within private health clubs, voluntary groups and partnerships. The range of activities is vast, but so too is the range of possible medical conditions, ability levels and interests of the clients.

Activity

1. In small groups, consider three of the above ageing factors and discuss why they would have an effect on the ageing process.
2. Once you are happy with your findings, present your results to the rest of the group using PowerPoint.

This group is defined as 4 to14-year-olds. There are a variety of points to consider about this group. Children have different body shapes. If a child is fat and muscular, then he or she may be taller and heavier than friends, and will mature earlier and so stop growing earlier. ten they will develop into shorter and more heavily built adults. A thin child will take longer to mature, but may develop into a taller adult.

Girls and boys also have different body shapes. Boys are larger than girls and usually have less body fat. Boys who mature early tend to be strong and more naturally able than those with average or delayed maturity. Girls who mature early are generally less naturally able in sport than those who are delayed in maturity (who tend to have leaner physiques). From this, you can understand that boys and girls show ability at different stages of development and it is the onset of puberty which begins these changes.

Think it over

Bring to class a photograph of yourself when you were between 8 and 12 years. Discuss how your body shape now relates to the image in your photograph.

▲ Children show sports ability at different stages of development

Referred clients

This group of people includes those who have been asked to join a fitness and exercise programme by their doctor or any other healthcare professional. There is a special process called the 'referral process', which introduces the referred client to trained people and facilities where structured and individually tailored physical activity programmes can be designed and delivered to them. There can be many reasons why someone is referred by a doctor or health specialist on to a referral programme. A person might have had a traffic accident or fall in the home. A doctor may refer a patient with a health problem on to an exercise programme and the patient would be known as a referred client. If someone had one of the problems below, then they might belong to this group:

- cardiovascular disease (high blood pressure)
- respiratory (asthma)
- neuromuscular (stroke, Parkinson's disease)
- musculoskeletal (osteoarthritis, rheumatoid arthritis, joint replacement, back pain)
- psychological/mental health (depression, stress, anxiety)
- metabolic/immunological (diabetes, osteoporosis, obesity).

All clients who are on a referral programme will have an initial appointment with an exercise consultant. Sessions will last from 45–60 minutes. The costs are low and each programme usually lasts for approximately 12 weeks.

Taking it further

Research in your locality any exercise establishments that offer referral programmes. This information could be obtained from your local leisure centre, clinic, local authority, private health clubs and care groups such as Age Concern.

Provision

Providers

Exercise for specific groups is provided through many channels. Providers may be found in the public, private and voluntary sector. You need to know what these terms mean and what provision is made by these sectors for your specific groups.

■ Public

Public sector organisations receive their funds from central and local government. Providers in this sector will be schools, local authority-run leisure centres, swimming pools, youth clubs and National Health Service (NHS) schemes.

■ Private

The private sector consists of commercially-run organisations that aim to make a profit. Under this heading you would find private health clubs, private leisure centres, physiotherapists, sports therapists, personal trainers, football clubs and rugby clubs.

Voluntary

Voluntary providers have charitable status and are run by volunteers, although some have paid employees. Voluntary organisations do not aim to make a profit and any profit is reinvested into the provider. An example of a voluntary provider is the YMCA. The YMCA offers many opportunities for young people with excellent facilities and coaches.

Partnerships

Partnerships occur when two or more of these providers come together. For example, football clubs in partnership with the FA have set up initiatives for young people and adults, and local authorities work in partnership with voluntary sector groups (such as the British Heart Foundation) to provide rehabilitation programmes for heart patients.

Policies in place for specific groups

What provision is made by these providers for identified specific groups?

Facilities

Sport England is responsible for developing government sporting policies and they work with local authorities, commercial organisations, the voluntary sector, health professionals, coaches and teachers. Sport England highlights exercise as the key to delivering a healthy nation.

There is an important link between health and sport. Physical activity is seen by the government and health professionals as a key preventative measure to ensure a healthy lifestyle. We must take care of our bodies from an early age. Children take part in sport for fun, adventure, challenge, achievement, socialising, competition, independence, release of energy and emotion. Facilities such as leisure centres, swimming pools, playing fields, parks, schools and clubs are provided for the use of identified specific groups.

The NHS provides facilities at, for example, hospitals, clinics and doctor's surgeries for exercise opportunities for prenatal and post-natal women. Exercise referral schemes will be held at facilities such as leisure centres, clinics and private health clubs.

The Pan Disability programme is funded by the FA, Regional FA officers and football clubs for people with disabilities. In 2005, Manchester FA established a County Disability Coaching Centre in partnership with Manchester United at Manchester United training ground. This coaching centre provides opportunities for children of primary school age, girls and boys at secondary schools and adults to take part in coaching and football leagues.

The FA and the Inclusive Fitness Initiative (IFI) is an example of a private sector provider which gives access to facilities for exercise. The IFI is spread across 150 sites over England and has been developed with the FA to support players with disabilities. This means that players will be able physically to access the facilities on offer and receive support and back up from specialist staff having received specific training.

Within the voluntary sector, the British Heart Foundation has linked up with schools to initiate a school project called the Active School Programme. This is an accreditation scheme for the primary sector. It recognises and rewards a school for its commitment to sport for promoting physical activity and offering good facilities and physical activity provision.

Classes

Exercise is provided in the form of classes for identified specific groups. The NHS provides schemes such as well-being classes, water aerobics, low impact aerobics, stretching, toning and breathing exercise classes for prenatal and post-natal women at leisure centres, swimming pools and clinics.

Private health clubs also provide prenatal and post-natal exercise classes, for example Pilates and Kegal exercises. Kegal exercises strengthen the group of muscles called the pelvic floor muscles, and classes are provided for women before and after pregnancy. The pelvic muscles become weakened during childbirth and this could lead to bladder control problems.

Yoga classes can be offered for women during pregnancy and these are provided at local leisure centres and privately by specialists in this field. Exercise on prescription classes are run for specific identified groups referred by their doctors to sports therapists/instructors who work at leisure centres or with other appropriate organisations. Children and young people may have classes provided through the Community Youth Provision (which is an initiative started in conjunction with Sport England), with the major aim being to increase the levels of sports participation and prevent inactivity and obesity in the young.

BUPA is a private health scheme which provides exercise opportunities for a variety of specific groups, for example well-being classes for prenatal, post-natal and older adults.

Classes are provided in mainstream sport. This is any sport which provides exercise provision for groups (including people with disabilities) depending on factors such as individual choice, level of ability, the sport involved and the opportunities available. Some sports may be adapted for people with disabilities.

Private health clubs provide initiatives such as walking groups, exercise on prescription, prenatal and post-natal classes, over 50s programmes, swimming, cycling and running.

Equipment

Fitness suites in leisure centres are fully equipped for exercise on referral schemes, both in machinery and personnel. Hospitals have specialist equipment for cardiac rehabilitation. Soccability is a programme whereby mainstream schools receive additional equipment aimed at providing teachers and coaches with options around the inclusion of young people with disabilities.

Range of activities

The range of activities offered to specific groups is extensive. Some local authorities provides an exercise referral scheme called Start Up. This is an example of exercise provision for referred clients and adults over 50. Referred clients can also include prenatal and post-natal groups. Exercise provision includes the following range of activities.

- Aqua mobility: this is low intensity exercise to music and takes place in water. The water is designed to help mobility and increase the range of movement around the joints.
- Long-term condition circuit classes: this is a low intensity circuit exercise class to music. The exercise caters for individual needs. This class has been designed to bridge the gap between rehabilitation and mainstream activity for stroke, Parkinson's disease, multiple sclerosis and chronic obstructive pulmonary patients.
- Healthy walks: this is for any group.
- Mighty movers: this is low impact exercise to music. The classes are specifically designed for exercise referrals. The classes come in three intensity levels.
- Rowing: this is in partnership with the amateur rowing association. There is an indoor facility in the event of poor weather.

Adult further education classes also provide a range of exercise opportunities for over the 50s, including aerobics classes, walking and golf.

Urban Cricket is another initiative run by the England and Wales Cricket Board in partnership with npower. This scheme is aimed at children between 7 and 12 years old. The major aim is simply for youngsters to go and play the game of cricket. This scheme will enable many more youngsters to experience the game of cricket and develop their skills.

The YMCA offers many sporting opportunities and activities for young people in the UK. There are also many registered charities providing opportunities for exercise for disabled and older people (for example, British Blind Sport and Cerebral Palsy Sport England and Wales).

The Sports Development Service works closely with community partners such as leisure centres and other departments within the council to coordinate a programme of activities in the school summer holidays. The aims of these activities are to meet the identified needs of a wide age range, to be fully inclusive for all children and to lead to long-term participation, for example by offering opportunities to join local sports clubs. Local authorities also work in partnership with companies such as Adidas to provide opportunities for young people.

Case study

Pan Disability Football

Paul is 12 years old and partially sighted. Football is his passion and he shows good technical skills. His dad is really keen that Paul has the opportunity to play at a competitive level. Paul has a friend Michael who played football last Saturday in a Pan Disability Tournament. Paul's dad wants to know more about this project. Can you provide him with the answers to the following questions?

1. **Who organises the Pan Disability Football Programme?**
2. **Is it a partnership venture?**
3. **What role does the fast-food chain McDonald's play?**
4. **What is meant by a Chartered Standard Club?**
5. **What support does the FA give to provide disability football provision?**
6. **What does the future hold for the provision of disability football?**

Assessment practice

The Johnson family has come to live in a new area. Attached to their house is a small flat so grandad and grandma have moved too. Mrs Johnson (aged 35) is five month's pregnant and feeling very well. Mr Johnson (aged 40) is diabetic but lives a healthy lifestyle and is fit. They have two children. Laura (aged 10) and Daniel (aged 8) both enjoy sport. Grandad is a healthy 74-year-old and plays golf and likes to walk, while grandma enjoys gardening but finds she is limited because of having osteoporosis. She was told by her previous GP that exercise would be beneficial. They would all like to make new friends.

The family would like you to help them research the provision of exercise in their new area. Choose three members of the family who you would like to help. These will be your three specific groups. (If you wish to choose other groups not represented here, you may do so, for example, disabled people.)

1. From your research, describe very clearly where the Johnson family can go to find provision for their needs. **P1**
2. After researching for the Johnson family, you find that there are far more opportunities for some groups than others. Having explained who the providers are for your specified groups, compare and contrast the opportunities available within those groups. **M1**
3. You now decide that the local authority should be made aware of what provision there is for specific groups for exercise in the area and you decide to write a short report based on your findings. Detail the information discovered about three specific groups, identify the strengths and weaknesses and make suggestions for improvement. Inform the local authority of good practice elsewhere in the country. **D1**

Grading Tip **P1**

To achieve a pass grade your description must include three different specific groups. You must describe the exercise provision for three members of the family.

Grading Tip **M1**

When comparing and contrasting the opportunities available discuss if there is a group that has more opportunities for exercise. Support your opinions with examples of groups with strong provision and also areas for improvement, that is groups with little provision.

Grading Tip **D1**

After analysing the provision of exercise available for three specific groups remember to recommend how the weaker areas can be improved and what benefits this would bring to each specific group.

Activity

Visit public and private sector organisations that provide exercise for specific groups.

1 Describe the difference between a public sector and private sector organisation.

2 Identify the specific groups who use the organisations for exercise programmes.

3 Interview an instructor from each sector and find out if the instructor believes there is sufficient provision of exercise for specific groups in their sector, for example the public sector.

22.2 Understand the benefits of exercise for different specific groups

Benefits

Physiological

The physical benefits of exercising regularly are increased muscle strength, increased energy and maintaining a healthy weight. Exercising greatly reduces the risk of having a heart attack because you lower your blood pressure and cholesterol level. Weight bearing exercise also reduces the risk of osteoporosis and can even reverse it by building bone tissue. Increased strength and stamina means that all physical tasks become easier in everyday life.

Exercise improves posture, makes the body more agile, reduces joint discomfort and enhances the immune system. You will increase your resistance to colds and other illnesses by exercising regularly. Circulation is improved, you will have more energy, and coordination and balance is enhanced through exercise.

Prenatal

Recent studies have identified several benefits of exercise during pregnancy, including:

- decreased backache
- increased well-being of the mother-to-be
- increased well-being of the foetus.

For example, at a referral clinic between 2000 and 2002, two groups of pregnant women aged 20 years or older (carrying a foetus with a gestational age of 20 weeks or less) participated in a study. One group participated in three one-hour aerobic sessions per week and the other group in three one-hour relaxation and group discussions. This lasted over a period of 12 weeks.

Compared with women in the relaxation group, those in the exercise group were approximately five times more likely to have regular or good cardio respiratory capacity. There was no apparent increase in adverse effects related to exercise intervention.

Here are some of the benefits of exercise for prenatal women:

- it helps women to remain healthy
- their weight is kept within a safe range
- exercise improves mood
- stress is reduced
- sleep patterns improve
- exercise improves muscle tone in the upper body and abdominal area.

Exercising abdominal muscles makes it easier for a woman to support the weight of the baby. Pelvic muscles are also important muscles in pregnancy. Strengthening these muscles allows the vagina to widen more during childbirth and prevents urinary problems after delivery. Strengthening back muscles improves posture and also minimises the strain of pregnancy on the lower back. Other exercises which will benefit the mother during the birth are pelvic floor exercises. She will be less likely to tear her perineum or need an episiotomy. The special exercise for this is called 'Kegal' exercise (see page 373).

Improved circulation

The better the cardiovascular system, the more stamina a woman will have for the birth. Exercise helps circulatory problems such as fatigue and varicose veins. Good circulation supplies the baby with more oxygen and nutrients (because the woman and the baby are linked by the placenta). Exercise improves circulation and, therefore, reduces the problem of haemorrhoids, varicose veins, cramps and constipation.

Reduced swelling

Another benefit of exercise for prenatal women is that it reduces swelling. During pregnancy there are increased fluid volumes and retention and reduced blood flow back to the heart. Exercise in water during pregnancy helps to improve venous blood flow and this can reduce swelling in the lower limbs. It also relaxes muscles and relieves pain and there is less muscle soreness than after exercising on land.

Enhanced muscular balance

As a woman's body grows during pregnancy, her centre of gravity changes and this affects her posture and balance. She may feel less coordinated as her pregnancy progresses. Exercise tones muscles and, because of this, balance is improved. The abdominal and pelvic floor muscles will also go back to normal more easily and quickly after the birth. Better muscle strength and coordination helps the woman to adjust to her changing shape.

Post-natal

Most women are concerned about their weight gain during pregnancy and how they are going to regain their figures. It is important that they do not go on a diet while they are breastfeeding. However, exercise in both prenatal and post-natal periods can have huge benefits, both to the way they look and the way they feel. There is evidence to show that exercise has a beneficial effect on the following:

- sleep pattern
- general weight loss
- energy levels
- muscle tone.

▲ New mothers enjoy the physiological benefits of exercise

Benefits of post-natal exercise also include:

- speedier healing and recovery from the birthing process
- a faster return to the woman's pre-pregnancy shape
- an increase in energy levels to cope with the demands of motherhood
- reduced likelihood of stress and depression.

After birth, your abdomen may look like a deflated ball with no muscle tone. The uterus will contract over the next few weeks and help to flatten the tummy. Post-natal exercises will help to regain shape, also ligaments and joints will still be soft for at least three months following the birth, so vigorous stretching and high impact activities should be avoided.

▲ Exercise is fun!

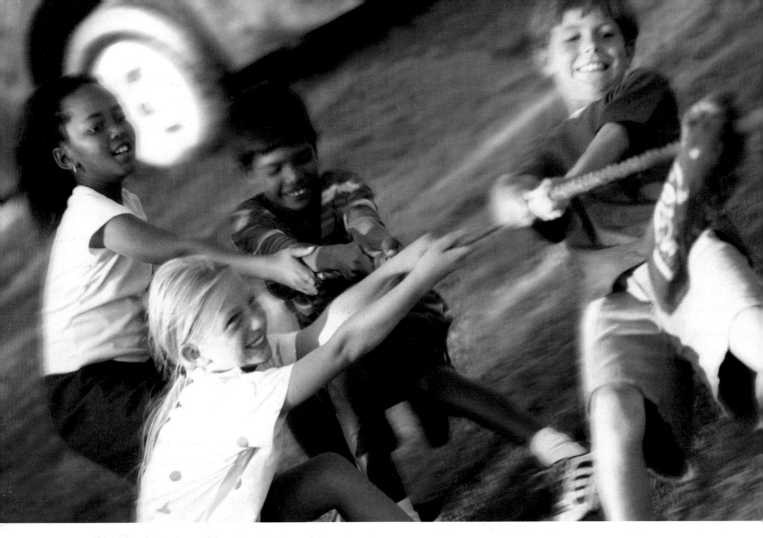

A Caesarean birth involves delivering the baby through an incision made through the abdominal wall and uterus. Gentle exercise can follow the Caesarean birth:

- leg movements and breathing exercises can reduce the risk of blood clots
- no exercise should involve heavy lifting
- regular aerobic exercise will not be recommended for several weeks.

After giving birth a woman should not expect too much too soon, especially while they are breastfeeding. A year should be allowed to get back into pre-pregnancy shape. Aqua fit sessions are particularly beneficial to prenatal and post-natal women, allowing greater flexibility, movement and a heightened degree of relaxation.

Improved posture

During pregnancy the weight of the baby altered the woman's centre of gravity. This, combined with the softening effects of the hormone relaxin on her ligaments, may have led to bad posture. Through exercise she can strengthen her abdominal and back muscles and this will improve posture and reduce her chances of backache while carrying the newborn baby.

Increased energy

Exercise increases energy levels to help cope with the demands of looking after the baby. A strengthened cardiovascular system will give the mother more endurance and stronger muscles will allow her to accomplish tasks with less effort. The new mother will have more energy to get her through the day.

Think it over

When you were at primary school, can you remember how you felt when you performed an activity well and received praise? Were there any occasions when you struggled with an activity and became de-motivated? Discuss these feelings in small groups in your class.

Increased self-confidence

A woman who has exercised during pregnancy will not have to lose a significant amount of weight. Post-natal exercise will help the new mother to lose weight and regain her shape. She should give herself time and not expect too much too soon, especially when breasfeeding. Through regular exercise the mother will feel good about herself, be positive about her shape and her ability to look after the baby. This will lead to increased confidence.

■ Children and young people

The benefits of exercise to children will vary according to the activity.

Learn

Providing exercise opportunities for children and young people develops their personal, physical and social skills. Through exercise programmes young people are introduced to sport, physical activities and new environments. Barriers can also be broken down between young people and adults. Discussion groups can be formed to evaluate and assess issues which may have been raised during activity sessions.

As young people grow older, exercise programmes can lead them to further exercise training opportunities and better employment prospects. This training could be at local, regional and national events.

The human nervous system does not reach full maturity until early adulthood. Therefore, younger children have limited ability and this makes it harder for them to learn specific skills. This does not just affect coordination but also the ability to concentrate and make decisions.

Children learn by doing, being motivated, achieving, through encouragement and by copying others. They need plenty of time to practise a skill, and the practice should be fun, varied, active and challenging. All children need to succeed.

Children learn and develop skills by:

- understanding the task
- performing and practising the task
- receiving feedback from performance which reinforces learning
- practising the skill until it becomes automatic
- evaluating their performance and the self-assessment process.

Think it over

Have you ever been taught a new sporting skill but not been given the time to practise that skill? Did you feel frustrated with yourself?

With a partner, discuss these feelings and write down three benefits you might have gained had you been allowed to practise further.

Socialise

Sport may help children to work together and develop positive attitudes and fair play but it can also have an effect upon a child's self-esteem. Sport involves competition and children soon learn about success and failure. Therefore, children need to play sport in a positive atmosphere where participation and effort is just as good as winning.

Children aged six years cooperate with others and are now less dependent on adults. Between the ages of six and nine years, friendships become very important, and around nine years children form groups and compete to see who is 'the best'. As they become older they learn to cooperate with others, enjoy teamwork and there is a greater awareness of their own and others' skills.

Through learning by doing, children will develop physically.

Increased motor skills

Motor skills can be divided into fine motor skills and gross motor skills.

- Fine motor skills are those skills that allow children to develop the ability to write, draw and manipulate.
- Gross motor skills are big motor skills which require balance and coordination.
- Exercise increases motor skills. Examples of gross motor skills include running, jumping, catching and throwing. For example, moving and passing a ball increases spatial awareness, and performing a tennis serve improves coordination and control. Holding a cricket bat increases manipulative skills.

Children will also develop mentally. Concentration, creativity, communication, cognitive skills and focus are all increased through exercise.

Case study

Responding to encouragement

Mark is 11 years old and a member of his local football club. The club provides coaching sessions twice a week with matches played on a weekend. He lives and breathes football and is only happy with the ball at his feet.

His parents have noticed a big difference in his personality since he was made captain three months ago. Mark used to be a very quiet and introvert character. His parents are very pleased with both his physical and psychological development.

They would like you to answer a few questions to help them understand the difference exercise (football) has made to Mark's personal development.

With a partner, prepare answers to the following questions. Your tutor will select students to present their findings to the rest of the class. Discuss the answers as a whole class.

1 **Mark's football skills have developed immensely. Can you describe why?**

2 **Mark has recently been made captain of the team. What opportunities does Mark now have to show his leadership qualities?**

3 **His parents have noticed that instead of playing as an individual, Mark is now far more aware of his fellow team-mates. Can you describe why?**

4 **Does Mark have opportunities to be creative in his role? Give detailed examples.**

5 **Mark's parents have heard the coaches at the club talk about the need to promote self-awareness. Can you explain what this means and give reasons why Mark is now showing an improvement in self-awareness?**

6 **Mark's academic work at school lacked personal organisational skills. His last academic report commented on a vast improvement in this area. Explain how Mark's sporting experiences have affected this?**

7 **Can you compare Mark's character before joining the football club with the young man he has now become?**

8 **What recommendations would you make to any parents about the benefits of belonging to a football or any sporting club?**

Remember!

The benefits of exercise to children and young people can be divided into:

- physiological benefits
- psychological benefits.

'Regular physical activity can assist in avoiding, minimising and/or reversing many of the physical, psychological and social hazards that accompany advancing age.'

(World Health Organization)

Referred clients

Referred clients are more likely to belong to the older adult group or a specific group, for example cardiac rehabilitation, mobility, exercise on prescription or accident.

Older people will have a more positive image through exercise. This can come about through an increased contribution to society.

Case study

Exercise brings rewards

Sheila Barker, aged 68, has always been healthy and active. However, lately she has been feeling tired and lacking in energy. Winter is approaching and she is certainly not enjoying the thought of dark nights and shutting out the world at 5 p.m.

Her friend Margaret is a member of her local gym and attends regularly twice a week. One of these sessions she follows with a swim at the local pool. Margaret invites Sheila to accompany her and, after much persuasion, Sheila agrees. The following spring Sheila looks back over the winter months and wonders where the time has gone. She is now an active member of her local gym, attends a weekly coffee morning and has found a new group of friends. She devotes one day a week to working in a charity shop. Sheila has even found time to start her spring cleaning.

1. **What have been the social benefits to Sheila through increasing her exercise pattern?**
2. **Could Sheila have gained the same social benefits from joining a 'book club'? Explain and give details to support your answer.**

The main physiological benefits of health and exercise for older adults are:

- the prevention and management of heart problems, possible strokes and diabetes type two (this type of diabetes is when the body cannot use insulin well, the condition usually starts in the over 40s age group but could start earlier)
- the development of motor skills
- the management of weight and obesity, and increased health and fitness
- the prevention of osteoporosis
- increased coordination and control, and a reduction of accidental falls
- the prevention of diseases, e.g. colon cancer
- the positive use of energy and an improvement in sleep patterns.

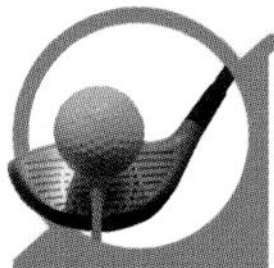

Think it over

Have you ever noticed an older person who is very round shouldered or stooped and begins to look smaller? Can you explain why they stoop and how exercise can be beneficial to them? You could research how many hip operations are performed in the UK per year on older people.

As a young person, what could you do now to build and maintain healthy bones?

Increased fitness

Referred clients increase fitness by exercising. The main three types of exercise which increase fitness for referred clients are flexibility (stretching) exercises, strengthening (resistance) exercises and cardiovascular (aerobic exercise). The client should always consult their doctor before embarking on an exercise programme.

Gentle stretching exercise can help a referred client warm up for more strenuous exercise by getting the body moving. Aerobic activity such as walking, dancing, swimming or cycling makes the heart, lungs, blood vessels and muscles work more efficiently. This results in improved endurance, stronger bones, improved sleep, and reduced stress, anxiety and depression.

Exercise helps all people to stay healthy. If referred clients exercise moderately on a regular basis, their stamina and energy levels increase and also their general sense of well-being.

Rehabilitation

Who can benefit from a rehabilitation programme? In the past, rehabilitation programmes were suggested for people who were young and needed to return to work after an illness or surgery. Today, with improved programmes and close monitoring, rehabilitation programmes are an option for people of all ages and with any form of disease or injury.

Increased bone density

Exercise will increase muscle strength, improve balance and reduce the risk of falls. Bones will suffer if they are not used and, therefore, need regular weight-bearing exercises. This will put a working force through the bone, stimulate growth and, therefore, strengthen the bone. Even a brisk walk or running up and down the stairs can be beneficial to bones.

Psychological

The psychological benefits of exercise include improved self-esteem, improved mental alertness and an increased perception of acceptance by others. You become less stressed and tense and are able to respond constructively to disappointments.

Exercise sharpens your brain well into old age and improves focus and concentration. Older adults have a better chance of avoiding diseases such as Alzheimer's and dementia through exercising.

■ Reduction in depression

In the early 1980s, a neuropeptide (a brain chemical) was discovered which showed remarkable morphine-like qualities. Very small amounts of beta-endorphin promoted feelings of exhilaration and reduced feelings of depression and anxiety. Aerobic activity increases the production of endorphins, and can improve mood and suppress depression.

Exercise may help balance brain chemicals and can help a person fighting depression to feel good, be less stressed and lift their mood. Exercise is now a major part of stress reduction programmes and self-care for depression.

■ Reduction in anxiety

People who exercise regularly suffer less from anxiety. They are able to concentrate more and sleep deeply at night. Exercise acts like a tranquillizer to reduce anxiety.

A recent study showed that people who are stressed and anxious get viral infections twice as frequently as non-stressed individuals. Regular exercise decreases the level of stress hormones released during stressful responses, such as anger and fear.

■ Improve self-confidence

Exercise increases self-confidence. When you are in control of your body size and weight through exercise your self-confidence and self-esteem are increased, and you will have the confidence to make other changes in your life.

For example, the strength and endurance gained from regular exercise makes you more confident going about your daily tasks, such as shopping, gardening and meeting other people.

Specific groups

Older adults

This specific group should exercise for many reasons. Examples of physiological benefits for older adults are as follows:

- exercise can reduce pain and stiffness
- it can build strong muscles around the joints
- exercise can build stronger bones
- there will be more flexibility and endurance
- the person will feel better because they will have more energy
- exercise will help them sleep better because they will be more active during the day
- exercise controls weight.

Through exercise, other related health problems such as heart disease and osteoporosis will be prevented.

Exercise sharpens the brain well into old age and improves focus and concentration. Therefore there is a better chance of avoiding age-related diseases such as dementia.

Exercise gives an older person more energy to go out and do tasks, and this increases confidence and well-being. Less stress and anxiety enables an older person to face daily tasks, and responsibilities.

Through exercise, older people feel better about themselves and more included in society. They are often more self-reliant and require less care.

Disabled people

In order to participate and benefit from exercise, a disabled person must be able to physically perform the skill that is required.

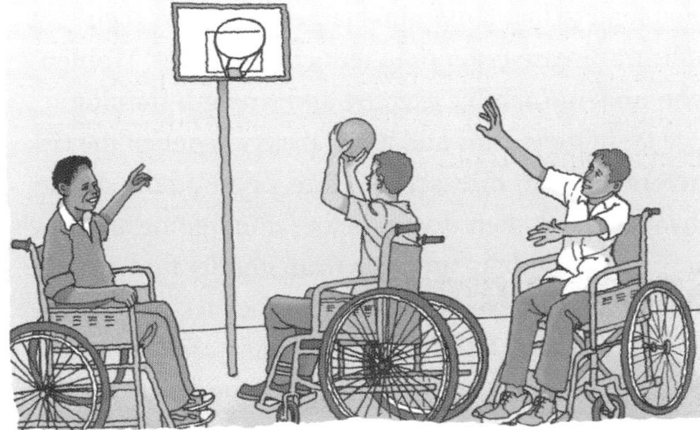

▲ Wheelchair-bound people can physically perform many tasks

Think it over

How many wheelchair-bound sports can you think of?

However, as you will learn later in the unit, there are different ways and levels of performing the same task. The physiological and psychological benefits can be similar as those covered in the section for children or older adults, as many people with disabilities are included in mainstream exercise. People with disabilities also enter mainstream activities with adaptations made around their disability. Below are examples of some psychological benefits that exercises can bring to disabled people.

- Spatial awareness: disabled people with spatial awareness problems would have special exercises which would relate them to exercise areas. This could mean touching lines or moving around the playing area.
- Awareness of others: this could involve discussing and watching how other participants move around the exercise space. For example, do they need wheelchairs, sticks or scooters to assist their mobility?
- Manipulation: here the disabled person would focus on the equipment. They will become familiar with, for example, the balls used – are they large or small? What colour are they and do they feel hard or soft?
- Concentration: this could be a very big problem for some people. Therefore, through exercise, they can be taught to focus on the task. For example, experimenting with different ways of travelling.

Prenatal and post-natal clients

Moderate exercise (which makes women feel slightly out of breath) is good for those who are pregnant, especially if the body is used to exercise. Being fit is excellent preparation for the physical effort which will be required during labour. Gentler exercises are more beneficial, but new intensive exercise programmes should be avoided (as overheating is not good for prenatal women). Jerky or violent impact exercises should be avoided because women's joints loosen up during pregnancy.

Many obstetricians recommend that exercise is reduced in the third trimester (both aerobic and resistance exercise). However, others say that a reduction in exercise after the first two trimesters results in the mother gaining unnecessary weight and foetal fat mass.

In 2006, a group of obstetricians and gynaecologists in a study in the USA made several recommendations about exercise for post-natal women. They advised sedentary women to begin a moderate exercise programme of aerobic exercise for 16–30 minutes three times a week. The exercise was to be limited to the intensity level of a heart rate of 140.

Exercise releases the 'feel good' endorphins into the woman's system. She already feels good about herself through exercising. She has a good body shape, no excess fat, a bright complexion and a very positive outlook. Regular exercise increases energy levels and certainly promotes a feeling of well-being during pregnancy.

Pilates is an excellent exercise programme and can be started by mothers in varying post-natal stages to assist recovery. It strengthens the core control muscles of the lower abdominal regional floor, strengthens and lengthens the back, and tones and stretches to relieve muscular tension from repetitive physical movements such as bending over, carrying and nursing. It also helps post-natal women to focus on balance, posture and breathing. Circulation is stimulated and this reduces water retained after the birth.

Children and young people

Children learn by taking part and doing exercises. All children should be set activities where they can achieve and be successful. This means that they remain motivated and on task. You should always encourage children, allow them to experiment, copy others and make mistakes. The motivation for doing exercise simply comes from enjoyment.

You will know that a good level of self-confidence comes through praise and achievement. Through exercise a child becomes independent, and accepts that exercise is a valuable way of releasing energy and emotions. You must realise that winning is not everything, exercise must be fun and all children must be made to feel equal.

Referred clients

As well as specific groups (such as older adults, disabled people, prenatal and post-natal clients, children and young people), you can also find others who benefit from exercise, such as those with:

- obesity problems
- sedentary lifestyles
- cardiac or metabolic disease
- injuries
- arthritis
- osteoporosis
- mobility problems.

Some of these you have already considered; others you will consider as referred clients. Many people who come under the category of referred clients are suffering stress as a result of pain. How does exercise help them to manage their pain?

Obesity

Being overweight forces the heart to work harder. Exercise will improve heart efficiency, lower blood pressure and lower blood cholesterol levels. It will also reduce weight, maintain weight loss and fight obesity. A fitter older adult is a healthier adult.

Exercise without dieting will also add benefits. One study, for example, found that overweight fit adults have half the death rate of overweight and unfit adults. As adults get older, they need to exercise more to keep the weight off. Men tend to lose abdominal fat which lowers their risk of heart disease faster than reducing body fat. Women who undergo aerobic exercise and strength training lose fat in their arms and legs. Obesity is one of the risk factors for heart disease, therefore, obese adults should always consult their doctor before undergoing an exercise programme. Adults suffering from obesity find it more difficult to start exercising because they feel unattractive and rejected and the strain emotionally can lead to 'comfort eating' for consolation. This food is usually high in fat, sugar and calories. This group of adults may eat because they are lonely.

There is increasing obesity in children. Recent findings show that 40 per cent of boys and 60 per cent of girls failed to meet the recommended one hour a day of moderate intensity exercise.

Activity

1. Did your school meals assist you in keeping a healthy body weight? Explain why.
2. Why are school meals so important to children and young adults?

Sedentary

If you do not walk briskly for 30 minutes each day or do not undertake leisure activities, then you are sitting too much. Sedentary living increases the risk of chronic health conditions.

When sedentary people become involved in regular exercise programmes they realise that muscle soreness and the trivialities of life no longer annoy them. Exercise can become a valued time when they can reflect upon their life. The physical benefits of exercise will indirectly influence their psychological well-being, as exercise gets rid of nervous energy and influences the relaxation response.

Sedentary people should start on an exercise programme slowly and choose an activity that they would enjoy, such as walking which requires no expensive equipment. They could walk 15–30 minutes every other day to begin with and then gradually increase the time and number of days – 30 minutes five or six days a week is ideal. For people who have been sedentary, they should keep the heart rate around 65–70 per cent of maximum heart rate. To work out the maximum, subtract your age from 220 and then multiply the number by 65 per cent and then by 80 per cent. This will give you a lower and an upper limit for your heart rate during exercise.

The number of overweight children and adolescents has accelerated over the last ten years and children now show risk factors for chronic health conditions related to their sedentary lifestyle.

■ Cardiac

Exercise strengthens the cardiovascular and respiratory systems and increases fitness, no matter what age or group.

The circulation of the blood goes through the heart and blood vessels. A build up of plaques in your arteries is caused by cholesterol and other products in the bloodstream. This can interrupt the blood flow and cause life-threatening damage to the cardiovascular system.

■ Pulmonary or metabolic disease

Exercise can prevent and manage heart problems and stroke.

> ‘*A stroke is more common among the elderly. However, over 50 per cent of strokes occur in people under the age of 75 and 5 per cent under the age of 45.*’
>
> (Angela Williams, 2005)

A stroke occurs when the blood supply to the brain is suddenly stopped by a blockage in a brain artery or bleeding in or around the brain. The brain, therefore, cannot get the oxygen it needs, brain cells in that area die and the brain may become permanently damaged. The patient is often left with some form of paralysis.

According to the American Stroke Association blood clots are the cause of 8 out of 10 strokes. Walking or cycling reduces the risk of blood clots in the brain. In 2003, researchers showed in a case-controlled study that moderate and high intensity exercise will reduce the risk of a stroke by 64 per cent.

Cardiac disease has been reported to occur in many stroke survivors. Therefore, exercise places a greater energy demand on a stroke survivor's cardiovascular system than able bodied adults. Stroke survivors do benefit from exercise but, in their case, rehabilitation programmes are hampered more by the associated cardiac disease than the stroke. A stroke survivor would initiate a programme of exercise to regain pre-stroke levels of activity as soon as possible. Recent research has shown that intensive work for several months after the stroke, including work on the treadmill, increases aerobic capacity and motor function. It has been well established that in stroke survivors there is a link between training and improved cardiovascular fitness and health. Strength exercises have also been found to have beneficial effects in patients with stroke history. Before undergoing an exercise programme a stroke patient would undergo an electrocardiograph (ECG) as part of a monitoring programme before beginning exercise.

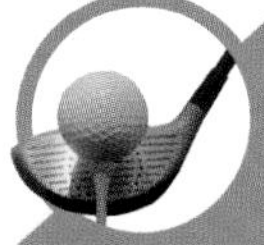

Think it over

Why are stroke victims at an increased health risk?

Metabolic diseases of the muscle are caused by a genetic defect which hinders the body's metabolism. This is the collection of chemicals which occur within cells during normal everyday living. Muscles need a lot of energy and when the energy levels become low, muscle weakness and exercise intolerance will occur and the person with this disease will experience muscle cramp.

A person with a metabolic disease has difficulty exercising. They become tired very easily. The degree of intolerance to exercise will depend on the severity of the metabolic disorder and within each disorder there will be varying degrees from person to person.

An example of a metabolic disease would be a person with a defect in their carbohydrate pathways. People with this disorder may recognise that they tire very easily at the beginning of exercise, but can feel more energetic after 10–15 minutes of exercise. Cramp (sharp contractions that temporarily seize up the muscle), which is exercise related, is especially noted in disorders of carbohydrate metabolism.

If a person with a metabolic disorder over-exerts themselves, they could experience severe muscle pain during exercise for several hours afterwards. Exercises such as running, jumping, pushing or pulling heavy objects and squatting can trigger such pain. For this group of people, prolonged moderate exercise may not be beneficial and, in fact, may be quite painful. It is, therefore, very important that professional therapists work with the individual to satisfy their exercise needs.

Injuries

If you have suffered a sporting injury, you will know that exercise is a vital part of the rehabilitation process. An athlete will receive a course of treatment from a physiotherapist but will also be set specific strengthening and flexibility exercises. For example, an athlete who is recovering from a hamstring strain would need to stretch and strengthen the injured hamstring so that flexibility and strength are equal for both the injured and uninjured side.

A study found that exercise had benefits for individuals with traumatic brain injuries. Those who exercised were found to be less depressed and their general state of health was better. It was found that exercise improved mood and general health, but did not affect aspects of disability and handicap. People who suffer from back pain have found that exercise and physical therapy aids recovery. Active exercise, as well as creating the physiological conditions for the injured area to heal, relieves emotional distress and this also aids recovery.

Arthritis

Arthritis is from the Greek words '*arthro*' meaning joint and '*itis*' meaning inflammation. Arthritis disease includes rheumatoid arthritis and psoriatic arthritis, which is septic arthritis caused by infection in the joints. Osteoarthritis mainly affects older people and is the degeneration of joint cartilage.

Research has shown that moderate exercise can bring a wide range of benefits to people with arthritis. Many years ago people would not have exercised as it was thought that this would damage joints. Now, however, exercise is seen as an essential part of pain management.

Arthritis sufferers benefit from flexibility exercises that involve basic stretching movements to improve their range of motion. After feeling comfortable with these, endurance exercise such as weight training and cardiovascular (aerobic) exercise can begin. If there is a great amount of pain, exercise programmes in water are better because the body's buoyancy reduces stress on the hips, knees and spine. Good exercises might include:

- walking
- yoga
- golf.

Before beginning an exercise programme arthritis sufferers will work with their health professionals to find the best referral scheme for them. In this way they will be guided towards the best practitioner in their area who can provide for their specific needs. This might be at their local leisure centre, swimming pool or private health club. A qualified instructor will assess their specific exercise and joint protection needs.

Exercises which are beneficial to clients with arthritis include the following.

- Gentle stretching exercises which can be done every day. These will help the client warm up and prepare for more strenuous exercise. They will also release tension and aid relaxation – 15 minutes of stretching would be beneficial.
- Strengthening exercises (resistance exercise) to make muscles stronger. If the muscles are strengthened, then there will be less stress on the joints. This will protect the joints from injury, as muscles will be strong enough to absorb shock. In order to make the muscles work harder, weights are used for exercise.

There are two types of strengthening exercises: isometric and isotonic. People with arthritis benefit from isometric exercises, because these exercises tighten the muscles without moving the joint.

Cardiovascular (aerobic) exercise uses large muscles of the body in rhythmic continuous movements (such as walking, dancing, swimming and cycling). This type of exercise makes your heart, lungs, blood vessels and muscles work more efficiently. Arthritis sufferers need to adopt aerobic exercise into their programmes. It may begin with just five minutes three to four times a week, increasing to 30 minutes. The client would work within their target heart rate.

Water exercises are very beneficial for people with arthritis. Exercising in warm water can:

- relax the muscles
- decrease pain and stiffness
- make you comfortable when performing exercises.

There are other reasons why an arthritic client might be referred to an exercise programme in water.

- The water is soothing and warm.
- Immersing in warm water raises the body temperature causing blood vessels to dilate. This increases circulation.
- Water exercise is a gentle, safe way to exercise muscles; joint movement is freer. Muscle strength can be built up because water acts as resistance.

There are many safe ways to exercise for people with this disability. It is vital that they work with the qualified referral specialists such as sports therapists and physiotherapists, or on an appropriate scheme recommended by their doctor.

Walking is beneficial exercise for anyone and, in particular, for people with arthritis. Walking is an endurance exercise. This means it strengthens the heart, the lungs work more efficiently and stamina is increased. Walking is a weight bearing exercise, i.e. one that puts full weight on a person's bones and so reduces the risk of osteoporosis.

Activity

Discuss what will be considered before an arthritic client embarks on an exercise programme. Consider the following headings:

- the type of arthritis the client has
- how it effects them
- the severity of the disease
- how their joints are affected.

Remember!

A referral professional will help the client to get going on the programme which could improve their quality of life.

Case study

The benefits of yoga

Michelle, aged 47, decided to start yoga classes after she began experiencing joint pain and general stiffness in her body five years ago. Her doctor had recommended that she kept her joints as flexible as possible, particularly with the knowledge that her mother and grandmother both suffered from rheumatoid arthritis. She found it quite difficult at first but decided to persevere. With more and more practice her joints began to feel less stiff in the mornings and the pain was reduced a little. She feels so much better now at the end of each day. 'I don't feel so stressed and anxious. I sleep much better. My attitude has improved and I am really proud of what I can now achieve. The more exercise I do, the more I know I can do.'

Write down all of the physical and psychological benefits of exercise to Michelle through attending her yoga classes.

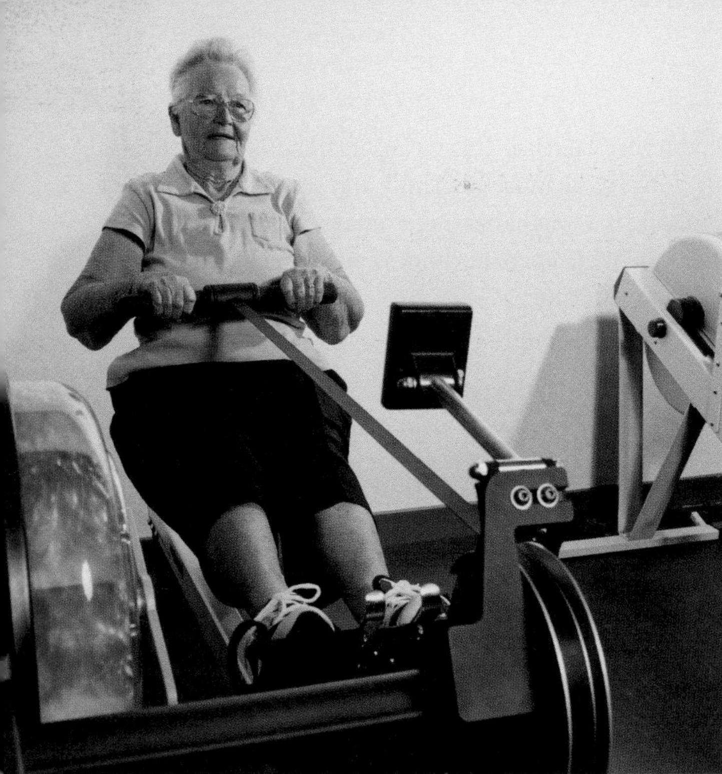

Enid suffers from osteoporosis and enjoys her referral programme

Osteoporosis

Three types of exercise will bring benefit to osteoporosis sufferers:

- strength-training exercises
- weight-bearing aerobic activities
- flexibility exercises.

A referral professional will decide what exercises will be appropriate.

Strength training can work directly on your bones to slow down mineral loss. Compression fractures resulting from osteoporosis leads to a stooped posture and this can result in more compression fractures. Exercises can gently stretch the upper back, improve posture and strengthen the muscles between the shoulder blades. Weight bearing exercises involving aerobic exercise on foot are also beneficial. This could be walking, dancing or gardening. These exercises work on the bones in your legs, hips and lower spine to reduce mineral loss. Swimming and water aerobics do not have an impact on bones (impact is needed to reduce mineral loss); therefore, this type of exercise is not so beneficial. Flexibility exercises increase the mobility in joints. If joints are stiff, then the abdominal and chest muscles tighten and this pulls the body forward giving the stooped position. Chest and shoulder stretches will benefit posture.

Our bones begin to thin after the age of 30. These changes may never be noticed. However, for 1 in 3 women and 1 in 12 men over the age of 50, the progressive thinning of the bones leads to osteoporosis. With this condition, a person can break a bone following a simple knock or fall because their bones have become so fragile. With osteoporosis the bones have become too porous. Often, it is only when someone fractures a bone that the disease is suspected. The wrist, hips, hands and spine are the sites where these fractures occur most commonly.

Regular exercise is the best thing an older person can do to prevent the bone-weakening disease osteoporosis. Strength and weight bearing exercises help preserve bone mass and may increase bone density. This means bones may even grow stronger. Strengthening bones and muscles can improve balance and coordination, and so reduce falls.

Women are at greater risk because they have smaller bones than men and their bones are less dense. Also, at the menopause the ovaries produce lower levels of the female hormone oestrogen which has a protective effect on their bones. It is, therefore, the lack of oestrogen which causes an increase in bone loss. Osteoporosis in men is less common, but is often the result of low levels of the male hormone testosterone. There may be no obvious signs, but some men may find that they need to shave less regularly and may feel excessively tired.

Mobility problems

Balance exercises improve agility and flexibility. Balance is important for everyday activities. As adults get older they need to exercise for many reasons and balance is one of them. The body is constantly moving and transferring energy and if it strays too far from where it should be, it needs to be pushed back. Older adults should safeguard and improve their balance. This is extremely important as lack of balance is the cause of many accidents.

Growing older does not mean that people have to lose their strength and agility and ability to do everyday tasks. Exercise helps older adults to feel good and enjoy good health. Muscles can be strengthened and bone density maintained. This decreases the risk of fractures should an older adult fall. Muscle strengthening also increases synovial fluid, which increases flexibility and, therefore, reduces the risk of falling. This helps older adults to avoid accidents.

Taking it further

1. Stand on one leg and stay as still as possible for as long as possible. Are you completely balanced? Is your body still? Could you explain why some people can remain balanced and others would find it very difficult?
2. Practise balancing activities. How good are you at balancing?

Assessment practice

On your recommendation, the Johnson family begins classes. Laura (10) joins a gymnastics class and the swimming club, while Daniel (8) becomes a member of a football team and a running club. Mr Johnson (40) joins a gym and plays badminton and Mrs Johnson (35) is referred to a prenatal exercise group and also enjoys taking the children swimming. Grandad (74) is now playing golf and walking. Finally, grandma has joined a rambling group and also an exercise (on prescription) class at the local gym.

The family is very interested in the benefits they will gain from exercise. Could you inform them of the benefits?

1. Create a wall chart that identifies the same three specific groups chosen earlier (through photographs or pictures). Next to the images, describe four different benefits of exercises for each group (that are specific to that group). **P2**
2. The family looks at the wall chart and would like further information. Explain to the members of the family why it is beneficial for them to exercise and how exercise increases their fitness levels. **M2**
3. Could you now add another section to the previous report for the local authority? In this section discuss the benefits of exercise for the chosen groups, and provide further evidence as to why these groups should have many opportunities locally for exercise. **M2**

▲ The Johnson family all enjoy exercise

Grading Tip P2

Remember to describe in detail four different benefits of exercise to each of three specific different groups.

Grading Tip M2

Once again remember to explain in detail four different benefits of exercise for three selected specific groups. Support your explanations with examples.

Exercise referral process

Initial screening procedures

The purpose of initial screening of participants is to identify those who have symptoms of a disease and also those who are at increased risk of disease. It is essential that each person is at no risk during the performance testing stage and during an exercise prescription programme. Screening establishes where the person is now and provides information from which future progress can be monitored.

There are two stages to the screening process. First, it identifies the participants who need medical checks before starting on performance testing and exercise. The second stage is the consent form on which the participant and their doctor will provide information. There will also be a questionnaire for the participant to complete. Screening is a legal procedure and is essential for all older adults, both for their safety and the effectiveness of their programme.

Referral professionals

The referral professionals can be sports therapists, physiotherapists, general practitioners or consultants.

■ Sports therapists

Sports therapists train specifically to work with people who have sport injuries. Many sports therapists work with professional, semi-professional and amateur football clubs and rugby teams, cyclists, hockey players and other sports. They also run private practices providing sport's therapy and rehabilitation services within health and leisure centres.

■ Physiotherapists

Physiotherapists play a big part in the healthcare system, particularly in rehabilitation programmes and intermediate care. A small example would be working with older people, and people with pain or cardiac problems. In primary care, physiotherapists work with general practitioners in residential homes, day centres, special units and also the person's own home.

■ General practitioners

Although therapists and nurses may initiate exercise referral schemes, the general practitioner is responsible for the overall management of the programme of exercise. The roles of the general practitioner are as follows.

- To decide which clients are to be transferred to an exercise referral scheme (using the criteria that meets the national guidelines on selecting patients), or to delegate this role to a nurse or therapist.
- To obtain consent from the client to pass on all confidential information relating to the client's health and the benefits of exercise for daily living.
- To inform the client about any symptoms that may occur which indicate that the programme is not suitable for the client.
- To refer the client to the most appropriate facility for their exercise prescription programme. This is normally their local fitness facility.
- To let the client know that there is always support available to them while on the programme.
- To consult with the client at the end of the programme and discuss their progress.
- To encourage an active lifestyle at the end of the programme.

The managers of referral schemes can come from a wide variety of professional backgrounds. They could be:

- general practitioners
- nurses
- therapists
- health promotion specialists
- exercise scientists
- appropriately qualified exercise instructors.

The role of the manager of the referral scheme is to:

- know the capabilities and roles of all the other professionals in the scheme
- have a good knowledge of both primary healthcare and exercise resources and facilities

- develop a network of people to exercise referral schemes, and so develop within this network an integrated system of client care.

Activity

Visit your local surgery or clinic and research the procedures for referring a client onto an exercise referral scheme.

1. A patient has asked the doctor if they can be referred onto an exercise programme. What is the doctor's role in the referral scheme?
2. What exercise programmes are available for this client in your local area and who will take care of them while on the programme?
3. What specific group does this client belong to?

Activity

Types of schemes

The types of schemes available are:

- exercise for the elderly
- multiple sclerosis
- prenatal and post-natal
- obesity
- fitness for life
- cardiac rehabilitation
- mobility
- diabetes.

Exercise for the elderly

'Steps to Health' is a physical activity referral scheme provided by the Active Living Team, which is set up by the local authority and works in partnership with local health services. This scheme is to encourage people who are inactive and may have health needs to take up some form of physical activity. Nurses, GPs and other health professionals refer clients on to an appropriate activity programme. The classes are held at local leisure centres and also within private health facilities. Health walks are organised by many local authorities for people of all ages who want to improve their general health and well-being. Exercise referral schemes have become a major route for promoting exercise for older adults. The success of the programme relies on the GP's recommendations, the experienced personnel and the attractiveness of the programme.

Multiple sclerosis

Multiple sclerosis is an autoimmune disease which mistakenly attacks the central nervous system. Most people with multiple sclerosis can expect to live a normal or nearly normal life. Only a small number of sufferers actually develop any serious disability as a result of having the disease. It is typically first diagnosed between the ages of 20 and 45 years, although very young children and very old people have developed the disorder. Some people may develop paralysis over time or severe motor disabilities.

It has been found that properly managed exercise programmes taking account of the individual's limitations, can be beneficial to these clients, both physically and mentally. Exercise referral schemes have been set up to provide exercise programmes for people with this disease. Exercise will increase mobility, strengthen muscles, combat depression and emotional problems. People with neurological conditions can be referred independently (with written agreement from their GP) to schemes at council-run leisure centres and gyms. In one local authority a physiotherapist attended the inductions with the client and the gym instructor to advise about the client's condition and suitable equipment. Some new clients needed assistance for up to six weeks before they could use equipment safely and independently. Exercise needs to become part of lifestyle changes to ensure there are long-term benefits.

Antenatal

Antenatal schemes are available for all pregnant women through their GP. For example, exercise in the form of yoga (which improves breathing, strength and stamina) and prenatal exercise designed for the special needs of expectant mothers. Many prenatal women benefit from Kegal exercises. These exercises strengthen the vaginal muscles to bring an easier birth. Swimming is also encouraged, as this keeps the body toned without putting weight and stress on the joints. Swimming raises the heart rate and is a safe cardiovascular exercise that is not likely to cause overheating. Walks are also organised from local leisure centres and this is easier on the knees than running. Cycling is also recommended on a stationary bike. There are also schemes which provide aerobic classes for prenatal women and most health clubs have them.

Post-natal

Examples of post-natal referral schemes can be found through your local authority, private health clubs and BUPA. Some local authorities have an Active Living Team that is responsible for helping many groups of people to get fit. Walks are organised for new mothers called 'Pram Push', which helps them to not only regain their shape but also meet other new mums. Kegal exercises are beneficial for post-natal mothers as they help to tone and strengthen the vaginal muscles. There are also breastfeeding support groups and referral schemes for mothers who may be suffering from 'baby blues'.

Obesity

Active for Health Schemes include referral schemes for clients with conditions that can improve through physical activity, including obesity. The scheme is designed to assist the client in beginning a healthy and active lifestyle. It consists of initial and final consultations, together with gym-based activity sessions (which can be adapted for differing levels of fitness and ability). Kids Active 4 Health is another scheme which targets obesity at its early stages, with a view to preventing it continuing into adult life. The scheme aims to address obesity in children at primary school between the ages of 8 and 11, as children of this age are beginning to have a greater influence over what they eat and their physical activity routines. This type of intervention is important for improving children's health and well-being.

Slimming on referral is a scheme set up in partnership with local authorities and Slimming World. Highly trained Slimming World consultants help those referred to improve their overall fitness. With individual guidance, in a caring environment, clients rebuild their confidence as they develop the skills needed to bring about the long-term changes needed to improve their lives.

Fitness for life

As you know, there are many benefits to be gained from regular exercise, but many people feel nervous about starting exercise because they do not know what to expect or are frightened of hurting themselves. For them, the Fitness for Life referral scheme is an ideal start. Fitness for Life is available in many areas. A GP or nurse can refer a client on to the scheme if they think that physical activity will be beneficial for that person. Suitable people include those who are currently inactive or have a specific medical condition (such as high blood pressure, diabetes or osteoporosis). A free initial consultation is included, discounted rates at the participating centres and a meeting with the health and fitness instructor (who, together with the client, will devise a specific exercise programme to meet individual needs).

Cardiac rehabilitation

This is an exercise and education programme which is designed to improve the quality of life after a heart attack. Exercising, under the supervision of referral professionals, may be the one chance of survival. A doctor will advise the client when and where to go. A cardiac rehabilitation programme:

- aids recovery
- prevents the problem getting worse
- reduces the risk of further heart problems.

There are four main strands to cardiac rehabilitation.

- Medical evaluation – a healthcare team evaluates and assesses the client's physical abilities and limitations depending upon the severity of the illness. Risk factors (such as strokes or high blood pressure) will be explored by the doctor in charge of each individual case. The doctor and referral professionals will tailor a cardiac rehabilitation programme specifically for the individual's situation. It will be an exercise programme which is both safe and effective.
- Physical activity – if a client has a serious heart problem, they are not encouraged to lead a sedentary lifestyle. They have to improve their fitness levels.

A cardiac rehabilitation programme will improve their cardiovascular fitness levels through exercises such as walking, cycling, rowing and even jogging.
- Lifestyle education – any excess weight will have to be lost as part of a cardiac rehabilitation programme and healthier food choices made (aiming at reducing fat, sodium and cholesterol). Opportunities will be given during the programme to ask questions and discuss any issues which may arise.
- Psychological benefits and support – it takes time to adjust to serious health problems. The client may have experienced anxiety and depression and lost contact with friends at work and socially. Cardiac rehabilitation will help to rebuild a person's life, both physically and emotionally.

In the past, cardiac rehabilitation programmes were often only suggested to younger people who had a heart attack or surgery to enable them to get back to work. Programmes have improved and people can now be monitored more closely by a team of health professionals – people of all ages and with a variety of cardiac problems can benefit from cardiac rehabilitation programmes. It may even be that an older person benefits more than a younger person, because older adults with heart disease are less able to exercise and have a higher disability rate.

Most programmes last 3–6 months and are tailored to the individual client's needs. During the programme the client may work with some or all of the following:

- cardiologists
- nurses
- dieticians
- exercise rehabilitation specialists
- occupational therapists
- psychologists.

A programme can be divided into three sections.

1. *Programme 1 – in hospital*: here, the client will begin with non-strenuous activities:
   - sitting up in bed
   - self-care
   - walking
   - limited stair climbing
   - being involved in the kind of activity they will face when at home.
2. *Programme 2 – early recovery*: this phase can last between 2 and 12 weeks and will begin when the client has left hospital. Under very close supervision from the cardiac rehabilitation team, the client will increase their activity level. Exercises introduced will be those that they can safely do at home, for example walking.
   The client will also learn about healthy diets and be told to give up smoking if necessary.
   If there is no medical facility with a cardiac rehabilitation centre, then the exercise rehabilitation therapist can work closely with the client's local fitness facility.
3. *Programme 3 – late recovery*: a person's exercise regime and lifestyle must become a long-term programme. If there are still health concerns, a client will remain under the care of the cardiac rehabilitation team. This programme will help a person return to an active lifestyle. There will be anxieties that can be worked through, as the client grows stronger and improves their quality of life.

Think it over

What is your image of a potential heart attack victim? Discuss this image with the rest of the group. Do you all have the same image?

Mobility

Exercise referral schemes for people with mobility problems are usually water based. Schemes offer 12 weeks of supervised water-based mobility exercises that are ideal for those with joint pains and mobility problems (such as arthritis or recovering from injuries). Active Lifestyle Exercise referral schemes provide a variety of programmes to meet the needs of defined medical problems (such as mobility), and these assist the individual to become more physically active.

Diabetes

Diabetes is a disease in which the body does not properly produce or use insulin. Insulin is the hormone that is needed to convert sugar, starches and other nutrients into energy.

Symptoms of diabetes include frequent urination, excessive thirst, extreme hunger, unusual weight loss, increased fatigue and blurred vision.

A risk factor for diabetes and heart disease is abdominal fat. Exercise is important because it will reduce the size of these cells.

Obese people who have more abdominal fat are at a higher risk than people who store fat in their hips and thighs.

Abdominal fat is associated with metabolic syndrome. This is a cluster of symptoms that increases the risk of heart disease and diabetes. This syndrome is diagnosed when someone has at least three of the following:

- abdominal obesity
- low levels of good cholesterol
- high blood pressure
- increased levels of sugar in their blood.

Diabetes wellness scheme is a referral scheme run by local authorities for clients with stable diabetes that can be improved through exercise. The scheme consists of circuit-based exercises adapted to differing levels of fitness and ability.

Another referral scheme is the Start Up exercise referral scheme run by the local authority. The referral process begins with the GP, nurse or health professional referring those clients who would benefit from structured, supervised exercise to the scheme. The referral form would be signed by the client's referee and shown at the first appointment. After 12 weeks, the client discusses their progress with the instructor who then reports back to the doctor, nurse or health professional. The client can continue exercising at a similar rate and be given guidance when needed.

Exercise prescription

This means that a person is prescribed an exercise programme by a professional in healthcare that matches the frequency, intensity, duration and type of exercise to meet the fitness and health needs of the client. This will minimise the risks and maximise the health gain. There is a register for exercise and fitness professionals in the UK. This is supported by Sport England and operated by the Fitness Industry Association. The quality assurance framework set up in 2000 for exercise referral recommends registration as a prerequisite for exercise instructors working at this level.

Recommended guidelines

These are the national guidelines set up by the National Assurance Quality Framework for Referral Schemes.

- Healthcare professionals are referral specialists who should keep a regularly-updated file of local physical opportunities and support groups for their prospective clients.
- Referral specialists will select the most appropriate strategy to encourage exercise outside the programme. There should always be a follow-up briefing at the end of the programme.
- The exercise programme must be tailored to the participant's needs and the professional's skills.
- Records of progress have to be filed or a log book kept by the participant.
- Records of all communication must be securely filed within the exercise setting.
- There should be a mid-point assessment (5–6 weeks), in order to monitor progress in terms of the change to a more active lifestyle.

Monitoring

There is strong evidence to support the positive impact of physical activity on a variety of health problems:

- coronary heart disease
- obesity
- blood pressure
- diabetes
- colon cancer
- depression
- anxiety
- arthritis
- osteoporosis.

National standards for GP exercise referral schemes were published in 2001. This has improved the delivery of existing referral schemes and encouraged the development of effective high-quality projects nationwide.

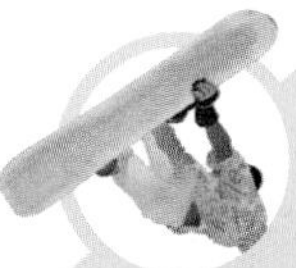

grading tips

Grading Tip 

Ensure that the description is detailed and gives the whole picture of the exercise referral process.

Assessment practice

Members of staff have complained about having no publicity and advertising about the exercise referral scheme that is available at their clinic.

Could you design a leaflet that describes the process of referral from the initial screening to the evaluation at the end of the programme. Describe the process by using an example, such as a patient with heart problems. You could get research locally or nationally. **P3**

22.4 Be able to plan and deliver an exercise session for a specific group

Plan session

This section will help you plan and deliver an exercise session for a specific group. The first stage of your planning is deciding who your group will be and what kind of session you want to deliver.

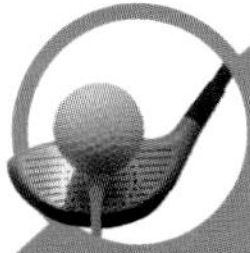

Think it over

Have you had experience of delivering activity sessions to a specific group before? Which specific groups would you have access to? What are the resources available to you?

When planning your session, you should think of the following words: 'Fun, inclusion, achievable tasks, imaginative use of facilities, who the participants are, age ability, gender, number, time constraints.'

Having chosen the specific group, you must decide the aims of the session.

Aims

These are the goals you are setting the individuals in your group – what they will be able to achieve by the end of the session. The aims of your exercise session can be divided into three areas.

- Cognitive: this is where you aim to develop the individual's knowledge and understanding and allow the individual to apply that knowledge and understanding.
- Affective: this is where you build confidence and promote a positive attitude.
- Psychomotor: here, you develop a skill and become competent at that skill.

Think it over

How do the aims of a session relate to the benefits of exercise?

Outcomes

These are the learning outcomes. What will you want your group to have learnt at the end of the activity session? You might want to say, 'At the end of this activity the individual can throw a ball four different ways.' It is vital that each taught exercise session has a clear and valid outcome.

Resources

These can be divided up into three areas: human, facilities and equipment.

Human

This resource is 'you' because you are leading the session (and also anyone else who is there to help you).

Facilities

You must know where your session is taking place, for example on a field, in a sports hall, a fitness room or a church hall. It is also important that you know how many are in the group and how large your delivery space is.

Equipment

This will depend very much upon your chosen group and topic. Whatever you use you must check for safety, and that you have sufficient equipment (and the right equipment for the group).

Your resources may also include any questionnaires, checklists and self-evaluation sheets for individuals:

Having chosen your group and activity, you can now begin your planning as follows:

- decide on the aims and objectives of the session
- plan when the session will be delivered, where and how
- prepare your session plan
- organise the activity area, check it for safety and lay out the equipment.

Screening and medical history

Before planning your activity session, you need to gather information about the participants, regardless of age. For the majority of participants, being involved in exercise will not pose a problem. However, you may have chosen a specific group with medical problems or you may be presented with an individual in your group who has a certain medical condition. It is vital, therefore, that before planning your exercise session you identify any individuals who may be at risk. Through the process of screening and medical history you will be able to refer some to seek further guidance from their doctor or other health professional before joining your exercise session. A simple questionnaire could provide you with the details required to identify the apparently healthy participants and those who might be at risk and, therefore, require clearance from their doctor. Before commencing your session, you must check that the participants have the correct clothing and footwear and have no problems which could affect participation in the activities.

Informed consent

The participant will receive consent from their GP, health professional or other qualified instructor regarding their ability for exercise. The participant will then sign an informed consent form for exercise participation along with the doctor or health professional. With this consent, the participant can be included and take part in the session at an appropriate level.

Other considerations

There are other considerations to take into account before you can deliver the session.

Health and safety

A successful session will be a safe and appropriate one. There are several considerations to be made under this heading and they are important.

- Have you carried out a risk assessment?
- Do you know where the nearest telephone is?
- Do you know where the first aid box is kept?
- Have you planned an appropriate warm up?
- Is there water available for the participants?
- Have you checked the condition of the equipment?
- What are your participants wearing, are they suitably dressed?
- Who are the participants? Have all the appropriate checks been made, for example the screening and medical history?

A risk assessment is a careful examination of what could be harmful to the participants while they are in the session for which you are responsible. Exercise sessions cannot be completely risk-free, especially when working with groups who have specific medical needs. The risk, therefore, must be contained to one that is as safe as possible.

While doing the risk assessment there is a lot for you to think about.

1. The type of activity, group and level to which these activities are being taken.
2. Consider the location – is it a field, a gym, a fitness room?
3. How experienced are you and the people who will be with you?
4. The participants – age, fitness and health levels, and their competence.
5. The ratio of experienced staff to participants.
6. The quality of the equipment.
7. The weather – if the session is outside.

Any risks must be assessed and recorded by you and the following identified:

- any hazards
- the risk and who it will affect
- how you can control the risk
- record the findings
- monitor the risk and review it for further sessions.

Activity

1. Obtain a risk assessment form.
2. In an activities session, set up a circuit in the sports hall.
3. Carry out a risk assessment prior to the session beginning. Record your findings.

It will also benefit you to know the correct procedure for reporting an accident.

An accident will be reported in writing and there will probably be an official document prepared by the management of wherever you choose to deliver the session.

On this document you will need to do the following:

- record the nature of the accident
- note when it happened
- list who was concerned
- give details about the type of injury
- record what action was taken, when and by whom
- state what recommendation was made to the casualty department.

The report needs to be signed by you, the person who had the accident and a witness.

Participants

These are the people/children who will take part in your exercise session. This group can be from any specific group. The specific group may be made up of disabled people, prenatal or post-natal women. The group may be older adults, children and young people or referred clients. Whichever group you choose, building a rapport with them will be very important. This will be done through effective communication.

Timing and sequencing of activities

Your session has to be delivered in a structured and logical way. If you do not do this, the participants will not understand, nor will they learn. In fact, you will just confuse them. The benefit of planning an exercise session is to assist you with the timing of each section so that you do not end up spending too much time on one area. Good preparation leads to good evaluation and review because you can approach each aspect logically. With a structured plan you can make changes but you also have the plan there to bring you back on track. A good plan will be very detailed.

■ Ability level

No one person has exactly the same ability as another. It is important that everyone in your group has the same opportunity to participate. Perhaps you will have some disabled children in a mainstream activity. You must allow for this by looking for ways to include them. Inclusion does not mean that the person with a disability will perform the task in the same way as a child without a disability. You have to find the most appropriate form of movement, and this may mean having to adapt the exercises and activities to meet their personal needs. Once you have assessed the child's mobility, you will analyse the purpose of the activity and then adapt the task. Later in the unit you will learn how to adapt exercises to suit individual needs.

■ Marketing

Marketing is the process by which you plan and execute your idea from the initial planning stages, the promotion of your ideas, the possible pricing and the exchange that satisfies the customer. You, therefore, have to think about the following:

- planning your session
- promoting your session
- if a fee should be payable
- how to satisfy the participants' needs.

You can think about positively promoting your session in a one page spread in a local newspaper, encouraging your selected group to participate in the activities at a local leisure centre.

Deliver session

Safe and effective

You will consider several factors when planning a safe and effective exercise session. Your first consideration will be the level of fitness of your participants. If you have been thorough with your screening methods, then you will pitch your session at just the right level. On meeting the participants you will immediately be aware of their body type. Do you have a participant who is very overweight or (within a group of children), is there a very small child? Other factors to consider are the range of movement of the participant, what type of exercise they enjoy doing, which exercises they will find comfortable and the speed of the activities. You will also consider the clothing and footwear, the equipment and how it is used, and during the exercise session will be aware of participants who may push themselves too far.

Warm-up

The purpose of a warm-up is to prepare the body for exercise, to improve performance and to help protect against injury. There should be no sudden activities in a warm-up, there is a whole body approach and you begin with small movements and work towards a full range of movements. A warm-up should link to skill development by introducing new movements which are developed later in the session or using skills learnt in previous sessions. Warm-ups become increasingly more energetic, so you will have to think about the following.

- Activities to raise the temperature and the heart rate.
- Movements that use joints. As older adults may be stiffer due to natural wear and tear you should choose

Activity

1 Design a poster promoting exercise.

2 Design a leaflet promoting exercise.

3 Design a poster advertising a specific exercise session for older people.

4 Write a newspaper article analysing the benefits of an exercise programme for older people. Use this to advertise your exercise session for a specific older group. Are you targeting a particular activity?

a warm-up which mobilises the joints thoroughly, slowly and progressively through a full range of movements. Do not over exercise one joint.
- Stretches which use the whole body or different muscle groups.
- Avoid making participants move from the floor.

Warm-ups focus the mind and body to work safely and effectively.

The aim of a warm-up is to promote circulation and generate heat. This will take longer with older adults, therefore, spend more time on this than you would with normal beginners. The warm-up should build up gradually. Strong exercise should be avoided. The central nervous system becomes less efficient with age and. Therefore, an older person may have poorer balance, less body awareness and poorer short-term memory. New skills and movements may need repeating several times. Always provide a relaxed atmosphere and allow social integration, as older adults are often looking for the social benefits of exercise.

Key Term

Warm-up Includes a pulse-raising activity, a mobility exercise and stretches. The group could also be introduced to any equipment.

Pulse raiser

The heart is a pump and exercise will enable the heart to work more effectively and efficiently. By building the exercise up gradually, you are preparing the heart for more strenuous exercise. You are allowing the heart and lungs time to provide the muscles with nutrients. As your muscles work harder, your heart also has to work harder to supply more oxygenated blood to them. Your heart rate gets faster and you begin to feel hotter. Pulse raising exercises for older people might be circling arms, leg extensions, or bending arms at elbows alternately. A pulse raiser for children could be a tag game as a warm-up for a rugby session.

Mobility and stretches

Stretching should be selected according to the type of activity which is to follow. It is important not to put undue pressure on another group of muscles or joint when stretching a selected muscle group. Stretches as part of a warm-up may involve stretching the front of the upper leg, the chest, and the muscles across your back or down the side of your upper body. Older adults may find stretching in certain positions more difficult and there may be a lack of muscular strength to assist in holding the required position for the stretch. In older people the joints are more vulnerable and stiffer, therefore, they should be mobilised thoroughly, slowly and progressively through their full range of movement. Joints should not be overworked and support given where necessary, for example a chair or partner. For a game, sport or walking session you would mobilise all the major joints with emphasis on the areas of the body which are to be used most, for example in walking it is the ankles, hips, knees and spine.

Maintenance component

Your exercise session is now broken down into teaching skills, followed by a game or mini game or appropriate activities for your group. Finally, you will conclude with a cool-down. Through your exercise session you are aiming to increase the physical fitness of your participants. To do this you will consider activities which will increase their stamina and aerobic fitness. This will increase the efficiency of their cardiovascular system to deliver oxygen to the working muscles and carry carbon dioxide and other waste products from the working muscles. The muscles will also be able to work harder and longer. Muscular strength will be increased and so will muscular endurance. Through flexibility exercises, participants will be more able to use muscles and joints throughout the full range of natural movement. Finally, participants will become more agile, have better coordination, reaction time, power and speed.

Session

In order to deliver your session you will need a plan. It will contain the following details:

- specific group (number of people and any related problems)

- details of the activity
- venue (date and time)
- number of helpers
- details of space to be used and equipment
- aims and objectives of the session
- details of the session content (introduction, warm-up, main body of the session, cool-down and evaluation).

The session content will have times marked against each section.

You will also have to detail the session content.

- Introduction – include the instructions you want to give, think about how you can get the group to bond with you quickly.
- Main content – individually introduce skills, followed by partner work and then small group skills and practices. Activities could introduce tactics, rules and a mini game. The cool-down will follow. This content will vary hugely according to your group choice.

After this, opportunity will be given for feedback and review.

Theory into practice

Design a session plan (just the headings). Check that you have included all the headings in your plan.

Skills

If you plan that your participants play a game, you must ensure they have the appropriate skills. For example, if you wish your group to progress into a game of basketball, you may teach individual skills such as dribbling and passing and team skills such as defending. If your session is planned for very young children, you might aim to introduce them to skills related to throwing and catching, kicking and dribbling or hitting in preparation for a mini game. The skills you teach will always relate to the game or activity which is to follow. During this part of the session adapt the skills so that the participants can progress. For example, with young children you may begin with large sized balls, underarm throwing and a short-distance from each other. This can progress to smaller balls, a faster pace, overarm and the distance adjusts as they progress. Skills can be introduced in a similar way with chair-based games for older people.

Activity

1 On your own, select a skill that you could teach to chair-based older adults for use in a games activity.

   a Why would this skill be physically beneficial to this group of people?

   b How could you add progression to challenge the participants?

2 What social benefits would your group gain from this activity?

Taking it further

Develop the activity or exercise into paired work (or small group work) with a competitive element.

Game

The games you select will depend on the participants. You may choose to play games such as tag rugby, high five netball, short tennis, mini soccer or Kwik cricket with young children. With adaptation, disabled children can be included into mainstream sports. However, specific games for disabled people would be Boccia, Polybat or Goalball. Older people can also enjoy games which might be adapted for them, such as archery, ten pin bowling, darts, curling, soft tennis, uni-hoc or mat ball.

Activity

Divide the class into four groups. Each group devises a small-sided game from the following list:

- invasion game
- net/wall game
- striking game
- target game.

Activity

If you select prenatal or post-natal as your specified group, you may wish to progress towards an activity rather than a game. During pregnancy, water-based activities are beneficial to the mother and baby as the weight of the uterus is supported and there is less stress on joints and ligaments. You may, therefore, choose gentle warm-up exercises followed by stretches and then progress to activities which involve swimming. There are a variety of chair-based activities which can provide enjoyment for older people with lessened mobility. They can pass balls in circles, catch and throw balls. Game activities can be introduced to add a competitive edge.

▲ Exercise and enjoy the environment

Walking is another activity which is beneficial to any group.

Walking is easily accessible, can have a comfortable level of intensity for each individual, and can have a low skill level. Health benefits can be obtained from walking at moderate levels of intensity. Individuals enjoy walking for many reasons.

- low to moderate intensity
- low skill requirement
- low risk of injury
- low cost
- walking can be done any time
- there are social opportunities
- to enjoy the environment.

Your group can walk briskly or at a more comfortable level.

Cool-down

Key Term

Cool-down A calming-down activity that lowers the pulse.

The cool-down is to decrease the intensity of movement developed in the main content of the session. It is also a calming down period for all. Cooling down prepares your body to stop exercising and reduces stiff and aching muscles.

Pulse lower and stretches

In an older person, the heart rate will take longer to recover from exercise, therefore, the intensity of the exercise should be brought slowly back down. Stiffness might make stretching the muscles more difficult, so more care is needed. The emphasis during the stretch should be on relaxation. All major muscles should be stretched and related to everyday activities. When cooling down, an older adult should not be asked to get up and down from the floor frequently. With children, a physical cool-down calms their emotions, so that they become calm at the end of a session. Young children do not need to do formal stretches, but more reaches up and down and to the side. Cool-downs gradually decrease the intensity of the exercise.

Consider the following points when planning a cool-down.

- The environment should be warm and comfortable, because at the end of exercise the body temperature decreases.
- You should give plenty of time for relaxation. To relax individual body parts needs concentration and

you should remember that older adults may not be familiar with this process.
- Try to keep the atmosphere friendly and build up a rapport with the group. Everyone should leave wanting to return the following week.

Delivery

One of the aims of your session will be to ensure an enjoyable and safe exercise session for all participants. Through detailed planning, your session will allow them the opportunity to participate fully and enjoy being with you and their group. You will motivate and guide each person through the session, imparting knowledge and skills at the right place and time. Everyone in your group should be encouraged to assist each other and share their ideas.

Rapport with participants

Above all, you and the group have to enjoy being with each other. This will happen if you build a rapport with your participants. Anyone who has come to an exercise session does not want to be put under pressure. At the same time they want to succeed. They also want to have fun. By listening to each other, laughing, having strong eye contact, and showing enthusiasm, you will soon build up a rapport with each individual. You must be able to judge just how far you can push them. You will have set clear and realistic goals for each individual and, as a teacher, it is your responsibility to inspire each person to achieve their goals. Remember, many in your group will be there to improve their well-being and quality of life but it must be achieved by having fun! The way you dress can be important when developing rapport and empathy with your participants.

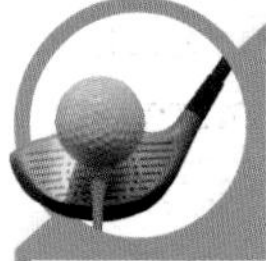

Think it over

Mary has come to your session today and tells you that you are the first person she has spoken to in three days. How does this make you feel? What could the leader in the group do to help Mary? How important is communication and motivation in this scenario?

Motivation

If you fail to motivate the participants in your exercise session, then they will not have fun nor will they achieve. You can encourage them in so many ways. Show enthusiasm, excitement and passion for whatever activity or task you are leading. Show an interest in each individual, make them feel important, value their contribution and be energetic in your praise. Value each small achievement and inspire them to improve progress and reach their goals. Your chosen group will also need motivating. To deliver an interesting and enjoyable exercise session, you will need to show the following characteristics:

- enjoyment and enthusiasm when working with people
- confidence
- ability to plan a session carefully
- energy
- ability to learn with your group
- ability to act responsibly.

Activity

How could you motivate an older person to participate in an exercise session? Write down six reasons. For example, 'You will get out of the house and get some fresh air.'

▲ Does everyone understand the instructions?

"It does not matter what you know about anything if you cannot communicate to your people. In that event you are not even a failure. You are just not there."

(Alinsky, 1972)

The communication process is the giving and using of information. Communication comes in many forms: speech, signals, signs, facial expressions, sounds, good eye contact, demonstrations, leaflets, gestures, electronically, written word, television, radio, video and Braille. Body language is also part of the communication process, as well as images such as clothing, attitudes and behaviours.

When delivering your session, you must do the following:

- communicate clearly using verbal and non-verbal skills
- always position yourself where you can see all of the group
- listen to what others are saying
- check that others have understood what you have communicated
- remember that body language is important.

Activity

1. Write an opening statement which could be used to begin a skills demonstration. For example, we are now going to look at the components of a serve (tennis).
2. Each person takes on the role of the teacher and reads the statement with a particular emotion. The rest of the group can say what emotion was used and how it made them feel. Emotions used could be enthusiastic, sad, angry, impatient, bored, happy, alert, unsure or miserable.
3. Also consider the type of body language and facial expression that would accompany each emotion. Can you now see why communication is important when delivering a session?

Listening is also part of the communication process. To be an active listener you must give full attention to what has been communicated. Listen carefully and show by your response that you understand what is being said. To be a good listener requires concentration and effort, and unless you have listened, you cannot give feedback.

Theory into practice

Ask one member of the group to give you the names of three favourite pop stars, films and television programmes. Do not write them down. Go round the rest of the group and see if each member can recall what they were told.

You must listen carefully to those around you. Communication skills may have to be adapted according to who you work with (for example you would you sign language with the deaf).

Communication skills can be divided into verbal (speaking) and non-verbal.

Verbal

Oral questioning is a powerful way for you to interact with participants. It involves you with the individual and also provides you with feedback on the level of their learning. Communication is a two-way process and question and answer is a good way to encourage this style of interaction. Technical language must be understood by the participants, so check that all instructions have been understood and are delivered clearly, at a good pace and the right volume. Make information giving fun and bright.

An older person may have a hearing aid. Remember to speak clearly and do not shout. The speed of learning slows down when you are older, so deliver the session at the appropriate pace. Any visual communication must be easy to read. Do not be afraid to ask the participants questions to check whether or not you are meeting their needs.

Communication is an important consideration when delivering a session for participants with a disability. You need to know how much sight a person has and think about describing the layout of the activity. Have you received permission to guide them through an activity? Also, if you have handouts, are they in large print or Braille?

Hearing impaired and deaf people may lip read, so you must remember to face the person and never shout. Listen carefully and try and learn simple sign language. Use your observation skills to check for understanding.

Non-verbal

Body language is important because you need to be able to 'read' the participant's body language and they need to be able to 'read' yours. Your mood is expressed through your body language and you need to appear to be feeling positive and enthusiastic. How you stand gives messages. Do you stand confidently? How you dress has an impact on those you meet, therefore, have you thought about the way you look? Does your style of dress communicate that you are about to organise and run an exercise session? Facial expression is a window on your feelings. Do you look nervous and anxious, or do you look happy and pleased to meet everyone? Do not invade anyone's personal space but, on the other hand, too much space can create a barrier.

You should always listen without interruptions when communicating with older people. Eye contact is important, shows concern and an interest in the individual. Therefore, even if only briefly, you should have eye contact with all participants in your group.

Think it over

Would you expect elderly ladies in a residential home to have good posture? Give reasons for your answer.

Observation skills

When delivering your session you will be expected to correct techniques according to the participant's ability.

Correction of technique

Correcting technique is important, especially if by performing the wrong technique a participant may be injured. However, some participants (especially older adults) may find the correct technique difficult, and in this case you would adapt the skill to suit them. If, for example, you decide to select walking as your chosen activity, then there are several points you should know. Posture is important and you can encourage good posture in the following ways.

- Head: this should be in a neutral position, chin parallel to the ground. If you need to look at the ground, the participant should be encouraged to maintain the neutral head position.
- Shoulders: these should be low and relaxed.
- Chest: the chest cavity should be lifted and open to help relaxed breathing.
- Abdominals: these should be contracted by keeping the natural arch of the lower spine.
- Buttocks: there should be gentle tension in the muscles.

For older participants, a very gentle, moderate walking pace with frequent opportunities to rest and provide social opportunities is very beneficial. The aim should be 30 minutes, five times a week. This may come in 5–10 minutes walk and then rest. If the participants are very frail, assisted walking is recommended.

Initiative and common sense should tell you when and how far to push for the correct technique. If the participant cannot achieve the task, then it should be modified.

Taking it further

Which specific groups would benefit from correcting techniques when exercising?

Modification of exercises

Games and exercise can be modified in a variety of ways. You can modify a game in the following ways by changing the: playing area, equipment, team structure, individual roles and positions, rules and scoring.

For example, you could modify an invasion game by doing the following:

- create a smaller or larger playing area (a wider playing area encourages attacking play and a narrower one encourages defence play)
- use different-sized balls

- group participants according to age
- have teams with unequal numbers
- decide that certain players cannot be marked.

Activity

1 Select one activity from netball, football, tennis, bowling or table tennis, and modify the game to suit a group of boys and girls aged between 8 and 12.

Work under the following headings:

- Equipment
- Rules, and
- Players

2 Explain your reasons for the modifications.

Adaptation of exercises

Many exercises can be adapted to suit the specific needs of individuals.

Ten pin bowling can be adapted by using skittles made from plastic bottles filled with sand, and the scores can then be painted on the bottles. This game could be played in a residential home with older adults. Archery could be adapted by making a target and allocating a score for different sections on the target. The target can be placed on the floor. The players can either be placed on a circle around the target or throw from behind a line. This could be played by participants in wheelchairs.

Exercise can be adapted for chair-based activities or for those who need the support of a chair:

- warm-up (e.g. wrist circling; knee out to the side of the chair and back in alternately)
- mobility (e.g. reaching up alternate arms; swim front crawl; push alternate knees forward to straighten the leg)
- stretch (e.g. sit on the edge of the chair and straighten one leg out in front of the chair, support back with hands on bent leg)
- aerobic (e.g. alternate heel digs forward and then to the side and then with both feet)
- cool-down (e.g. relax using the basic sitting position going through each body part).

Disabled children can be included in adapted games but you must find out what they can do and then you can help them to enjoy the session. Children and young people can experiment with different-sized balls, with different methods of throwing and catching and kicking the ball. All these skills can be adapted for children with disabilities.

Taking it further

In groups, adapt and make the equipment (if necessary) for a game for disabled children.

1 Plan a warm-up for the adapted game.
2 Deliver the warm-up to the other groups.
3 Analyse the warm-up. Discuss whether the aims were fulfilled.
4 Did the key sections relate well to the activity?
5 How could the warm-up be improved?

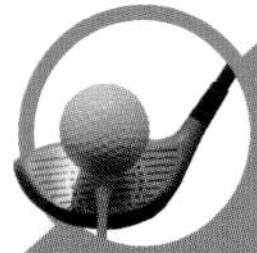

Think it over

How many ways can you perform the same skill, for example travel with a ball? This may include travelling with the ball in your arms, carrying it on your lap if you are in a wheelchair, holding it under your chin, holding it in a receptacle, pushing it along with one or two hands (or one or two feet.)

How many ways can you send and receive a ball?

Can you experiment with many different ways of sending and receiving a ball?

Case study

Planning an exercise session for older people

Mary is 78, lives alone and is an intelligent and lively lady. She has had a hip replacement and is having to stay in a nursing home until she is well enough to look after herself. She is very keen to return home even though her arthritis is quite severe. Therefore, it is essential that she regains her mobility. She read an article in the local newspaper describing the benefits of exercise for specific selected groups. Mary has asked the matron to explore a class for her. The matron has telephoned you to ask if you could deliver an exercise session for a group of older people in a similar condition to Mary. You agree to explore the possibilities by agreeing to deliver a trial session. Having visited the nursing home, gone through the screening process and obtained informed consent from the participants, you are now ready to consider the planning.

1 **Select an aim from one of the following for the exercise session with Mary and her colleagues.**
   - **Improve posture.**
   - **Promote circulation.**
   - **Improve motor skills.**
   - **Increase body awareness.**

   Plan a warm-up which would be suitable for your selected aim and is appropriate for the skills you wish to teach and develop.

2 **Explain why you have selected this warm-up and how the warm-up links to the skills you wish to teach. Remember, appropriate physical activities are those which meet the specific needs of the participants. These should be planned in close consultation with older people themselves.**

3 **Describe the main activity you have selected for Mary and her colleagues.**

4 **Explain how this activity relates to the aim of the session (for example, increased body awareness), and give reasons why you have chosen these exercises.**

5 **Mary really enjoys herself. Explain what benefits Mary has received from the session and how and why the exercises brought her benefit.**

Remember!

When delivering an exercise session for older adults:

- encourage good posture, a good starting position and ensure effective and safe techniques
- keep balance to a minimum and give support if it is needed
- do not spend long periods with the knees bent
- emphasise that participants should work at their own level
- ensure that the older participant does work
- give clear instructions (as someone may have a hearing problem)
- deliver the warm-up where you can be seen by everyone
- encourage chatting and laughter
- encourage partner work for social interaction
- allow time for the heart rate to return to pre-exercise rate.

Feedback

Participants can give feedback at any time during the session. Through questioning you can check knowledge and understanding. The cool-down period also provides an opportunity for you to ask questions which would give you feedback on the session.

The body language of participants also provides feedback. While observing the group, what is the body language of participants telling you? Are they enjoying the session or looking hot and uncomfortable?

You may even give the participants a questionnaire. Questions would be a mixture of open or closed questions. An open question could be: 'What part of the basketball session did you find stimulating?' This would be answered by writing a few words or a sentence. A closed question would be answered by ticking a box or answering 'Yes' or 'No'. For example, 'Did you enjoy the basketball session?' – 'Yes'.

Assessment practice

1 Plan and deliver an exercise session.

A nearby special school has asked you to help them with sports activities. They have a small indoor hall that is used on many occasions and for lunch. They have an outdoor concrete playground. There is no grassed area for sport. The group will be a specific age range and you can select whichever age you wish. They have children and young people aged 3–14 years. The session will last for 30 minutes. The school has many balls, all shapes, sizes and colour, also cones, beanbags, hoops, skipping ropes, bats, rackets and other small equipment.

You may use this scenario or devise your own scenario around the group you have selected for your planning and delivering of an exercise session. Remember, the group can be your choice and you may have the support of your teacher if you wish. The session will include, the warm-up, skills practice, exercises (or a game, adapted game or fun game), the cool-down and a session debrief.

You will need to provide a session plan. Use the following headings: Aims, Outcomes, Equipment, Venue, Time, Forms of adaptation to be used, Warm-up, Main content, Cool-down, Debrief. Deliver the session to your selected specified group with support. **P4**

2 You may have chosen to complete the session plan and delivery of an exercise session for a selected group without support. Explain why you chose the specific exercise and activities for this group. Give reasons for selecting the warm-up, main content and cool-down. **M3**

3 Having completed the session plan and delivery of an exercise session for a selected group, justify why you selected the exercise and activities with the warm-up, main content and cool-down sections. Support your reasons for selecting the chosen exercises and activities by providing evidence that the selections achieved the aims of the chosen components. **D2**

grading tips

Grading Tip 

Remember to ask for support with the planning and delivery of the exercise session for a selected specific group if you find this necessary.

Grading Tip 

To achieve M3 the planning and delivery of the exercise seaaion for a selected group is conducted with no support. You must also clearly explain the components of your exercise session.

Grading Tip D2

Having explained the chosen components of your exercise session you must say why you selected these components and how they will benefit your selected group.

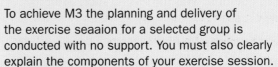

Review of session

Reviewing is the process of looking back over the planning and delivery of a session and evaluating what was successful and what could be improved.

Your participants and peers can give you feedback by identifying what was good and what could be improved.

Your teacher can also help by discussing the strengths and weaknesses.

There are several methods that will help you to review the planning and delivery of an exercise session.

Methods

Methods of evaluation (e.g. questionnaires to provide feedback from participants and peers, feedback observation sheets, charts, checklists and self-evaluation methods) can assist you in identifying areas of strength and areas for improvement. You can also receive feedback from questioning during and at the end of your exercise session, as well as using observation skills.

Through feedback, you can ascertain whether the aim was achieved, whether the participants enjoyed themselves, how safe the session was and if it was well organised. It is important that you are able to review your session as you progress through it and be able to make decisions and adjustments accordingly.

Questionnaires

Questionnaires can be used to provide feedback from participants, peers, teachers and for self-assessment. Questions can be open or closed. Open questions would give you more information and are answered through writing words or sentences.

- Open question: 'What do you think went very well?'
- Closed question: 'Was the session successful?' Yes/No

It may be that certain participants (such as young children and older adults) would find questionnaires difficult to fill in. You could obtain feedback through a 'chuff chart'.

Activity

Design a chart that could easily be completed by children or an older person which would give you feedback from your session.

Consider the following headings.

- Start of warm-up
- End of warm-up
- Skills practice
- The game
- Cool-down

Peer feedback

Feedback from your peers should be given back to you in such a manner that it will assist you with self-evaluation.

Your peers can give you information which would be difficult for you to gather while you are delivering your session. The observer will collect data that you can analyse.

A feedback observation sheet which could be completed by your peers would consider the following key factors: preparation, equipment used, organisation of the space, organisation of the group, other safety issues, the structure and progression of the activities, time management, communication, motivation, improvisation, inclusion, and any additional comments.

Activity

1 Design a simple feedback observation sheet that could be used by your peers to evaluate your session.

2 Ask one of your friends to complete the observation sheet during a practice session.

Checklist

Direct observation assessment techniques can assess the process of your delivery session as well as the overall session. By using a checklist your peers or teacher can, by marking a tick or a cross, assess whether you did or did not carry out all the aspects of the session successfully. The following may assist you in designing a checklist that can be used by your peers or teachers.

Warm-up:

- ☐ Did you explain the warm-up activities clearly to the participants?
- ☐ Did the activity relate to the game/sport?
- ☐ Was everyone involved?
- ☐ Were the participants made aware of safety issues?
- ☐ Were your aims achieved?

Skills practice:

- ☐ Did you follow a progressive structure?
- ☐ Did the methods of adaptation work well?
- ☐ Was the practice session enjoyable?
- ☐ Did you achieve your aims?

The game:

- ☐ Were the instructions clear?
- ☐ What methods of adaptations were used and were they successful?
- ☐ Did everyone have the chance to participate?
- ☐ Was everyone enjoying themselves?

Cool-down:

- ☐ Was the cool-down activity explained clearly to the participants?
- ☐ Was everyone involved in the activity?
- ☐ Did the activity achieve its aims?

General:

- ☐ What could have been improved? Be specific.
- ☐ Did you manage to include everyone?
- ☐ Did you communicate well?
- ☐ What was really good about the session?

Theory into practice

Design a checklist and ask one of your peers or teachers to use this while observing your practice session. This will be good preparation for your final practical delivery session.

Self-evaluation

At the end of your session you can reflect on how well or how badly your session went. You can think about the 'highlights' and 'lowlights'. If you are to get a realistic picture that will help you progress and improve, then you should have a system that will help you do this. The only true evaluation is self-evaluation, therefore, it is important to assess your own performance and make judgements that will identify your strengths and areas for improvement.

Checklists, rating scales and questionnaires will all help you evaluate the session you have delivered. Headings that you have used in a checklist can be turned into a questionnaire, or you can rate yourself using a scale (1 = poor, 4 = excellent).

Activity

Use the checklist you designed and change it into a questionnaire for self-evaluation.

Strengths

Strengths can be determined by completing a SWOT analysis. The information you have collected from questionnaires, observation sheets, teachers and self-evaluation will help you complete the analysis.

Your SWOT analysis will be divided into:

- strengths
- weaknesses
- opportunities
- threats.

Under strengths, you might consider the following:

- What did you do well?
- Which part of the session was the most enjoyable?
- What do you feel confident doing?
- What did your participants achieve?
- How did you encourage your participants?

Areas for improvement

Under areas for improvement you can consider your weaknesses, threats and opportunities. For example, you could ask yourself the following questions:

- What else do you need to learn to improve?
- What barriers do you need to overcome?
- How can you overcome your weaknesses?

Development plan

After considering your strengths and areas for improvement, you are now ready to consider a development plan. A development plan is a specific plan which sets out in writing/diagrams what you want to achieve. You will make specific proposals in the form of targets to guide you through your development. The plan is the starting point from where you will move forward. It will contain short-term and long-term goals.

SMART targets

When designing your development plan think of the word SMART. This means that any targets you set yourself should be:

S – **S**pecific: identify your targets.

M – **M**easurable: how many weeks will you give yourself to achieve the targets?

A – **A**chievable: how will you achieve your targets?

R – **R**ealistic: check that your targets can be achieved.

T – **T**ime-bound: what time will you give yourself before re-assessing the target?

Assessment practice

Review the planning and delivery of your exercise session for a specific group. Here are some ideas to help you.

- Ask your participants to fill in a questionnaire which you could have prepared.
- Listen to feedback from your peers.
- Use the feedback from your teacher.
- Complete a self-evaluation form.

1 In the review, describe what went well and why it went well.
2 Explain why your session was a success.
3 Think about what you might change.
4 What were the strengths of the session and what could be improved? **P5**

grading tips

Grading Tip 

When reviewing your planning use all the information you have gathered from peers, teachers, etc.

Knowledge check

1 Identify three different specific groups. Give a short description of each group.

2 Give short explanations of the meaning of the following sectors:
- public
- private
- voluntary
- partnerships.

3 Give two examples of exercise provision for specific groups from each sector.

4 Choose three specific groups and explain the physiological and psychological benefits of exercise for these groups.

5 Why is maintaining bone density important? What benefits are there in exercise for someone with:
- osteoporosis
- diabetes
- multiple sclerosis?

6 What do you mean by a rehabilitation programme? Describe a rehabilitation programme for a specific group.

7 What do you mean by the exercise referral process?

8 What is the role of managers of referral schemes?

9 When planning a session, why would you consider factors such as aims, outcomes, resources, health and safety?

10 What do you mean by participants of an exercise programme?

11 Why is communication so important when delivering an exercise session to people with a disability, or older adults?

12 Why is it important to warm-up when delivering an exercise session?

13 When would you adapt a game when planning and delivering an exercise session?

14 Explain how SMART will help you to set targets.

Preparation for assessment

You are a sports therapist and have recently opened your own private health club. Your previous work was within the public sector. You would like to develop this club particularly for specific groups who will benefit from exercise programmes. Working in the public sector has awakened your interest in this area as you have seen the need for individual care and tailored programmes for each client through your hospital work.

Having dealt mainly with sporting injuries, you know that to run a successful business means planning carefully and researching the exercise provision already existing in the area for specific groups. You are prepared to take on extra qualified staff. You set yourself an action plan.

1 This task is a written task in the style of a short report.

a Visit public/private/voluntary sectors where exercise for specific groups is provided. Describe the provision of exercise for three specific groups. You may find that partnerships are involved in some of the ventures. **P1**

b Compare and contrast the provision of exercise for your three selected specific groups. You can do this by looking at the similarities and differences. After considering these factors, identify the strengths of the providers and the areas that you think should be improved. **M1**

c If you are to offer specialist exercise programmes for your three selected groups, then you must analyse carefully the existing exercise provision for these groups. Having analysed the provision, make recommendations for improvements that relate to the identified areas. What benefits would your selected three groups gain from your recommendations? **D1**

grading tips

Grading Tip P1

Remember, you need to give a clear and full description and include all the relevant points.

Grading Tip M1

Remember to explain the similarities in detail and consider the differences carefully.

Grading Tip D1

When analysing the provision, identify the provision of exercise for each selected group and then discuss this provision in relation to each group.

Grading Tip P2

The poster should allow the viewer to have a clear picture of the benefits of exercise.

Grading Tip M2

Remember to give a detailed explanation of four benefits of exercise to each of three specific groups and always give reasons to support your answers.

Grading Tip P3

The reader has very little knowledge of the referral process. Therefore, your description must include all the relevant details.

Grading Tip P4

Your plan must be organised and in detail, and include all the relevant sections – that is warm up, development and cool down. You are allowed support from your teacher

2 The next stage of your plan is to have an Open Day and invite three specific groups to the event. You will market the Open Day through a poster that will be displayed in doctors' surgeries, day centres, support groups, free press and radio.

a In your poster, describe four different benefits of exercise to each of the three specific groups. **P2**

b Use the poster as part of a short presentation at your Open Day. Explain in detail four different benefits of exercise to each of your three selected groups. You may wish to use demonstrations and visual aids. **M2**

3 You have now employed two fitness instructors and they want to know more about the exercise referral process.

You already have some background knowledge, but it would be beneficial if you could visit a leisure centre/health club/doctor's surgery to find out more about this scheme. Write a description of the exercise referral process for your instructors.

4 Your club is now operating, but the fitness instructors need some guidance from you about planning and delivering exercise sessions for specific groups. With your support, they are to plan and deliver an exercise session to a specific group.

a You are now taking the role of an instructor. Invite a specific group of your choice to your health club. With the support of the owner of the club, write a plan and deliver an exercise session for the selected group. **P4**

b You have to do the next session without support. Select a specific group and write a plan and deliver an exercise session. The owner of the club would like you to explain why you chose the aims and objectives and the reasons for your selected warm-up, development and cool-down for this specific group. In your explanation, set out in detail the reasons and give evidence to support them. This can be written or explained verbally to the owner/tutor. **M3**

c Having planned and delivered the session and explained your reasons for choosing the components of the session in the previous task, the owner/tutor asks you to say why you chose these components. Either in writing or in a verbal presentation to the owner/tutor, justify and say how you came to choose the components of the exercise session. **D2**

5 The owner of the club would like to monitor your progress and has asked for a meeting. He would like you to prepare for this meeting by reviewing the planning of the exercise session for your specific group, describing what you felt was strong about the planning and delivery of the session, and what you need to improve on.

grading tips

Grading Tip 

Remember to explain in detail and give examples to support the chosen components of the exercise session

Grading Tip 

Say how and why you chose the components of the exercise session. What beneefits would the chosen components bring to your specific group?

Grading Tip 

Remember the words SMART and SWOT, and use the evaluations of participants, peers and self-evaluation to assist you with the review.

Grading criteria		
To achieve a pass grade the evidence must show that the learner is able to:	**To achieve a merit grade the evidence must show that, in addition to the pass criteria, the learner is able to:**	**To achieve a distinction grade the evidence must show that, in addition to the pass and merit criteria, the learner is able to:**
P1 describe the provision of exercise for three different specific groups **Assessment practice pages 375, 412**	**M1** compare and contrast the provision of exercise for three different specific groups, identifying strengths and areas for improvement **Assessment practice pages 375, 412**	**D1** analyse the provision of exercise for three different specific groups, providing recommendations relating to identified areas for improvement, and the benefits specific to each group **Assessment practice pages 375, 412**
P2 describe four different benefits of exercise to each of three different specific groups **Assessment practice pages 389, 413**	**M2** explain four different benefits of exercise to each of three different specific groups **Assessment practice pages 389, 413**	
P3 describe the exercise referral process **Assessment practice page 395**		
P4 plan and deliver an exercise session for a selected specific group, with support **Assessment practice pages 407, 413**	**M3** plan and deliver an exercise session for a selected specific group, explaining chosen components **Assessment practice pages 407, 413**	**D2** plan and deliver an exercise session for a selected specific group, justifying chosen components **Assessment practice pages 407, 413**
P5 review the planning and delivery of an exercise session for a specific group, describing strengths and areas for improvement **Assessment practice page 410**		

Index

Note: Page numbers in **bold** type point to definitions of key terms. Page numbers in *italic* type indicate a diagram, table or illustration.